Econometric Methods

2nd Edition

J. Johnston

Stanley Jevons Professor of Econometrics, University of Manchester, England

McGraw-Hill Book Company · New York

St. Louis · San Francisco · Düsseldorf · Johannesburg · Kuala Lumpur
London · Mexico · Montreal · New Delhi · Panama · Rio de Janeiro
Singapore · Sydney · Toronto

By the same author

Statistical Cost Analysis

(McGraw-Hill, New York, 1960)

For A., R., and M.

Econometric Methods

Library of Congress Catalog Card Number: 79-142968

07-032679-7

6 7 8 9 0 D O D O 7 9 8 7 6

Contents

Preface to the Second Edition

I have attempted in this second edition to cover the main topics in the rapid development of Econometrics since the first edition appeared in 1963. The book still starts at the same level as its predecessor and as far as possible I have integrated the new developments into the structure and notation of the first book.

A new introductory chapter has been added on The Nature of Econometrics. Chapters 2 and 3 treat the two-variable linear model and its extensions as before. Chapter 4 on Matrix Algebra has been considerably expanded with greater attention to partitioned matrices, rank and the solution of homogeneous equations, quadratic forms and positive definite matrices. Chapter 5 on the general linear model contains substantial amounts of additional material on such topics as the correlation matrix, prediction, linear restrictions, multicollinearity and specification error. Chapter 6 is essentially new; it contains all the material on dummy variables and pays especial attention to covariance analysis. The treatment of generalized least squares has been simplified in Chapter 7 and new material added on pure and mixed estimation, grouping of observations and grouping of equations. Autocorrelation still receives a chapter to itself and recent important results have been included. Chapter 9 introduces some important asymptotic results and also treats instrumental variables and errors in variables. Two entirely new chapters follow, namely Chapter 10, which is concerned solely with the problems raised by lagged variables and Chapter 11, which covers other important multivariate techniques. The final two chapters on simultaneous equation problems have also been expanded and include among other things an assessment of the latest simulation studies of the small sample properties of various estimators. I have not included Bayesian techniques or spectral analysis for, at the present stage of their development in econometrics, they are best treated in specialized monographs and, at the level of prior knowledge assumed for this book, their treatment would have taken up an inordinate amount of space in relation to the rest of the material.

The revision of the book was begun during my tenure of a visiting professorship at Baruch College and the Graduate Centre of the City University of New York. It has been influenced by the comments and criticisms of the first edition that I have received from friends, colleagues and students in many parts of the world. In particular I must acknowledge my debt to S. D. Silvey, Professor of Mathematical Statistics in the University of Glasgow, who made invaluable criticisms of various drafts of the present manuscript, and also to my colleagues R. W. Farebrother, S. A. Moore and J. Stewart for comments and help with proofs and index. I am also very grateful to Pauline Millward and Dolores Whittaker for the speed and efficiency with which they typed a difficult manuscript.

Finally I am indebted to the Literary Executor of the late Sir Ronald Fisher, F.R.S. to Dr. Frank Yates, F.R.S. and to Oliver and Boyd, Edinburgh, for permission to reprint Table A-2 from *Statistical Tables for Biological, Agricultural and Medical Research*. Similar debts are acknowledged to the Biometrika Trustees and to the Editors of the Annals of Mathematical Statistics for permission to reprint Tables A-4, A-5 and A-6. I am also grateful to various authorities for permission to use questions from examination papers of the Universities of Cambridge, London, Manchester and Oxford.

J. Johnston.

Preface to the First Edition

The purpose of this book is to provide a fairly self-contained development and explanation of econometric methods for students who have already done about one year's work in statistical theory and method. It is divided into two parts. Part 1 contains a full exposition of the linear normal regression model. This serves as an essential basis for the theory of econometrics in Part 2. This latter part expounds the main statistical methods now available for the estimation of econometric models.

Students who have already done a year's work in mathematical statistics will be able to skip much of the first two chapters, which have been inserted as a link with the conventional courses in statistical methods taken by most students in the social sciences. Chapter 1 is a complete treatment of the two-variable linear model, including all the problems of estimation, hypothesis testing, and forecasting which arise in the context of this model. Most students will already be familiar with many of the topics treated in this chapter. An elementary knowledge of probability distributions, expected values, estimation, and hypothesis testing is assumed. Anyone who experiences difficulty with the material in Chap. 1 should refer to a good introductory book on statistics before proceeding any further.[1] As well as providing useful review material, Chap. 1 introduces all the basic inference problems, which will be considered in more complicated contexts throughout the rest of the book.

Chapter 2 deals with extensions of the two-variable linear model to embrace nonlinearities and also increases in the number of variables. One does not travel far along this road before the notational and other complexities call for a more powerful technique. Chapter 3 thus provides the essentials of matrix algebra, which is then used as the basic method of exposition throughout the rest of the book. Chapter 4 deals with the general linear model in k variables. This is the basic and final chapter in Part 1, and it contains a development of all the important results for this model. Chapters 1, 2 and 3 provide preparatory material which different readers will

[1] For example, P. G. Hoel, *Introduction to Mathematical Statistics*, 2d ed., Wiley, New York, 1954. A. M. Mood, *Introduction to the Theory of Statistics*, McGraw-Hill, New York, 1950. D. A. S. Fraser, *Statistics: An Introduction*, Wiley, New York, 1958.

have to use more or less intensively before tackling Chap. 4. The material in Chap. 4 is an essential prerequisite for understanding the developments in econometric methods described in Part 2.

After a short introductory chapter, Part 2 contains a treatment of errors in variables in Chap. 6. This is a topic which sometimes receives scant attention in econometric work, but which is often of great practical importance. Chapter 7 gives a unified treatment of problems arising from autocorrelated disturbances, and various other problems which can arise in a single equation context such as multicollinearity, heteroscedasticity, lagged variables, and dummy variables are covered in Chap. 8. The final two chapters deal with simultaneous-equation problems, including identification problems, indirect least squares, two-stage least squares, limited-information methods, full-information, and three-stage least squares.

The emphasis throughout is on the rationale of the various methods. I have attempted to explain as fully as possible the assumptions underlying the various techniques and to give a fairly extensive development of the various results, in the hope that readers of varying backgrounds will be able to work through the material on their own and develop a real appreciation of the advantages and limitations of the various techniques in different practical applications. Numerical examples are given in the text, and theoretical and numerical exercises at the end of most chapters. I am grateful to various authorities for permission to use examples from examination papers of the Royal Statistical Society and the Universities of Cambridge, London, Manchester and Oxford. I have given no treatment of computational problems since an ever-increasing number of research workers are now using various electronic computers with associated programs.

I am heavily indebted to certain individuals. The project would not have been undertaken at all had it not been for the encouragement and support that I received at a crucial stage from Prof. Guy H. Orcutt at the University of Wisconsin. J. Parry Lewis of the University of Manchester checked through the algebra, and he and R. J. Ball, also of Manchester, made many valuable suggestions. I am very grateful to them both. I am also greatly indebted to Prof. A. S. Goldberger of the University of Wisconsin for sending me his mimeographed lecture notes, which have materially improved my exposition at several points. Thanks also go to Profs. R. G. Lipsey and W. M. Gorman of London and Oxford, respectively, for valuable comments. Miss Pamela Drake checked the numerical examples, and L. T. Simister helped with the survey of empirical studies in Chap. 10. It is also a pleasure to acknowledge the patience and skill with which Mrs. Katherine Norrie and Miss Pauline O'Brien typed several versions of this manuscript. The final burden of proof correction was greatly eased by assistance from David Bugg.

J. Johnston

1
The Nature of Econometrics

1-1 RELATIONSHIPS BETWEEN VARIABLES

The first basic idea to which the student of economics is introduced is that of relationships between economic variables. The quantity demanded of a commodity in a market is regarded as a function of its price, the costs of producing a product are assumed to be a function of the amount produced, consumption expenditure is taken as a function of income, and so forth. These are all examples of two-variable relations, but more realistic formulations require the specification of several variables in each relation. Thus, quantity demanded may be regarded as a function of price, disposable income, and prices of related commodities; production costs will depend on rate of production, factor prices, and changes in production rate; and consumption expenditure may be specified as a function of income, liquid assets, and previous consumption levels.

1-2 ECONOMIC MODELS

The next step in the development of economic theories is the grouping of relationships to form a model. The number of relationships included in an economic model depends on the objectives for which the model is constructed and the degree of explanation that is being sought. For example, the traditional supply and demand model seeks to explain price–quantity combinations in a particular market; it consists of three equations, namely, a demand equation, a supply equation, and a market adjustment equation. These equations will contain other variables in addition to the quantity and price of the commodity in question, such as disposable income in the demand equation and factor prices in the supply equation. The explanation achieved by the model is then conditional on the values of these other variables and in this sense the model is a *partial* or *conditional* one. More ambitious models contain many more equations and attempt to explain the behavior of many more variables, yet most models are still conditional ones, in the sense that they contain some variables which are not determined or explained by the model.

All economic models, whether macro or micro, whether pertaining to an economy, an industry, a firm, or a market have certain basic features in common. First there is the assumption that the behavior of economic variables is determined by the joint and simultaneous operation of a number of economic relations. Second is the assumption that the model, though admittedly a simplification of the complexities of reality, will capture the crucial features of the economic sector or system being studied, and third is the hope that from the understanding that the model gives of the system we may predict the future movements of the system and possibly control those movements to improve economic welfare.

1-3 EXAMPLE OF A SIMPLE MACRO-MODEL

To illustrate these points and to pave the way for an explanation of the specific contribution of econometrics let us consider an extremely crude macro-model. Suppose an economic theorist suggests three propositions:

Consumption is an increasing function of Disposable Income, but likely to increase by less than the increase in Disposable Income.

Investment is an increasing function of National Income and a decreasing function of a Government Regulator, (for example, a rate of interest).

National Income is the sum of Consumption, Investment, and Government Spending on Goods and Services.

Our first task is to translate these propositions into mathematical form and here we immediately face a bewildering variety of possible specifications that would satisfy these *a priori* specifications of the theorist. Should the relations be linear in the variables or nonlinear, and if nonlinear should they be logarithmic, polynomial, or what? Even when the form of the relationship is specified there is still the problem of specifying the time-lags in the various equations. Does investment in the current time period, for instance, respond to last period's national income or to several previous values of national income? The conventional response to these difficulties is to postulate, in the first instance, as simple a form as possible for these relations. Thus one might translate the above propositions into the following model.

$$C_t = \alpha_0 + \alpha_1(Y_t - T_t) \tag{1-1}$$

$$I_t = \beta_1 Y_{t-1} + \beta_2 R_t \tag{1-2}$$

$$Y_t \equiv C_t + I_t + G_t \tag{1-3}$$

where the *a priori* restrictions on the model are expressed by

$$0 < \alpha_1 < 1, \qquad \beta_1 > 0, \qquad \beta_2 < 0$$

These three relations, together with the restrictions, constitute the model. C denotes consumption, I investment, Y national income, G government expenditure on goods and services, T taxes on income, and R the government regulator.

The model consists of two behavioral relations explaining consumption and investment and one identity. We have formulated the model to refer to discrete time periods and specified a one-period lag for national income in the investment equation. The behavioral relations are specified for the moment as exact functions but, as we shall see later, this is unrealistic and econometric work cannot proceed without some additional stochastic specifications.

In order to illustrate the functioning of the model we first classify the variables in the model as follows:

C_t, I_t, and Y_t are classified as *current, endogenous* variables
T_t, R_t, and G_t are classified as *current, exogenous* variables
and Y_{t-1} is classified as a *lagged, endogenous* variable.

The rationale of this classification is that the model purports to explain the values of the endogenous variables in the current time period (t) on the basis of the values taken by the exogenous and lagged endogenous variables. The model, however, tells us nothing about how the exogenous variables have been determined; the implication, of course, is that the values of these exogenous variables might be set to produce certain desired values of the endogenous variables. There is, however, a constraint on that process since, as the model shows, past values of one endogenous variable also play a part in influencing the current endogenous variables. More generally lagged exogenous variables will appear in a model and the two sets of exogenous variables (current and lagged) and lagged endogenous variables are labeled *predetermined* variables. Schematically the workings of the model, period by period, may be pictured

thus

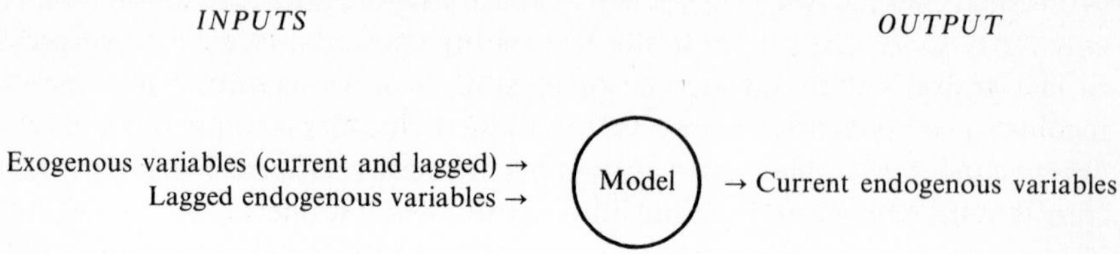

Relations (1-1) to (1-3) are usually described as the *structural form* of the model. The process by which the current endogenous variables are determined, however, may be more clearly seen if we cast the model into its *reduced form.* This is done by successive substitution in order to express each current endogenous variable as a function only of the predetermined variables. For example, substituting (1-2) and (1-3) in (1-1) gives

$$C_t = \alpha_0 + \alpha_1(C_t + \beta_1 Y_{t-1} + \beta_2 R_t + G_t - T_t)$$

or

$$C_t = \frac{\alpha_0}{1-\alpha_1} + \frac{\alpha_1\beta_1}{1-\alpha_1}Y_{t-1} + \frac{\alpha_1\beta_2}{1-\alpha_1}R_t + \frac{\alpha_1}{1-\alpha_1}(G_t - T_t) \tag{1-4}$$

The investment equation is already in reduced form since it contains no current endogenous variable other than I_t, so we simply rewrite (1-2) as

$$I_t = \beta_1 Y_{t-1} + \beta_2 R_t \tag{1-5}$$

Using (1-3), (1-4), and (1-5) we then obtain

$$Y_t = \frac{\alpha_0}{1-\alpha_1} + \frac{\beta_1}{1-\alpha_1}Y_{t-1} + \frac{\beta_2}{1-\alpha_1}R_t + \frac{1}{1-\alpha_1}G_t - \frac{\alpha_1}{1-\alpha_1}T_t \tag{1-6}$$

Equations (1-4), (1-5), and (1-6) constitute the reduced form of the model. The coefficients of the reduced form are all functions of the original structural coefficients and special significance attaches to the coefficients of exogenous variables: they are often referred to as *impact multipliers*, for they show the effect on each endogenous variable *in the current period* of a change in any current exogenous variable. For example a unit increase in the government regulator would change C_t by $\alpha_1\beta_2/(1-\alpha_1)$ and I_t by β_2. Since the model is linear the effect of changing several exogenous variables at the same time is simply the sum of the separate effects. Thus a unit increase in both government spending and tax collections would leave consumption and investment unchanged but increase national income by one unit.

In this simple model the *a priori* restrictions $0 < \alpha_1 < 1$, $\beta_1 > 0$, and $\beta_2 < 0$ on the structural parameters are sufficient to determine unequivocally the signs of the reduced form parameters in equations (1-4) to (1-6). There are at least five main reasons, however, why *qualitative* information about the signs of structural parameters is inadequate and must, if possible, be replaced by *quantitative* information. Firstly the qualitative information that we have so far about this model is purely of an *a priori* kind. It is desirable to see if the data confirm these *a priori* suppositions and, moreover, the simple linear specification of the model likewise needs to be tested against the data to see if it gives an adequate representation of observed behavior or whether a more complicated specification is required. Secondly, in more complicated models valid information just about the signs of structural parameters may not give unambiguous indications of the signs of the impact multipliers. Thirdly, for effective policy purposes it is desirable to have some indication of the magnitudes of the impact multipliers since some exogenous variables may be much more effective policy instruments than others. Fourthly, if we wish to analyze the type of behavior (whether damped or explosive, oscillatory or montonic) implied by the model it is essential to have numerical estimates of the structural coefficients. For example, (1–6) is a non-homogeneous first-order difference equation in national income, whose solution path depends on the numerical values of the α and β coefficients. If the structural equations had contained lags of more than one period, (1-6) would have been a difference equation of second or higher order in national income and the nature of the solution could not be determined simply from a knowledge of the signs of the coefficients of the difference equations. Finally, numerical forecasts of the effects on the endogenous variables of different combinations of exogenous variables can only be obtained from numerical estimates of the reduced form parameters.[1]

1-4 THE ROLE OF ECONOMETRICS

The essential role of econometrics is the estimation and testing of economic models. The first step in the process is the specification of the model in mathematical form, for as we have seen the *a priori* restrictions derived from economic theory are not usually sufficient to yield a precise mathematical form. Next we must assemble appropriate and relevant data from the economy or sector that the model purports to describe. Thirdly we use the data to estimate the parameters of the model and finally we carry out tests on the estimated model in an attempt to judge whether it constitutes a sufficiently realistic picture of the economy being studied or whether a somewhat

[1] For an extremely lucid illustration of the uses to which numerical estimates of economic models can be put the reader should consult D. B. Suit's "Forecasting and Analysis with an Econometric Model," *American Economic Review*, vol. LII, pp. 104–132, 1962. Those with a knowledge of matrix algebra could also usefully consult H. Theil and J. G. G. Boot, "The Final Form of Econometric Equation Systems," *Rev. Intern. Statist. Inst.*, vol. 30, pp. 136–152, 1962.

different specification has to be estimated. It should also be pointed out that the assumption of exact relations such as those in Eqs. (1-1) and (1-2) has to be removed in econometric work. No economic data ever give an exact fit to simple relations of this kind since linear or other simple forms are only an approximation to possibly complex but unknown forms and also since only a small subset of all possible explanatory variables can usually be included in any specification. These factors require the specification of a stochastic error or disturbance term in each relation other than identities and indeed a very useful product of the econometric process is an estimate of the error variance in each relation. These estimates shed crucial light on the quality of the econometric relations and they are also vital for the assessment of the estimated coefficients and for the use of the estimated model for forecasting purposes.

The field covered by econometrics is indicated in the accompanying diagram. Most of the titles in the diagram will not be meaningful at this stage, but the scheme will help to keep the reader oriented as he works his way through the book. This book is concerned with econometric methods, that is with the top half of the tree in the diagram, and the objective of the study is to learn how to make the best possible estimates of the parameters of econometric models for applied work.

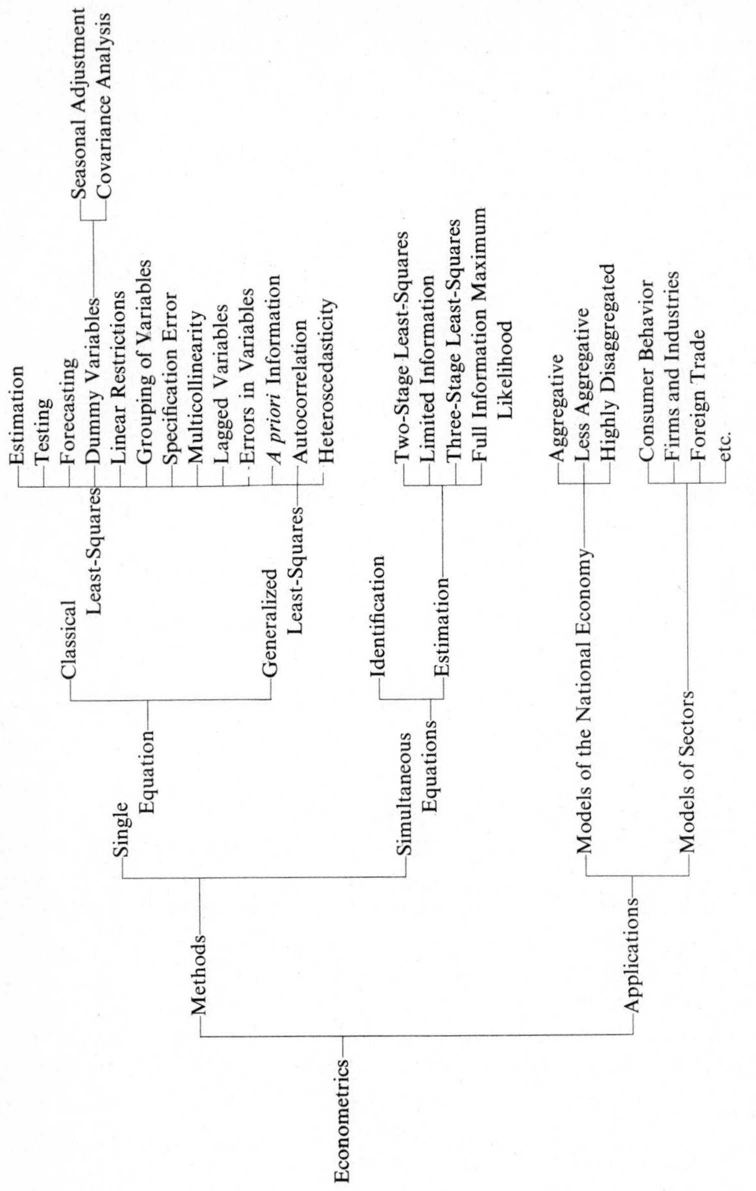
Econometrics
Methods
Applications
Single Equation
Simultaneous Equations
Classical Least-Squares
Generalized Least-Squares
Estimation
Testing
Forecasting
Dummy Variables
Seasonal Adjustment
Covariance Analysis
Linear Restrictions
Grouping of Variables
Specification Error
Multicollinearity
Lagged Variables
Errors in Variables
A priori Information
Autocorrelation
Heteroscedasticity
Identification
Estimation
Two-Stage Least-Squares
Limited Information
Three-Stage Least-Squares
Full Information Maximum Likelihood
Models of the National Economy
Aggregative
Less Aggregative
Highly Disaggregated
Models of Sectors
Consumer Behavior
Firms and Industries
Foreign Trade
etc.

2
The Two-variable Linear Model

2-1 ASSUMPTIONS

We have seen in Chap. 1 that econometrics is concerned with the estimation of the parameters of economic models. Such models typically contain a number of equations and each equation contains a number of variables. Given the possible complexity of the models and also the virtual impossibility of conducting controlled experiments in economics one might expect that formidable estimation problems occur and this is indeed the case. However, complicated methods are built up from simpler basic techniques and a thorough understanding of the latter is essential for proceeding to the more difficult cases. In particular a complete grasp of the least-squares principle is required for all that follows and so we begin with the most simple and elementary case by making the twin assumptions that we are dealing only with a single relation and that it contains only two variables.

Denoting the variables by Y and X, we postulate

$$Y = f(X) \tag{2-1}$$

This step merely identifies the variable X, which is thought to influence the other variable Y.

The second step is to specify the form of the relation between Y and X. The theory underlying the development of (2-1) may suggest the precise functional form to use, or it may merely suggest certain side conditions on the intercept, slope, and curvature of the function. Such conditions may be satisfied by a variety of functions, and we then look to statistical analysis for some help in choosing between them.

The simplest relationship between two variables is a linear one, namely,

$$Y = \alpha + \beta X \tag{2-2}$$

where α and β are unknown parameters indicating the intercept and slope of the function. Other relationships between two variables include

$$Y = \alpha e^{\beta X} \qquad Y = \alpha X^{\beta} \qquad Y = \alpha + \beta \frac{1}{X}$$

The third relation is linear in the variables Y and $1/X$, and the first and second can be reduced to a linear form in transformed variables by taking logs of both sides to give

$$\log_e Y = \log_e \alpha + \beta X$$

and

$$\log_e Y = \log_e \alpha + \beta \log_e X$$

respectively. The first is linear in log Y and X, and the second is linear in the logs of both variables.

The bulk of conventional economic theory, whether expressed in diagrammatic or algebraic form, postulates exact functional relationships between variables. The most elementary acquaintance with economic data, however, indicates that points do not lie exactly on straight lines or other smooth functions. Thus, for measurement and testing purposes, formulations such as (2-1) and the various functional forms associated with it are inadequate. The extension employed is the introduction of a stochastic term into economic relationships.

Suppose, for example, that we are investigating the relationship between consumption expenditure and disposable income in a cross section of households for some given period in time. Letting Y denote consumption expenditure and X denote disposable income, completed budget data for, say, 10,000 households would provide 10,000 pairs of associated measurements X_i, Y_i ($i = 1, 2, \ldots, 10{,}000$). Let us suppose that we have already divided our households into various groups on the basis of household size and composition and are looking at the relationship between Y and X *within* a given group. We do not expect that all households within the group which have some given income X' will display an identical consumption expenditure Y'. Some will spend more than others, some will spend less, but we do expect a clustering of the expenditure figures around a value which is geared to the income value in question. These ideas may be expressed more formally in a new linear hypothesis

$$Y = \alpha + \beta X + u \tag{2-3}$$

where u denotes a variable which may take on positive or negative values. Thus, if we consider the subgroup of those households with a given income X', the central value of consumption expenditure for them will be $\alpha + \beta X'$, but actual consumption figures for individual households in the subgroup will be indicated by $\alpha + \beta X' + u_1$, $\alpha + \beta X' + u_2$, etc., where $u_1, u_2, \ldots$ indicate the amounts by which the expenditures of particular households exceed or fall short of the central value $\alpha + \beta X'$.

There are three possible, though not mutually exclusive, ways of rationalizing the insertion of the u term in (2-3). First, we may say that the consumption expenditure of each and every household could be fully explained if we knew all the factors at work and had all the necessary data. Even among households of the same size and composition, there will be variations in the precise ages of the parents and children, in the number of years since marriage, in whether the husband is a golfer, drinker, poker player, or birdwatcher, in whether the wife is addicted to spring hats, Paris fashions, swimming pools, or foreign sports cars, in whether the household income has been increasing or decreasing, in whether the parents are themselves the children of thrifty, cautious folk or of carefree spendthrifts, and so forth. In explaining human behavior the list of relevant factors may be extended *ad infinitum.* Many of the factors, however, will not be quantifiable, and even if they are, it is not usually possible in practice to obtain data on them all. Even if one can do that, the number of factors is still almost certain to exceed the feasible number of observations, so that no statistical means exist for estimating their influence. Moreover, many variables may have very slight effects, so that even with substantial quantities of data, the statistical estimation of their influence will be difficult and uncertain. This case then amounts to saying that $Y = f(X_1, X_2, \ldots, X_n)$ where n is an impracticably large number, so that we choose instead to represent Y as an explicit function of just a small number of what are thought to be the more important X's and let the net effect of the excluded variables be represented by u. In the limiting case of a single, explicit variable we have

$$Y = f(X_1, u) \tag{2-4}$$

Since many factors may be at work and in a given household many may be pulling in opposite directions, we should expect small values of u to occur more frequently than large values. We are thus led to think of u

as a variable with a probability distribution centered at zero and having a finite variance σ_u^2. This is why u is referred to as a stochastic disturbance (or error) term. In view of the many factors involved, and their likely independence, an appeal to the Central Limit Theorem would suggest a normal distribution for u.[1]

A second justification for the presence of a disturbance term in economic relations is to assume that, over and above the total effect of all relevant factors, there is a basic and unpredictable element of randomness in human responses which can be adequately characterized only by the inclusion of a random variable term. For purposes of practical statistics the distinction between these two rationalizations does not matter since, for reasons of both theory and data, we hardly ever claim to have included all distinguishable and relevant factors in any relationship, so that the insertion of a stochastic term is essential on the first count, and the second, if present, merely adds to its variance. Both these types of stochastic terms are sometimes referred to as disturbances, or errors, in the equation.

A third source of error lies in errors of observation or measurement. It may be that a variable Z is exactly related in a linear fashion to X by the relation $Z = \alpha + \beta X$, but errors of measurement obscure the true value Z, and instead of Z we observe $Y = Z + u$ where u denotes the measurement error. We have then

$$Y = Z + u$$

that is,

$$Y = \alpha + \beta X + u$$

It is possible, of course, to have a measurement error superimposed on an equation error as in the case

$$Z = \alpha + \beta X + u \qquad \text{equation error}$$

$$Y = Z + v \qquad \text{measurement error}$$

therefore

$$Y = \alpha + \beta X + w$$

where $w = u + v$. It is probably unrealistic to consider measurement error as being present in only one variable, so we postpone a complete treatment of measurement errors to Chap. 9 and concentrate in the intervening chapters on equation error.

The initial specification of the relationship must now include some assumptions about the probability distribution of the disturbance term.

[1] See W. Feller, *An Introduction to Probability Theory and Its Applications*, 2d ed., Wiley, New York, 1957, vol. I, pp. 238–241.

These must relate to mean, variance, and covariance. The simplest possible assumptions are to assume the mean to be zero, the variance to be constant and independent of X, and the various values of u to be drawn independently of one another. To continue our example, suppose we distinguish various levels of disposable income, which we shall enumerate for convenience from the smallest to the highest as $X_1, X_2, \ldots, X_n$. If a linear hypothesis is true and if the above assumptions about the disturbance term hold, the situation can be pictured as in Fig. 2-1. The distributions centered around the line $\alpha + \beta X$ are the assumed distribution for u. It might be more realistic in this particular example to assume that the variance of the disturbance term increases with X, but we postpone examination of this case until Chap. 7.

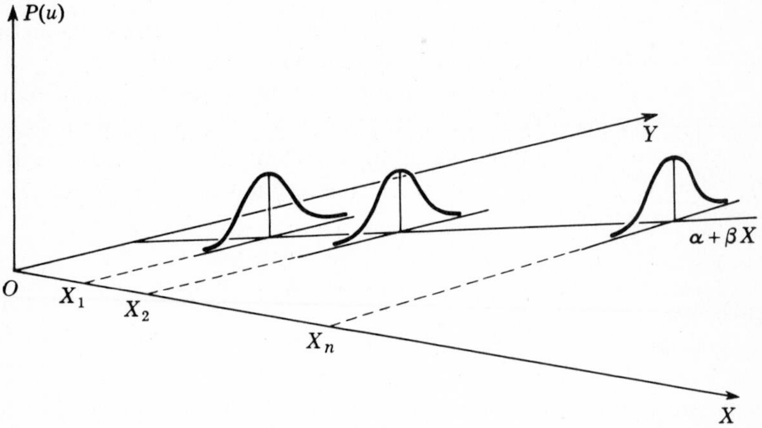

Fig. 2-1.

If we now select a sample of n households, one from each income level, the sample points can be represented on a scatter diagram, as in Fig. 2-2. If the u values have been drawn independently, the sample points will cluster more or less randomly around the straight line. This would be the case if a positive (or negative) value for u_1 did not in any way influence the $u_2, u_3, \ldots$ values. If, on the other hand, the people with lower incomes tended to be younger people in the early stages of married life and those with higher incomes older people with an eye on retirement, we should expect positive disturbances for lower values of X and negative disturbances for higher values. The nonrandom character of the disturbances would here be an indication that an important explanatory variable, age, had been omitted and that its inclusion in the disturbance term was preventing that term from displaying random behavior.

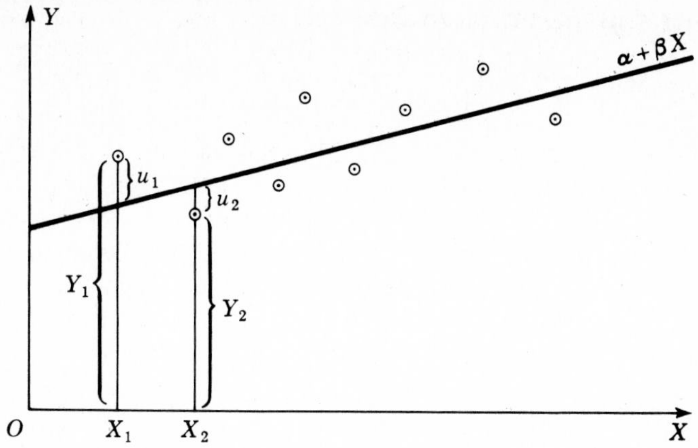

Fig. 2-2.

The practical situation then is that we have n pairs of sample observations on X, Y, which can be represented on a scatter diagram as in Fig. 2-2 above. The essential difference from that figure is that in practice the line $\alpha + \beta X$ is unknown. Instead we have a set of hypotheses

$$\begin{aligned} Y_i &= \alpha + \beta X_i + u_i && i = 1, 2, \ldots, n \\ E(u_i) &= 0 && \text{for all } i \\ E(u_i u_j) &= \begin{cases} 0 & \text{for } i \neq j;\ i, j = 1, 2, \ldots, n \\ \sigma_u^2 & \text{for } i = j;\ i, j = 1, 2, \ldots, n \end{cases} \end{aligned} \tag{2-5}$$

In (2-5), α, β, and σ_u^2 are unknown parameters. We wish to estimate these parameters statistically on the basis of our sample observations on X and Y, and we may also wish to test hypotheses about these parameters. For example, should we regard consumption as proportional to income ($\alpha = 0$)? Is the marginal propensity to consume, β, greater than one-half? Is a linear function an adequate representation of the data? Does the assumption of a constant variance for the disturbance term seem reasonable in the light of our sample data? These are typical problems of statistical inference, and our immediate task is to review what standard methods are available for dealing with them. As we shall see later, much of econometric theory is concerned with the development of new methods of dealing with statistical inference problems in the context of economic models, because standard methods are sometimes inapplicable, but a thorough grasp of the standard methods is an essential prerequisite for the understanding of more complicated techniques.

2-2 LEAST-SQUARES ESTIMATORS

The statistical inference problem outlined above may be treated in a variety of ways according to the precise assumptions made. Let us first make the assumptions set out in (2-5) above. We denote the sample observations by

$$X_1, X_2, \ldots, X_n$$

$$Y_1, Y_2, \ldots, Y_n$$

We can denote the arithmetic means by

$$\bar{X} = \frac{1}{n}\sum_{i=1}^{n} X_i \quad \text{and} \quad \bar{Y} = \frac{1}{n}\sum_{i=1}^{n} Y_i$$

On the scatter diagram in Fig. 2-3 insert perpendiculars to the axes at $\bar{X}$ and $\bar{Y}$ as shown. We wish to pass a line through the observations as our estimate of the true line $\alpha + \beta X$. Denote the estimated line by

$$\hat{Y} = \hat{\alpha} + \hat{\beta}X \tag{2-6}$$

where $\hat{\alpha}$, $\hat{\beta}$ are estimates of the unknown parameters α and β and $\hat{Y}$ is the ordinate on the line for any given value of X. To fit such a line we must develop formulae for $\hat{\alpha}$ and $\hat{\beta}$ in terms of the sample observations. We shall show how this is done by the principle of least-squares and then examine the properties of the resultant estimators.

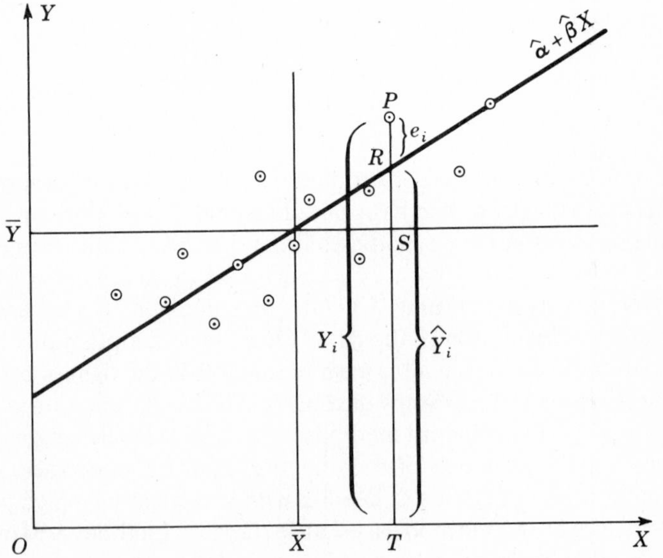

Fig. 2-3.

Take any point P with coordinates, say, (X_i, Y_i) in the scatter. Drop a perpendicular from P to the X axis, intersecting our estimated line at R, the $\bar{Y}$ line at S, and the X axis at T. Then $OT = X_i$, $PT = Y_i$, and $RT = \hat{Y}_i$. Define the vertical difference between P and the estimated line by

$$e_i = Y_i - \hat{Y}_i = PR$$

These residuals, or deviations, from the estimated line will be positive or negative as the actual point lies above or below the line. If they are squared and summed, the resultant quantity must be nonnegative and will vary directly with the spread of the points from the line. Different pairs of values for $\hat{\alpha}$ and $\hat{\beta}$ will give different lines and hence different values for the sum of the squared residuals about the line. Thus we have

$$\sum_{i=1}^{n} e_i^2 = f(\hat{\alpha}, \hat{\beta})$$

The principle of least squares is that the $\hat{\alpha}$, $\hat{\beta}$ values should be chosen so as to make Σe^2 as small as possible. A necessary condition is that the partial derivatives of the sum with respect to $\hat{\alpha}$ and $\hat{\beta}$ should both be zero. We thus have

$$\sum_{i=1}^{n} e_i^2 = \sum_{i=1}^{n} (Y_i - \hat{Y}_i)^2$$

$$= \sum_{i=1}^{n} (Y_i - \hat{\alpha} - \hat{\beta}X_i)^2$$

so that

$$\frac{\partial}{\partial\hat{\alpha}}\left(\sum_{i=1}^{n} e_i^2\right) = -2\sum_{i=1}^{n} (Y_i - \hat{\alpha} - \hat{\beta}X_i) = 0$$

$$\frac{\partial}{\partial\hat{\beta}}\left(\sum_{i=1}^{n} e_i^2\right) = -2\sum_{i=1}^{n} X_i(Y_i - \hat{\alpha} - \hat{\beta}X_i) = 0$$

Simplifying these two equations gives the standard form of the normal equations for a straight line:

$$\begin{aligned} \sum_{i=1}^{n} Y_i &= n\hat{\alpha} + \hat{\beta}\sum_{i=1}^{n} X_i \\ \sum_{i=1}^{n} X_iY_i &= \hat{\alpha}\sum_{i=1}^{n} X_i + \hat{\beta}\sum_{i=1}^{n} X_i^2 \end{aligned} \qquad (2\text{-}7)$$

When the indicated values from the sample observations are inserted, they give two simultaneous equations, which may be solved for $\hat{\alpha}$ and $\hat{\beta}$.

Alternatively, we see that if we divide through the first equation in (2-7) by n, we obtain

$$\bar{Y} = \hat{\alpha} + \hat{\beta}\bar{X} \tag{2-8}$$

that is, the least-squares estimates are such that the estimated line passes through the point of means $(\bar{X}, \bar{Y})$. If we subtract (2-8) from (2-6), there results

$$\hat{Y} - \bar{Y} = \hat{\beta}(X - \bar{X})$$

Using the convention that lowercase letters denote deviations from means, so that

$$x_i = X_i - \bar{X} \qquad y_i = Y_i - \bar{Y} \qquad \hat{y}_i = \hat{Y}_i - \bar{Y}$$

we now have an alternative way of writing the equation of the least-squares line, namely,

$$\hat{y} = \hat{\beta}x \tag{2-9}$$

Referring to Fig. 2-3, the residual e_i may be indicated by

$$e_i = y_i - \hat{y}_i = y_i - \hat{\beta}x_i$$

so that the sum of squared residuals is

$$\sum_{i=1}^{n} e_i^2 = \sum_{i=1}^{n} (y_i - \hat{\beta}x_i)^2$$

Minimizing this last expression with respect to $\hat{\beta}$ gives

$$\hat{\beta} = \frac{\sum_{i=1}^{n} x_i y_i}{\sum_{i=1}^{n} x_i^2} \tag{2-10}$$

and we also see that

$$\frac{\partial^2(\Sigma e^2)}{\partial \hat{\beta}^2} = 2\sum_{i=1}^{n} x_i^2$$

which is positive, so that a true minimum has been obtained. The intercept $\hat{\alpha}$ is then obtained from the condition that the line passes through the point of means, namely,

$$\hat{\alpha} = \bar{Y} - \hat{\beta}\bar{X} \tag{2-11}$$

Equation (2-10) might also have been obtained merely by rewriting the second equation of (2-7) in deviation form and remembering that for any variable the sum of the deviations around the arithmetic mean is identically zero.

To illustrate the calculation of a least-squares relationship, consider the data in Table 2-1. The original data have been expressed in figures of approximately the same order of magnitude. It is important to choose units of measurement for the variables to achieve this result, especially in cases of three or more variables, in order to avoid having too few significant figures in some of the calculations.

Table 2-1 Road casualties and licensed vehicles in the United Kingdom

Year (1)	*Road casualties* (000) Y (2)	*Licensed vehicles* (0,000) X (3)	$y = Y - \bar{Y}$ (4)	$x = X - \bar{X}$ (5)
1947	166	352	−51.8	−167.2
1948	153	373	−64.8	−146.2
1949	177	411	−40.8	−108.2
1950	201	441	−16.8	−78.2
1951	216	462	−1.8	−57.2
1952	208	490	−9.8	−29.2
1953	227	529	9.2	9.8
1954	238	577	20.2	57.8
1955	268	641	50.2	121.8
1956	268	692	50.2	172.8
1957	274	743	56.2	223.8

Source: Oxford P.P.E., 1959.

From columns 2 and 3 we calculate the following quantities required for Eqs. (2-7):

$$n = 11 \qquad \Sigma X = 5{,}711 \qquad \Sigma Y = 2{,}396$$

$$\Sigma X^2 = 3{,}134{,}543 \qquad \Sigma XY = 1{,}296{,}836$$

Substitution in (2-7) gives

$$2{,}396 = 11\hat{\alpha} + 5{,}711\hat{\beta}$$

$$1{,}296{,}836 = 5{,}711\hat{\alpha} + 3{,}134{,}543\hat{\beta}$$

which solve to give

$$\hat{\alpha} = 55.85 \qquad \hat{\beta} = 0.3120$$

and the estimated relationship is written

$$\hat{Y} = 55.85 + 0.3120X$$

As an alternative method we compute the deviations from the arithmetic means in columns 4 and 5, and then from (2-10) and (2-11) obtain

$$\hat{\beta} = 52{,}876.36/169{,}495.64 \qquad = 0.3120$$

$$\hat{\alpha} = (217.818) - (0.31196)(519.182) = 55.85$$

as before. Notice that one should always retain more significant places in parameters that are reused in subsequent calculations than one may wish to use in writing the final estimate.

Next we establish the properties of these estimators.[1] We assume that the X_i values are fixed constants. This is equivalent to assuming that in an experimental setup we can choose a set of X values and hold them constant in repeated samples. Alternatively, one may think of establishing the properties of $\hat{\alpha}$ and $\hat{\beta}$ *conditional* upon the given values of X and then, if for some applications it is more appropriate to consider X a random variable as well, to see how these properties hold up for this change of assumption about X.

Let us hold the X_i fixed and imagine repeated samples of size n being taken. The Y values will vary from sample to sample as a consequence of different drawings from the u distribution in each sample. Applying the formulae for $\hat{\alpha}$ and $\hat{\beta}$ to each set of sample observations would generate a series of $\hat{\alpha}$, $\hat{\beta}$ values. The distribution of these values is the joint sampling distribution of the least-squares estimators. Looking at the two marginal distributions for $\hat{\alpha}$ and $\hat{\beta}$, we are interested in the means and variances of these distributions and also in the comparison between these distributions and those of other possible estimators.

The first point to notice about the least-squares estimators is that they are *linear* functions of the actual observations on Y. From (2-10) we can write

$$\begin{aligned} \hat{\beta} &= \frac{\Sigma x_i y_i}{\Sigma x_i^2} \\ &= \frac{\Sigma x_i Y_i}{\Sigma x_i^2} - \frac{\bar{Y}\Sigma x_i}{\Sigma x_i^2} \\ &= \sum_{i=1}^{n} w_i Y_i \qquad \text{since } \sum_{i=1}^{n} x_i \equiv 0 \end{aligned} \tag{2-12}$$

where

$$w_i = \frac{x_i}{\sum_{i=1}^{n} x_i^2} \tag{2-13}$$

[1] Strictly speaking, estimator refers to a method, or formula, of estimation, and estimate to a particular numerical value yielded by that formula.

These w_i are fixed constants in repeated sampling, and it also follows directly that

$$\sum_{i=1}^{n} w_i = 0 \qquad \sum_{i=1}^{n} w_i^2 = \frac{1}{\sum_{i=1}^{n} x_i^2} \qquad \sum_{i=1}^{n} w_i x_i = \sum_{i=1}^{n} w_i X_i = 1 \tag{2-14}$$

By a similar algebraic manipulation of (2-11), $\hat{\alpha}$ may be expressed as a linear function of the Y_i, namely,

$$\hat{\alpha} = \sum_{i=1}^{n} \left(\frac{1}{n} - \bar{X}w_i\right) Y_i \tag{2-15}$$

To establish the means of the sampling distributions, we substitute for Y_i from (2-5), namely,

$$Y_i = \alpha + \beta X_i + u_i$$

Thus

$$\begin{aligned} \hat{\beta} &= \Sigma w_i Y_i \\ &= \Sigma w_i(\alpha + \beta X_i + u_i) \\ &= \beta + \sum_{i=1}^{n} w_i u_i \quad \text{using (2-14)} \end{aligned} \tag{2-16}$$

Hence

$$\begin{aligned} E(\hat{\beta}) &= \beta + \sum_{i=1}^{n} w_i E(u_i) \\ &= \beta \end{aligned}$$

since $E(u_i) = 0$ for all i by assumption (2-5). The significance of the assumption of constant X values is seen in the above manipulations, in that the operation of taking expected values is applied to the u and Y values but not to X. Thus $\hat{\beta}$ is seen to be an unbiased linear estimator of β. Similarly, $\hat{\alpha}$ is an unbiased linear estimator of α. For

$$\begin{aligned} \hat{\alpha} &= \Sigma\left(\frac{1}{n} - \bar{X}w_i\right)(\alpha + \beta X_i + u_i) \\ &= \alpha - \alpha\bar{X}\Sigma w_i + \beta\bar{X} - \beta\bar{X}\Sigma w_i X_i + \Sigma\left(\frac{1}{n} - \bar{X}w_i\right)u_i \\ &= \alpha + \Sigma\left(\frac{1}{n} - \bar{X}w_i\right)u_i \quad \text{using (2-14)} \end{aligned} \tag{2-17}$$

Hence

$$E(\hat{\alpha}) = \alpha$$

since $E(u_i) = 0$ for all i by assumption (2-5).

The variances of the estimates may be obtained from (2-16) and (2-17). We have, first, that

$$\hat{\beta} - \beta = \sum_{i=1}^{n} w_i u_i$$

$$\begin{aligned}\text{var}(\hat{\beta}) &= E[(\hat{\beta} - \beta)^2] \\ &= E[(\Sigma w_i u_i)^2] \\ &= E(w_1^2 u_1^2 + \cdots + w_n^2 u_n^2 + 2w_1 w_2 u_1 u_2 + \cdots + 2w_{n-1} w_n u_{n-1} u_n) \\ &= \sigma_u^2 \sum_{i=1}^{n} w_i^2\end{aligned}$$

since $E(u_i^2) = \sigma_u^2$ and $\underset{i \neq j}{E}(u_i u_j) = 0$ by assumption (2-5). Thus

$$\text{var}(\hat{\beta}) = \frac{\sigma_u^2}{\sum_{i=1}^{n} x_i^2} \quad \text{from (2-14)} \tag{2-18}$$

Using (2-17), we derive in a similar fashion the variance of $\hat{\alpha}$.

$$\begin{aligned}\text{var}(\hat{\alpha}) &= E[(\hat{\alpha} - \alpha)^2] \\ &= \sigma_u^2 \sum_{i=1}^{n} \left(\frac{1}{n} - \bar{X} w_i\right)^2 \\ &= \sigma_u^2 \left(\frac{1}{n} + \bar{X}^2 \Sigma w_i^2 - \frac{2\bar{X}}{n} \Sigma w_i\right) \\ &= \sigma_u^2 \left(\frac{1}{n} + \frac{\bar{X}^2}{\sum_{i=1}^{n} x_i^2}\right) \quad \text{using (2-14)}\end{aligned}$$

or rearranging slightly,

$$\text{var}(\hat{\alpha}) = \frac{\sum_{i=1}^{n} X_i^2}{n \sum_{i=1}^{n} x_i^2} \sigma_u^2 \tag{2-19}$$

Likewise, we may deduce that the covariance of the estimates is

$$\operatorname{cov}(\hat{\alpha}, \hat{\beta}) = E[(\hat{\alpha} - \alpha)(\hat{\beta} - \beta)]$$

$$= \frac{-\bar{X}}{\sum_{i=1}^{n} x_i^2}\sigma_u^2 \tag{2-20}$$

Next we shall establish that these estimators are *best* linear unbiased, that is, that of the class of linear unbiased estimators, the least-squares estimators have the smallest variance. Define any arbitrary linear estimator of β as

$$\hat{\hat{\beta}} = \sum_{i=1}^{n} c_i Y_i$$

where

$$c_i = w_i + d_i \tag{2-21}$$

the w_i being defined in (2-13) and the d_i being arbitrary constants. For $\hat{\hat{\beta}}$ to be an unbiased estimator of β, the d_i must fulfill certain conditions.

$$\hat{\hat{\beta}} = \Sigma c_i(\alpha + \beta X_i + u_i)$$

$$= \alpha\Sigma c_i + \beta\Sigma c_i X_i + \Sigma c_i u_i$$

therefore

$$E(\hat{\hat{\beta}}) = \alpha\Sigma c_i + \beta\Sigma c_i X_i$$

$$= \beta$$

which is true for all α and β if and only if $\Sigma c_i = 0$ and $\Sigma c_i X_i = 1$. These two conditions, in conjunction with (2-21) and the properties of w in (2-14), give the required conditions on the d_i, namely,

$$\sum_{i=1}^{n} d_i = 0 \quad \text{and} \quad \sum_{i=1}^{n} d_i X_i = \Sigma d_i x_i = 0 \tag{2-22}$$

The variance of this arbitrary linear unbiased estimator is then

$$\operatorname{var}(\hat{\hat{\beta}}) = E\left[\left(\sum_{i=1}^{n} c_i u_i\right)^2\right]$$

$$= \sigma_u^2 \sum_{i=1}^{n} c_i^2$$

but

$$\sum_{i=1}^{n} c_i^2 = \sum_{i=1}^{n} w_i^2 + \sum_{i=1}^{n} d_i^2 + 2\sum_{i=1}^{n} w_i d_i$$

$$\sum_{i=1}^{n} w_i d_i = \frac{\Sigma x_i d_i}{\Sigma x_i^2} = 0 \quad \text{by (2-22)}$$

Thus

$$\text{var}(\hat{\hat{\beta}}) = \text{var}(\hat{\beta}) + \sigma_u^2 \sum_{i=1}^{n} d_i^2$$

Σd_i^2 is necessarily nonnegative and is zero only if each value of d is zero. Thus the least-squares estimator has the smallest variance of all linear unbiased estimates. A similar result may be demonstrated for var $(\hat{\alpha})$.

An alternative development is to obtain best linear unbiased estimators directly, and it can then be seen that they coincide with the least-squares estimators. This approach also illustrates a method which will find fruitful applications in later problems. Let us make the same assumptions (2-5) as before and define

$$\hat{\beta} = \sum_{i=1}^{n} c_i Y_i$$

where the problem is to choose the weights c_i to make $E(\hat{\beta}) = \beta$ and to make the variance of $\hat{\beta}$ as small as possible. From the definition of Y_i in (2-5),

$$\hat{\beta} = \alpha\Sigma c_i + \beta\Sigma c_i X_i + \Sigma c_i u_i$$

$$E(\hat{\beta}) = \alpha\Sigma c_i + \beta\Sigma c_i X_i$$

Thus $\hat{\beta}$ is an unbiased estimator of β if and only if

$$\sum_{i=1}^{n} c_i = 0 \quad \text{and} \quad \sum_{i=1}^{n} c_i X_i = 1 \tag{2-23}$$

Using these conditions, the variance of $\hat{\beta}$ is

$$\text{var}(\hat{\beta}) = \sigma_u^2 \sum_{i=1}^{n} c_i^2$$

The problem now is to minimize var $(\hat{\beta})$ subject to the conditions (2-23). We define

$$\varphi = \sum_{i=1}^{n} c_i^2 - 2\lambda \sum_{i=1}^{n} c_i - 2\mu\left(\sum_{i=1}^{n} c_i X_i - 1\right)$$

where λ and μ are Lagrangian multipliers. Differentiating φ partially with respect to c_i $(i = 1, \ldots, n)$, λ, and μ and equating to zero and rearranging gives the equations

$$c_i = \lambda + \mu X_i \qquad i = 1, \ldots, n \tag{2-24}$$

$$\Sigma c_i = 0 \tag{2-25}$$

$$\Sigma c_i X_i = 1 \tag{2-26}$$

Summing (2-24) over all values of i gives $\lambda = -\mu\bar{X}$, which on resubstitution in (2-24) yields

$$c_i = \mu(X_i - \bar{X}) = \mu x_i$$

Multiplying through this equation by X_i, summing over i, and using (2-26) gives

$$\mu \Sigma x_i X_i = \Sigma c_i X_i = 1$$

Hence

$$\mu = \frac{1}{\Sigma x_i X_i} = \frac{1}{\sum_{i=1}^{n} x_i^2}$$

Therefore

$$c_i = \frac{x_i}{\sum_{i=1}^{n} x_i^2} \qquad i = 1, \ldots, n \tag{2-27}$$

It is seen that the weights c_i are identical with the least-squares weights w_i, as defined in (2-13), so that the best linear unbiased estimator of β is $\Sigma x_i y_i/\Sigma x_i^2$ as before. A similar development to the above can also be obtained for $\hat{\alpha}$. This is a simple case of the famous Gauss–Markoff result on least squares.[1]

Summarizing the results so far, we have that if $Y_i = \alpha + \beta X_i + u_i$ $(i = 1, \ldots, n)$, where the u_i have zero expectation, constant variance σ_u^2, and zero covariances and the X_i are fixed constants, then the least-square estimators

$$\hat{\beta} = \frac{\sum_{i=1}^{n} x_i y_i}{\sum_{i=1}^{n} x_i^2} = \frac{\sum_{i=1}^{n} x_i Y_i}{\sum_{i=1}^{n} x_i^2} = \frac{n \sum_{i=1}^{n} X_i Y_i - \left(\sum_{i=1}^{n} X_i\right)\left(\sum_{i=1}^{n} Y_i\right)}{n \sum_{i=1}^{n} X_i^2 - \left(\sum_{i=1}^{n} X_i\right)^2}$$

$$\hat{\alpha} = \bar{Y} - \hat{\beta}\bar{X}$$

[1] F. N. David and J. Neyman, "Extension of the Markoff Theorem on Least Squares," *Statist. Research Mems.*, vol. 2, pp. 105–116, 1938.

are best linear unbiased estimators of α and β, and their variances are

$$\operatorname{var}(\hat{\alpha}) = \frac{\sigma_u^2 \Sigma X_i^2}{n \Sigma x_i^2} \qquad \operatorname{var}(\hat{\beta}) = \frac{\sigma_u^2}{\Sigma x_i^2}$$

It seems intuitively plausible to base an estimate of the variance of the disturbance term σ_u^2 on the squared residuals about the least-squares line. Referring to Fig. 2-3, we have

$$e_i = y_i - \hat{\beta} x_i$$

and if we average $Y_i = \alpha + \beta X_i + u_i$ over the n sample values, we obtain $\bar{Y} = \alpha + \beta \bar{X} + \bar{u}$, so that

$$y_i = \beta x_i + (u_i - \bar{u})$$

Hence

$$e_i = -(\hat{\beta} - \beta) x_i + (u_i - \bar{u})$$

Therefore

$$\sum_{i=1}^{n} e_i^2 = (\hat{\beta} - \beta)^2 \sum_{i=1}^{n} x_i^2 + \sum_{i=1}^{n} (u_i - \bar{u})^2 - 2(\hat{\beta} - \beta) \sum_{i=1}^{n} x_i (u_i - \bar{u})$$

Taking expected values of each term on the right-hand side gives

$$E[(\hat{\beta} - \beta)^2 \Sigma x_i^2] = \sigma_u^2 \qquad \text{using (2-18)}$$

$$E\left[\sum_{i=1}^{n} (u_i - \bar{u})^2\right] = E\left[\sum_{i=1}^{n} u_i^2 - \frac{1}{n}\left(\sum_{i=1}^{n} u_i\right)^2\right]$$
$$= (n-1)\sigma_u^2$$

$$E[(\hat{\beta} - \beta) \Sigma x_i (u_i - \bar{u})] = E\left[\frac{\Sigma u_i x_i}{\Sigma x_i^2} (\Sigma u_i x_i - \bar{u} \Sigma x_i)\right] \qquad \text{using (2-16)}$$
$$= E\left[\frac{(\Sigma u_i x_i)^2}{\Sigma x_i^2}\right] \qquad \text{since } \Sigma x_i = 0$$
$$= \sigma_u^2$$

Hence

$$E\left(\sum_{i=1}^{n} e_i^2\right) = \sigma_u^2 + (n-1)\sigma_u^2 - 2\sigma_u^2$$
$$= (n-2)\sigma_u^2$$

Thus if we define

$$\hat{\sigma}_u^2 = \frac{\sum_{i=1}^{n} e_i^2}{n-2} \tag{2-28}$$

$\hat{\sigma}_u^2$ is an unbiased estimator of σ_u^2.

So far we have made no assumptions about the probability distribution of the u_i beyond those of zero mean, constant variance, and zero covariances. If we postulate a normal distribution, then we can obtain maximum-likelihood estimators. Assumptions (2-5) combined with normality give the probability of obtaining the observed u's as

$$p(u_1 u_2 \cdots u_n) = \frac{1}{(\sigma_u^2 2\pi)^{n/2}} \exp\left(-\frac{1}{2\sigma_u^2}\sum_{i=1}^{n} u_i^2\right) du_1 \cdots du_n$$

Since $Y_i = \alpha + \beta X_i + u_i$ $(i = 1, \ldots, n)$ gives a linear transformation of u_i into Y_i and the Jacobian of the transformation is unity, the likelihood function for the sample is

$$L = \frac{1}{(\sigma_u^2 2\pi)^{n/2}} \exp\left[-\frac{1}{2\sigma_u^2}\sum_{i=1}^{n}(Y_i - \alpha - \beta X_i)^2\right]$$

and

$$\log_e L = -\frac{n}{2}\log 2\pi - \frac{n}{2}\log \sigma_u^2 - \frac{1}{2\sigma_u^2}\sum_{i=1}^{n}(Y_i - \alpha - \beta X_i)^2$$

Differentiating partially with respect to α, β, and σ_u^2 gives

$$\frac{\partial(\log L)}{\partial\alpha} = \frac{1}{\sigma_u^2}\Sigma(Y_i - \alpha - \beta X_i)$$

$$\frac{\partial(\log L)}{\partial\beta} = \frac{1}{\sigma_u^2}\Sigma X_i(Y_i - \alpha - \beta X_i)$$

$$\frac{\partial(\log L)}{\partial\sigma_u^2} = \frac{n}{2\sigma_u^2} + \frac{1}{2\sigma_u^4}\Sigma(Y_i - \alpha - \beta X_i)^2$$

On equating to zero and simplifying, the first two equations reduce to the least-squares equations already obtained.

$$\Sigma Y_i = n\tilde{\alpha} + \tilde{\beta}\Sigma X_i$$

$$\Sigma X_i Y_i = \tilde{\alpha}\Sigma X_i + \tilde{\beta}\Sigma X_i^2$$

where we use the tilde over a parameter to indicate a maximum-likelihood estimate of that parameter. The third equation then gives the maximum-likelihood estimate of the variance of the disturbance term as

$$\tilde{\sigma}_u^2 = \frac{1}{n}\sum_{i=1}^{n}(Y_i - \tilde{\alpha} - \tilde{\beta}X_i)^2 \qquad (2\text{-}29)$$

Since $\tilde{\alpha}$ and $\tilde{\beta}$ are identical with the least-squares estimators, it follows from (2-16) and (2-17) that they are linear functions of the u_i, which have a multivariate normal distribution. Thus $\tilde{\alpha}$ and $\tilde{\beta}$ themselves are normally distributed.[1] The means are α and β, since we have already shown these estimators to be unbiased, and the variances and covariance are given in formulae (2-18) to (2-20) above, so that the bivariate distribution of $\tilde{\alpha}$ and $\tilde{\beta}$ is determined. The variances and covariance, however, involve the unknown variance of the disturbance term σ_u^2. In order to test hypotheses about α and β and compute interval estimates, we need one further result. This is that $n\tilde{\sigma}_u^2/\sigma_u^2$ has a χ^2 distribution with $n - 2$ degrees of freedom and that this statistic is distributed independently of $\tilde{\alpha}$ and $\tilde{\beta}$.[2]

Let us recall the definition of the t distribution, that if z has a standard normal distribution $N(0, 1)$ and v^2 has an independent χ^2 distribution with r degrees of freedom, the quantity

$$t = \frac{z\sqrt{r}}{v}$$

has *Student's* distribution with r degrees of freedom.[3] The equation of the t distribution is

$$f(t) = c\left(1 + \frac{t^2}{r}\right)^{-(r+1)/2}$$

where c is an appropriate constant. This is symmetrical about a zero mean, and it approaches $N(0, 1)$ as r tends to infinity.

[1] See R. L. Anderson and T. A. Bancroft, *Statistical Theory in Research*, McGraw-Hill, New York, 1952, pp. 63–64.

[2] See A. M. Mood and F. A. Graybill, *Introduction to the Theory of Statistics*, McGraw-Hill, New York, 1963, pp. 328–333. This result will be proved for the general case of k variables in Chap. 5.

[3] See P. G. Hoel, *Introduction to Mathematical Statistics*, 3rd ed., Wiley, New York, 1962, pp. 271–275, or Mood and Graybill, *op. cit.*, p. 233. $N(\mu, \sigma^2)$ indicates a normal distribution with mean μ and variance σ^2.

For tests on $\hat{\alpha}$ we have[1]

$$\hat{\alpha} \text{ is } N\left(\alpha, \frac{\sigma_u^2 \Sigma X^2}{n \Sigma x^2}\right)$$

Hence

$$z = \frac{(\hat{\alpha} - \alpha)\sqrt{n\Sigma x^2}}{\sigma_u \sqrt{\Sigma X^2}} \quad \text{is } N(0, 1)$$

Further,

$$v^2 = \frac{\sum_{i=1}^{n} e_i^2}{\sigma_u^2} = \frac{(n-2)\hat{\sigma}_u^2}{\sigma_u^2}$$

has an independent χ^2 distribution with $n - 2$ degrees of freedom. Hence

$$t = \frac{(\hat{\alpha} - \alpha)\sqrt{n\Sigma x^2}}{\hat{\sigma}_u \sqrt{\Sigma X^2}} \tag{2-30}$$

has the t distribution with $n - 2$ degrees of freedom. In formula (2-30), $\hat{\sigma}_u$ is the estimated disturbance standard deviation, as defined in (2-28). It can be seen that the unknown true disturbance variance σ_u^2 has disappeared on the formation of the t quantity and we have a test function which depends solely on the sample observations and the hypothetical value of α.

To perform a two-tailed test of the hypothesis that $\alpha = \alpha_0$, we should substitute α_0 for α in (2-30) and see whether the resultant t value falls within an appropriate critical region determined from the t distribution with $n - 2$ degrees of freedom. To obtain a 95 per cent confidence-interval estimate for α, we should proceed as follows:

$$\Pr(-t_{0.025} < t < t_{0.025}) = 0.95$$

where $t_{0.025}$ is the value of t such that

$$0.025 = \int_{t_{0.025}}^{\infty} f(t)\, dt$$

[1] We are using two separate results here which are very important.
(1) If x is a random variable with mean $E(x) = \mu$ and y is defined as $x - k$, where k is a constant, then the mean of y is the mean of x less k.

$$E(y) = E(x - k) = \mu - k$$

(2) If x is a random variable with mean μ and variance $\sigma^2 = E[(x - \mu)^2]$, and y is defined as kx, where k is a constant, then the variance of y is k^2 times the variance of x.

$$E\{[y - E(y)]^2\} = E[(kx - k\mu)^2] = k^2 E[(x - \mu)^2]$$
$$= k^2\sigma^2$$

Substituting for t from (2-30) gives

$$\Pr\left[-t_{0.025} < \frac{(\hat{\alpha} - \alpha)\sqrt{n\Sigma x^2}}{\hat{\sigma}_u\sqrt{\Sigma X^2}} < t_{0.025}\right] = 0.95$$

The inequality statements inside the brackets may be rearranged to isolate α on one side of the inequality sign, and the probability statement rewritten as

$$\Pr\left(\hat{\alpha} - t_{0.025}\frac{\hat{\sigma}_u\sqrt{\Sigma X^2}}{\sqrt{n\Sigma x^2}} < \alpha < \hat{\alpha} + t_{0.025}\frac{\hat{\sigma}_u\sqrt{\Sigma X^2}}{\sqrt{n\Sigma x^2}}\right) = 0.95 \qquad (2\text{-}31)$$

so that the 95 per cent confidence limits for α are

$$\hat{\alpha} \pm t_{0.025}\frac{\hat{\sigma}_u\sqrt{\Sigma X^2}}{\sqrt{n\Sigma x^2}} \qquad (2\text{-}32)$$

In general, the 100 $(1 - \varepsilon)$ per cent confidence limits are

$$\hat{\alpha} \pm t_{\varepsilon/2}\frac{\hat{\sigma}_u\sqrt{\Sigma X^2}}{\sqrt{n\Sigma x^2}} \qquad (2\text{-}33)$$

In a similar fashion, to carry out tests on β, we have

$$\hat{\beta} \text{ is } N\left(\beta, \frac{\sigma_u^2}{\Sigma x^2}\right)$$

Hence

$$z = \frac{(\hat{\beta} - \beta)\sqrt{\Sigma x^2}}{\sigma_u} \quad \text{is } N(0, 1)$$

$$v^2 = \frac{(n - 2)\hat{\sigma}_u^2}{\sigma_u^2}$$

is an independent χ^2 distribution with $n - 2$ degrees of freedom. Hence

$$t = \frac{(\hat{\beta} - \beta)\sqrt{\Sigma x^2}}{\hat{\sigma}_u} \qquad (2\text{-}34)$$

has the t distribution with $n - 2$ degrees of freedom. It follows that a $100(1 - \varepsilon)$ per cent confidence interval for β is given by

$$\hat{\beta} \pm t_{\varepsilon/2}\frac{\hat{\sigma}_u}{\sqrt{\Sigma x^2}} \qquad (2\text{-}35)$$

These are tests on α and β separately. Joint tests can be obtained from the following result. The quadratic form of the joint distribution of $\hat{\alpha}$ and $\hat{\beta}$,

$$Q = \frac{1}{\sigma_u^2}[n(\hat{\alpha} - \alpha)^2 + 2n\bar{X}(\hat{\alpha} - \alpha)(\hat{\beta} - \beta) + \Sigma X_i^2(\hat{\beta} - \beta)^2]$$

has a χ^2 distribution with 2 degrees of freedom.[1] The quantity $(n - 2)\hat{\sigma}_u^2/\sigma_u^2$ has an independent χ^2 distribution with $n - 2$ degrees of freedom. Recalling the definition of the F distribution, it then follows that

$$F = \frac{Q/2}{\hat{\sigma}_u^2/\sigma_u^2} \tag{2-36}$$

has the F distribution with 2 and $n - 2$ degrees of freedom.[2] In (2-36) the unknown σ_u^2 will cancel out, leaving only the unknown parameters α and β. If we use the inequality

$$\Pr(F < F_\varepsilon) = 1 - \varepsilon$$

to read off the appropriate F_ε from the table of the F distribution and substitute this value for F in (2-36), we obtain a 100 $(1 - \varepsilon)$ per cent elliptical confidence region for α and β in the α, β plane. To test a joint hypothesis at the 100ε per cent level of significance that $\alpha = \alpha_0$ and $\beta = \beta_0$, we should substitute these values for α and β in (2-36) and observe whether or not the resultant F value exceeds F_ε, indicating rejection of the hypothesis.

Tests on σ_u^2 may be obtained by use of the χ^2 distribution. The probability statement

$$\Pr\left[\chi_{0.975}^2 < \frac{(n-2)\hat{\sigma}_u^2}{\sigma_u^2} < \chi_{0.025}^2\right] = 0.95$$

gives 95 per cent confidence limits for σ_u^2 as

$$\frac{(n-2)\hat{\sigma}_u^2}{\chi_{0.025}^2} \quad \text{and} \quad \frac{(n-2)\hat{\sigma}_u^2}{\chi_{0.975}^2}$$

and the same result may be used to test hypotheses about σ_u^2.

All the tests and estimation procedures derived so far in this chapter rest on the assumption that $X_1, X_2, \ldots, X_n$ are constants. It is important to understand the economic and statistical significance of this assumption and to see what would happen to our test procedure if it were relaxed. Statistically, the meaning of the assumption is that, if one computes, say, a 95 per cent confidence interval for β, this implies that if one were to take repeated samples of size n, with the X_i fixed, and compute an interval for each sample from (2-35), then approximately 95 per cent of these intervals would include the true value of β. Economically, this assumption is sometimes interpreted as a condition that the econometrician in obtaining his data must be able to hold one variable constant at predetermined levels, and that the usual statistical inferences do not hold if the data have not been obtained in this fashion. Since experimental control over variables is usually impossible in economics,

[1] See Mood and Graybill, *op. cit.*, p. 333.
[2] *Ibid.*, pp. 231–232.

the outlook seems bleak and most of this statistical theory irrelevant, but fortunately the state of affairs is not quite as black as this.

There are, in fact, two possible lines of approach. One is to say that no matter how the X, Y data have been obtained, if the assumptions about the *conditional* distribution of Y_i, given X_i, made in (2-5) are valid, then our probability statements about confidence intervals and powers of tests are still valid, but they are statements of *conditional* probabilities for the given X values. These conditional statements, valid as they are, may not, however, seem very interesting or relevant for the economic or social situation under study. The alternative is to assume that the X_i are also random variables and to examine what meaning or usefulness now attaches to our procedures.

Assume that the X_i have a multivariate density function $g(X_1, X_2, \ldots, X_n)$ and assume also that the conditional distributions of the Y_i, given X_i, are normal and independent with expectations given by $E(Y_i|X_i) = \alpha + \beta X_i$ and with constant variance denoted by σ_u^2. The likelihood function for the sample observations is then

$$L = g(X_1, X_2, \ldots, X_n)\frac{1}{(2\pi\sigma_u^2)^{n/2}} \exp\left[-\frac{1}{2\sigma_u^2}\sum_{i=1}^{n}(Y_i - \alpha - \beta X_i)^2\right] \tag{2-37}$$

On the assumption that the distribution $g(X_1, X_2, \ldots, X_n)$ does *not* involve the parameters $\alpha, \beta, \sigma_u^2$, the maximum-likelihood estimators of these parameters (from 2-37) are easily shown to be

$$\tilde{\beta} = \frac{\Sigma x_i y_i}{\Sigma x_i^2}$$

$$\tilde{\alpha} = \bar{Y} - \tilde{\beta}\bar{X}$$

$$\tilde{\sigma}_u^2 = \frac{1}{n}\Sigma(Y_i - \tilde{\alpha} - \tilde{\beta}X_i)^2$$

which are exactly the same as those obtained on page 26 above for the case of fixed X_i. These may be shown to have the same means as before by the use of the following important lemma.

Lemma: If $f(X, Y)$ is the joint distribution of two random variables X and Y and if $h(X, Y)$ is any function such that $E[h(X, Y)]$ exists, then

$$E[h(X, Y)] = E_X\{E_{Y|X}[h(X, Y)]\}$$

where $E_{Y|X}$ = expected value in the *conditional* distribution of Y, given X

E_X = expected value in the *marginal* distribution of X

Proof. Let $f(X, Y) = k(Y|X)g(X)$.

$$E[h(X, Y)] = \int_{-\infty}^{\infty}\int_{-\infty}^{\infty} h(X, Y)f(X, Y)\,dY\,dX$$

$$= \int_{-\infty}^{\infty}\int_{-\infty}^{\infty} h(X, Y)k(Y|X)g(X)\,dY\,dX$$

$$= \int_{-\infty}^{\infty}\left[\int_{-\infty}^{\infty} h(X, Y)k(Y|X)\,dY\right] g(x)\,dX$$

The term in brackets is $E_{Y|X}[h(X, Y)]$, which is a function of X only. Thus

$$E[h(X, Y)] = \int_{-\infty}^{\infty} E_{Y|X}[h(X, Y)]g(X)\,dX$$

$$= E_X\{E_{Y|X}[h(X, Y)]\}$$

We have already shown in (2-12) and (2-13) that

$$\tilde{\beta} = \hat{\beta} = \Sigma w_i Y_i$$

where $w_i = x_i/\Sigma x_i^2$, and in (2-16) that the expected value of $\tilde{\beta}$, for given X, is β, that is, that

$$E_{Y|X}(\tilde{\beta}) = \beta$$

For the case of X and Y both being random variables, we have

$$E(\tilde{\beta}) = E_X[E_{Y|X}(\tilde{\beta})]$$

$$= E_X(\beta)$$

$$= \beta$$

since the distribution of the X values does not involve β. Similarly, it may be shown that $E(\tilde{\alpha}) = \alpha$ and $E(\tilde{\sigma}_u^2) = (n - 2)\sigma_u^2/n$.

Turning now to probability statements such as (2-31) and the associated confidence intervals for α and β, we recall that these involve *Student's t* distribution on the assumption of fixed X_i. The type of probability statement is

$$\Pr(-t_{\varepsilon/2} < t < t_{\varepsilon/2}) = 1 - \varepsilon$$

where t is some function of the observations on X and Y. Denote the conditional distribution of this t variable for given X_i by $f(t|X_1, \ldots, X_n)$ and let the density function of the X_i be $g(X_1, X_2, \ldots, X_n)$. The joint density for t, $X_1, X_2, \ldots, X_n$ is then given by

$$h(t, X_1, \ldots, X_n) = f(t|X_1, \ldots, X_n)g(X_1, \ldots, X_n).$$

Our probability statement is

$$1 - \varepsilon = \Pr(-t_{\varepsilon/2} < t < t_{\varepsilon/2})$$

$$= \int_{-t_{\varepsilon/2}}^{t_{\varepsilon/2}} f(t|X_1, \dots, X_n)\, dt$$

$$= \int_{-\infty}^{\infty} \cdots \int_{-\infty}^{\infty} \int_{-t_{\varepsilon/2}}^{t_{\varepsilon/2}} f(t|X_1, \dots, X_n) g(X_1, \dots, X_n)\, dt\, dX_1 \dots dX_n$$

since the integral of $g(X_1, \dots, X_n)$ over the range of the X_i values is unity. Thus

$$1 - \varepsilon = \int_{-\infty}^{\infty} \cdots \int_{-\infty}^{\infty} \int_{-t_{\varepsilon/2}}^{t_{\varepsilon/2}} h(t, X_1, \dots, X_n)\, dt\, dX_1 \cdots dX_n \qquad \text{(2-38)}$$

Thus our original probability statement is still true when the X_i are random variables. We can therefore compute confidence intervals by formulae (2-33) and (2-35) exactly as before, but the interpretation of the confidence coefficient is now that if we take repeated samples where the X_i as well as the Y_i may change from sample to sample, approximately $100(1 - \varepsilon)$ per cent of our confidence intervals will contain the true value.

The probabilities of type I error for our initial tests on α and β also depend on these same t distributions. By a similar argument to the above it can be seen that these probabilities remain unaltered when the X_i are taken to be random variables. Thus our original procedures turn out to be still valid and important when our original assumptions are extended to make the X_i random variables. It is important, however, to emphasize that this extended validity of the initial results depends upon the X, Y distribution being such that the conditional distribution of Y, given X, still fulfills the assumptions made in (2-5) above.

2-3 THE CORRELATION COEFFICIENT

Elementary treatments of the relationship between two variables usually emphasize the correlation coefficient as well as the principle of least squares. We have developed the application of least squares and also of maximum-likelihood estimators in the context of specific assumptions about the generation of the X, Y values and the nature of the disturbance term. We now proceed to show the link between correlation analysis and our treatment above and also to develop the analysis of variance for the two-variable case.

Assume a sample of X_i, Y_i observations ($i = 1, \dots, n$) which are represented on a scatter diagram as in Fig. 2-4. Divide the diagram into four quadrants by erecting perpendiculars to the axes at $\bar{X}$ and $\bar{Y}$. For any point P with coordinates (X_i, Y_i), define the deviations $x_i = X_i - \bar{X}$ and $y_i = Y_i - \bar{Y}$.

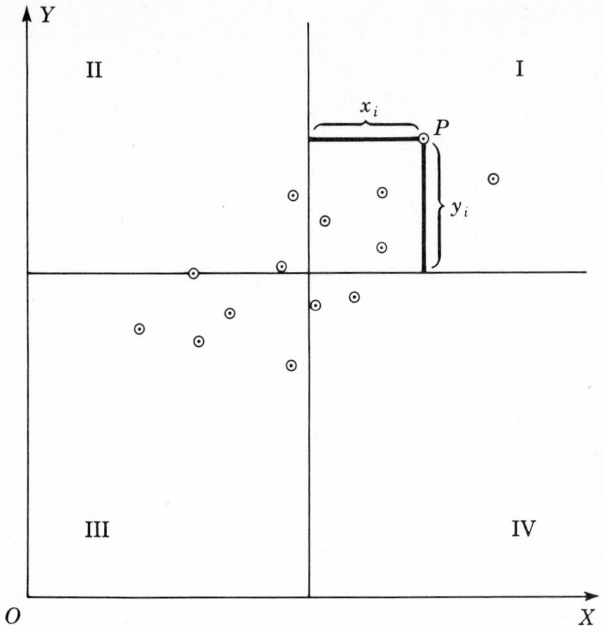

Fig. 2-4.

It is clear from inspection of the diagram that

For all points in quadrant I the product $x_i y_i$ is positive
For all points in quadrant II the product $x_i y_i$ is negative
For all points in quadrant III the product $x_i y_i$ is positive
For all points in quadrant IV the product $x_i y_i$ is negative

Hence the quantity $\sum_{i=1}^{n} x_i y_i$ serves as a measure of association between X and Y, for if the association is positive, so that most points lie in quadrants I and III, Σxy tends to be positive, while if the association is negative, so that most points lie in quadrants II and IV, Σxy tends to be negative, while if no relation exists between X and Y, the points will be scattered over all four quadrants and Σxy will tend to be very small.

The measure has two defects as it stands. Its numerical value can be increased arbitrarily by adding further observations, and it is also arbitrarily influenced by the units of measurement for X and Y. These defects are corrected by expressing the deviations in standard-deviation units and averaging to give the Pearsonian, or product-moment, coefficient of correlation

$$r = \frac{\Sigma x_i y_i}{n s_x s_y} \tag{2-39}$$

where

$$s_x = \sqrt{\frac{\Sigma x_i^2}{n}} \quad \text{and} \quad s_y = \sqrt{\frac{\Sigma y_i^2}{n}}$$

Alternative forms for r such as

$$r = \frac{\Sigma xy}{\sqrt{(\Sigma x^2)(\Sigma y^2)}} = \frac{n\Sigma XY - (\Sigma X)(\Sigma Y)}{\sqrt{n\Sigma X^2 - (\Sigma X)^2}\sqrt{n\Sigma Y^2 - (\Sigma Y)^2}} \tag{2-40}$$

are easily developed from the basic definition in (2-39).

If we fit a least-squares line $\hat{Y} = \hat{\alpha} + \hat{\beta}X$ to the observations by (2-7) above, then we have some interesting relations. First,

$$\hat{\beta} = \frac{\Sigma xy}{\Sigma x^2} \quad \text{(2-10)}$$

$$= r\frac{s_y}{s_x} \quad \text{using (2-40)} \tag{2-41}$$

Second, from the definition of the least-squares line,

$$y_i = \hat{y}_i + e_i$$

Thus

$$\Sigma y_i^2 = \Sigma \hat{y}_i^2 + \Sigma e_i^2 + 2\Sigma \hat{y}_i e_i$$

But

$$\Sigma \hat{y}_i e_i = \hat{\beta}\Sigma e_i x_i \quad \text{using (2-9)}$$

$$= \hat{\beta}\Sigma x_i(y_i - \hat{\beta}x_i)$$

$$= 0 \quad \text{using (2-10)}$$

Thus

$$\Sigma y_i^2 = \Sigma \hat{y}_i^2 + \Sigma e_i^2 \tag{2-42}$$

In words, the total variation of the Y values about their sample mean can be partitioned into two parts. The first is the variation of the $\hat{Y}$ values about their mean $\bar{\hat{Y}}$.[1] This is often referred to as the sum of squares "due to," or "explained by," the linear influence of X. The second component is the *residual*, or "unexplained," variation of the Y values about the least-squares line. As we shall see below, (2-42) is the basis of the analysis-of-variance treatment of the two-variable case.

[1] Notice that $\bar{\hat{Y}} = \bar{Y}$; that is, the mean of the values on the least-squares line is equal to the mean of the actual Y values, for

$$\hat{Y} = \hat{\alpha} + \hat{\beta}X$$

$$\bar{\hat{Y}} = \hat{\alpha} + \hat{\beta}\bar{X} = (\bar{Y} - \hat{\beta}\bar{X}) + \hat{\beta}\bar{X} = \bar{Y}$$

Taking the ratio of the explained to the total sum of squares, we have

$$\begin{aligned}\frac{\Sigma\hat{y}_i^2}{\Sigma y_i^2} &= \frac{\Sigma(\hat{\beta}x_i)^2}{\Sigma y_i^2} \\ &= \hat{\beta}^2\frac{\Sigma x_i^2}{\Sigma y_i^2} \\ &= r^2 \quad \text{using (2-41)}\end{aligned} \tag{2-43}$$

Thus the square of the correlation coefficient, sometimes called the coefficient of determination, is equal to the proportion of the Y variance explained by the linear influence of X. An r value of 0.9, therefore, indicates that the least-squares regression of Y on X accounts for 81 per cent of the variance in Y.

Combining (2-42) and (2-43), we may write

$$r^2 = 1 - \frac{\Sigma e_i^2}{\Sigma y_i^2} \tag{2-44}$$

from which it is clear that the maximum value of r^2 must be unity, and this can occur only when $\Sigma e_i^2 = 0$, that is, when each and every e_i is zero, so that the points on the scatter diagram lie on a straight line. Thus the limits of r are ± 1, the sign being determined by the sign of the product-moment term Σxy. The minimum value of r^2 is zero, which occurs when $\Sigma e_i^2 = \Sigma y_i^2$, that is when the regression line is $\hat{Y} = \bar{Y}$ and the explained variation is zero.

2-4 THE ANALYSIS OF VARIANCE IN REGRESSION

The analysis of variance may be developed as follows. We have shown that

$$\frac{\hat{\beta} - \beta}{\sigma_u/\sqrt{\Sigma x^2}} \quad \text{is } N(0, 1)$$

Hence $(\hat{\beta} - \beta)^2\Sigma x^2/\sigma_u^2$ has the χ^2 distribution with 1 degree of freedom.[1] $\Sigma e^2/\sigma_u^2$ has an independent χ^2 distribution with $n - 2$ degrees of freedom. Hence

$$F = \frac{(\hat{\beta} - \beta)^2\Sigma x^2}{\Sigma e^2/(n - 2)}$$

has the F distribution with $(1, n - 2)$ degrees of freedom. If $\beta = 0$, then our F

[1] Using the basic theorem that if x is normally distributed with zero mean and unit variance, the sum of the squares of n random sample values of x has a χ^2 distribution with n degrees of freedom. See Mood and Graybill, *op. cit.*, pp. 226–227.

ratio reduces to

$$F = \frac{Q_1}{Q_2/(n-2)} \tag{2-45}$$

where

$$\begin{aligned} Q_1 &= \hat{\beta}^2\Sigma x^2 \\ &= \Sigma\hat{y}_i^2 \quad \text{using the development of (2-43)} \\ &= \text{“explained” sum of squares} \end{aligned}$$

and

$$Q_2 = \Sigma e^2 = \text{“unexplained” sum of squares}$$

Hence the hypothesis of no relationship between Y and X ($\beta = 0$) may be tested by computing the F value defined in (2-45) and rejecting the hypothesis at the 100ε level of significance if $F > F_\varepsilon$. This calculation is usually set out in an analysis-of-variance table as in Table 2-2. The explained sum ot squares may be computed variously as

$$Q_1 = \hat{\beta}^2\Sigma x^2 = r^2\Sigma y^2 = \hat{\beta}\Sigma xy$$

Table 2-2

Source of variation	*Sum of squares*	*Degrees of freedom*	*Mean square*
X	$Q_1 = \Sigma\hat{y}_i^2$	1	$\Sigma\hat{y}_i^2$
Residual	$Q_2 = \Sigma e_i^2$	$n-2$	$\Sigma e_i^2/(n-2)$
Total	$\Sigma y^2 = Q_1 + Q_2$	$n-1$	

The unexplained sum of squares is obtained simply as

$$Q_2 = \Sigma y^2 - Q_1$$

and the appropriate F value is the ratio of the two mean squares in the final column of the table.

Exactly the same test is performed when one tests the significance of a sample correlation coefficient. This test is performed by computing

$$t = \frac{r\sqrt{n-2}}{\sqrt{1-r^2}}$$

and inferring a significant correlation between X and Y if $|t| > t_\varepsilon$, where t_ε

is an appropriate value from the t distribution with $n - 2$ degrees of freedom.

$$t = \frac{r\sqrt{n-2}}{\sqrt{1-r^2}}$$

$$= \frac{\hat{\beta}s_x\sqrt{n-2}}{s_y\sqrt{1-r^2}} \quad \text{using (2-41)}$$

$$= \frac{\hat{\beta}\sqrt{\Sigma x^2}}{\sqrt{\Sigma y^2(1-r^2)/(n-2)}}$$

$$= \frac{\hat{\beta}\sqrt{\Sigma x^2}}{\hat{\sigma}_u}$$

since

$$\hat{\sigma}_u^2 = \frac{\Sigma e^2}{n-2} \quad \text{defined in (2-28)}$$

$$= \frac{\Sigma y^2(1-r^2)}{n-2} \quad \text{using (2-44)}$$

If one looks at (2-34), this is exactly the t quantity that would test the hypothesis $\beta = 0$. Squaring this quantity gives $t^2 = \hat{\beta}^2\Sigma x^2/\hat{\sigma}_u^2$, which is identical with the analysis-of-variance test described above, since the square of a t variable with γ degrees of freedom is an F variable with $(1, \gamma)$ degrees of freedom. Thus correlation, regression, and variance tests are all equivalent ways of testing the basic hypothesis of no linear relationship between Y and X.

To continue the numerical example on road casualties and licensed vehicles from Table 2-1:

$$\Sigma xy = 52{,}876.36 \qquad \Sigma x^2 = 169{,}495.64$$

$$\hat{\beta} = 0.31196 \qquad \Sigma y^2 = 17{,}619.64$$

Hence the explained sum of squares is

$$Q_1 = \hat{\beta}\Sigma xy = (0.31196)(52{,}876.36) = 16{,}495.31$$

and the unexplained sum of squares is

$$Q_2 = \Sigma y^2 - Q_1 = 17{,}619.64 - 16{,}495.31 = 1{,}124.33$$

The analysis of variance is shown in Table 2-3. $F = 16{,}495.31/124.93 = 132.0$ with $(1, 9)$ degrees of freedom. For these degrees of freedom $F_{0.01} = 10.56$, so that the data decisively reject the hypothesis of no relation between the two variables.

Table 2-3

Source of variation	*Sum of squares*	*Degrees of freedom*	*Mean square*
X	16,495.31	1	16,495.31
Residual	1,124.33	9	124.93
Total	17,619.64	10	

To obtain, say, a 95 per cent confidence interval for β, we substitute in (2-35)

$$\hat{\beta} \pm \frac{t_{\varepsilon/2}\hat{\sigma}_u}{\sqrt{\Sigma x^2}}$$

where

$$\hat{\sigma}_u = \sqrt{\frac{Q_2}{n-2}} = \sqrt{\frac{1{,}124.33}{9}} = 11.18$$

For 9 degrees of freedom, $t_{0.025} = 2.262$. Hence the 95 per cent interval is

$$0.3120 \pm \frac{(2.262)(11.18)}{(411.7)}$$

that is,

0.2506 to 0.3734

2-5 PREDICTION

Suppose we continue our two-variable model and pose the problem of predicting the *mean* value of Y corresponding to some given value of X, say, X_0, which may or may not lie within the range of the sample observations X_1 to X_n. Our prediction may take the form of a point or interval prediction. To take a point prediction first, suppose we define the predictor as an arbitrary linear function of the Y_i $(i = 1, \ldots, n)$, say,

$$\hat{Y}_0 = \sum_{i=1}^{n} c_i Y_i \tag{2-46}$$

where the weights c_i are to be chosen so as to make $\hat{Y}_0$ a best linear unbiased predictor.

Since we are still assuming

$$Y_i = \alpha + \beta X_i + u_i$$

we have

$$E(Y_0|X_0) = \alpha + \beta X_0 \tag{2-47}$$

and

$$\hat{Y}_0 = \alpha \sum_{i=1}^{n} c_i + \beta \sum_{i=1}^{n} c_i X_i + \sum_{i=1}^{n} c_i u_i$$

so that

$$E(\hat{Y}_0|X_0) = \alpha \sum_{i=1}^{n} c_i + \beta \sum_{i=1}^{n} c_i X_i$$

Hence $\hat{Y}_0$ will be an unbiased linear predictor of $E(Y_0|X_0)$ if and only if

$$\sum_{i=1}^{n} c_i = 1 \quad \text{and} \quad \sum_{i=1}^{n} c_i X_i = X_0 \tag{2-48}$$

The variance of $\hat{Y}_0$ is given by

$$\begin{aligned} E\{[\hat{Y}_0 - E(\hat{Y}_0|X_0)]^2\} &= E[(\Sigma c_i u_i)^2] \\ &= \sigma_u^2 \sum_{i=1}^{n} c_i^2 \end{aligned}$$

We thus define the function

$$\varphi = \Sigma c_i^2 - 2\lambda(\Sigma c_i - 1) - 2\mu(\Sigma c_i X_i - X_0)$$

which, on taking partial derivatives, gives

$$\frac{\partial \varphi}{\partial c_i} = 2c_i - 2\lambda - 2\mu X_i = 0 \qquad i = 1, \ldots, n$$

$$\frac{\partial \varphi}{\partial \lambda} = -2(\Sigma c_i - 1) = 0$$

$$\frac{\partial \varphi}{\partial \mu} = -2(\Sigma c_i X_i - X_0) = 0$$

From the first two of these equations we obtain

$$\Sigma c_i = n\lambda + \mu \Sigma X_i = 1$$

giving

$$\lambda = \frac{1}{n} - \mu \bar{X}$$

which, on substitution in the first equation again, gives

$$c_i = \frac{1}{n} + \mu x_i$$

Multiplying this by X_i, summing over i, and using the third equation gives

$$\Sigma c_i X_i = \bar{X} + \mu \Sigma x_i X_i = X_0$$

which gives

$$\mu = \frac{X_0 - \bar{X}}{\Sigma x_i X_i}$$

$$= \frac{X_0 - \bar{X}}{\Sigma x_i^2}$$

since

$$X_i = x_i + \bar{X} \quad \text{and} \quad \sum_{i=1}^{n} x_i = 0$$

Hence

$$c_i = \frac{1}{n} + \frac{(X_0 - \bar{X})x_i}{\Sigma x_i^2}$$

Substitution in (2-46) gives the best linear unbiased estimator as

$$\hat{Y}_0 = \Sigma\left[\frac{1}{n} + \frac{(X_0 - \bar{X})x_i}{\Sigma x_i^2}\right]Y_i$$

$$= \Sigma\left[\frac{1}{n} - \bar{X}\frac{x_i}{\Sigma x_i^2} + X_0\frac{x_i}{\Sigma x_i^2}\right]Y_i$$

$$= (\bar{Y} - \hat{\beta}\bar{X}) + \hat{\beta}X_0 \quad \text{using (2-10) and (2-11)}$$

$$= \hat{\alpha} + \hat{\beta}X_0$$

Thus the best unbiased linear estimator of $\alpha + \beta X_0$ is $\hat{\alpha} + \hat{\beta}X_0$, where $\hat{\alpha}$ and $\hat{\beta}$ are the familiar least-squares estimators.

It follows immediately that the variance of Y_0 is

$$E\{[\hat{Y}_0 - E(\hat{Y}_0|X_0)]^2\} = E\{[(\hat{\alpha} - \alpha) + (\hat{\beta} - \beta)X_0]^2\}$$

$$= \text{var}(\hat{\alpha}) + X_0^2 \,\text{var}(\hat{\beta}) + 2X_0 \,\text{cov}(\hat{\alpha}, \hat{\beta})$$

$$= \sigma_u^2\left[\frac{1}{n} + \frac{(X_0 - \bar{X})^2}{\sum_{i=1}^{n} x_i^2}\right] \quad \text{using (2-18) to (2-20)} \tag{2-49}$$

so that the variance of the prediction increases the further the X_0 value lies from the mean of the sample values employed to compute $\hat{\alpha}$ and $\hat{\beta}$. Since $\hat{Y}_0$ is a linear function of $\hat{\alpha}$ and $\hat{\beta}$, which have a bivariate normal distribution, it will have a normal distribution with mean $\alpha + \beta X_0$ and variance as given by (2-49). Since $(n-2)\hat{\sigma}_u^2/\sigma_u^2$ has an independent χ^2 distribution with $n-2$ degrees of freedom, the quantity

$$t = \frac{\hat{Y}_0 - E(Y_0|X_0)}{\hat{\sigma}_u\sqrt{1/n + (X_0 - \bar{X})^2/\Sigma x_i^2}}$$

has the t distribution with $n-2$ degrees of freedom. Thus a $100(1-\varepsilon)$ confidence interval for $E(Y_0|X_0)$ is

$$(\hat{\alpha} + \hat{\beta}X_0) \pm t_{\varepsilon/2}\hat{\sigma}_u\sqrt{\frac{1}{n} + \frac{(X_0 - \bar{X})^2}{\Sigma x_i^2}} \qquad \text{(2-50)}$$

The above development has concentrated upon obtaining a confidence interval for the *mean* value of Y associated with a given X value, X_0. Sometimes we may be more interested in obtaining a confidence interval for the individual Y_0 value associated with X_0, or alternatively, the problem may occur in a slightly different form, with a new pair of observations (X_0, Y_0) being obtained and the question arising of whether they belong to the same linear structure.

To deal with these problems we proceed as follows. If the same linear relationship holds, then

$$Y_0 = \alpha + \beta X_0 + u_0$$

$$\hat{Y}_0 = \hat{\alpha} + \hat{\beta}X_0$$

Define

$$z = Y_0 - \hat{Y}_0 = u_0 - (\hat{\alpha} - \alpha) - (\hat{\beta} - \beta)X_0 \qquad \text{(2-51)}$$

It follows immediately that $E(z) = 0$.

Squaring (2-51) and taking expected values,

$$\operatorname{var}(z) = E(Y_0 - \hat{Y}_0)^2 = E(u_0^2) + E\{[(\hat{\alpha} - \alpha) + (\hat{\beta} - \beta)X_0]^2\}$$

since u_0 is independent of the $u_1 \ldots u_n$ values influencing $\hat{\alpha}$ and $\hat{\beta}$. Thus

$$E(Y_0 - \hat{Y}_0)^2 = \sigma_u^2\left[1 + \frac{1}{n} + \frac{(X_0 - \bar{X})^2}{\sum_{i=1}^{n} x_i^2}\right] \quad \text{using (2-49)} \qquad \text{(2-52)}$$

Since z is a linear combination of normal variables it too is normally distributed. Thus $z/\sqrt{\operatorname{var}(z)}$ is $N(0, 1)$. The σ_u^2 term occurring in var (z) is unknown, but by the usual shift to the t distribution,

$$t = \frac{Y_0 - \hat{Y}_0}{\hat{\sigma}_u \sqrt{1 + 1/n + (X_0 - \bar{X})^2 \bigg/ \left(\sum_{i=1}^{n} x_i^2 \right)}} \tag{2-53}$$

has a t distribution with $n - 2$ degrees of freedom, and a $100(1 - \varepsilon)$ per cent confidence interval for Y_0 is

$$(\hat{\alpha} + \hat{\beta} X_0) \pm t_{\varepsilon/2} \hat{\sigma}_u \sqrt{1 + \frac{1}{n} + \frac{(X_0 - \bar{X})^2}{\sum_{i=1}^{n} x_i^2}} \tag{2-54}$$

To continue the previous numerical example, suppose the number of licensed vehicles rises to 10 million. What prediction should we make for road casualties on the basis of the estimated linear relationship for the decade 1947–1957? It should perhaps be emphasized that in a real situation one would not make a simple prediction from the statistical relationship unless a thorough examination of relevant factors such as road and travel developments, the nature and type of additional vehicles, and the uses to which they were to be put seemed to indicate the complex of accident-producing forces to be substantially unchanged.

Ten million vehicles gives $X_0 = 1{,}000$. Substitution in

$$\hat{Y} = 55.85 + 0.3120X$$

gives

$$\hat{Y}_0 = 367.85$$

that is, 367,850, as the expected number of road casualties. Applying (2-50), a 95 per cent confidence interval for this expected figure would be

$$367.85 \pm (2.262)(11.18)\sqrt{\frac{1}{11} + \frac{(1{,}000 - 519.18)^2}{169{,}495.64}}$$

i.e., 367.85 ± 30.50, or 337,350 to 398,350 road casualties.

Suppose much sterner penalties are introduced for dangerous driving and in the following year there are 8 million licensed vehicles and 270,000 road casualties. Does this indicate a significant change in the relationship, or might these figures easily come from the same relationship as before?

$$X_0 = 800 \qquad Y_0 = 270$$

$$\hat{Y}_0 = 305.45$$

$$\hat{\sigma}_u\sqrt{1+\frac{1}{n}+\frac{(X_0-\bar{X})^2}{\Sigma x^2}} = 11.18\sqrt{1+\frac{1}{11}+\frac{(280.82)^2}{169{,}495.64}}$$

$$= 13.95$$

Substituting in (2-53),

$$t = \frac{-35.45}{13.95} = -2.54$$

Since we are testing here for a reduction in road casualties, it is appropriate to use a one-tailed test. The 5 per cent value of t for 9 degrees of freedom is -1.833, and the 1 per cent value is -2.821. The computed value is suggestive of a reduction, being significant at the 5 per cent, but not at the 1 per cent, level.

REFERENCES

The elementary statistical theory used in this chapter is fully described in

1. A. M. Mood and F. A. Graybill; *Introduction to the Theory of Statistics*, McGraw-Hill, New York, 1963,

or in

2. P. G. Hoel: *Introduction to Mathematical Statistics*, 3rd ed., Wiley, New York, 1962.

A very lucid and compact survey of the same material is also available in

3. R. L. Anderson and T. A. Bancroft: *Statistical Theory in Research*, McGraw-Hill, New York, 1952, Chaps. 1–12.

The *algebra* of correlation and regression analysis is well set out in

4. G. U. Yule and M. G. Kendall: *An Introduction to the Theory of Statistics*, 14th ed., Griffin, London, 1950.

An excellent short treatment of estimation theory for the two-variable linear case is given in Anderson and Bancroft, Ref. 3, Chap. 13.

EXERCISES

2-1. The two normal equations for a least-squares line are

$$\Sigma Y = n\hat{\alpha} + \hat{\beta}\Sigma X$$

$$\Sigma XY = \hat{\alpha}\Sigma X + \hat{\beta}\Sigma X^2$$

Show by direct substitution from the first into the second that these are equivalent to

$$\hat{\beta} = \frac{\Sigma xy}{\Sigma x^2}$$

$$\hat{\alpha} = \bar{Y} - \hat{\beta}\bar{X}$$

where

$$x = X - \bar{X} \quad \text{and} \quad y = Y - \bar{Y}$$

2-2. The least-squares estimate of α in $Y = \alpha + \beta X + u$ is $\hat{\alpha} = \Sigma(1/n - \bar{X}w_i)Y_i$ where $w_i = x_i/\Sigma x_i^2$ with

$$\operatorname{var}(\hat{\alpha}) = \sigma_u^2\left(1/n + \bar{X}^2 \Big/ \sum_{i=1}^{n} x_i^2\right)$$

Show that no other linear unbiased estimate of α can be constructed with a smaller variance.

2-3. Let $\hat{\alpha} = \sum_{i=1}^{n} c_i Y_i$, where $Y_i = \alpha + \beta X_i + u_i$. Using Lagrangian multipliers, find the weights c_i $(i = 1, \ldots, n)$ which will make $\hat{\alpha}$ a best linear unbiased estimate of α and show that

$$c_i = \frac{1}{n} - \frac{\bar{X}x_i}{\sum_{i=1}^{n} x_i^2}$$

2-4. Show that if z_i are independent quantities from the same population, with variance σ^2, then the sampling variance of

$$b = \sum_{i=1}^{n} a_i z_i$$

is $\sigma^2 \sum_{i=1}^{n} a_i^2$. Observations Y_i are related to fixed quantities X_i and the quantities z_i above by the relations $Y_i = \alpha + \beta X_i + z_i$ $(i = 1, \ldots, n)$. If the values of X_i are

X_1	X_2	X_3	X_4	X_5	X_6
1	2	3	4	5	6

an alternative estimate of β is

$$\tfrac{1}{8}(Y_6 + Y_5 - Y_2 - Y_1)$$

Deduce the sampling variance of this estimate and compare it with the sampling variance of the least-squares estimate. (Oxford, Diploma, 1958)

2-5. From a sample of 200 pairs of observations the following quantities were calculated:

$$\Sigma X = 11.34 \qquad \Sigma Y = 20.72 \qquad \Sigma X^2 = 12.16$$

$$\Sigma Y^2 = 84.96 \qquad \Sigma XY = 22.13$$

Estimate the two regression lines and the variance of the estimated regression coefficient of Y on X. (R.S.S. Certificate, 1956)

(*Note*: The exposition in Chap. 2 concentrated upon the estimation of $\hat{\alpha}$ and $\hat{\beta}$ in $\hat{Y} = \hat{\alpha} + \hat{\beta}X$. One may similarly minimize the sum of the squared residuals measured in the X direction by fitting the line $\hat{X} = \hat{\gamma} + \hat{\sigma}Y$, where $\hat{\gamma}$ and $\hat{\sigma}$ are obtained from the formulae for $\hat{\alpha}$ and $\hat{\beta}$ by interchanging X and Y.)

2-6. Show that if r is the correlation coefficient between n pairs of values (X_i, Y_i), then the correlation coefficient between the n pairs $(aX_i + b, cY_i + d)$, where a, b, c, d, are constants, is also r. (R.S.S. Certificate, 1956)

2-7. Fat percentage (X) and solids-nonfat percentage (Y) are measured on milk samples of a number of dairy cows in two herds. A summary of the data is set out below. Calculate the linear regression equations of Y on X for each herd, and test whether the two lines differ in slope.

Herd A. Number of cows = 16.

$$\Sigma X = 51.13 \qquad \Sigma Y = 117.25 \qquad \Sigma x^2 = 1.27 \qquad \Sigma y^2 = 4.78 \qquad \Sigma xy = 1.84$$

Herd B. Number of cows = 10.

$\Sigma X = 37.20 \quad \Sigma Y = 78.75 \quad \Sigma x^2 = 1.03 \quad \Sigma y^2 = 2.48 \quad \Sigma xy = 1.10$

(R.S.S. Certificate, 1956)

[Note: If $\hat{\beta}_1$ is $N(\beta_1, \sigma_1^2/\Sigma x_1^2)$ and $\hat{\beta}_2$ is $N(\beta_2, \sigma_2^2/\Sigma x_2^2)$, where $\hat{\beta}_1$ and $\hat{\beta}_2$ are independent, then $\hat{\beta}_1 - \hat{\beta}_2$ is $N(\beta_1 - \beta_2, \sigma_1^2/\Sigma x_i^2 + \sigma_2^2/\Sigma x_2^2)$. If σ_1^2 and σ_2^2 are unknown, then a shift to the t distribution can be made if we assume $\sigma_1^2 = \sigma_2^2 = \sigma^2$ and pool the sum of squared residuals from each regression so that $(\Sigma e_1^2 + \Sigma e_2^2)/\sigma^2$ has a χ^2 distribution with $n_1 + n_2 - 4$ degrees of freedom.]

2-8. If $u = ax + by$ and $v = bx - ay$, where x and y are in deviation form, and if the correlation coefficient between x and y is r but u and v are uncorrelated, show that

$$s_u s_v = (a^2 + b^2) s_x s_y \sqrt{1 - r^2}$$

where s indicates standard deviation. (L.S.E., 1948)

2-9. For certain data, $\hat{y} = 1.2x$ and $\hat{x} = 0.6y$ are the regression lines expressed in deviation form. Compute r_{xy} and s_x/s_y. If $y = x + u$, compute r_{xu}, r_{yu}, and s_u/s_y.

(R.S.S. Certificate, 1948)

2-10. The table below gives the means and standard deviations of two variables X and Y and the correlation between them for each of two samples.

Sample	*No. in sample*	$\bar{X}$	$\bar{Y}$	s_x	s_y	r_{xy}
1	600	5	12	2	3	0.6
2	400	7	10	3	4	0.7

Calculate the correlation between X and Y for the composite sample consisting of the two samples taken together. Comment on the fact that this correlation is lower than either of the two original values. (R.S.S. Certificate, 1955)

2-11. Calculate the coefficient of correlation between the two following series:

	1935	1936	1937	1938	1939	1940	1941	1942	1943	1944	1945	1946
Deaths of children under 1 year (000)	60	62	61	55	53	60	63	53	52	48	49	43
Consumption of beer, bulk barrels	23	23	25	25	26	26	29	30	30	32	33	31

Eliminate the trend from *one* of the series graphically or otherwise and recalculate the correlation. Comment on the difference between the two values. (R.S.S. Certificate, 1954)

2-12. A sample of 20 observations corresponding to the regression model

$$Y = \alpha + \beta X + \varepsilon$$

where ε is normal with zero mean and unknown variance σ^2, gave the following data:

$\Sigma Y = 21.9 \quad \Sigma(Y - \bar{Y})^2 = 86.9 \quad \Sigma(X - \bar{X})(Y - \bar{Y}) = 106.4$

$\Sigma X = 186.2 \quad \Sigma(X - \bar{X})^2 = 215.4$

Estimate α and β and calculate estimates of variance of your estimates. Estimate the (conditional) mean value of Y corresponding to a value of X fixed at $X = 10$ and find a 95 per cent confidence interval for this (conditional) mean. (L.S.E., 1958)

2-13. Suppose that, for a set of T observations on x_t and y_t (denoted by $t = 1, 2, \ldots, T$) y_t is determined by

$$y_t = \alpha + \beta x_t + v_t \tag{1}$$

where α and β are unknown constants, the x_t are constants, and the v_t are random variables independently and normally distributed with zero mean and variance σ_v^2. Obtain confidence intervals for α and β. Suppose that, with the same model, Eq. (1) is written in the form

$$y_t = \gamma + \beta\left(x_t - \frac{1}{T}\sum_{t=1}^{T} x_t\right) + v_t$$

What would be the confidence intervals for β and γ, and what advantage would there be in this alternative procedure? (Cambridge Economics Tripos, 1968)

3
Extensions of the Two-variable Linear Model

The theory of Chap. 2 has been wholly concerned with linear relationships between two variables. Obvious extensions are now required, first to cover the case of nonlinear relationships between two variables, and then more generally to treat relationships between *more than* two variables.

3-1 TWO-VARIABLE NONLINEAR RELATIONSHIPS

Economic theory may suggest that the relationship between a certain pair of variables can be adequately represented only by a nonlinear form. Or, in the absence of any firm theoretical indications, an inspection of the scatter diagram may indicate the inappropriateness of attempting to fit a linear relationship. In such a case the two possibilities are to attempt to fit an appropriate nonlinear relationship directly to the data or else to seek an initial transformation of the data such that the relationship between the transformed data appears approximately linear and the techniques of Chap. 2 may be applied.

The most commonly used transformations are the logarithmic and the reciprocal, and a judicious choice of these can encompass a wide variety of nonlinear relationships. The difficulty is that making transformations to keep the calculations in a simple linear framework may lead to a violation of some of the basic assumptions underlying the linear techniques of Chap. 2. One has to guard against this by making those tests, described in subsequent chapters, which are available to check on some of the basic underlying assumptions. On the other hand, there are sometimes cases where transformations substantially improve the validity of certain basic assumptions; examples are given in Chaps. 7 and 8, in the treatments of autocorrelation and heteroscedasticity.

To illustrate the use of transformations, suppose we have a variable Z, growing at approximately a constant rate of $100g$ per cent per unit of time t. We then have the following table.

t	Z
0	$Z_0 = A$
1	$Z_1 = A(1+g)$
2	$Z_2 = A(1+g)^2$
3	$Z_3 = A(1+g)^3$
.	.
.	.
.	.

Since this is only an approximate relation, let us postulate a disturbance term v. If we assume here that the effect of a disturbance is, say, proportional to the trend value of Z, we may write

$$Z_t = AB^t v_t \tag{3-1}$$

where

$$B = 1 + g \tag{3-2}$$

Taking logs of both sides of (3-1) gives

$$\log Z_t = \log A + (\log B)t + \log v_t \tag{3-3}$$

and if we define

$$\begin{aligned} Y_t &= \log Z_t \\ X_t &= t \\ \alpha &= \log A \\ \beta &= \log B \\ u_t &= \log v_t \end{aligned} \tag{3-4}$$

(3-3) may be rewritten as

$$Y_t = \alpha + \beta X_t + u_t \tag{3-5}$$

The assumption of a multiplicative disturbance in (3-1) conveniently yields an additive disturbance in the transformed relation (3-5). One often has no strong *a priori* information on the appropriate assumptions, and in such a case one starts with the simplest possible assumptions and attempts, as far as possible, to check from the data on the validity of the assumptions made.

The coefficients α and β in (3-5) may be estimated by applying least squares to Y and X. By use of the transformations defined in (3-4) we can then estimate A and B of (3-1) and from B obtain an estimate of g, the rate of growth. An example is given in Table 3-1.

Table 3-1 Bituminous coal output in the United States, 1841–1910

Decade	*Average annual output* (1,000 *net tons*) Z	$Y = \log_{10} Z$	$X = t$
1841–1850	1,837	3.2641	−3
1851–1860	4,868	3.6873	−2
1861–1870	12,411	4.0937	−1
1871–1880	32,617	4.5135	0
1881–1890	82,770	4.9179	1
1891–1900	148,457	5.1718	2
1901–1910	322,958	5.5092	3

Inspection of the two least-squares equations in (2-7) shows that they could be further simplified if the X variable had zero sample mean. Since X stands for time in this example, we can easily achieve this result by taking the origin of time at the middle of the 1871–1880 decade and then inserting ± 1, ± 2, ± 3 in column 4 of Table 3-1, using 10 years as our unit of measurement for the variable X. The least-squares equations then become

$$\hat{\alpha} = \bar{Y}$$

$$\hat{\beta} = \frac{\Sigma X_i Y_i}{\Sigma X_i^2}$$

which give

$$\hat{\alpha} = 31.1575/7 = 4.4511$$

$$\hat{\beta} = 10.5285/28 = 0.3760$$

Taking antilogs, we have

$$\hat{A} = 28{,}260 \quad \text{and} \quad \hat{B} = 2.377$$

Thus

$$\hat{g} = \hat{B} - 1 = 1.377$$

This gives a rate of increase of 137.7 per cent per decade. The corresponding annual rate of increase is given by g', where

$$(1 + g')^{10} = 2.377$$

yielding

$$g' = 0.09$$

that is, a 9 per cent annual increase. The problem might also have been worked by taking X in units of a year so that the X values read -30, -20, -10, etc. This would give $\hat{\beta} = 105.285/2{,}800 = 0.0376$, with an antilog of 1.09 and an annual growth rate of 9 per cent as before. The coefficient of determination for (3-5) is 0.994, which indicates that the assumption of constant growth in (3-1) seems very reasonable for this series.

It is useful to have an idea of the various nonlinearities that can be transformed by using logarithms and reciprocals. The accompanying figures illustrate some of the main cases, where α and β are positive parameters and logs are always taken to base e. We also confine the illustrations to the positive X, Y quadrant.

Semilog transformation $Y = \alpha + \beta \log X;\ X = AB^Y$.

$$\frac{dY}{dX} = \frac{\beta}{X}$$

so that the slope decreases steadily as X increases. When $Y = 0, \log X = -\alpha/\beta$,

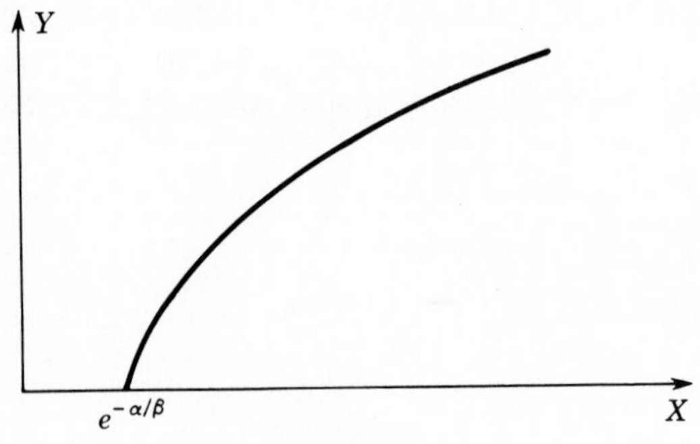

Fig. 3-1.

so that the point of intersection on the X axis is at $e^{-\alpha/\beta}$. The inverse of this function is $X = e^{-\alpha/\beta}e^{Y/\beta}$, which may be written

$$X = AB^Y$$

where

$$A = e^{-\alpha/\beta}$$

$$B = e^{1/\beta}$$

This is the steady-growth function employed in the previous example.

Double-log transformation

$$\text{(a)}\ \log Y = \alpha + \beta \log X \qquad \text{(b)}\ \log Y = \alpha - \beta \log X$$

These functions may also be written

$$\text{(a)}\ Y = AX^{\beta} \qquad \text{(b)}\ Y = AX^{-\beta}$$

where $\log A = \alpha$. For case (a),

$$\frac{dY}{dX} = A\beta X^{\beta-1}$$

so that, if β is greater than unity, the slope continually increases as X increases, while if β lies between zero and unity, the slope continually decreases, as shown in Fig. 3-2a. For either value of β, Y tends to infinity as X tends to infinity. For case (b), a value of unity for β produces a rectangular hyperbola, that is, the locus of a point such that the product of its coordinates XY is a constant. The double-log transformation is commonly employed by econometricians because it corresponds to the assumption of a *constant*

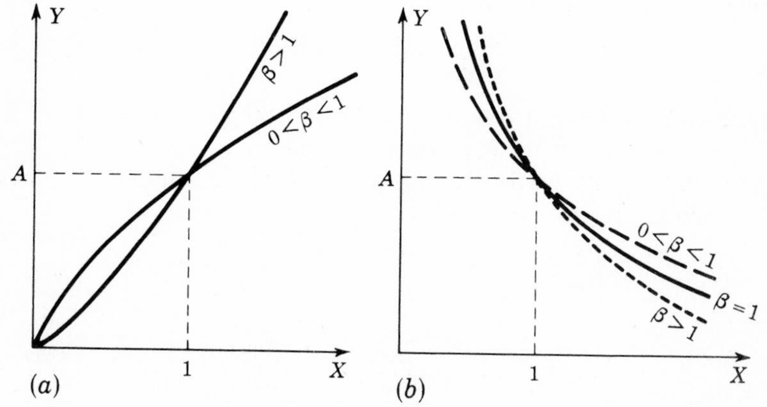

Fig. 3-2.

elasticity between Y and X and the simple application of linear methods to the logarithms of the variables produces directly an estimate of that elasticity.[1]

Reciprocal transformation

$$\text{(a)}\ Y = \alpha + \frac{\beta}{X} \qquad \text{(b)}\ Y = \alpha - \frac{\beta}{X}$$

Taking case (a) first of all, $dY/dX = -\beta/X^2$, so that the slope is everywhere negative and decreases in absolute value as X increases. As $X \to 0$, $Y \to \infty$, and as $X \to \infty$, $Y \to \alpha$. With a similar analysis for case (b) we have Fig. 3-3. The reciprocal transformation is thus useful if one wishes to build in the assumption of an asymptotic level, and an estimate of α is an estimate of the asymptotic level.

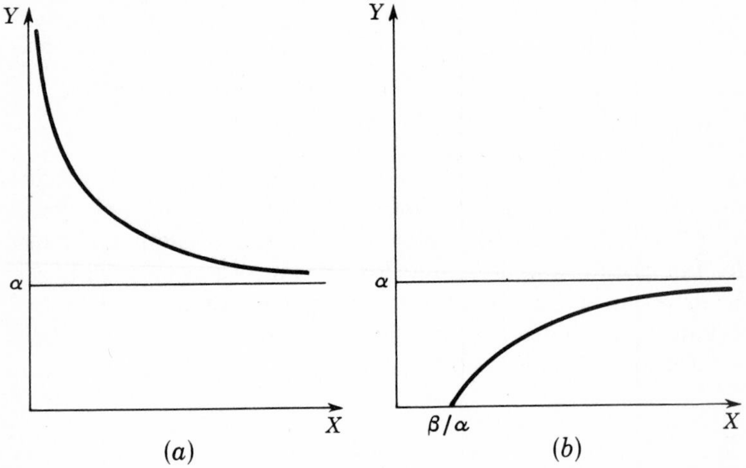

Fig. 3-3.

Logarithmic, reciprocal transformation Log $Y = \alpha - \beta/X$, or $Y = e^{\alpha - \beta/X}$. Y is not defined for X equal to zero but as $X \to 0$, $Y \to 0$ so we can define $Y(0)$ as zero and we then have a function which is right-hand continuous at the origin.

$$\frac{dY}{dX} = e^{\alpha - \beta/X}\left(\frac{\beta}{X^2}\right)$$

[1] The elasticity of Y with respect to X is defined as $(X/Y)(dY/dX)$. For case (a) this gives $(X/AX^{\beta})A\beta X^{\beta-1} = \beta$. For extensive illustrations of double-log applications in statistical demand analysis, see J. R. N. Stone, *The Measurement of Consumers' Expenditure and Behaviour in the United Kingdom*, 1920–1938, Cambridge, London, 1954.

Thus the slope is positive for positive X.

$$\frac{d^2Y}{dX^2} = e^{\alpha-\beta/X}\left(\frac{\beta^2}{X^4} - \frac{2\beta}{X^3}\right)$$

Hence there is a point of inflection where $X = \beta/2$. To the left of this point the slope increases with X; to the right of it the slope diminishes. As $X \to \infty$, $Y \to e^\alpha$. Thus we have Fig. 3-4. Curves of these types have been extensively used in the statistical analysis of consumer-budget data, where the assumptions of asymptotic levels of expenditure, varying marginal consumption rates, threshold levels of income for expenditure on certain commodities, and so forth, are often appropriate.[1]

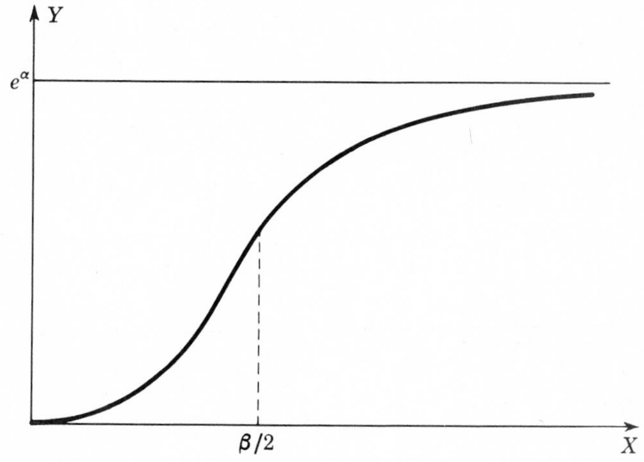

Fig. 3-4.

The second method of dealing with nonlinear relations is to fit nonlinear functions directly to the original data without the help of prior transformations. Unfortunately, standard principles like least squares or maximum likelihood often yield extremely complicated, or even insoluble, estimating equations, even for very simple nonlinear forms. For example, applying least squares to

$$Y = AB^X + u$$

[1] For detailed illustrations and examples the reader should consult S. J. Prais and H. S. Houthakker, *The Analysis of Family Budgets*, Cambridge, London, 1955.

would give

$$\Sigma Y_i B^{X_i} = A \Sigma B^{2X_i}$$

$$A \Sigma Y_i X_i B^{X_i - 1} = A^2 \Sigma X_i B^{2X_i - 1}$$

which would have to be solved for A and B.

One case where such difficulties do not arise is where Y is approximated by means of a simple polynomial in X. Two points can, of course, always be fitted *exactly* by a straight line (polynomial of the first degree), three points by a second-degree function, and n points by a polynomial of degree $n - 1$. One seeks, however, for a polynomial of as low a degree as possible. Suppose one attempts to represent Y by

$$Y_i = a + bX_i + cX_i^2 \tag{3-6}$$

The residual sum of squares is then

$$\sum_{i=1}^{n} (Y_i - a - bX_i - cX_i^2)^2$$

Applying the least-squares principle then gives the following set of normal equations to be solved for the unknowns a, b, and c.

$$\begin{aligned} \Sigma Y_i &= na + b\Sigma X_i + c\Sigma X_i^2 \\ \Sigma X_i Y_i &= a\Sigma X_i + b\Sigma X_i^2 + c\Sigma X_i^3 \\ \Sigma X_i^2 Y_i &= a\Sigma X_i^2 + b\Sigma X_i^3 + c\Sigma X_i^4 \end{aligned} \tag{3-7}$$

The fit obtained by such a nonlinear function may be measured by a coefficient analogous to the coefficient of determination r^2 of Chap. 2. One can measure the residual variance of the Y_i about the fitted function and then define the coefficient as 1 minus the ratio of the residual variance to the total variance in Y. The above approach may also be easily extended to polynomials of higher degree, but there is no need to elaborate this case further as it is really a special case of functions of three or more variables, to which we turn in the next section.

To illustrate the fitting of parabolas, consider the observations shown in Table 3-2 on page 55 of temperature made at intervals of 5 minutes during a chemical experiment.

To simplify the calculations we have defined

$$X = \frac{t - 30}{5}$$

$$Y = (T - 99.0) \times 10$$

Table 3-2

Time t, min (1)	*X* (2)	*Temperature T, °C* (3)	*Y* (4)	X^2	X^4
5	−5	99.2	2	25	625
10	−4	99.7	7	16	256
15	−3	99.9	9	9	81
20	−2	100.2	12	4	16
25	−1	100.3	13	1	1
30	0	100.4	14	0	0
35	1	100.4	14	1	1
40	2	100.3	13	4	16
45	3	100.0	10	9	81
50	4	99.8	8	16	256
55	5	99.4	4	25	625

Source: R.S.S. Certificate, 1955.

Equations (3-7) then give

$$106 = 11a + 110c$$

$$20 = 110b$$

$$688 = 110a + 1{,}958c$$

These give the parabolic regression of Y on X as

$$\hat{Y} = 13.9721 + 0.1818X - 0.4336X^2$$

Substituting for X and Y from the above relations gives

$$\hat{T} = 98.727 + 0.1077t - 0.001734t^2$$

To find the time at which maximum temperature occurs,

$$\frac{d\hat{T}}{dt} = 0.1077 - 0.003{,}468t = 0$$

giving

$$t = 31.06 \text{ min}$$

3-2 RELATIONS BETWEEN THREE VARIABLES

Suppose we have three associated variables, which we shall denote by Y, X_2, and X_3. For example, Y might represent the quantity of a commodity purchased by a household, X_2 the price of the commodity to that household, and X_3 the household income. A sample of n households would give related observations, which we can denote in general by

Y	X_2	X_3
Y_1	X_{21}	X_{31}
Y_2	X_{22}	X_{32}
$\vdots$	$\vdots$	$\vdots$
Y_i	X_{2i}	X_{3i}
$\vdots$	$\vdots$	$\vdots$
Y_n	X_{2n}	X_{3n}

where X_{ki} denotes the value of the variable X_k for the ith household. A linear hypothesis might then be written

$$Y_i = \beta_1 + \beta_2 X_{2i} + \beta_3 X_{3i} + u_i \qquad i = 1, \ldots, n \tag{3-8}$$

and the problem formulated as that of estimating the βs and the variance of the disturbance term. Relation (3-8) might also be written as

$$Y_i = \sum_{j=1}^{3} \beta_j X_{ji} + u_i$$

where $X_{1i} = 1$ for all i; that is, Y can be regarded as a linear function of X's, the sample values of the first X variable always being a set of units.

The full treatment of the general model for k variables will be given in Chap. 5. Our present objective is to give the reader a firm grasp and understanding of the basic concepts required in the analysis of a relationship between three variables so that extension to the general case is facilitated. For this purpose we concentrate upon the algebra of the analysis, and the connection between the various statistical measures will be simplified if we use a slightly different notation for our estimators than that developed in Chap. 2.

Let the least-squares estimate of the relationship (3-8) be denoted by

$$\hat{Y}_i = a_{1\cdot 23} + b_{12\cdot 3} X_{2i} + b_{13\cdot 2} X_{3i} \tag{3-9}$$

where we also define

$$e_i = Y_i - \hat{Y}_i \tag{3-10}$$

Relation (3-9) is referred to as the equation of the regression of Y on X_2 and X_3. It represents a plane in three-dimensional space: $a_{1\cdot 23}$ is the intercept made by the plane on the Y axis and is an estimate of the parameter β_1 in (3-8); $b_{12\cdot 3}$ denotes the amount by which a unit change in X_2 is expected to affect Y and is an estimate of β_2, while $b_{13\cdot2}$ is the amount by which a unit change in X_3 is expected to affect Y and is an estimate of β_3. The advantage of the subscript notation in (3-9) is that it clearly indicates the number of variables in the analysis. The figure 1 in the subscripts refers to the variable Y, the figure 2 to X_2, and 3 to X_3. The subscript 1·23 on a indicates that this is the intercept in the regression of Y on X_2 and X_3 since the figure 1 comes before the point and the figures 2 and 3 after it. In the subscripts to the b coefficients, the first figure indicates the variable on the left-hand side of the equation, the second indicates the variable to which this b coefficient is attached, and figures after the point indicate which other variables have also been taken into account in the estimation of the relationship.

There are three sets of sample statistics that may be employed in describing the relationship between three (or more) variables. The first set consists of the regression coefficients $a_{1\cdot23}$, $b_{12\cdot3}$, and $b_{13\cdot2}$. These are a simple extension of the regression coefficients in the two-variable case, the only difference being that in the computation of these estimates several explanatory variables have been taken into consideration.

In the two-variable case the coefficient of correlation r was defined in (2-44) as

$$r^2 = 1 - \frac{\Sigma e_i^2}{\Sigma y_i^2}$$

that is, the fit of a straight line to the two-variable scatter was measured in terms of the ratio of the sum of squared deviations of Y about the line to the total sum of squared deviations of Y about the mean. In the three-variable case we define the *coefficient of multiple correlation* $R_{1\cdot23}$ analogously in terms of the residual variation about the regression *plane*; i.e.,

$$R_{1\cdot23}^2 = 1 - \frac{\Sigma e_i^2}{\Sigma y_i^2} = 1 - \frac{s_{1\cdot23}^2}{s_1^2} \tag{3-11}$$

where

$$s_{1\cdot23}^2 = \frac{1}{n}\Sigma(Y_i - \hat{Y}_i)^2 = \frac{1}{n}\Sigma(Y_i - a_{1\cdot23} - b_{12\cdot3}X_{2i} - b_{13\cdot2}X_{3i})^2 \tag{3-12}$$

and

$$s_1^2 = \frac{1}{n}\Sigma y_i^2 \tag{3-13}$$

A new concept is that of the partial correlation coefficient. For example, we may ask whether an observed correlation between Y and X_2 is merely due to the fact that each is influenced by X_3 or whether there is a net association between Y and X_2, over and above the association due to the common influence of X_3. Thus in computing a partial correlation between Y and X_2, one attempts to remove the influence of X_3 from each and see what correlation exists between the "unexplained" residuals that remain. This is the statistical equivalent of the economic theorist's technique of impounding certain variables in a *ceteris paribus* clause. These partial correlation coefficients are denoted as follows:

$r_{12\cdot3}$ = partial correlation between Y and X_2, when X_3 is held constant

$r_{13\cdot2}$ = partial correlation between Y and X_3, when X_2 is held constant

$r_{23\cdot1}$ = partial correlation between X_2 and X_3, when Y is held constant

As we shall see, these partial correlation coefficients are intimately related to the regression coefficients in (3-9). Using the same subscript notation, we can indicate the simple correlation coefficients.

$$r_{12} = \frac{\Sigma(yx_2)}{\sqrt{(\Sigma y^2)(\Sigma x_2^2)}} = \text{simple correlation between } Y \text{ and } X_2$$

$$r_{13} = \frac{\Sigma(yx_3)}{\sqrt{(\Sigma y^2)(\Sigma x_3^2)}} = \text{simple correlation between } Y \text{ and } X_3$$

$$r_{23} = \frac{\Sigma(x_2x_3)}{\sqrt{(\Sigma x_2^2)(\Sigma x_3^2)}} = \text{simple correlation between } X_2 \text{ and } X_3$$

Similarly, we may indicate simple regression coefficients in the two-variable case, for example, $b_{12} = \Sigma yx_2/\Sigma x_2^2$ = coefficient of X_2 in the regression of Y on X_2.

We have, in fact, a hierarchy of coefficients. Examples of zero-order coefficients are r_{12}, r_{23}, s_1, etc. These coefficients have no *secondary* subscripts, that is, no subscripts after the point. Examples of first-order coefficients are $r_{13\cdot2}$ and $s_{1\cdot2}$, where

$$s_{1\cdot2} = \sqrt{\frac{1}{n}\Sigma(y - b_{12}x_2)^2}$$

the standard deviation of the Y values measured about the regression line of Y on X_2. An example of a second-order coefficient is $s_{1\cdot23}$, defined in (3-12). Coefficients of a given order can, in general, be expressed in terms of coefficients of the next lower order, and for three or four variables this often provides the simplest computational approach. For larger numbers of variables and extensive computations the general formulae developed in Chap. 5 are more useful.

3-3 FITTING THE REGRESSION PLANE

Using (3-9) and (3-10), the sum of squared residuals about the plane is

$$\sum_{i=1}^{n} e_i^2 = \sum_{i=1}^{n} (Y_i - a_{1\cdot 23} - b_{12\cdot 3}X_{2i} - b_{13\cdot 2}X_{3i})^2$$

Taking the partial derivative with respect to $a_{1\cdot 23}$ and equating to zero gives

$$\Sigma Y_i = na_{1\cdot 23} + b_{12\cdot 3}\Sigma X_{2i} + b_{13\cdot 2}\Sigma X_{3i}$$

i.e.,

$$\bar{Y} = a_{1\cdot 23} + b_{12\cdot 3}\bar{X}_2 + b_{13\cdot 2}\bar{X}_3 \tag{3-14}$$

Thus the least-squares plane passes through the point of means. Subtracting (3-14) from (3-9) we can rewrite the regression equation in deviation form,

$$\hat{y}_i = b_{12\cdot 3}x_{2i} + b_{13\cdot 2}x_{3i} \tag{3-15}$$

and express the sum of squared residuals as

$$\Sigma e_i^2 = \Sigma(y_i - b_{12\cdot 3}x_{2i} - b_{13\cdot 2}x_{3i})^2 \tag{3-16}$$

Minimizing with respect to $b_{12\cdot 3}$ and $b_{13\cdot 2}$ gives the two normal equations

$$\begin{aligned} b_{12\cdot 3}\Sigma x_2^2 + b_{13\cdot 2}\Sigma x_2x_3 &= \Sigma yx_2 \\ b_{12\cdot 3}\Sigma x_2x_3 + b_{13\cdot 2}\Sigma x_3^2 &= \Sigma yx_3 \end{aligned} \tag{3-17}$$

Solving these for $b_{12\cdot 3}$ and $b_{13\cdot 2}$ and substituting the results in (3-14) gives $a_{1\cdot 23}$ as

$$a_{1\cdot 23} = \bar{Y} - b_{12\cdot 3}\bar{X}_2 - b_{13\cdot 2}\bar{X}_3$$

Alternatively, (3-17) may be solved algebraically to give

$$b_{12\cdot 3} = \frac{(\Sigma yx_2)(\Sigma x_3^2) - (\Sigma yx_3)(\Sigma x_2x_3)}{(\Sigma x_2^2)(\Sigma x_3^2) - (\Sigma x_2x_3)^2}$$

which may be reduced to the following expression in terms of zero-order coefficients:

$$b_{12\cdot 3} = \frac{r_{12} - r_{13}r_{23}}{1 - r_{23}^2}\,\frac{s_1}{s_2} \tag{3-18}$$

Similarly,

$$b_{13\cdot 2} = \frac{r_{13} - r_{12}r_{23}}{1 - r_{23}^2}\,\frac{s_1}{s_3} \tag{3-19}$$

3-4 THE COEFFICIENT OF MULTIPLE CORRELATION

This is defined in (3-11) above but for practical computation it is more convenient to obtain a simpler expression for the residual variance $s_{1\cdot 23}^2$.

$$\begin{aligned} ns_{1\cdot 23}^2 &= \Sigma e_i^2 \\ &= \Sigma e_i(y_i - b_{12\cdot 3}x_{2i} - b_{13\cdot 2}x_{3i}) \quad \text{using (3-10) and (3-15)} \\ &= \Sigma e_i y_i - b_{12\cdot 3}\Sigma e_i x_{2i} - b_{13\cdot 2}\Sigma e_i x_{3i} \end{aligned}$$

but from (3-16)

$$\frac{\partial(\Sigma e_i^2)}{\partial b_{12\cdot 3}} = -2\Sigma e_i x_{2i} = 0 \tag{3-20}$$

and

$$\frac{\partial(\Sigma e_i^2)}{\partial b_{13\cdot 2}} = -2\Sigma e_i x_{3i} = 0 \tag{3-21}$$

since both these partial derivatives are equated to zero in obtaining $b_{12\cdot 3}$ and $b_{13\cdot 2}$. Thus

$$\begin{aligned} \Sigma e_i^2 &= \Sigma e_i y_i \\ &= \Sigma y_i(y_i - b_{12\cdot 3}x_{2i} - b_{13\cdot 2}x_{3i}) \quad \text{using (3-10) and (3-15)} \\ &= \Sigma y_i^2 - b_{12\cdot 3}\Sigma y_i x_{2i} - b_{13\cdot 2}\Sigma y_i x_{3i} \end{aligned} \tag{3-22}$$

Thus, since $R_{1\cdot 23}^2 = 1 - \Sigma e_i^2/\Sigma y_i^2$, we have

$$R_{1\cdot 23}^2 = \frac{b_{12\cdot 3}\Sigma y_i x_{2i} + b_{13\cdot 2}\Sigma y_i x_{3i}}{\Sigma y_i^2} \tag{3-23}$$

Substituting from (3-18) and (3-19), we may derive an alternative expression for $R_{1\cdot 23}^2$ in terms of simple correlation coefficients, namely,

$$R_{1\cdot 23}^2 = \frac{r_{12}^2 + r_{13}^2 - 2r_{12}r_{13}r_{23}}{1 - r_{23}^2} \tag{3-24}$$

From (3-20) and (3-21) we see that the residual term is uncorrelated with each explanatory variable X_2 and X_3. Hence the residual term is uncorrelated with the regression values $\hat{Y}_i$, for

$$\begin{aligned} \Sigma e_i \hat{y}_i &= b_{12\cdot 3}\Sigma e_i x_{2i} + b_{13\cdot 2}\Sigma e_i x_{3i} \\ &= 0 \end{aligned}$$

Thus, since $y_i = \hat{y}_i + e_i$, we can write

$$\Sigma y_i^2 = \Sigma \hat{y}_i^2 + \Sigma e_i^2$$

which is an exact parallel of the result obtained in (2-42) for the two-variable case, that the total variation in Y can be partitioned into two components, the "explained" variation due to the linear influence of X_2 and X_3 and the residual variation. From (3-23) it then follows that the explained variation may be computed from

$$\Sigma \hat{y}_i^2 = b_{12\cdot 3}\Sigma y_i x_{2i} + b_{13\cdot 2}\Sigma y_i x_{3i} \tag{3-25}$$

and $R^2_{1\cdot 23}$, called the coefficient of multiple determination, has the familiar interpretation of the proportion of the Y variance accounted for by the linear influence of X_2 and X_3.

Another illuminating way of looking at $R_{1\cdot 23}$ is that it is the simple correlation coefficient between the actual values Y_i and the regression values $\hat{Y}_i$, given by (3-9). To see this we write

$$\begin{aligned} r^2_{Y\hat{Y}} &= \frac{(\Sigma y_i \hat{y}_i)^2}{(\Sigma y_i^2)(\Sigma \hat{y}_i^2)} \\ &= \frac{(\Sigma \hat{y}_i^2)^2}{(\Sigma y_i^2)(\Sigma \hat{y}_i^2)} \end{aligned}$$

since

$$\Sigma y_i \hat{y}_i = \Sigma(\hat{y}_i + e_i)\hat{y}_i = \Sigma \hat{y}_i^2 \quad \text{for } \Sigma \hat{y}_i e_i = 0$$

Thus

$$\begin{aligned} r^2_{Y\hat{Y}} &= \frac{\Sigma \hat{y}_i^2}{\Sigma y_i^2} \\ &= R^2_{1\cdot 23} \end{aligned}$$

This result is perfectly general and holds for cases of one, two, three or more explanatory variables.

3-5 PARTIAL CORRELATION COEFFICIENTS

To calculate, say, $r_{12\cdot 3}$, we first of all eliminate the linear influence of X_3 from Y and from X_2. To do this we take the linear regression of Y on X_3, giving

$$Y_i = a_{1\cdot 3} + b_{13}X_{3i} + u_i$$

which may be written in deviation form as

$$y_i = b_{13}x_{3i} + u_i$$

The unexplained residuals in Y_i from this regression are given by

$$u_i = Y_i - a_{1\cdot 3} - b_{13}X_{3i} = y_i - b_{13}x_{3i}$$

Similarly, the unexplained residuals in X_2 after the removal of the linear influence of X_3 may be defined by

$$v_i = X_{2i} - a_{2\cdot 3} - b_{23}X_{3i} = x_{2i} - b_{23}x_{3i}$$

The partial correlation coefficient between Y and X_2, with X_3 held constant, is then defined as the simple correlation coefficient between u_i and v_i; that is,

$$r_{12\cdot 3} = \frac{\Sigma u_i v_i}{\sqrt{\Sigma u_i^2}\sqrt{\Sigma v_i^2}}$$

where we notice that u and v, being themselves residuals from least-squares regressions, have zero means. Thus

$$r_{12\cdot 3} = \frac{\Sigma(y_i - b_{13}x_{3i})(x_{2i} - b_{23}x_{3i})}{\sqrt{\Sigma y_i^2(1 - r_{13}^2)}\sqrt{\Sigma x_{2i}^2(1 - r_{23}^2)}}$$

applying (2-44) to each regression. Thus

$$r_{12\cdot 3} = \frac{\Sigma y_i x_{2i} - r_{13}(s_1/s_3)\Sigma x_{2i}x_{3i} - r_{23}(s_2/s_3)\Sigma y_i x_{3i} + r_{13}r_{23}(s_1 s_2/s_3^2)\Sigma x_{3i}^2}{\sqrt{\Sigma y_i^2}\sqrt{\Sigma x_{2i}^2}\sqrt{1 - r_{13}^2}\sqrt{1 - r_{23}^2}}$$

applying (2-41). Hence

$$r_{12\cdot 3} = \frac{ns_1 s_2(r_{12} - r_{13}r_{23})}{ns_1 s_2\sqrt{1 - r_{13}^2}\sqrt{1 - r_{23}^2}}$$

Thus

$$r_{12\cdot 3} = \frac{r_{12} - r_{13}r_{23}}{\sqrt{1 - r_{13}^2}\sqrt{1 - r_{23}^2}} \tag{3-26}$$

Similarly,

$$r_{13\cdot 2} = \frac{r_{13} - r_{12}r_{23}}{\sqrt{1 - r_{12}^2}\sqrt{1 - r_{23}^2}} \tag{3-27}$$

and

$$r_{23\cdot 1} = \frac{r_{23} - r_{12}r_{13}}{\sqrt{1 - r_{12}^2}\sqrt{1 - r_{13}^2}} \tag{3-28}$$

Comparing (3-18) and (3-26), we see that

$$b_{12\cdot 3} = \frac{r_{12} - r_{13}r_{23}}{1 - r_{23}^2}\,\frac{s_1}{s_2}$$

$$= \frac{r_{12} - r_{13}r_{23}}{\sqrt{1 - r_{13}^2}\sqrt{1 - r_{23}^2}}\,\frac{s_1\sqrt{1 - r_{13}^2}}{s_2\sqrt{1 - r_{23}^2}}$$

that is,

$$b_{12\cdot3} = r_{12\cdot3}\frac{s_{1\cdot3}}{s_{2\cdot3}} \tag{3-29}$$

Similarly,

$$b_{13\cdot2} = r_{13\cdot2}\frac{s_{1\cdot2}}{s_{3\cdot2}} \tag{3-30}$$

These last two formulae are the first-order equivalent of the zero-order relationship obtained in (2-41) for the two-variable case, namely,

$$b_{12} = r_{12}\frac{s_1}{s_2}$$

They show that the least-squares coefficients of the regression plane are, in fact, the simple regression coefficients between the pairs of residuals which are obtained by eliminating from each variable the linear influence of the third variable.

Finally, we may derive a further revealing way of looking at the partial correlation coefficients. It may be shown that[1]

$$s_{1\cdot23}^2 = s_{1\cdot2}^2(1 - r_{13\cdot2}^2) = s_1^2(1 - r_{12}^2)(1 - r_{13\cdot2}^2) \tag{3-31}$$

$$s_{1\cdot23}^2 = s_{1\cdot3}^2(1 - r_{12\cdot3}^2) = s_1^2(1 - r_{13}^2)(1 - r_{12\cdot3}^2) \tag{3-32}$$

Using (3-32) we can write

$$\begin{aligned} r_{12\cdot3}^2 &= \frac{s_{1\cdot3}^2 - s_{1\cdot23}^2}{s_{1\cdot3}^2} \\ &= \frac{s_1^2(1 - r_{13}^2) - s_1^2(1 - R_{1\cdot23}^2)}{s_1^2(1 - r_{13}^2)} \\ &= \frac{R_{1\cdot23}^2 - r_{13}^2}{1 - r_{13}^2} \end{aligned} \tag{3-33}$$

Now

$$\begin{aligned} s_1^2(1 - r_{13}^2) &= \text{variation in } Y \text{ unexplained by } X_3 \\ s_1^2 r_{13}^2 &= \text{variation in } Y \text{ explained by } X_3 \\ s_1^2 R_{1\cdot23}^2 &= \text{variation in } Y \text{ explained by } X_2 \text{ and } X_3 \\ s_1^2(R_{1\cdot23}^2 - r_{13}^2) &= \text{increase in explained variation in } Y \text{ due to } X_2 \end{aligned}$$

[1] For example, using (3-24), $s_{1\cdot23}^2$ may be expressed in terms of zero-order coefficients as $s_1^2(1 - r_{12}^2 - r_{13}^2 - r_{23}^2 + 2r_{12}r_{13}r_{23})/(1 - r_{23}^2)$, and the expressions of the right-hand sides of (3-31) and (3-32) may easily be seen to reduce to the same quantity.

so that $r_{12\cdot3}^2$ measures the proportion of the Y variation unaccounted for by X_3 that has been explained by the addition of X_2.

Similarly, from (3-31) we can derive

$$r_{13\cdot2}^2 = \frac{R_{1\cdot23}^2 - r_{12}^2}{1 - r_{12}^2} \tag{3-34}$$

that is, $r_{13\cdot2}^2$ measures the proportion of the Y variation unaccounted for by X_2 that is explained by the addition of X_3.

3-6 SUMMARY OF CALCULATIONS FOR THE THREE-VARIABLE CASE

1. First calculate the means $\overline{Y}$, $\overline{X}_2$, and $\overline{X}_3$, the zero-order standard deviations s_1, s_2, and s_3, and the zero-order correlations r_{12}, r_{13}, and r_{23}.
2. From the statistics in step 1 compute

$$r_{12\cdot3} = \frac{r_{12} - r_{13}r_{23}}{\sqrt{1 - r_{13}^2}\sqrt{1 - r_{23}^2}} \qquad r_{13\cdot2} = \frac{r_{13} - r_{12}r_{23}}{\sqrt{1 - r_{12}^2}\sqrt{1 - r_{23}^2}}$$

and

$$s_{1\cdot2} = s_1\sqrt{1 - r_{12}^2}$$

$$s_{1\cdot3} = s_1\sqrt{1 - r_{13}^2}$$

$$s_{2\cdot3} = s_2\sqrt{1 - r_{23}^2}$$

$$s_{3\cdot2} = s_3\sqrt{1 - r_{23}^2}$$

3. From the quantities in step 2 calculate the regression coefficients

$$b_{12\cdot3} = r_{12\cdot3}\frac{s_{1\cdot3}}{s_{2\cdot3}} \qquad b_{13\cdot2} = r_{13\cdot2}\frac{s_{1\cdot2}}{s_{3\cdot2}}$$

and

$$a_{1\cdot23} = \overline{Y} - b_{12\cdot3}\overline{X}_2 - b_{13\cdot2}\overline{X}_3$$

4. Finally, $R_{1\cdot23}^2$ may be computed from

$$R_{1\cdot23}^2 = \frac{b_{12\cdot3}\Sigma yx_2 + b_{13\cdot2}\Sigma yx_3}{\Sigma y^2}$$

or

$$s_{1\cdot23}^2 = s_{1\cdot2}^2(1 - r_{13\cdot2}^2) = s_{1\cdot3}^2(1 - r_{12\cdot3}^2)$$

and

$$R_{1\cdot23}^2 = 1 - \frac{s_{1\cdot23}^2}{s_1^2}$$

One may similarly build up to the four-variable case with coefficients of second and third order, which may in turn be expressed in terms of coefficients of lower order, but this approach becomes excessively tedious and cumbersome. The formulae also mushroom exponentially in number and complexity. We have, moreover, said nothing about the inference problems for the case of three and more variables. All these problems can be treated more efficiently if we make use of matrix algebra to cut through the jungle of subscripts and summation signs. This is done in Chap. 5. Chapter 4 presents a summary of the necessary matrix algebra, for those not already familiar with it.

REFERENCES

For practical illustrations of the use of logarithmic and inverse transformations, see

1. S. J. Prais and H. S. Houthakker: *The Analysis of Family Budgets*, Cambridge, London, 1955.

For the algebra of three and more variables consult

2. G. U. Yule and M. G. Kendall: *An Introduction to the Theory of Statistics*, 14th ed., Griffin, London, 1950.

EXERCISES

3-1. Given five observations $u_{-2}, u_{-1}, u_0, u_1, u_2$ at equally spaced points of time $t = -2, -1, 0, 1, 2$, show how to fit a parabola to the observations by least squares and show that the value given by the parabola at time $t = 0$ is

$$\tfrac{1}{35}(-3u_{-2} + 12u_{-1} + 17u_0 + 12u_1 - 3u_2)$$

(R.S.S. Certificate, 1955)

3-2. The "firmness" of cheese depends upon the time allowed for a certain process in the manufacture. In an experiment on this topic, 18 cheeses were taken and at each of several times firmness was determined on samples from three of the cheeses. The results (on an arbitrary scale) are given below:

Time, hr	$\frac{1}{2}$	1	$1\frac{1}{2}$	2	3	4
Firmness	102 105 115	110 120 115	126 128 119	132 143 139	160 149 147	164 166 172

Estimate the parameters in a linear regression of firmness on time. Give standard errors of the estimates and test the adequacy of a linear regression to describe the results.

(R.S.S. Certificate, 1955)

(*Note*: For the description of a test of linearity, see Yule and Kendall, Ref. 2, pp. 519–520.)

3-3. Discuss briefly the advantages and disadvantages of the relation

$$v_i = \alpha + \beta \log v_0$$

as a representation of an Engel curve, where v_i is expenditure per person on commodity i and v_0 is income per person. Fit such a curve to the following data, and from your results estimate the income elasticity at an income of £5 per week.

Pounds per week

v_i	0.8	1.2	1.5	1.8	2.2	2.3	2.6	3.1
v_0	1.7	2.7	3.6	4.6	5.7	6.7	8.1	12.0

(Manchester, 1956)

[*Note*: The elasticity of y with respect to x is defined as

$$\frac{x}{y}\frac{dy}{dx}.$$

But notice that the use of $d(\log x)/dx = 1/x$ implies that logs have been taken to base e. If logs to base 10 are used in the calculations, an adjustment must be made before a correct estimate of the elasticity is obtained.]

3-4.

Response rates at various levels of rateable values

Range of rateable value	A	B	C	D	E	F	G	H	I	J
Assumed central value, £/annum (X)	3	7	12	17	25	35	45	55	70	120
Response rate, per cent (Y)	86	79	76	69	65	62	52	51	51	48

The data relate to a survey recently conducted in England. Estimate the constants in the regression equation

$$\frac{100}{100 - Y} = a + \frac{b}{X}$$

(Oxford, Diploma, 1955)

3-5. In the following equation,

$$Y = a + bX + ct$$

the coefficients a, b, and c are estimated by least squares from n annual observations of X and Y; t is time measured in years. Show that the estimate of b is the same as that obtained from a simple regression of Y on X after a linear time trend has been removed from X.

(Cambridge, Economics Tripos, Part II, 1960)

3-6. X_1, X_2, and X_3 are three correlated variables, where $s_1 = 1$, $s_2 = 1.3$, $s_3 = 1.9$, and $r_{12} = 0.370$, $r_{13} = -0.641$, and $r_{23} = -0.736$. Compute $r_{13\cdot2}$. If $X_4 = X_1 + X_2$, obtain r_{42}, r_{43}, and $r_{43\cdot2}$. Verify that the two partial coefficients are equal and explain this result.

(L.S.E., 1952)

3-7. A steel bar 18 inches long is subjected to a carefully regulated hardening process. The hardness is determined at the extremities of the bar and at nine positions between the ends. The following results are obtained:

Distance from end of bar, d, in.	0	1.8	3.6	5.4	7.2	9.0	10.8	12.6	14.4	16.2	18.0
Vickers hardness number, h	250	276	298	335	374	414	454	503	558	604	671

It is required to determine a mathematical function to graduate the change in hardness along the bar. Two forms of function are suggested:

(a) $h = A + Bd + Cd^2$

(b) $h = \alpha e^{\beta d}$

Which of these formulae appears to give the better representation of the changes in hardness along the bar? (R.S.S. Certificate, 1951)

3-8. In the regression equation

$$y_t = \beta x_{1t} + \gamma x_{2t} + u_t \quad (t = 1, \ldots, n)$$

all variables are expressed as deviations from their sample means. Consider the following alternative procedures for estimating β.

(a) Calculate the estimates $\hat{\beta}$ and $\hat{\gamma}$ in a regression of y on x_1 and x_2.

(b) Regress y on x_2 and calculate the regression residuals y_t^*: regress x_1 on x_2 and calculate the regression residuals x_{1t}^*: regress y^* on x_1^* to obtain an estimate b of β.

Show that the two procedures give the same result, that is, $\hat{\beta} = b$.

Show that the regression residuals given by each procedure, that is,

$$y_t - \hat{\beta} x_{1t} - \hat{\gamma} x_{2t} \quad \text{and} \quad y_t^* - b x_{1t}^*$$

are the same. (L.S.E. 1969)

4
Elements of Matrix Algebra

It is clear from Chap. 3 that it would be excessively tedious and complicated to build up to the general case of k variables in a stepwise fashion. Fortunately, by the use of matrix algebra we can obtain a compact and powerful way of treating the general case, and we shall see that all the results of Chaps. 2 and 3 may be obtained from a few very simple matrix formulae. The rest of this chapter presents the elements of matrix algebra necessary for following the treatment in the remainder of the book.

We may write the linear relation in k variables as

$$Y = \beta_1 + \beta_2 X_2 + \cdots + \beta_k X_k + u$$

If we have n observations, they give the following set of equations:

$$\begin{aligned} Y_1 &= \beta_1 + \beta_2 X_{21} + \cdots + \beta_k X_{k1} + u_1 \\ Y_2 &= \beta_1 + \beta_2 X_{22} + \cdots + \beta_k X_{k2} + u_2 \\ &\vdots \\ Y_n &= \beta_1 + \beta_2 X_{2n} + \cdots + \beta_k X_{kn} + u_n \end{aligned} \tag{4-1}$$

When systems of equations like (4-1) occur frequently, it is convenient to have a neater and more powerful notation for handling them. The method we adopt allows us to write this system of equations as

$$\mathbf{y} = \mathbf{X}\boldsymbol{\beta} + \mathbf{u} \tag{4-2}$$

where the boldface letters indicate appropriately specified vectors or matrices.

4-1 MATRICES

A matrix is defined as a rectangular array of elements arranged in rows or columns as in

$$\mathbf{A} = \begin{bmatrix} a_{11} & a_{12} & \cdots & a_{1n} \\ a_{21} & a_{22} & \cdots & a_{2n} \\ \vdots & \vdots & & \vdots \\ a_{m1} & a_{m2} & \cdots & a_{mn} \end{bmatrix}$$

If it has mn elements arranged in m rows and n columns, it is said to be of order m by n, which is often written $m \times n$.

The element in the ith row and jth column is represented by a_{ij}. The matrix may be indicated even more concisely by

$$\mathbf{A} = [a_{ij}]$$

Alternatives to the use of brackets for enclosing the elements of a matrix are parentheses or pairs of parallel vertical lines.

A matrix of order $1 \times n$ contains only a single row of elements and is commonly referred to as a *row vector*, for example,

$$\mathbf{b} = [b_1 \quad b_2 \quad \cdots \quad b_n]$$

while a matrix of order $m \times 1$ is a *column vector*,

$$\mathbf{c} = \begin{bmatrix} c_1 \\ c_2 \\ \vdots \\ c_m \end{bmatrix}$$

To economize space, column vectors will be written in horizontal position but enclosed in braces, thus:

$$\mathbf{c} = \{c_1 \quad c_2 \quad \cdots \quad c_m\}$$

We now require a set of rules and definitions for operating with matrices.

Equality of two matrices Two matrices **A** and **B** are said to be equal when they are of the same order and $a_{ij} = b_{ij}$ for all i, j: that is, the matrices are equal, element by element.

Addition of two matrices If **A** and **B** are of the same order, then we define $\mathbf{A} + \mathbf{B}$ to be a new matrix **C** of the same order in which

$$c_{ij} = a_{ij} + b_{ij} \qquad \text{for all } i, j$$

that is, we add corresponding elements of **A** and **B** to obtain the elements of $\mathbf{C} = \mathbf{A} + \mathbf{B}$. For example if

$$\mathbf{A} = \begin{bmatrix} 2 & 0 \\ -5 & 6 \end{bmatrix} \quad \text{and} \quad \mathbf{B} = \begin{bmatrix} -3 & 6 \\ 4 & 1 \end{bmatrix}$$

then

$$\mathbf{C} = \mathbf{A} + \mathbf{B} = \begin{bmatrix} -1 & 6 \\ -1 & 7 \end{bmatrix}$$

Scalar multiplication If λ is a scalar, then we define scalar multiplication such that

$$\lambda\mathbf{A} = [\lambda a_{ij}]$$

that is, each element of **A** is multiplied by λ. For example, if

$$\mathbf{A} = \begin{bmatrix} 2 & 0 \\ -5 & 6 \end{bmatrix} \quad \text{and} \quad \lambda = -5$$

then

$$\lambda\mathbf{A} = \begin{bmatrix} -10 & 0 \\ 25 & -30 \end{bmatrix}$$

It follows from the rules for addition and scalar multiplication that

$$\mathbf{A} - \mathbf{B} = [a_{ij} - b_{ij}]$$

Matrix multiplication If **A** is of order $m \times n$ and **B** is of order $n \times p$, then the product **AB** is defined to be a matrix of order $m \times p$ whose ijth element is

$$c_{ij} = \sum_{k=1}^{n} a_{ik}b_{kj}$$

that is, the ijth element in the product matrix is found by multiplying the elements of the ith row of the first matrix by the corresponding elements of the jth column of the second matrix and summing over all terms. For this to be possible it is clear that the number of elements in a *row* of the first matrix has to be equal to the number of elements in a *column* of the second matrix, that is, that the number of *columns* in the first should equal the numbers of *rows* in the second. The matrices are then said to be *conformable* with respect to multiplication.

It is also of crucial importance to note the order of the matrices in multiplication.

In **AB** we refer to **A** being postmultiplied by **B** or to **A** premultiplying **B**. **BA** is usually different from **AB** and may not exist. The two products **AB** and **BA** will exist only if the matrices are of order $m \times n$ and $n \times m$. In this case the first product will be of order $m \times m$, and the second $n \times n$.

Example

$$\mathbf{A} = \begin{bmatrix} a_{11} & a_{12} & a_{13} \\ a_{21} & a_{22} & a_{23} \end{bmatrix} \qquad \mathbf{B} = \begin{bmatrix} b_{11} & b_{12} \\ b_{21} & b_{22} \\ b_{31} & b_{32} \end{bmatrix}$$

Then **AB** is a 2×2 matrix:

$$\mathbf{AB} = \begin{bmatrix} a_{11}b_{11} + a_{12}b_{21} + a_{13}b_{31} & a_{11}b_{12} + a_{12}b_{22} + a_{13}b_{32} \\ a_{21}b_{11} + a_{22}b_{21} + a_{23}b_{31} & a_{21}b_{12} + a_{22}b_{22} + a_{23}b_{32} \end{bmatrix}$$

while **BA** is a 3×3 matrix:

$$\mathbf{BA} = \begin{bmatrix} b_{11}a_{11} + b_{12}a_{21} & b_{11}a_{12} + b_{12}a_{22} & b_{11}a_{13} + b_{12}a_{23} \\ b_{21}a_{11} + b_{22}a_{21} & b_{21}a_{12} + b_{22}a_{22} & b_{21}a_{13} + b_{22}a_{23} \\ b_{31}a_{11} + b_{32}a_{21} & b_{31}a_{12} + b_{32}a_{22} & b_{31}a_{13} + b_{32}a_{23} \end{bmatrix}$$

We must be careful not to assume that the laws of ordinary scalar algebra necessarily hold for matrix algebra. Most do, but some do not. The following are the more important laws which we shall need for subsequent operations with matrices.

I. $\mathbf{A} + \mathbf{B} = \mathbf{B} + \mathbf{A}$: that is, the commutative law of addition holds. **A** and **B** must, of course, be of the same order, and the result follows directly from the definition of the addition of matrices.

Example

$$\begin{bmatrix} 2 & 3 \\ -5 & 0 \end{bmatrix} + \begin{bmatrix} 0 & -1 \\ -2 & 6 \end{bmatrix} = \begin{bmatrix} 0 & -1 \\ -2 & 6 \end{bmatrix} + \begin{bmatrix} 2 & 3 \\ -5 & 0 \end{bmatrix} = \begin{bmatrix} 2 & 2 \\ -7 & 6 \end{bmatrix}$$

II. $\mathbf{AB} \neq \mathbf{BA}$ except for rather special square matrices: i.e., the commutative law of multiplication does not, in general, hold. If the matrices are of order $m \times n$ and $n \times m$, then both products will exist, but they will be of different orders and hence cannot be equal. If both are square matrices of the same order, then both products will exist and will be of the same order but not necessarily equal, as the following examples show.

Examples

$$\mathbf{A} = \begin{bmatrix} 2 & 1 \\ 1 & 1 \end{bmatrix} \qquad \mathbf{B} = \begin{bmatrix} 3 & 0 \\ 1 & 2 \end{bmatrix}$$

$$\mathbf{AB} = \begin{bmatrix} 7 & 2 \\ 4 & 2 \end{bmatrix} \qquad \mathbf{BA} = \begin{bmatrix} 6 & 3 \\ 4 & 3 \end{bmatrix}$$

whereas if

$$\mathbf{A} = \begin{bmatrix} 2 & 1 \\ 1 & 1 \end{bmatrix} \qquad \mathbf{B} = \begin{bmatrix} 1 & -1 \\ -1 & 2 \end{bmatrix}$$

then

$$\mathbf{AB} = \begin{bmatrix} 1 & 0 \\ 0 & 1 \end{bmatrix} = \mathbf{BA}$$

III. $(\mathbf{A} + \mathbf{B}) + \mathbf{C} = \mathbf{A} + (\mathbf{B} + \mathbf{C})$: that is, the associative law of addition holds. Since addition of matrices is simply achieved by the addition of corresponding elements and since it does not matter in which order elements are added together, the associative law holds.

IV. $(\mathbf{AB})\mathbf{C} = \mathbf{A}(\mathbf{BC})$: that is, the associative law of multiplication holds. We can first form **AB** and then postmultiply by **C**, or first form **BC** and premultiply by **A**, for suppose

$$\mathbf{A} = [a_{ir}] \text{ of order } m \times n$$

$$\mathbf{B} = [b_{rs}] \text{ of order } n \times p$$

$$\mathbf{C} = [c_{sj}] \text{ of order } p \times q$$

then **AB** is a matrix of order $m \times p$ whose isth element is $\sum_{r=1}^{n} a_{ir}b_{rs}$. The matrix **ABC** formed by postmultiplying **AB** by **C** is a matrix of order $m \times q$, whose ijth element is

$$\sum_{s=1}^{p}\left(\sum_{r=1}^{n} a_{ir}b_{rs}\right)c_{sj} = \sum_{s=1}^{p}\sum_{r=1}^{n} a_{ir}b_{rs}c_{sj}$$

Similarly, the rjth element in (**BC**) is $\sum_{s=1}^{p} b_{rs}c_{sj}$, and the ijth element in **A**(**BC**) is

$$\sum_{r=1}^{n} a_{ir}\left(\sum_{s=1}^{p} b_{rs}c_{sj}\right) = \sum_{s=1}^{p}\sum_{r=1}^{n} a_{ir}b_{rs}c_{sj} = ij\text{th element in } (\mathbf{AB})\mathbf{C}$$

V. $\mathbf{A}(\mathbf{B} + \mathbf{C}) = \mathbf{AB} + \mathbf{AC}$, and $(\mathbf{B} + \mathbf{C})\mathbf{A} = \mathbf{BA} + \mathbf{CA}$: that is, the distributive law holds. For

$$\begin{aligned} ij\text{th element in } \mathbf{A}(\mathbf{B} + \mathbf{C}) &= \sum_k a_{ik}(b_{kj} + c_{kj}) \\ &= \sum_k a_{ik}b_{kj} + \sum_k a_{ik}c_{kj} \\ &= ij\text{th element in } \mathbf{AB} + ij\text{th element in } \mathbf{AC} \end{aligned}$$

VI. $\lambda(\mathbf{A} + \mathbf{B}) = \lambda\mathbf{A} + \lambda\mathbf{B}$, and $(\lambda + \mu)\mathbf{A} = \lambda\mathbf{A} + \mu\mathbf{A}$: that is, the distributive law of scalar multiplication holds.

These six results are important for the manipulation of matrices, and the student should get a firm grasp of them by working out arbitrary numerical examples.

Unit, or identity, matrix This is defined by

$$\mathbf{I}_n = \begin{bmatrix} 1 & 0 & \cdots & 0 \\ 0 & 1 & \cdots & 0 \\ \vdots & \vdots & & \vdots \\ 0 & 0 & \cdots & 1 \end{bmatrix}$$

a square matrix of order $n \times n$ with units in the principal diagonal and zeros everywhere else.

It is easy to verify that premultiplying or postmultiplying any matrix $\mathbf{A}$ by the unit matrix of appropriate order leaves $\mathbf{A}$ unchanged: that is,

$$\mathbf{IA} = \mathbf{AI} = \mathbf{A}$$

Scalar matrix A scalar matrix has a common scalar element in the principal diagonal and zeros everywhere else: e.g.,

$$\lambda\mathbf{I} = \begin{bmatrix} \lambda & 0 & \cdots & 0 \\ 0 & \lambda & \cdots & 0 \\ \vdots & \vdots & & \vdots \\ 0 & 0 & \cdots & \lambda \end{bmatrix}$$

For this reason we can always replace a scalar in a matrix product by a scalar matrix and choose the order of that matrix to suit our convenience. Scalar multiplication (already defined) is thus equivalent to matrix multiplication and may be thought of as pre- or postmultiplication, since

$$\lambda\mathbf{A} = (\lambda\mathbf{I})\mathbf{A} = \mathbf{A}(\lambda\mathbf{I}) = \mathbf{A}\lambda$$

For example,

$$\lambda\mathbf{A} = \lambda\mathbf{IA} = \begin{bmatrix} \lambda & 0 & 0 \\ 0 & \lambda & 0 \\ 0 & 0 & \lambda \end{bmatrix} \begin{bmatrix} a_{11} & a_{12} & a_{13} \\ a_{21} & a_{22} & a_{23} \\ a_{31} & a_{32} & a_{33} \end{bmatrix} = \begin{bmatrix} \lambda a_{11} & \lambda a_{12} & \lambda a_{13} \\ \lambda a_{21} & \lambda a_{22} & \lambda a_{23} \\ \lambda a_{31} & \lambda a_{32} & \lambda a_{33} \end{bmatrix}$$

$$= \mathbf{A}\lambda\mathbf{I} = \mathbf{A}\lambda$$

We thus see that the unit matrix may be inserted or suppressed at will in matrix expressions without altering their value.

Diagonal matrix A diagonal matrix has scalar elements, not necessarily equal, in the principal diagonal and zeros in the off-diagonal positions, i.e.,

$$\mathbf{A} = [a_{ij}] \qquad i, j = 1, 2, \ldots, n$$

$$a_{ij} = 0, i \neq j$$

that is,

$$\mathbf{A} = \begin{bmatrix} a_{11} & 0 & \cdots & 0 \\ 0 & a_{22} & \cdots & 0 \\ \vdots & \vdots & & \vdots \\ 0 & 0 & \cdots & a_{nn} \end{bmatrix} = \text{diag}\,[a_{11}\; a_{22} \ldots a_{nn}]$$

A scalar matrix is thus a special form of diagonal matrix.

Transposition In scalar algebra division follows simply as the inverse of multiplication. In matrix algebra it is less simple, and before we can usefully consider the problem, we have to introduce an operation on the matrix **A** that has no equivalent in scalar algebra.

The transpose of **A** is defined to be the matrix obtained from **A** by interchanging rows and columns: that is, the first row of **A** becomes the first column of the transpose, the second row of **A** becomes the second column of the transpose, and in general the jith element in the transpose is the ijth element of the original matrix. We indicate the transposed matrix by $\mathbf{A}'$: for example,

$$\mathbf{A} = \begin{bmatrix} a_{11} & a_{12} & a_{13} \\ a_{21} & a_{22} & a_{23} \end{bmatrix}$$

$$\mathbf{A}' = \begin{bmatrix} a_{11} & a_{21} \\ a_{12} & a_{22} \\ a_{13} & a_{23} \end{bmatrix}$$

If $\mathbf{A}' = \mathbf{A}$, then $\mathbf{A}$ is said to be a *symmetric* matrix: it must obviously be a square matrix such that

$$a_{ij} = a_{ji} \qquad i \neq j; i, j = 1, 2, \ldots, n.$$

Let $\mathbf{A}$ be as defined above: viz,

$$\mathbf{A} = \begin{bmatrix} a_{11} & a_{12} & a_{13} \\ a_{21} & a_{22} & a_{23} \end{bmatrix}$$

then

$$\mathbf{AA}' = \begin{bmatrix} a_{11}^2 + a_{12}^2 + a_{13}^2 & a_{11}a_{21} + a_{12}a_{22} + a_{13}a_{23} \\ a_{21}a_{11} + a_{22}a_{12} + a_{23}a_{13} & a_{21}^2 + a_{22}^2 + a_{23}^2 \end{bmatrix}$$

and

$$\mathbf{A}'\mathbf{A} = \begin{bmatrix} a_{11}^2 + a_{21}^2 & a_{11}a_{12} + a_{21}a_{22} & a_{11}a_{13} + a_{21}a_{23} \\ a_{12}a_{11} + a_{22}a_{21} & a_{12}^2 + a_{22}^2 & a_{12}a_{13} + a_{22}a_{23} \\ a_{13}a_{11} + a_{23}a_{21} & a_{13}a_{12} + a_{23}a_{22} & a_{13}^2 + a_{23}^2 \end{bmatrix}$$

Notice that both $\mathbf{AA}'$ and $\mathbf{A}'\mathbf{A}$ are symmetric. Since $\mathbf{A}$ is not square, these products are of different orders, but their *traces* are equal, the trace of a square matrix being defined as the sum of the elements in the principal diagonal. The trace of $\mathbf{AA}'$, denoted by tr $(\mathbf{AA}')$, is in fact the sum of the squares of the elements of $\mathbf{A}$.

Notice that if $\mathbf{x}$ is a column vector of n elements, $\mathbf{x}'$ is then a row vector of n elements and

$$\mathbf{x}'\mathbf{x} = \sum_{i=1}^{n} x_i^2$$

and

$$\mathbf{xx}' = \begin{bmatrix} x_1^2 & x_1x_2 & \cdots & x_1x_n \\ x_2x_1 & x_2^2 & \cdots & x_2x_n \\ \vdots & \vdots & & \vdots \\ x_nx_1 & x_nx_2 & \cdots & x_n^2 \end{bmatrix}$$

Theorems about transposed matrices

$$(\mathbf{A}')' = \mathbf{A} \tag{4-3}$$

$$(\mathbf{A} + \mathbf{B})' = \mathbf{A}' + \mathbf{B}' \tag{4-4}$$

$$(\mathbf{AB})' = \mathbf{B}'\mathbf{A}' \tag{4-5}$$

The first two are obvious from the definition of transposition. To prove (4-5) we note that

$$\begin{aligned} ji\text{th element in } \mathbf{B}'\mathbf{A}' &= j\text{th row of } \mathbf{B}' \text{ into } i\text{th column of } \mathbf{A}' \\ &= j\text{th column of } \mathbf{B} \text{ into } i\text{th row of } \mathbf{A} \\ &= ij\text{th element in } \mathbf{AB} \end{aligned}$$

It also follows that

$$(\mathbf{ABC})' = \mathbf{C}'\mathbf{B}'\mathbf{A}' \tag{4-6}$$

for

$$(\mathbf{ABC})' = [(\mathbf{AB})\mathbf{C}]' = \mathbf{C}'(\mathbf{AB})' = \mathbf{C}'\mathbf{B}'\mathbf{A}'$$

The following examples illustrate some simple operations with matrices and also serve to introduce some algebraic expressions, which will be of subsequent use.

Example i The set of simultaneous equations

$$\begin{aligned} a_{11}x_1 + a_{12}x_2 + \cdots + a_{1n}x_n &= h_1 \\ a_{21}x_1 + a_{22}x_2 + \cdots + a_{2n}x_n &= h_2 \\ &\vdots \\ a_{n1}x_1 + a_{n2}x_2 + \cdots + a_{nn}x_n &= h_n \end{aligned}$$

may be written

$$\mathbf{Ax} = \mathbf{h}$$

where

$\mathbf{A}$ = matrix of a_{ij} coefficients of order $n \times n$
$\mathbf{x}$ = column vector of n elements $\{x_1 \quad x_2 \quad \cdots \quad x_n\}$
$\mathbf{h}$ = column vector of n elements $\{h_1 \quad h_2 \quad \cdots \quad h_n\}$

The product of the matrix $\mathbf{A}$ and the vector $\mathbf{x}$ gives a column vector of n elements, which is then equated, element by element, with the $\mathbf{h}$ vector. The first element in the vector $\mathbf{Ax}$ is $a_{11}x_1 + a_{12}x_2 + \cdots a_{1n}x_n$, which is equated to h_1 and similarly for the other elements, giving n simultaneous equations in all.

Example ii Sum of squares

$$\begin{aligned} e_1^2 + e_2^2 + \cdots + e_n^2 &= \sum_{i=1}^{n} e_1^2 \\ &= \mathbf{e}'\mathbf{e} \end{aligned}$$

where

$$\mathbf{e} = \{e_1 \quad e_2 \quad \cdots \quad e_n\}$$

Example iii A weighted sum of squares

$$a_{11}x_1^2 + a_{22}x_2^2 + \cdots + a_{nn}x_n^2 = \mathbf{x}'\mathbf{A}\mathbf{x}$$

where

$\mathbf{A}$ = a diagonal matrix of order $n \times n$
$\mathbf{x}$ = a column vector of n elements

This result may be seen by a straightforward application of the multiplication rule. As an illustration of the 3×3 case,

$$\mathbf{x}'\mathbf{A}\mathbf{x} = [x_1 \; x_2 \; x_3]\begin{bmatrix} a_{11} & 0 & 0 \\ 0 & a_{22} & 0 \\ 0 & 0 & a_{33} \end{bmatrix}\begin{bmatrix} x_1 \\ x_2 \\ x_3 \end{bmatrix}$$

$$= [x_1 \; x_2 \; x_3]\begin{bmatrix} a_{11}x_1 \\ a_{22}x_2 \\ a_{33}x_3 \end{bmatrix}$$

$$= a_{11}x_1^2 + a_{22}x_2^2 + a_{33}x_3^2$$

Example iv Quadratic forms. $\mathbf{x}'\mathbf{A}\mathbf{x}$. A very important function in statistics is obtained when we consider the general expression $\mathbf{x}'\mathbf{A}\mathbf{x}$, without the restriction that $\mathbf{A}$ is a diagonal matrix, but postulating simply that $\mathbf{A}$ is *symmetric.* For the 2×2 case, we obtain, on multiplying out,

$$\mathbf{x}'\mathbf{A}\mathbf{x} = a_{11}x_1^2 + 2a_{12}x_1x_2 + a_{22}x_2^2$$

and for the 3×3 case,

$$\mathbf{x}'\mathbf{A}\mathbf{x} = a_{11}x_1^2 + 2a_{12}x_1x_2 + 2a_{13}x_1x_3 + a_{22}x_2^2 + 2a_{23}x_2x_3 + a_{33}x_3^2$$

The restriction that the matrix $\mathbf{A}$ of the quadratic form be symmetric is not a serious one, since if we have a nonsymmetric matrix $\mathbf{A}^*$, a typical cross-product term would be $(a_{ij}^* + a_{ji}^*)x_ix_j$. If we now define

$$a_{ij} = a_{ji} = \frac{a_{ij}^* + a_{ji}^*}{2}$$

this term becomes $2a_{ij}x_ix_j$ and the associated matrix is a symmetric one.

The general quadratic form may be written

$$
\begin{aligned}
\mathbf{x}'\mathbf{A}\mathbf{x} = a_{11}x_1^2 + 2a_{12}x_1x_2 + \cdots &+ 2a_{1n}x_1x_n \\
+ a_{22}x_2^2 + \cdots &+ 2a_{2n}x_2x_n \\
&+ \cdots \\
&\quad \vdots \\
&+ a_{nn}x_n^2
\end{aligned}
$$

where $\mathbf{A}$ is a symmetric matrix of order $n \times n$ and $\mathbf{x}$ is a column vector of n elements.

As an illustration, if we are given the quadratic form

$$x_1^2 + 3x_2^2 - 5x_3^2 + 2x_1x_2 - 8x_2x_3$$

we can by inspection write

$$\mathbf{x} = \begin{bmatrix} x_1 \\ x_2 \\ x_3 \end{bmatrix} \quad \text{and} \quad \mathbf{A} = \begin{bmatrix} 1 & 1 & 0 \\ 1 & 3 & -4 \\ 0 & -4 & -5 \end{bmatrix}$$

since the coefficients of the terms in x_i^2 appear on the principal diagonal of $\mathbf{A}$ and the symmetric off-diagonal terms are one-half the coefficients of the x_ix_j terms.

The inverse matrix The matrix form $\mathbf{Ax} = \mathbf{h}$ of the set of equations in Example i suggests that if it were possible and meaningful to divide each side of the equation by $\mathbf{A}$, by analogy with division in scalar algebra, we should obtain as a solution

$$\mathbf{x} = \mathbf{A}^{-1}\mathbf{h}$$

If $\mathbf{A}^{-1}$ is an $n \times n$ matrix with elements which are functions of the elements of $\mathbf{A}$, then the right-hand side of the above equation becomes a column vector of n elements, which we equate, element by element, with the unknown x_i, and so obtain a solution to the original set of equations.

In order to establish the nature of the matrix $\mathbf{A}^{-1}$, we need a few results on determinants.

4-2 DETERMINANTS

Associated with any square matrix $\mathbf{A}$ there is a *scalar* quantity, called the determinant of $\mathbf{A}$, which is indicated by det $\mathbf{A}$ or by the special symbol $|\mathbf{A}|$. This quantity is obtained by summing various products of the elements of $\mathbf{A}$.

For example, the determinant of a 2 × 2 matrix is defined to be

$$\begin{vmatrix} a_{11} & a_{12} \\ a_{21} & a_{22} \end{vmatrix} = a_{11}a_{22} - a_{12}a_{21}$$

and of a 3 × 3 matrix

$$\begin{vmatrix} a_{11} & a_{12} & a_{13} \\ a_{21} & a_{22} & a_{23} \\ a_{31} & a_{32} & a_{33} \end{vmatrix} = a_{11}a_{22}a_{33} - a_{12}a_{21}a_{33} + a_{12}a_{23}a_{31} - a_{13}a_{22}a_{31} + a_{13}a_{21}a_{32} - a_{11}a_{23}a_{32}$$

We notice various features of the above determinants.

1. Each term on the right-hand side is the product of the same number of elements as the order of **A**, namely, two elements for a 2 × 2 matrix and three elements for a 3 × 3 matrix. In general, we then expect n elements in each term.

2. In each term there is one and only one element from each row and one and only one element from each column of **A**. Thus no element appears twice in the same term.

3. The number of terms in the expansions are $2 = 2!$ and $6 = 3!$, respectively, and all terms are different. In general, we expect $n!$ different terms, where $n! = n(n-1)(n-2)\cdots 3 \cdot 2 \cdot 1$.

4. In the subscripts attaching to the elements in each term the elements have been written so that *within* each term the first subscripts are in natural order, that is, 1, 2, 3, etc. The second subscripts, however, are various permutations of the n numbers. Since there are $n!$ permutations of n distinct objects, this gives the $n!$ different terms as noted in item 3 above.

5. Half the terms have positive signs, and half have negative signs. The sign depends upon the second subscripts. An *inversion* of natural order is said to occur when of two integers the larger precedes the smaller. The number of inversions in a permutation of n integers is the number of pairs of elements, not necessarily adjacent, in which a larger integer precedes a smaller one. A permutation is *even* when the number of inversions is even and *odd* when the number of inversions is odd. Even permutations carry a positive sign, and odd permutations a negative sign. For example, the second term in the expansion of the third-order determinant has second subscripts in the order 2 1 3, which contains only one inversion, 2 before 1, and is therefore odd and has a negative sign. The next term has second subscripts in the order 2 3 1, which contains two inversions since 2 comes before 1 and 3 comes before 1: it is therefore even and carries a plus sign.

These five points lead to the general definition of the determinant of an nth-order matrix **A** as

$$|\mathbf{A}| = \Sigma \pm a_{1i}a_{2j}\cdots a_{nr}$$

the sum being taken over all permutations of the second subscripts, with a positive sign attached to even permutations and a negative one to odd permutations.

Properties of determinants

$$|\mathbf{A}'| = |\mathbf{A}| \tag{4-7}$$

i.e., the determinant of the transposed matrix is equal to the determinant of the original matrix. To prove this result let $\mathbf{B} = \mathbf{A}'$. We require to find the determinant of **B** in terms of the determinant of **A**. The proof is illustrated by considering a matrix of order 3×3. In this the term $b_{13}b_{21}b_{32}$ in the expansion of **B** consists of the product of the three elements a_{31}, a_{12}, and a_{23}. Its sign in the determinant of **B** is given by the number of inversions in 3 1 2 (second subscripts of the b expression) and is thus positive. The sign of $a_{31}a_{12}a_{23}$ in the determinant of **A** can be found when these three terms are rearranged with the first subscript in natural order. This rearrangement, however, will give exactly the same number of inversions in the second subscripts as it removes from the first subscripts. For example, as the first element is moved into third position, two inversions are removed from the first subscripts as the integer 3 now comes after 1 and 2, but two inversions are created in the second subscript as the integer 1 moves to the right of 2 and 3. Thus $a_{31}a_{12}a_{23}$ will have the same sign in the expansion of the determinant of **A** as in the expansion of the determinant of **B**. This will apply to any term and so the result is proved.

Interchanging any two columns (or rows) of **A** *changes the sign of the determinant of* **A** (4-8)

To prove this we notice that the interchange of any two elements in a permutation must always change the class of the permutation from odd to even, or vice versa. Suppose, for example, that we are interchanging j and k, which are separated by m numbers as in Fig. 4-1. To achieve the interchange, k must move over $m + 1$ numbers and j must pass over m numbers. Any time one number passes over another, an inversion is either introduced or removed. Thus the interchange of any two numbers j and k separated by m numbers

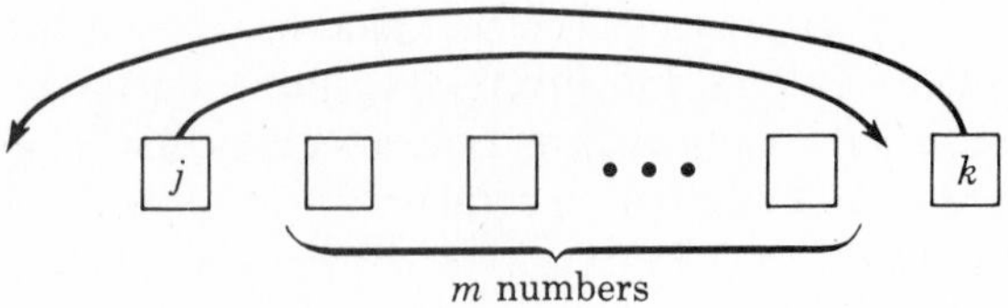

m numbers

Fig. 4-1.

causes $2m + 1$ inversion changes, and since this must be an odd number, the class of the permutation changes.

Interchanging any two columns of **A** thus means that the first subscripts in all terms in $|\mathbf{A}|$ are unchanged but the sign of each term changes, so that the sign of $|\mathbf{A}|$ changes.

Let **B** denote the matrix obtained from **A** by interchanging columns j and k. We have thus shown that

$$|\mathbf{B}| = -|\mathbf{A}|$$

Then $\mathbf{B}'$ is the matrix obtained from $\mathbf{A}'$ by interchanging *rows* j and k.

We then have

$$\begin{aligned} |\mathbf{B}'| &= |\mathbf{B}| && \text{by (4.7)} \\ &= -|\mathbf{A}| && \text{just proved} \\ &= -|\mathbf{A}'| && \text{by (4.7)} \end{aligned}$$

Thus interchanging any two columns (or rows) of a matrix changes the sign of the determinant.

The determinant of a matrix with two rows (or columns) identical is zero (4-9)

This follows directly from (4-8) for the interchanging of two rows (or columns) gives a new determinant equal to $-|\mathbf{A}|$. Yet if the two rows are identical, their interchange must leave **A** unaltered. Thus

$$|\mathbf{A}| = -|\mathbf{A}|$$

that is,

$$|\mathbf{A}| = 0$$

If every element of a row (or column) of **A** *is multiplied by a scalar λ to give a new matrix* **B**, *then*

$$|\mathbf{B}| = \lambda|\mathbf{A}| \tag{4-10}$$

If every element of an nth order matrix **A** *is multiplied by λ, then*

$$|\lambda\mathbf{A}| = \lambda^n|\mathbf{A}| \tag{4-11}$$

These two results follow directly from the fact that each term in the expansion of a determinant contains one element and one element only from each row (or column) of the matrix.

If we consider

$$|\mathbf{A}| = \Sigma \pm a_{1\alpha}a_{2\beta}\cdots a_{n\nu}$$

and collect all the terms in the expansion containing a_{11}, the coefficient of the element a_{11} is

$$\Sigma \pm a_{2\beta}a_{3\gamma}\cdots a_{n\nu} \tag{4-12}$$

where the summation takes place over all $(n-1)!$ permutations of the integers $2, 3, \ldots, n$. Since the row and column suffixes 1, 1 in a_{11} are in correct natural order, they make no contribution to the sign of any term in (4-12). This sign is therefore given by the permutation $(\beta, \gamma, \ldots, \nu)$ of the natural order $(2, 3, \ldots, n)$. In fact,

$$\Sigma \pm a_{2\beta}a_{3\gamma}\cdots a_{n\nu}$$

is the determinant of order $n-1$.

$$\begin{vmatrix} a_{22} & \cdots & a_{2n} \\ \vdots & & \vdots \\ a_{n2} & \cdots & a_{nn} \end{vmatrix}$$

of the matrix obtained from $\mathbf{A}$ by deleting its first row and first column.

Minor Such a determinant is called a minor. Denote it by $|\mathbf{A}_{11}|$. In general,

$$|\mathbf{A}_{ij}| = \begin{vmatrix} a_{11} & a_{12} & \cdots & a_{1,j-1} & a_{1,j+1} & \cdots & a_{1n} \\ \vdots & & & & & & \vdots \\ a_{i-1,1} & a_{i-1,2} & \cdots & a_{i-1,j-1} & a_{i-1,j+1} & \cdots & a_{i-1,n} \\ a_{i+1,1} & a_{i+1,2} & \cdots & a_{i+1,j-1} & a_{i+1,j+1} & \cdots & a_{i+1,n} \\ \vdots & & & & & & \vdots \\ a_{n1} & a_{n2} & \cdots & a_{n,j-1} & a_{n,j+1} & \cdots & a_{nn} \end{vmatrix} \tag{4-13}$$

We have thus shown that the sum of all terms in $|\mathbf{A}|$ involving a_{11} as a factor is given by $a_{11}|\mathbf{A}_{11}|$.

Next we ask what is the sum of all terms in $|\mathbf{A}|$ involving a_{ij} as a factor? Consider the matrix $\mathbf{B}$ obtained from $\mathbf{A}$ by (1) interchanging row i of $\mathbf{A}$ with the row above it and repeating this process until after $i-1$ interchanges: row i of $\mathbf{A}$ is now the first row, and the lower rows are in normal order except for the omission of row i: and (2) interchanging column j of $\mathbf{A}$ step by step with the one on its left until after $j-1$ steps it is the first column. Thus

$$|\mathbf{B}| = (-1)^{i+j-2}|\mathbf{A}| = (-1)^{i+j}|\mathbf{A}|$$

$$b_{11} = a_{ij}$$

and

$$|\mathbf{B}_{11}| = |\mathbf{A}_{ij}|$$

since

$$|\mathbf{B}_{11}| = \begin{vmatrix} a_{11} & \cdots & a_{1,j-1} & a_{1,j+1} & \cdots & a_{1n} \\ \vdots & & & & & \cdot \\ a_{i-1,1} & & & & & \cdot \\ a_{i+1,1} & & & & & \\ \vdots & & & & & \cdot \\ a_{n1} & & \cdots & & & a_{nn} \end{vmatrix}$$

Thus the sum of all terms in $|\mathbf{B}|$ which involve $a_{ij}(=b_{11})$ as a factor is $b_{11}|\mathbf{B}_{11}|$. It is seen above that when the terms in $|\mathbf{B}|$ are multiplied by $(-1)^{i+j}$, they become terms in $|\mathbf{A}|$. Thus the sum of all terms in $|\mathbf{A}|$ involving a_{ij} as a factor is

$$(-1)^{i+j}a_{ij}|\mathbf{A}_{ij}|$$

Co-factor Let us define these co-factors (coefficients) as

$$c_{ij} = (-1)^{i+j}|\mathbf{A}_{ij}| \tag{4-14}$$

so that

$$c_{11} = |\mathbf{A}_{11}| \qquad c_{12} = -|\mathbf{A}_{12}| \qquad c_{22} = |\mathbf{A}_{22}| \quad \text{etc.}$$

Now consider the expression

$$a_{i1}c_{i1} + a_{i2}c_{i2} + \cdots + a_{in}c_{in}$$

There are altogether $(n-1)!n = n!$ terms in this expression, *all different* and all occurring with correct sign in $|\mathbf{A}|$. But the expansion of $|\mathbf{A}|$ has only $n!$ terms, all different. Thus

$$|\mathbf{A}| = a_{i1}c_{i1} + a_{i2}c_{i2} + \cdots + a_{in}c_{in} \tag{4-15}$$

This gives us the expansion of $|\mathbf{A}|$ in terms of the elements of the ith row and their co-factors. $|\mathbf{A}|$ may be similarly expanded in terms of the elements of *any row* (or column).

A determinant is unaltered in value when to any row (column) is added a constant multiple of any other row (column) (4-16)

Proof Consider

$$\begin{vmatrix} a_{11} + \lambda\alpha & a_{12} + \lambda\beta & a_{13} + \lambda\gamma \\ a_{21} & a_{22} & a_{23} \\ a_{31} & a_{32} & a_{33} \end{vmatrix}$$

Using (4-15) to expand this determinant, Δ, in terms of the elements of the first row gives

$$\Delta = (a_{11} + \lambda\alpha)\begin{vmatrix} a_{22} & a_{23} \\ a_{32} & a_{33} \end{vmatrix} - (a_{12} + \lambda\beta)\begin{vmatrix} a_{21} & a_{23} \\ a_{31} & a_{33} \end{vmatrix}$$

$$+ (a_{13} + \lambda\gamma)\begin{vmatrix} a_{21} & a_{22} \\ a_{31} & a_{32} \end{vmatrix}$$

$$= \begin{vmatrix} a_{11} & a_{12} & a_{13} \\ a_{21} & a_{22} & a_{23} \\ a_{31} & a_{32} & a_{33} \end{vmatrix} + \lambda \begin{vmatrix} \alpha & \beta & \gamma \\ a_{21} & a_{22} & a_{23} \\ a_{31} & a_{32} & a_{33} \end{vmatrix}$$

If

$$[\alpha \quad \beta \quad \gamma] = [a_{21} \quad a_{22} \quad a_{23}]$$

or

$$[\alpha \quad \beta \quad \gamma] = [a_{31} \quad a_{32} \quad a_{33}]$$

the last determinant on the right-hand side vanishes because of two identical rows, and thus the right-hand side reduces to the value of the original determinant. This result is often useful in the numerical evaluation of determinants.

Example Evaluate

$$|\mathbf{A}| = \begin{vmatrix} 2 & 4 & 6 \\ 3 & 2 & 3 \\ 1 & 4 & 9 \end{vmatrix}$$

Expanding in terms of the elements of the first row,

$$|\mathbf{A}| = 2\begin{vmatrix} 2 & 3 \\ 4 & 9 \end{vmatrix} - 4\begin{vmatrix} 3 & 3 \\ 1 & 9 \end{vmatrix} + 6\begin{vmatrix} 3 & 2 \\ 1 & 4 \end{vmatrix}$$

$$= 2(6) - 4(24) + 6(10)$$

$$= -24$$

Alternatively, subtract twice the second row from the first to give

$$|\mathbf{A}| = \begin{vmatrix} -4 & 0 & 0 \\ 3 & 2 & 3 \\ 1 & 4 & 9 \end{vmatrix}$$

Expanding this in terms of the elements in the first row

$$|\mathbf{A}| = -4(6) = -24$$

As a corollary it is easily seen that the same result holds when to any row (column) is added a linear combination of other rows (columns).

Expansions in Terms of Alien Co-factors Vanish Identically. Consider

$$a_{i1}c_{j1} + a_{i2}c_{j2} + \cdots + a_{in}c_{jn} \qquad i \neq j$$

The elements are those of row i, and the co-factors are those of row j. This is the expression we should obtain for the determinant of a matrix in which rows i and j are identical, which, from (4-9), is zero. Thus

$$\begin{aligned} \sum_{r=1}^{n} a_{ir}c_{jr} &= 0 \qquad i \neq j \\ \sum_{s=1}^{n} a_{sk}c_{sl} &= 0 \qquad k \neq l \end{aligned} \tag{4-17}$$

The inverse, or reciprocal, matrix In scalar algebra we have

$$xx^{-1} = x^{-1}x = 1 \qquad \text{(unity)}$$

This suggests that in matrix algebra we ask whether a *matrix* $\mathbf{A}^{-1}$ exists such that

$$\mathbf{AA}^{-1} = \mathbf{A}^{-1}\mathbf{A} = \mathbf{I} \quad \text{(unit matrix)}$$

$\mathbf{A}^{-1}$ is defined as the inverse (or reciprocal) of $\mathbf{A}$.

The steps in its construction are as follows:

1. From $\mathbf{A}$ of order $n \times n$ form a new matrix where a_{ij} is replaced by its co-factor c_{ij} and transpose this new matrix. The resulting matrix is called the *adjoint* of $\mathbf{A}$.

$$(\text{adj } \mathbf{A}) = \begin{bmatrix} c_{11} & c_{21} & \cdots & c_{n1} \\ c_{12} & c_{22} & \cdots & c_{n2} \\ \vdots & \vdots & & \vdots \\ c_{1n} & c_{2n} & \cdots & c_{nn} \end{bmatrix}$$

We can then see that

$$\mathbf{A}(\text{adj } \mathbf{A}) = (\text{adj } \mathbf{A})\mathbf{A} = \begin{bmatrix} |\mathbf{A}| & 0 & \cdots & 0 \\ 0 & |\mathbf{A}| & \cdots & 0 \\ \vdots & \vdots & & \vdots \\ 0 & 0 & \cdots & |\mathbf{A}| \end{bmatrix} = |\mathbf{A}|\mathbf{I}$$

using the result about expansions in terms of alien co-factors.

2. Define $\mathbf{A}^{-1}$ as

$$\frac{1}{|\mathbf{A}|}(\text{adj }\mathbf{A}) = \begin{bmatrix} \frac{c_{11}}{|\mathbf{A}|} & \frac{c_{21}}{|\mathbf{A}|} & \cdots & \frac{c_{n1}}{|\mathbf{A}|} \\ \vdots & & & \vdots \\ \frac{c_{1n}}{|\mathbf{A}|} & & \cdots & \frac{c_{nn}}{|\mathbf{A}|} \end{bmatrix}$$

This last step is possible only if $|\mathbf{A}| \neq 0$, in which case the matrix $\mathbf{A}$ is said to be *nonsingular*. When $|\mathbf{A}| = 0$, the matrix $\mathbf{A}$ is said to be *singular*.

$\mathbf{A}^{-1}$ is also unique; for suppose $\mathbf{B}$ exists such that $\mathbf{AB} = \mathbf{I}$, then

$$\begin{aligned} \mathbf{A}^{-1} &= \mathbf{A}^{-1}\mathbf{I} \\ &= \mathbf{A}^{-1}\mathbf{AB} \\ &= \mathbf{B} \end{aligned}$$

Likewise, if $\mathbf{C}$ exists such that $\mathbf{CA} = \mathbf{I}$, $\mathbf{C} = \mathbf{A}^{-1}$.

Example The calculation of an inverse matrix.

$$\mathbf{A} = \begin{bmatrix} 1 & 2 & 3 \\ 1 & 3 & 5 \\ 1 & 5 & 12 \end{bmatrix}$$

Replacing elements by co-factors gives

$$\begin{bmatrix} \begin{vmatrix} 3 & 5 \\ 5 & 12 \end{vmatrix} & -\begin{vmatrix} 1 & 5 \\ 1 & 12 \end{vmatrix} & \begin{vmatrix} 1 & 3 \\ 1 & 5 \end{vmatrix} \\ -\begin{vmatrix} 2 & 3 \\ 5 & 12 \end{vmatrix} & \begin{vmatrix} 1 & 3 \\ 1 & 12 \end{vmatrix} & -\begin{vmatrix} 1 & 2 \\ 1 & 5 \end{vmatrix} \\ \begin{vmatrix} 2 & 3 \\ 3 & 5 \end{vmatrix} & -\begin{vmatrix} 1 & 3 \\ 1 & 5 \end{vmatrix} & \begin{vmatrix} 1 & 2 \\ 1 & 3 \end{vmatrix} \end{bmatrix} = \begin{bmatrix} 11 & -7 & 2 \\ -9 & 9 & -3 \\ 1 & -2 & 1 \end{bmatrix}$$

Therefore

$$(\text{adj } \mathbf{A}) = \begin{bmatrix} 11 & -9 & 1 \\ -7 & 9 & -2 \\ 2 & -3 & 1 \end{bmatrix}$$

$$\text{Now } |\mathbf{A}| = \begin{vmatrix} 1 & 2 & 3 \\ 0 & 1 & 2 \\ 0 & 3 & 9 \end{vmatrix} \quad \text{subtracting first row from second and third}$$

$$= 3$$

Therefore

$$\mathbf{A}^{-1} = \begin{bmatrix} \frac{11}{3} & -3 & \frac{1}{3} \\ -\frac{7}{3} & 3 & -\frac{2}{3} \\ \frac{2}{3} & -1 & \frac{1}{3} \end{bmatrix}$$

Check

$$\mathbf{AA}^{-1} = \begin{bmatrix} 1 & 2 & 3 \\ 1 & 3 & 5 \\ 1 & 5 & 12 \end{bmatrix} \begin{bmatrix} \frac{11}{3} & -3 & \frac{1}{3} \\ -\frac{7}{3} & 3 & -\frac{2}{3} \\ \frac{2}{3} & -1 & \frac{1}{3} \end{bmatrix}$$

$$= \begin{bmatrix} 1 & 0 & 0 \\ 0 & 1 & 0 \\ 0 & 0 & 1 \end{bmatrix}$$

Second Example Leontief Static Input–Output System.

Let a_{ij} = input of product i per unit output of product j
X_i = total (gross) output of product i
C_i = consumption (final demand) of product i

Suppose we have just two products. Then we may write

$$a_{11}X_1 + a_{12}X_2 + C_1 = X_1$$
$$a_{21}X_1 + a_{22}X_2 + C_2 = X_2$$

assuming no waste or excess production. Rearranging gives

$$(1 - a_{11})X_1 - a_{12}X_2 = C_1$$
$$-a_{21}X_1 + (1 - a_{22})X_2 = C_2$$

or

$$\mathbf{A}\mathbf{x} = \mathbf{c}$$

where

$$\mathbf{A} = \begin{bmatrix} 1 - a_{11} & -a_{12} \\ -a_{21} & 1 - a_{22} \end{bmatrix}$$

We may solve for $\mathbf{x}$ in terms of $\mathbf{c}$; that is, we can find what total gross outputs X_1 and X_2 would be required to support a given program of final demand C_1, C_2.

$$\mathbf{x} = \mathbf{A}^{-1}\mathbf{c}$$

where

$$\mathbf{A}^{-1} = \frac{1}{(1 - a_{11})(1 - a_{22}) - a_{12}a_{21}} \begin{bmatrix} 1 - a_{22} & a_{12} \\ a_{21} & 1 - a_{11} \end{bmatrix}$$

so that

$$X_1 = \frac{1 - a_{22}}{\Delta} C_1 + \frac{a_{12}}{\Delta} C_2$$

$$X_2 = \frac{a_{21}}{\Delta} C_1 + \frac{1 - a_{11}}{\Delta} C_2$$

where

$$\Delta = (1 - a_{11})(1 - a_{22}) - a_{12}a_{21}$$

Cramer's rule If $\mathbf{A}\mathbf{x} = \mathbf{h}$, where $\mathbf{A}$ is a nonsingular matrix, premultiplication of both sides by $\mathbf{A}^{-1}$ gives

$$\mathbf{x} = \mathbf{A}^{-1}\mathbf{h}$$

For the 3×3 case this gives

$$\begin{bmatrix} x_1 \\ x_2 \\ x_3 \end{bmatrix} = \frac{1}{|\mathbf{A}|} \begin{bmatrix} c_{11} & c_{21} & c_{31} \\ c_{12} & c_{22} & c_{32} \\ c_{13} & c_{23} & c_{33} \end{bmatrix} \begin{bmatrix} h_1 \\ h_2 \\ h_3 \end{bmatrix}$$

where the c's denote co-factors. Thus

$$x_1 = \frac{h_1c_{11} + h_2c_{21} + h_3c_{31}}{|\mathbf{A}|}$$

The numerator in this expression for x_1 is the expression of a determinant by the elements of the first column where this column is $\{h_1\ h_2\ h_3\}$ and the remaining two columns are the second and third columns of **A**. Thus in a set of simultaneous equations, x_i is found as the ratio of two determinants, the first being that of the matrix of coefficients, in which the h vector has replaced the ith column, and the second being the determinant of the coefficient matrix.

$$x_1 = \frac{\begin{vmatrix} h_1 & a_{12} & a_{13} \\ h_2 & a_{22} & a_{23} \\ h_3 & a_{32} & a_{33} \end{vmatrix}}{|\mathbf{A}|} \qquad x_2 = \frac{\begin{vmatrix} a_{11} & h_1 & a_{13} \\ a_{21} & h_2 & a_{23} \\ a_{31} & h_3 & a_{33} \end{vmatrix}}{|\mathbf{A}|} \qquad x_3 = \frac{\begin{vmatrix} a_{11} & a_{12} & h_1 \\ a_{21} & a_{22} & h_2 \\ a_{31} & a_{32} & h_3 \end{vmatrix}}{|\mathbf{A}|}$$

Properties of inverse matrices

$$(\mathbf{AB})^{-1} = \mathbf{B}^{-1}\mathbf{A}^{-1} \tag{4-18}$$

Proof:

$$\begin{aligned}(\mathbf{AB})(\mathbf{B}^{-1}\mathbf{A}^{-1}) &= \mathbf{A}(\mathbf{BB}^{-1})\mathbf{A}^{-1} \\ &= \mathbf{AIA}^{-1} \\ &= \mathbf{AA}^{-1} \\ &= \mathbf{I}\end{aligned}$$

Similarly,

$$(\mathbf{B}^{-1}\mathbf{A}^{-1})(\mathbf{AB}) = \mathbf{I}$$

It is easy to extend this result to obtain

$$(\mathbf{ABC})^{-1} = \mathbf{C}^{-1}\mathbf{B}^{-1}\mathbf{A}^{-1} \tag{4-19}$$

By the definition of an inverse,

$$(\mathbf{A}^{-1})(\mathbf{A}^{-1})^{-1} = \mathbf{I}$$

Premultiplying both sides by **A**,

$$\begin{aligned}\mathbf{AA}^{-1}(\mathbf{A}^{-1})^{-1} &= \mathbf{AI} \\ \mathbf{I}(\mathbf{A}^{-1})^{-1} &= \mathbf{A} \\ (\mathbf{A}^{-1})^{-1} &= \mathbf{A}\end{aligned} \tag{4-20}$$

Thus taking the inverse of an inverse reproduces the original matrix. Another important result is expressed by

$$(\mathbf{A}')^{-1} = (\mathbf{A}^{-1})' \tag{4-21}$$

i.e., the inverse of the transpose equals the transpose of the inverse.

Proof

$$\mathbf{AA}^{-1} = \mathbf{I}$$

Transposing,

$$(\mathbf{A}^{-1})'\mathbf{A}' = \mathbf{I}$$

Postmultiply by $(\mathbf{A}')^{-1}$.

$$(\mathbf{A}^{-1})'\mathbf{A}'(\mathbf{A}')^{-1} = (\mathbf{A}')^{-1}$$

Thus

$$(\mathbf{A}^{-1})' = (\mathbf{A}')^{-1}$$

Finally we note that

$$|\mathbf{A}^{-1}| = \frac{1}{|\mathbf{A}|} \tag{4-22}$$

There is an important result on determinants that $|\mathbf{AB}| = |\mathbf{A}| \cdot |\mathbf{B}|$.[1] We have $\mathbf{A}^{-1}\mathbf{A} = \mathbf{I}$. Therefore

$$|\mathbf{I}| = 1 = |\mathbf{A}^{-1}\mathbf{A}| = |\mathbf{A}^{-1}| \cdot |\mathbf{A}|$$

Therefore

$$|\mathbf{A}^{-1}| = \frac{1}{|\mathbf{A}|}$$

4-3 PARTITIONED MATRICES

Since a matrix is a rectangular array of elements, we may divide it by means of horizontal and vertical lines into smaller arrays or submatrices. For example,

$$\mathbf{A} = \left[\begin{array}{ccc|c} a_{11} & a_{12} & a_{13} & a_{14} \\ a_{21} & a_{22} & a_{23} & a_{24} \\ \hline a_{31} & a_{32} & a_{33} & a_{34} \end{array}\right]$$

may be partitioned by means of the two lines shown to give the four submatrices

$$\begin{aligned} \mathbf{A}_{11} &= \begin{bmatrix} a_{11} & a_{12} & a_{13} \\ a_{21} & a_{22} & a_{23} \end{bmatrix} & \mathbf{A}_{12} &= \begin{bmatrix} a_{14} \\ a_{24} \end{bmatrix} \\ \mathbf{A}_{21} &= [a_{31} \quad a_{32} \quad a_{33}] & \mathbf{A}_{22} &= [a_{34}] \end{aligned} \tag{4-23}$$

[1] See G. Hadley, *Linear Algebra*, Addison-Wesley, Reading, Mass., 1961, pp. 99–100.

and **A** may then be written

$$\mathbf{A} = \begin{bmatrix} \mathbf{A}_{11} & \mathbf{A}_{12} \\ \mathbf{A}_{21} & \mathbf{A}_{22} \end{bmatrix}$$

Notice that the partitioning lines must extend all the way across or up and down the original matrix.

The basic operations of addition and multiplication still apply to partitioned matrices, but the matrices must have been partitioned conformably. For example, if **B** is also of order 3 × 4 and is partitioned,

$$\mathbf{B} = \begin{bmatrix} \mathbf{B}_{11} & \mathbf{B}_{12} \\ \mathbf{B}_{21} & \mathbf{B}_{22} \end{bmatrix}$$

where $\mathbf{B}_{ij}$ is of the same order as $\mathbf{A}_{ij}$, then the sum **A** + **B** can be written

$$\mathbf{A} + \mathbf{B} = \begin{bmatrix} \mathbf{A}_{11} + \mathbf{B}_{11} & \mathbf{A}_{12} + \mathbf{B}_{12} \\ \mathbf{A}_{21} + \mathbf{B}_{21} & \mathbf{A}_{22} + \mathbf{B}_{22} \end{bmatrix}$$

To consider multiplication, suppose **B** is of order 4 × 2:

$$\mathbf{B} = \begin{bmatrix} b_{11} & b_{12} \\ b_{21} & b_{22} \\ b_{31} & b_{32} \\ b_{41} & b_{42} \end{bmatrix}$$

The product **AB** can be formed and will be of order 3 × 2. For the product to be expressed in terms of partitioned matrices, the only condition is that the partitioning of the *rows* of **B** should conform to the partitioning of the *columns* of **A**. For example, let us partition **B** as follows:

$$\mathbf{B} = \begin{bmatrix} \mathbf{B}_{11} \\ \mathbf{B}_{21} \end{bmatrix}$$

where

$$\mathbf{B}_{11} = \begin{bmatrix} b_{11} & b_{12} \\ b_{21} & b_{22} \\ b_{31} & b_{32} \end{bmatrix} \quad \text{and} \quad \mathbf{B}_{21} = [b_{41} \quad b_{42}] \tag{4-24}$$

If we treated the submatrices as ordinary elements, we should write the product **AB** as

$$\mathbf{AB} = \begin{bmatrix} \mathbf{A}_{11} & \mathbf{A}_{12} \\ \mathbf{A}_{21} & \mathbf{A}_{22} \end{bmatrix} \begin{bmatrix} \mathbf{B}_{11} \\ \mathbf{B}_{21} \end{bmatrix}$$

$$\begin{bmatrix} \mathbf{A}_{11}\mathbf{B}_{11} + \mathbf{A}_{12}\mathbf{B}_{21} \\ \mathbf{A}_{21}\mathbf{B}_{11} + \mathbf{A}_{22}\mathbf{B}_{21} \end{bmatrix} \tag{4-25}$$

Inspection of the elements in the products of the submatrices shows that (4-25) does in fact give the same result as would be obtained by straightforward multiplication of the original unpartitioned matrices. Thus the submatrices can be treated as ordinary elements provided the matrices have been partitioned conformably.

The condition for conformable partitioning would also have been satisfied by

$$\mathbf{B} = \begin{bmatrix} \mathbf{B}_{11} & \mathbf{B}_{12} \\ \mathbf{B}_{21} & \mathbf{B}_{22} \end{bmatrix}$$

where

$$\mathbf{B}_{11} = \begin{bmatrix} b_{11} \\ b_{21} \\ b_{31} \end{bmatrix} \qquad \mathbf{B}_{12} = \begin{bmatrix} b_{12} \\ b_{22} \\ b_{32} \end{bmatrix} \qquad \mathbf{B}_{21} = [b_{41}] \qquad \mathbf{B}_{22} = [b_{42}]$$

and the product would then appear as

$$\mathbf{AB} = \begin{bmatrix} \mathbf{A}_{11}\mathbf{B}_{11} + \mathbf{A}_{12}\mathbf{B}_{21} & \mathbf{A}_{11}\mathbf{B}_{12} + \mathbf{A}_{12}\mathbf{B}_{22} \\ \mathbf{A}_{21}\mathbf{B}_{11} + \mathbf{A}_{22}\mathbf{B}_{21} & \mathbf{A}_{21}\mathbf{B}_{12} + \mathbf{A}_{22}\mathbf{B}_{22} \end{bmatrix}$$

in terms of the new submatrices.

Another important form of matrix multiplication is the *direct* or Kronecker product of two matrices. If **A** is of order $m \times n$ and **B** is of order $p \times q$, the direct (or Kronecker) product $\mathbf{A} \otimes \mathbf{B}$ is defined as

$$\mathbf{A} \otimes \mathbf{B} = \begin{bmatrix} a_{11}\mathbf{B} & a_{12}\mathbf{B} & \cdots & a_{1n}\mathbf{B} \\ a_{21}\mathbf{B} & a_{22}\mathbf{B} & \cdots & a_{2n}\mathbf{B} \\ \vdots & \vdots & & \vdots \\ a_{m1}\mathbf{B} & a_{m2}\mathbf{B} & \cdots & a_{mn}\mathbf{B} \end{bmatrix} \tag{4-26}$$

$\mathbf{A} \otimes \mathbf{B}$ is thus of order $mp \times nq$. If **A** and **B** are square matrices of the same order and both nonsingular it is easy to show that

$$(\mathbf{A} \otimes \mathbf{B})^{-1} = \mathbf{A}^{-1} \otimes \mathbf{B}^{-1} \tag{4-27}$$

Notice the contrast between this result and (4-18) where the order of multiplication is reversed whereas in (4-27) the order remains the same on both sides. The reader should prove (4-27) as an exercise.

We often require the inverse of a partitioned matrix and indeed the computation of an inverse is often simplified by a suitable partitioning of the original matrix. Let $\mathbf{A}$ be a nonsingular matrix, which is partitioned

$$\mathbf{A} = \begin{bmatrix} \mathbf{A}_{11} & \mathbf{A}_{12} \\ \mathbf{A}_{21} & \mathbf{A}_{22} \end{bmatrix}$$

where $\mathbf{A}_{11}$ and $\mathbf{A}_{22}$ are both square and non-singular.

Let the inverse be partitioned conformably and write it as

$$\mathbf{A}^{-1} = \begin{bmatrix} \mathbf{E} & \mathbf{F} \\ \mathbf{G} & \mathbf{H} \end{bmatrix}$$

Using the equations

$$\mathbf{A}\mathbf{A}^{-1} = \mathbf{A}^{-1}\mathbf{A} = \begin{bmatrix} \mathbf{I} & \mathbf{0} \\ \mathbf{0} & \mathbf{I} \end{bmatrix}$$

where the unit matrix has also been partitioned conformably it is simple but tedious to show that the inverse $\mathbf{A}^{-1}$ may be expressed as

$$\mathbf{A}^{-1} = \begin{bmatrix} \mathbf{E} & -\mathbf{E}\mathbf{A}_{12}\mathbf{A}_{22}^{-1} \\ -\mathbf{A}_{22}^{-1}\mathbf{A}_{21}\mathbf{E} & \mathbf{A}_{22}^{-1} + \mathbf{A}_{22}^{-1}\mathbf{A}_{21}\mathbf{E}\mathbf{A}_{12}\mathbf{A}_{22}^{-1} \end{bmatrix} \tag{4-28}$$

where

$$\mathbf{E} = (\mathbf{A}_{11} - \mathbf{A}_{12}\mathbf{A}_{22}^{-1}\mathbf{A}_{21})^{-1} \tag{4-29}$$

This is only one of several forms in which the inverse of a partitioned matrix may be expressed. It is useful for computational purposes if $\mathbf{A}_{22}^{-1}$ happens to be particularly simple. An alternative form[1] may be derived based on $\mathbf{A}_{11}^{-1}$.

A useful application of (4-28) which arises in Chap. 6 is the determination of the inverse of the matrix

$$\mathbf{A} = \begin{bmatrix} \mathbf{X}'\mathbf{X} & \mathbf{X}'\mathbf{D} \\ \mathbf{D}'\mathbf{X} & \mathbf{D}'\mathbf{D} \end{bmatrix}$$

where $\mathbf{X}$ is some $n \times k$ matrix of observations on certain variables and $\mathbf{D}$ is an $n \times s$ matrix of suitably specified dummy variables. Applying (4-28) and (4-29) gives

$$\mathbf{A}^{-1} = \begin{bmatrix} \mathbf{E} & -\mathbf{E}(\mathbf{X}'\mathbf{D})(\mathbf{D}'\mathbf{D})^{-1} \\ -(\mathbf{D}'\mathbf{D})^{-1}(\mathbf{D}'\mathbf{X})\mathbf{E} & (\mathbf{D}'\mathbf{D})^{-1} + (\mathbf{D}'\mathbf{D})^{-1}(\mathbf{D}'\mathbf{X})\mathbf{E}(\mathbf{X}'\mathbf{D})(\mathbf{D}'\mathbf{D})^{-1} \end{bmatrix} \tag{4-30}$$

[1] The reader should derive the alternative form as an exercise.

where

$$\mathbf{E} = (\mathbf{X}'\mathbf{M}\mathbf{X})^{-1} \quad \text{and} \quad \mathbf{M} = \mathbf{I} - \mathbf{D}(\mathbf{D}'\mathbf{D})^{-1}\mathbf{D}' \tag{4-31}$$

It also follows immediately from (4-28) and (4-29) that if **A** is nonsingular and of the form

$$\mathbf{A} = \begin{bmatrix} \mathbf{A}_{11} & \mathbf{0} \\ \mathbf{0} & \mathbf{A}_{22} \end{bmatrix}$$

then

$$\mathbf{A}^{-1} = \begin{bmatrix} \mathbf{A}_{11}^{-1} & \mathbf{0} \\ \mathbf{0} & \mathbf{A}_{22}^{-1} \end{bmatrix} \tag{4-32}$$

Matrices of this form are called *block-diagonal* and clearly the result (4-32) holds for matrices which can be partitioned to show more than two submatrices along the principal diagonal.

We sometimes need to find the determinants of partitioned matrices. To begin with we note that

$$\begin{vmatrix} \mathbf{A}_{11} & \mathbf{0} \\ \mathbf{0} & \mathbf{I} \end{vmatrix} = |\mathbf{A}_{11}| \tag{4-33}$$

for if we evaluate the determinant on the left-hand side by expanding in terms of the elements of the last row the only nonzero term is the last one, which is unity multiplied by a determinant of the same form except that the order of **I** has been reduced by one. Proceeding in this way the result then follows. The determinant of a block diagonal matrix is then

$$\begin{aligned} \begin{vmatrix} \mathbf{A}_{11} & \mathbf{0} \\ \mathbf{0} & \mathbf{A}_{22} \end{vmatrix} &= \begin{vmatrix} \mathbf{A}_{11} & \mathbf{0} \\ \mathbf{0} & \mathbf{I} \end{vmatrix} \cdot \begin{vmatrix} \mathbf{I} & \mathbf{0} \\ \mathbf{0} & \mathbf{A}_{22} \end{vmatrix} \\ &= |\mathbf{A}_{11}| \cdot |\mathbf{A}_{22}| \end{aligned} \tag{4-34}$$

Now consider

$$\begin{vmatrix} \mathbf{A}_{11} & \mathbf{A}_{12} \\ \mathbf{0} & \mathbf{I} \end{vmatrix}$$

By a similar argument to that establishing (4-33) this may be seen to be $|\mathbf{A}_{11}|$. This enables us to establish the determinant of a block-triangular matrix for

$$\begin{aligned} \begin{vmatrix} \mathbf{A}_{11} & \mathbf{A}_{12} \\ \mathbf{0} & \mathbf{A}_{22} \end{vmatrix} &= \begin{vmatrix} \mathbf{I} & \mathbf{0} \\ \mathbf{0} & \mathbf{A}_{22} \end{vmatrix} \cdot \begin{vmatrix} \mathbf{A}_{11} & \mathbf{A}_{12} \\ \mathbf{0} & \mathbf{I} \end{vmatrix} \\ &= |\mathbf{A}_{11}| \cdot |\mathbf{A}_{22}| \end{aligned} \tag{4-35}$$

This is a matrix generalization of the simple result that the determinant of a triangular matrix is the product of the diagonal elements.[1] Finally to establish the determinant of a general partitioned matrix let

$$\mathbf{A} = \begin{bmatrix} \mathbf{A}_{11} & \mathbf{A}_{12} \\ \mathbf{A}_{21} & \mathbf{A}_{22} \end{bmatrix}$$

as before and on the assumption that $\mathbf{A}_{22}$ is nonsingular define

$$\mathbf{B}_1 = \begin{bmatrix} \mathbf{I} & -\mathbf{A}_{12}\mathbf{A}_{22}^{-1} \\ \mathbf{0} & \mathbf{I} \end{bmatrix} \qquad \mathbf{B}_2 = \begin{bmatrix} \mathbf{I} & \mathbf{0} \\ -\mathbf{A}_{22}^{-1}\mathbf{A}_{21} & \mathbf{I} \end{bmatrix}$$

Then

$$\mathbf{B}_1\mathbf{A}\mathbf{B}_2 = \begin{bmatrix} \mathbf{A}_{11} - \mathbf{A}_{12}\mathbf{A}_{22}^{-1}\mathbf{A}_{21} & \mathbf{0} \\ \mathbf{0} & \mathbf{A}_{22} \end{bmatrix}$$

and since $|\mathbf{B}_1| = |\mathbf{B}_2| = 1$

$$|\mathbf{A}| = |\mathbf{A}_{22}| \cdot |\mathbf{A}_{11} - \mathbf{A}_{12}\mathbf{A}_{22}^{-1}\mathbf{A}_{21}| \tag{4-36}$$

In a similar fashion, if $\mathbf{A}_{11}$ is nonsingular it may be shown that

$$|\mathbf{A}| = |\mathbf{A}_{11}| \cdot |\mathbf{A}_{22} - \mathbf{A}_{21}\mathbf{A}_{11}^{-1}\mathbf{A}_{12}| \tag{4-37}$$

4-4 LINEAR DEPENDENCE, RANK, AND THE SOLUTION OF HOMOGENEOUS EQUATIONS

Consider the set of homogeneous equations

$$\mathbf{A}\mathbf{x} = \mathbf{0} \tag{4-38}$$

where $\mathbf{A}$ is an $m \times n$ matrix of known constants and $\mathbf{x}$ a column vector of n unknowns. If we denote the columns of $\mathbf{A}$ by $\mathbf{a}_1, \mathbf{a}_2, \ldots, \mathbf{a}_n$ (4-38) may be written as

$$x_1\mathbf{a}_1 + x_2\mathbf{a}_2 + \cdots + x_n\mathbf{a}_n = \mathbf{0} \tag{4-39}$$

where the left-hand side denotes a linear combination of the columns of $\mathbf{A}$. If the *only* solution to (4-39) is the trivial one $\mathbf{x} = \mathbf{0}$, (that is, *every* element of $\mathbf{x}$ is zero), then the vectors $\mathbf{a}_1, \mathbf{a}_2, \ldots, \mathbf{a}_n$ are said to be *linearly independent*. If, however, there is some $\mathbf{x} \neq \mathbf{0}$ (that is, not all the elements of $\mathbf{x}$ are zero), which satisfies (4-39) then the columns of $\mathbf{A}$ are said to be *linearly dependent*. The *rank* of $\mathbf{A}$ is defined as the *maximum number of linearly independent columns in* $\mathbf{A}$.

Consider for a moment only square matrices ($m = n$). If $\mathbf{A}$ is nonsingular, $|\mathbf{A}| \neq 0$ and the only solution to (4-38) is $\mathbf{x} = \mathbf{0}$. The n columns of $\mathbf{A}$

[1] See Exercise 4-13.

are thus linearly independent and the rank of $\mathbf{A}$ is n, which we shall write in the notation

$$\rho(\mathbf{A}) = n.$$

Clearly the n *rows* of $\mathbf{A}$ are also linearly independent, for $\mathbf{y}'\mathbf{A}$, where $\mathbf{y}'$ is an n-element row vector, represents a linear combination of the rows of $\mathbf{A}$ and the only solution to $\mathbf{y}'\mathbf{A} = \mathbf{0}$ is $\mathbf{y} = \mathbf{0}$. Thus in the case of a square, nonsingular $\mathbf{A}$, $|\mathbf{A}| \neq 0$ and the rank of $\mathbf{A}$ is given by the number of columns (or rows) in $\mathbf{A}$, which is then said to be of *full rank*. If we are to have a nontrivial solution to $\mathbf{Ax} = 0$ then $|\mathbf{A}|$ must be zero and in this case the n columns (or rows) of $\mathbf{A}$ will be linearly dependent and $\rho(\mathbf{A}) < n$.

To illustrate these points, consider the set of equations

$$\begin{bmatrix} 1 & 2 & -3 \\ 2 & 0 & 2 \\ 4 & 1 & 3 \end{bmatrix} \begin{bmatrix} x_1 \\ x_2 \\ x_3 \end{bmatrix} = \begin{bmatrix} 0 \\ 0 \\ 0 \end{bmatrix} \tag{4-40}$$

The only solution is $x_1 = x_2 = x_3 = 0$, for $|\mathbf{A}| = -4$. The columns (and rows) of $\mathbf{A}$ are linearly independent and $\rho(\mathbf{A}) = 3$. If we now look at the set

$$\begin{bmatrix} 1 & 2 & -3 \\ 2 & 0 & 2 \\ 4 & 1 & 2 \end{bmatrix} \begin{bmatrix} x_1 \\ x_2 \\ x_3 \end{bmatrix} = \begin{bmatrix} 0 \\ 0 \\ 0 \end{bmatrix} \tag{4-41}$$

$|\mathbf{A}| = 0$. This means that we should now be able to find a set of x's, not all zero, such that

$$x_1 \begin{bmatrix} 1 \\ 2 \\ 4 \end{bmatrix} + x_2 \begin{bmatrix} 2 \\ 0 \\ 1 \end{bmatrix} + x_3 \begin{bmatrix} -3 \\ 2 \\ 2 \end{bmatrix} = \begin{bmatrix} 0 \\ 0 \\ 0 \end{bmatrix} \tag{4-42}$$

By inspection it is seen that $x_1 = 1$, $x_2 = -2$, $x_3 = -1$, or any scalar multiple of these values, will satisfy (4-42). Denoting the column vectors in (4-42) by $\mathbf{a}_1$, $\mathbf{a}_2$, and $\mathbf{a}_3$ we have

$$\mathbf{a}_1 - 2\mathbf{a}_2 - \mathbf{a}_3 = \mathbf{0} \tag{4-43}$$

and the vectors are linearly dependent. Equation (4-43) means that any one of the three vectors can be expressed as a linear combination of the other two, for instance

$$\mathbf{a}_2 = 0.5\mathbf{a}_1 - 0.5\mathbf{a}_3$$

It is also clear by inspection that any pair of vectors in (4-42) is linearly independent, and so we conclude that the rank of the $\mathbf{A}$ matrix in (4-41) is two. We also note that all minors of order two from **A** are nonzero, for example,

$$\begin{vmatrix} 1 & 2 \\ 2 & 0 \end{vmatrix} = -4, \qquad \begin{vmatrix} 2 & 2 \\ 4 & 2 \end{vmatrix} = -4, \qquad \begin{vmatrix} 1 & 2 \\ 4 & 1 \end{vmatrix} = -7 \text{ etc.}$$

Just as we have found the columns of **A** to be linearly dependent so may the rows be shown to be linearly dependent. We seek a nonnull **y** vector such that

$$y_1 \begin{bmatrix} 1 \\ 2 \\ -3 \end{bmatrix} + y_2 \begin{bmatrix} 2 \\ 0 \\ 2 \end{bmatrix} + y_3 \begin{bmatrix} 4 \\ 1 \\ 2 \end{bmatrix} = \begin{bmatrix} 0 \\ 0 \\ 0 \end{bmatrix} \tag{4-44}$$

Such a vector is $y_1 = -0.5$, $y_2 = -1.75$, $y_3 = 1$ (or any scalar multiple thereof).[1] Clearly any pair of vectors in (4-44) is linearly independent.

Next consider the set of equations

$$\begin{bmatrix} 1 & 2 & 2 \\ 2 & 0 & 4 \\ 4 & 1 & 8 \end{bmatrix} \begin{bmatrix} x_1 \\ x_2 \\ x_3 \end{bmatrix} = \begin{bmatrix} 0 \\ 0 \\ 0 \end{bmatrix} \tag{4-45}$$

Again $|\mathbf{A}| = 0$. The linear dependence of the columns of **A** may now be expressed by

$$2\mathbf{a}_1 + 0 \cdot \mathbf{a}_2 - \mathbf{a}_3 = \mathbf{0}$$

or simply

$$2\mathbf{a}_1 - \mathbf{a}_3 = \mathbf{0}$$

We see that $\mathbf{a}_2$ cannot now be expressed as a linear combination of the $\mathbf{a}_1$ and $\mathbf{a}_3$ vectors, or, to put it in other words, not all pairs of column vectors are linearly independent. The vectors $\mathbf{a}_1$ and $\mathbf{a}_2$ are linearly independent, so are $\mathbf{a}_2$ and $\mathbf{a}_3$ but not $\mathbf{a}_1$ and $\mathbf{a}_3$. The same fact is revealed by the minors of order two. Replacing each element of **A** by its minor gives the matrix

$$\begin{bmatrix} -4 & 0 & 2 \\ 14 & 0 & -7 \\ 8 & 0 & -4 \end{bmatrix}$$

[1] When a solution is not obvious from inspection it may be obtained by dropping one equation, setting one of the y's at unity and solving for the remaining two. For example, dropping the third equation and setting $y_3 = 1$ gives

$$y_1 + 2y_2 = -4$$
$$2y_1 = -1$$

which yield $y_1 = -0.5$ and $y_2 = -1.75$ to which we add $y_3 = 1$.

where the linear dependence of $\mathbf{a}_1$ and $\mathbf{a}_3$ shows up in the zero minors in the $\mathbf{a}_2$ column. The rank of $\mathbf{A}$ in this example is still two since all three columns are linearly dependent but we can find two columns which are linearly independent.

Finally consider the set of equations

$$\begin{bmatrix} 1 & 2 & 6 \\ 2 & 4 & 12 \\ 4 & 8 & 24 \end{bmatrix} \begin{bmatrix} x_1 \\ x_2 \\ x_3 \end{bmatrix} = \begin{bmatrix} 0 \\ 0 \\ 0 \end{bmatrix}$$

Again $|\mathbf{A}| = 0$, but in addition all second-order minors are zero and it is now impossible to find any pair of column vectors that are linearly independent. The rank of $\mathbf{A}$ is now one.

Returning now to the more general case, let $\mathbf{A}$ be $m \times n$ and let r indicate the maximum number of linearly independent columns in $\mathbf{A}$. We can see right away that r cannot exceed m. Suppose that $r > m$ and that the first r columns of $\mathbf{A}$ are linearly independent. The first m columns are then linearly independent and so if $\mathbf{A}_1$ denotes the square matrix of order m consisting of the first m columns of $\mathbf{A}$ we have $|\mathbf{A}_1| \neq 0$ Thus for any one of the remaining linearly independent vectors $\mathbf{a}_i$ $(i = m + 1, \ldots, r)$ the equation

$$\mathbf{A}_1\mathbf{b} = \mathbf{a}_i$$

has non-zero solution

$$\mathbf{b} = \mathbf{A}_1^{-1}\mathbf{a}_i$$

which contradicts the assumption that there are more than m linearly independent columns. Thus

$$\rho(\mathbf{A}) \leq \min\{m, n\} \tag{4-46}$$

If $\rho(\mathbf{A}) = r$ and if we again assume that the columns of $\mathbf{A}$ are so numbered that the first r are linearly independent the only solution to

$$x_1\mathbf{a}_1 + x_2\mathbf{a}_2 + \cdots + x_r\mathbf{a}_r = \mathbf{0} \tag{4-47}$$

is

$$x_1 = x_2 = \cdots = x_r = 0$$

If $r = m$ the square matrix of order r formed by the vectors $\mathbf{a}_1, \mathbf{a}_2, \ldots, \mathbf{a}_r$ has a nonzero determinant. If $r < m$ we can drop $(m - r)$ linearly dependent equations from the set (4-47) to obtain

$$x_1\mathbf{a}_1^* + x_2\mathbf{a}_2^* + \cdots + x_r\mathbf{a}_r^* = \mathbf{0} \tag{4-48}$$

where the $\mathbf{a}_i^*$ denote column vectors of r elements. The only solution to (4-48) is still

$$x_1 = x_2 = \cdots = x_r = 0$$

and so there is at least one minor of order r from **A** which is nonzero. Since any set of $r + 1$ columns of **A** is a linearly dependent set all minors of order $r + 1$ must be zero, and the same applies to minors of order $r + 2$, $r + 3$ etc. Also since the implications of a nonzero minor for the linear independence of rows and columns are identical it follows that the rank of a matrix may be defined equivalently as the maximum number of linearly independent rows, the maximum number of linearly independent columns or the maximum order of non-zero minors.

As an example, the rank of

$$\mathbf{A} = \begin{bmatrix} 4 & 8 & 2 \\ 2 & 4 & 4 \\ 2 & 4 & -2 \end{bmatrix}$$

is seen to be two, for $|\mathbf{A}| = 0$ and though some minors of order two are zero others are nonzero. It is clear from the definition of rank that $\rho(\mathbf{I}_n) = n$ and that the rank of a diagonal matrix is equal to the number of nonzero elements on the diagonal. Further, it was shown in (4-22) that if **A** is a nonsingular matrix $|\mathbf{A}^{-1}| = 1/|\mathbf{A}|$. Thus $\mathbf{A}^{-1}$ has full rank.

We state without proof an important theorem concerning the rank of the product of two matrices, namely

$$\rho(\mathbf{AB}) \leq \min\,[\rho(\mathbf{A}), \rho(\mathbf{B})] \tag{4-49}$$

This states that the rank of the product **AB** cannot exceed the smaller of the ranks of **A** and **B**. An important corollary follows immediately. It is that pre- or postmultiplication of **A** by a nonsingular matrix gives products whose ranks are equal to the rank of **A**. Let **A** be $m \times n$ and let $\rho(\mathbf{A}) = r$. Let **B** be a nonsingular matrix of order n so that $\rho(\mathbf{B}) = n$. Let $\rho(\mathbf{AB}) = k$. Then by (4-49)

$$k \leq \min\,[r, n]$$

that is

$$k \leq r \quad \text{since} \quad r \leq n.$$

But

$$\mathbf{A} = (\mathbf{AB})\mathbf{B}^{-1}$$

Therefore

$$r \leq \min\,[k, n]$$

that is

$$r \leq k$$

and so

$$k = r$$

and we have

$$\rho(\mathbf{AB}) = \rho(\mathbf{A}) \text{ where } \mathbf{B} \text{ is nonsingular} \tag{4-50}$$

A similar proof shows

$$\rho(\mathbf{CA}) = \rho(\mathbf{A}) \text{ where } \mathbf{C} \text{ is nonsingular} \tag{4-51}$$

and

$$\rho(\mathbf{CAB}) = \rho(\mathbf{A}) \text{ where } \mathbf{C} \text{ and } \mathbf{B} \text{ are nonsingular} \tag{4-52}$$

Finally in this section on rank we need to establish one important result on the solution of homogeneous equations, which will be particularly useful in the treatment of identification in Chap. 12. Consider again the set of equations in (4-41)

$$\begin{bmatrix} 1 & 2 & -3 \\ 2 & 0 & 2 \\ 4 & 1 & 2 \end{bmatrix} \begin{bmatrix} x_1 \\ x_2 \\ x_3 \end{bmatrix} = \begin{bmatrix} 0 \\ 0 \\ 0 \end{bmatrix}$$

As we have seen $\rho(\mathbf{A}) = 2$ and any row in $\mathbf{A}$ can be expressed as a linear combination of the other two rows. Thus any one of the three equations may be discarded without losing any information. Let us drop the third equation and rewrite the first two in the form

$$\begin{bmatrix} 1 & 2 \\ 2 & 0 \end{bmatrix} \begin{bmatrix} x_1 \\ x_2 \end{bmatrix} = - \begin{bmatrix} -3 \\ 2 \end{bmatrix} x_3$$

Solving gives

$$\begin{bmatrix} x_1 \\ x_2 \end{bmatrix} = \begin{bmatrix} -x_3 \\ 2x_3 \end{bmatrix}$$

The solution vector to (4-41) is thus

$$\mathbf{x} = \{-x_3 \quad 2x_3 \quad x_3\} = \{-1 \quad 2 \quad 1\}x_3 \tag{4-53}$$

The x_3 value is arbitrary and so there is an infinite set of solutions but once any specific x_3 value has been selected the x_1 and x_2 values are given as certain multiples of that value. In other words the *ratios* of the elements in the solution vector are *uniquely* determined and all possible solutions lie on a single ray through the origin in three-dimensional space. Geometrically one says that the *dimension* of the subspace of solutions to (4-41) is one, and we notice that in this example the dimension is equal to the difference between the number of unknowns ($n = 3$) and the rank of $\mathbf{A}$ ($\rho(\mathbf{A}) = 2$).

If we now consider the set

$$\begin{bmatrix} 1 & 2 & 6 \\ 2 & 4 & 12 \\ 4 & 8 & 24 \end{bmatrix} \begin{bmatrix} x_1 \\ x_2 \\ x_3 \end{bmatrix} = \begin{bmatrix} 0 \\ 0 \\ 0 \end{bmatrix}$$

$\rho(\mathbf{A}) = 1$, that is, there is only one independent equation, which we may write

$$x_1 = -2x_2 - 6x_3 \tag{4-54}$$

Two elements of the solution vector are now arbitrary and the set of solutions (4-54) constitutes a plane through the origin in three dimensional space. The dimension of the subspace of solutions is again equal to the number of unknowns ($n = 3$) minus the rank of $\mathbf{A}(\rho(\mathbf{A}) = 1)$.[1]

These examples illustrate and suggest the general result that if $\mathbf{A}$ is $m \times n$ with $\rho(\mathbf{A}) = r$ then the dimension of the solution space for $\mathbf{Ax} = \mathbf{0}$ is $(n - r)$. This may be shown as follows. Partition $\mathbf{Ax} = \mathbf{0}$ in the form

$$\begin{bmatrix} \mathbf{A}_{11} & \mathbf{A}_{12} \\ \mathbf{A}_{21} & \mathbf{A}_{22} \end{bmatrix} \begin{bmatrix} \mathbf{x}_1 \\ \mathbf{x}_2 \end{bmatrix} = \mathbf{0} \tag{4-55}$$

where $\mathbf{A}_{11}$ is square and nonsingular of order r and $\mathbf{A}_{12}$ is of order $r \times (n - r)$ etc. Since the last $(m - r)$ rows of (4-55) are redundant we have

$$\mathbf{A}_{11}\mathbf{x}_1 + \mathbf{A}_{12}\mathbf{x}_2 = \mathbf{0}$$

giving

$$\mathbf{x}_1 = -\mathbf{A}_{11}^{-1}\mathbf{A}_{12}\mathbf{x}_2$$

[1] The dimension of a space is defined as the maximum number of linearly independent vectors in the space. In the first example $\{-x_3 \quad 2x_3 \quad x_3\}$ is one vector in the solution space and all other vectors in the space are given by $\{-cx_3 \quad 2cx_3 \quad cx_3\}$ where c is an arbitrary constant. Clearly any two solution vectors are linearly dependent and so the dimension is one. In the second example the general solution vector is given by $\{-2x_2-6x_3 \quad x_2 \quad x_3\}$ and so the general solution may be expressed as a linear combination of just two linearly independent vectors, namely,

$$\mathbf{x} = x_2 \begin{bmatrix} -2 \\ 1 \\ 0 \end{bmatrix} + x_3 \begin{bmatrix} -6 \\ 0 \\ 1 \end{bmatrix}$$

and so the dimension of the solution space is two.

Thus all solutions to $\mathbf{Ax} = \mathbf{0}$ are of the form

$$\mathbf{x} = \begin{bmatrix} -\mathbf{A}_{11}^{-1}\mathbf{A}_{12}\mathbf{x}_2 \\ \mathbf{x}_2 \end{bmatrix} = \begin{bmatrix} -\mathbf{A}_{11}^{-1}\mathbf{A}_{12} \\ \mathbf{I}_{(n-r)} \end{bmatrix}\mathbf{x}_2 \tag{4-56}$$

The matrix on the right-hand side of (4-56) is of order $n \times (n - r)$, has rank $(n - r)$, and $\mathbf{x}_2$ denotes an arbitrary vector of $(n - r)$ elements. Thus all vectors in the solution space have been expressed as linear combinations of $(n - r)$ linearly independent vectors and so the dimension of the solution space for $\mathbf{Ax} = \mathbf{0}$ is $n - \rho(\mathbf{A})$.

In identification problems we are particularly concerned with solution vectors which lie on a single ray and from the above it follows that solutions to $\mathbf{Ax} = \mathbf{0}$, where $\mathbf{A}$ is $m \times n$ and $\mathbf{x}$ is $n \times 1$, lie on a single ray if and only if $\rho(\mathbf{A}) = n - 1$.

4-5 CHARACTERISTIC ROOTS AND VECTORS

The characteristic value problem is defined as that of finding values of a scalar λ and an associated vector $\mathbf{x} \neq \mathbf{0}$ which satisfy,

$$\mathbf{Ax} = \lambda\mathbf{x} \tag{4-57}$$

where $\mathbf{A}$ is some $n \times n$ matrix. λ is called a characteristic root of $\mathbf{A}$ and $\mathbf{x}$ a characteristic vector. Alternative names are latent roots and vectors and eigenvalues and eigenvectors. If we take the 2×2 case as an illustration of (4-57) we have

$$(a_{11} - \lambda)x_1 + a_{12}x_2 = 0$$

$$a_{21}x_1 + (a_{22} - \lambda)x_2 = 0$$

which may be put back in matrix form as

$$(\mathbf{A} - \lambda\mathbf{I})\mathbf{x} = \mathbf{0} \tag{4-58}$$

Equation (4-58) only has a nontrivial solution, $\mathbf{x} \neq \mathbf{0}$, if $(\mathbf{A} - \lambda\mathbf{I})$ is singular, that is, if

$$|\mathbf{A} - \lambda\mathbf{I}| = 0 \tag{4-59}$$

Equation (4-59) yields a polynomial in the unknown λ, which may be solved for λ and then the characteristic vectors obtained. For example, in the 2×2 case, (4-59) gives

$$(a_{11} - \lambda)(a_{22} - \lambda) - a_{12}a_{21} = 0$$

that is

$$\lambda^2 - (a_{11} + a_{22})\lambda + (a_{11}a_{22} - a_{12}a_{21}) = 0$$

with roots

$$\lambda_1 = \tfrac{1}{2}[(a_{11} + a_{22}) + \sqrt{(a_{11} + a_{22})^2 - 4(a_{11}a_{22} - a_{12}a_{21})}]$$

$$\lambda_2 = \tfrac{1}{2}[(a_{11} + a_{22}) - \sqrt{(a_{11} + a_{22})^2 - 4(a_{11}a_{22} - a_{12}a_{21})}]$$

In the special case of a symmetric matrix, $a_{12} = a_{21}$, the roots become

$$\lambda = \tfrac{1}{2}[(a_{11} + a_{22}) \pm \sqrt{(a_{11} - a_{22})^2 + 4a_{12}^2}] \tag{4-60}$$

and since the content of the square root sign is the sum of two squares, the roots λ_1 and λ_2 are necessarily real for a symmetric matrix.

For a numerical example, consider

$$\mathbf{A} = \begin{bmatrix} 4 & 2 \\ 2 & 1 \end{bmatrix}$$

Substitution in (4-60) gives $\lambda_1 = 5$ and $\lambda_2 = 0$. To find the characteristic vector associated with each root we substitute for λ in (4-58). For $\lambda_1 = 5$

$$\mathbf{A} - \lambda\mathbf{I} = \begin{bmatrix} -1 & 2 \\ 2 & -4 \end{bmatrix}$$

and (4-58) gives

$$-x_1 + 2x_2 = 0$$

$$2x_1 - 4x_2 = 0$$

that is,

$$x_1 = 2x_2$$

Thus one element in the characteristic vector is arbitrary, and so if $\mathbf{x}$ satisfies (4-58) for a given λ, then so does kx, where k is an arbitrary constant. We may normalize the vector by setting its length at unity, that is, by making

$$x_1^2 + x_2^2 = 1$$

which, with $x_1 = 2x_2$, gives

$$x_2 = \frac{1}{\sqrt{5}} \quad \text{and} \quad x_1 = \frac{2}{\sqrt{5}}$$

so that the characteristic vector associated with $\lambda_1 = 5$ is

$$\mathbf{x}_1 = \left\{ \frac{2}{\sqrt{5}} \quad \frac{1}{\sqrt{5}} \right\}$$

Similarly it may be shown that the characteristic vector associated with $\lambda_2 = 0$ is

$$\mathbf{x}_2 = \left\{ \frac{1}{\sqrt{5}} \quad \frac{-2}{\sqrt{5}} \right\}$$

We notice that $\mathbf{x}_1'\mathbf{x}_2 = 0$, so the characteristic vectors of this symmetric matrix are orthogonal.[1]

In general we will only be concerned with real symmetric matrices. The two properties of real roots and orthogonal characteristic vectors hold in the general case, for real symmetric matrices of order n.[2] Furthermore, if a characteristic root λ, has multiplicity k (i.e., is repeated k times) there will be k orthogonal vectors corresponding to this root.[3]

The nth order symmetric matrix $\mathbf{A}$ has characteristic roots $\lambda_1, \lambda_2, \ldots, \lambda_n$, possibly not all distinct. Corresponding to these roots are a set of orthogonal characteristic vectors $\mathbf{x}_1, \mathbf{x}_2, \ldots, \mathbf{x}_n$ such that

$$\mathbf{x}_i'\mathbf{x}_j = 0 \qquad i \neq j, \quad i, j = 1, 2, \ldots, n$$

We can normalize the vectors so that $\mathbf{x}_i'\mathbf{x}_i = 1$ for all i. A set of normalized orthogonal vectors is called an *orthonormal* set. We can then write the conditions on the $\mathbf{x}$ vectors as

$$\mathbf{x}_i'\mathbf{x}_j = \delta_{ij} \qquad \delta_{ij} = \begin{cases} 0 & i \neq j \\ 1 & i = j \end{cases} \tag{4-61}$$

where δ_{ij} is the Kronecker delta. If $\mathbf{X}$ denotes the nth order matrix whose columns are the vectors $\mathbf{x}_1, \mathbf{x}_2, \ldots, \mathbf{x}_n$ it then follows that

$$\mathbf{X}'\mathbf{X} = \mathbf{I}_n \tag{4-62}$$

so that

$$\mathbf{X}' = \mathbf{X}^{-1} \tag{4-63}$$

that is, the transpose of $\mathbf{X}$ is equal to its inverse. Such a matrix is said to be an *orthogonal matrix*. It also follows directly that $\mathbf{X}\mathbf{X}' = \mathbf{I}$. If we now form the product $\mathbf{X}'\mathbf{A}\mathbf{X}$, the ijth element in the resulting nth order matrix is

$$\mathbf{x}_i'\mathbf{A}\mathbf{x}_j = \lambda_j\mathbf{x}_i'\mathbf{x}_j$$

applying (4-57) since $\mathbf{x}_j$ is the characteristic vector corresponding to λ_j. Thus

$$\mathbf{x}_i'\mathbf{A}\mathbf{x}_j = \lambda_j\delta_{ij} \text{ using (4-61)}$$

[1] Two vectors $\mathbf{x}$ and $\mathbf{y}$ are said to be orthogonal if $\mathbf{x}'\mathbf{y} = \mathbf{y}'\mathbf{x} = 0$ and $\mathbf{x}'\mathbf{x} \neq 0$, $\mathbf{y}'\mathbf{y} \neq 0$.

[2] See G. Hadley, *Linear Algebra*, Addison Wesley, Reading, Mass., 1961, pp. 240–241.

[3] *Ibid*., pp. 243–245.

Hence

$$\mathbf{X}'\mathbf{A}\mathbf{X} = \begin{bmatrix} \lambda_1 & 0 & 0 & \cdots & 0 \\ 0 & \lambda_2 & 0 & \cdots & 0 \\ 0 & 0 & \lambda_3 & \cdots & 0 \\ \vdots & \vdots & \vdots & & \vdots \\ 0 & 0 & 0 & \cdots & \lambda_n \end{bmatrix} \tag{4-64}$$

Thus assembling the characteristic vectors of $\mathbf{A}$ as the columns of $\mathbf{X}$ and forming the product $\mathbf{X}'\mathbf{A}\mathbf{X}$ has produced a diagonal matrix with the characteristic roots of $\mathbf{A}$ displayed on the principal diagonal. Equation (4-64) is an example of the diagonalizing of a symmetric matrix.

4-6 QUADRATIC FORMS AND POSITIVE DEFINITE MATRICES

Quadratic forms have already been introduced on page 77. Recapping, if $\mathbf{x}$ denotes an n-element column vector and $\mathbf{A}$ an nth order real symmetric matrix, then $\mathbf{x}'\mathbf{A}\mathbf{x}$ defines a quadratic form in the elements of $\mathbf{x}$. The quadratic form is said to be positive definite and the matrix $\mathbf{A}$ is said to be positive definite if and only if

$$\mathbf{x}'\mathbf{A}\mathbf{x} > 0 \quad \text{for all} \quad \mathbf{x} \neq \mathbf{0}$$

The quadratic form and associated matrix are said to be positive semidefinite if $\mathbf{x}'\mathbf{A}\mathbf{x} \geq 0$ for all $\mathbf{x}$. It follows immediately that if $\mathbf{A}$ is positive definite it must be nonsingular, for if it were singular the equation $\mathbf{A}\mathbf{x} = \mathbf{0}$ has a nontrivial solution and so $\mathbf{x}'\mathbf{A}\mathbf{x} = 0$ for $\mathbf{x} \neq \mathbf{0}$, contradicting the assumption of positive definiteness.

In the rest of this section we will assume, unless otherwise stated, that $\mathbf{A}$ is an nth order, symmetric, positive definite matrix. If $\mathbf{B}$ denotes a matrix of order $n \times s (s \leq n)$ with $\rho(\mathbf{B}) = s$, then

$$\mathbf{B}'\mathbf{A}\mathbf{B} \text{ is positive definite} \tag{4-65}$$

$\mathbf{B}'\mathbf{A}\mathbf{B}$ is clearly symmetric of order s. Consider any non-zero vector $\mathbf{y}$ of s elements and let $\mathbf{x} = \mathbf{B}\mathbf{y}$. It then follows that $\mathbf{x} \neq \mathbf{0}$. If $s < n$ we can write this equation as

$$\begin{bmatrix} \mathbf{x}_1 \\ \mathbf{x}_2 \end{bmatrix} = \begin{bmatrix} \mathbf{B}_1 \\ \mathbf{B}_2 \end{bmatrix} \mathbf{y}$$

where the partitioning is by the first s and the remaining $(n - s)$ rows. Since $\mathbf{B}$ has rank s we can assume that $\mathbf{B}_1$ is non-singular and so $\mathbf{y} = \mathbf{B}_1^{-1}\mathbf{x}_1$. If $\mathbf{x}$ were $\mathbf{0}$ then $\mathbf{x}_1 = \mathbf{0}$ and this would give $\mathbf{y} = \mathbf{0}$, contrary to assumption, so

$\mathbf{x} \neq \mathbf{0}$. If $s = n$ the same result follows immediately. Thus

$$\mathbf{y}'(\mathbf{B}'\mathbf{A}\mathbf{B})\mathbf{y} = \mathbf{x}'\mathbf{A}\mathbf{x} > 0$$

and so

$\mathbf{B}'\mathbf{A}\mathbf{B}$ is positive definite

A special case of (4-65) arises when $s = n$ and $\mathbf{B}$ is nonsingular. The conditions for the theorem are still satisfied and so

$$\mathbf{B}'\mathbf{A}\mathbf{B} \quad \text{is positive definite for nonsingular } \mathbf{B} \tag{4-66}$$

If $\mathbf{B}$ in (4-66) is replaced by $\mathbf{A}^{-1}$, $\mathbf{B}'\mathbf{A}\mathbf{B} = (\mathbf{A}^{-1})' = \mathbf{A}^{-1}$ since the inverse of a symmetric matrix is also symmetric. Thus

$$\mathbf{A}^{-1} \text{ is positive definite} \tag{4-67}$$

From the definition of a positive definite matrix it follows that the unit matrix $\mathbf{I}$ is positive definite for

$$\mathbf{x}'\mathbf{I}\mathbf{x} = \mathbf{x}'\mathbf{x} > 0 \quad \text{for } \mathbf{x} \neq \mathbf{0}$$

Replacing $\mathbf{A}$ in (4-65) by $\mathbf{I}$ gives

$$\mathbf{B}'\mathbf{B} \text{ is positive definite} \tag{4-68}$$

and so $\mathbf{B}'\mathbf{B}$ is nonsingular, or in other words

$$\rho(\mathbf{B}'\mathbf{B}) = s = \rho(\mathbf{B}) \tag{4-69}$$

A very important property of positive definite matrices is embodied in the following result

$\mathbf{A}$ is positive definite if and only if all the characteristic roots of $\mathbf{A}$ are positive (4-70)

Let $\mathbf{X}$ be the orthogonal matrix that diagonalizes $\mathbf{A}$, that is,

$$\mathbf{X}'\mathbf{A}\mathbf{X} = \begin{bmatrix} \lambda_1 & 0 & \cdots & 0 \\ 0 & \lambda_2 & \cdots & 0 \\ \vdots & \vdots & & \vdots \\ 0 & 0 & \cdots & \lambda_n \end{bmatrix} = \mathbf{\Lambda} \tag{4-71}$$

where the λ_i are the characteristic roots of $\mathbf{A}$. Let $\mathbf{z}$ be any nonnull n element column vector and define $\mathbf{y} = \mathbf{X}'\mathbf{z}$. Then

$$\mathbf{z} = \mathbf{X}\mathbf{y} \text{ since } \mathbf{X} \text{ is orthogonal}$$

Thus

$$\mathbf{z}'\mathbf{A}\mathbf{z} = \mathbf{y}'\mathbf{X}'\mathbf{A}\mathbf{X}\mathbf{y} = \sum_{i=1}^{n} \lambda_i y_i^2$$

To prove sufficiency, let all λ_i be positive, then $\mathbf{z}'\mathbf{A}\mathbf{z} > 0$ and $\mathbf{A}$ is positive definite. To prove necessity, let $\mathbf{A}$ be positive definite so that

$$\mathbf{z}'\mathbf{A}\mathbf{z} = \sum_{i=1}^{n} \lambda_i y_i^2 > 0$$

Suppose that λ_1, say, is not positive. Choose $\mathbf{y} = \{1 \quad 0 \quad \cdots \quad 0\}$. From $\mathbf{z} = \mathbf{X}\mathbf{y}$ it is clear that $\mathbf{z}$ is nonnull, being in fact the first column of $\mathbf{X}$, and so we have

$$\mathbf{z}'\mathbf{A}\mathbf{z} = \lambda_1 \leq 0$$

which contradicts the assumption that $\mathbf{A}$ is positive definite and thus completes the proof of (4-70).

From $\mathbf{X}'\mathbf{X} = \mathbf{I}$ it follows that

$$|\mathbf{X}|^2 = 1 \quad \text{for } |\mathbf{X}'| = |\mathbf{X}|$$

and so

$$|\mathbf{X}| = \pm 1.$$

That is, the determinant of an orthogonal matrix is plus or minus unity. Applying this result to (4-71) gives

$$|\mathbf{A}| = \lambda_1 \lambda_2 \ldots \lambda_n$$

and so

$$|\mathbf{A}| > 0 \tag{4-72}$$

Thus a positive definite matrix is nonsingular, has positive characteristic roots and a positive determinant. It also follows that all the principal minors of a positive definite matrix are positive. The principal minors of a matrix are the determinants of the various submatrices formed by deleting corresponding rows and columns from the original matrix. The principal minors of order one are a_{ii} $(i = 1, \ldots, n)$, obtained by deleting all rows and columns except the ith,

$$\text{of order two are } \begin{vmatrix} a_{ii} & a_{ij} \\ a_{ji} & a_{jj} \end{vmatrix},$$

obtained by deleting all rows and columns except the ith and jth, and so forth. This result on principal minors follows from (4-65) by taking an $n \times n$ identity matrix, deleting the columns corresponding to those deleted from $\mathbf{A}$, and calling the result **B**. For example, if

$$\mathbf{B} = \begin{bmatrix} 1 & 0 \\ 0 & 1 \\ 0 & 0 \\ \vdots & \vdots \\ 0 & 0 \end{bmatrix}$$

$$\mathbf{B}'\mathbf{A}\mathbf{B} = \begin{bmatrix} a_{11} & a_{12} \\ a_{21} & a_{22} \end{bmatrix}$$

and since **B′AB** is positive definite by (4-65), it then follows from (4-72) that

$$\begin{vmatrix} a_{11} & a_{12} \\ a_{21} & a_{22} \end{vmatrix} > 0$$

and similarly for all the other principal minors.

Equation (4-71) can also be adapted to give another result which we shall find very useful in the treatment of generalized least squares in Chap. 7. Since the λ_i are all positive we can define a diagonal matrix **D** as

$$\mathbf{D} = \begin{bmatrix} \frac{1}{\sqrt{\lambda_1}} & 0 & \cdots & 0 \\ 0 & \frac{1}{\sqrt{\lambda_2}} & \cdots & 0 \\ \vdots & \vdots & & \vdots \\ 0 & 0 & \cdots & \frac{1}{\sqrt{\lambda_n}} \end{bmatrix}$$

Pre- and postmultiplying (4-71) by **D** gives

$$(\mathbf{XD})'\mathbf{A}(\mathbf{XD}) = \mathbf{I}_n$$

or

$$\mathbf{Q}'\mathbf{A}\mathbf{Q} = \mathbf{I}_n \tag{4-73}$$

where

$$\mathbf{Q} = \mathbf{XD}$$

Since **X** and **D** are both nonsingular **Q** is nonsingular. With suitable multiplication (4-73) gives

$$\mathbf{A} = (\mathbf{Q}^{-1})'\mathbf{Q}^{-1} \tag{4-74}$$

Thus if $\mathbf{A}$ is positive definite we can find a nonsingular matrix $\mathbf{P} = (\mathbf{Q}^{-1})'$ such that

$$\mathbf{A} = \mathbf{P}\mathbf{P}' \tag{4-75}$$

Another useful result that follows directly from (4-71) is that the trace of $\mathbf{A}$ is the sum of its characteristic roots for

$$\sum_{i=1}^{n} \lambda_i = \text{tr}\,(\mathbf{X}'\mathbf{A}\mathbf{X}) = \text{tr}\,(\mathbf{A}\mathbf{X}\mathbf{X}') = \text{tr}\,(\mathbf{A}) \tag{4-76}$$

In proving (4-70) we have considered the transformation $\mathbf{y} = \mathbf{X}'\mathbf{z}$ and shown that

$$\mathbf{z}'\mathbf{A}\mathbf{z} = \lambda_1 y_1^2 + \lambda_2 y_2^2 + \cdots + \lambda_n y_n^2 \tag{4-77}$$

When $\mathbf{z}$ consists of normally distributed variables $\mathbf{z}'\mathbf{A}\mathbf{z}$ is a quadratic form in normal variables and reference to the general expression for a quadratic form on page 78 will show that the right-hand side of (4-77) represents a considerable simplification. The fact that the transformation matrix $\mathbf{X}$ is orthogonal means that the distribution of the elements of $\mathbf{y}$ may be derived easily from that of the elements of $\mathbf{z}$. Suppose that the $\mathbf{z}$ vector consists of normally and independently distributed variables with zero mean and constant variance σ^2, that is

$$E(z_i) = 0 \qquad i = 1, \ldots, n$$

$$E(z_i^2) = \sigma^2 \qquad i = 1, \ldots, n$$

$$E(z_i z_j) = 0 \qquad i \neq j$$

These conditions are written more compactly as

$$\mathbf{z} \text{ is } N(\mathbf{0}, \sigma^2\mathbf{I})$$

where $\mathbf{0}$ indicates the vector of zero means and $\sigma^2\mathbf{I}$ the scalar variance–covariance matrix. Since $\mathbf{y} = \mathbf{X}'\mathbf{z}$, $\mathbf{y}$ also has a multivariate normal distribution

$$E(\mathbf{y}) = \mathbf{X}'E(\mathbf{z}) = \mathbf{0}$$

The variance–covariance matrix for a vector $\mathbf{y}$ with zero mean is defined as

$$E(\mathbf{y}\mathbf{y}') = \begin{bmatrix} E(y_1^2) & E(y_1y_2) & \cdots & E(y_1y_n) \\ E(y_2y_1) & E(y_2^2) & \cdots & E(y_2y_n) \\ \vdots & \vdots & & \vdots \\ E(y_ny_1) & E(y_ny_2) & \cdots & E(y_n^2) \end{bmatrix}$$

where the elements on the principal diagonal are seen to be variances and the off-diagonal elements covariances. Thus

$$E(\mathbf{yy}') = E(\mathbf{X}'\mathbf{zz}'\mathbf{X})$$

$$= \mathbf{X}'E(\mathbf{zz}')\mathbf{X}$$ since the elements of **X** are constants, depending only on **A**.

$$= \sigma^2\mathbf{X}'\mathbf{I}\mathbf{X}$$ since a constant such as σ^2 can be moved from the middle to the front (or back) of a matrix expression.

$$= \sigma^2\mathbf{X}'\mathbf{X}$$

$$= \sigma^2\mathbf{I}$$ since $\mathbf{X}'\mathbf{X} = \mathbf{I}$.

Thus the elements of **y** are also normally distributed with the same zero mean vector and the same scalar, variance–covariance matrix as **z**.

An especially important case of (4-77) arises when **A** is an *idempotent* matrix. We are concerned only with symmetric idempotent matrices which are defined as

$$\mathbf{A} = \mathbf{A}' \qquad \mathbf{A}^2 = \mathbf{A} \tag{4-78}$$

that is, an idempotent matrix is one which on multiplication by itself remains unchanged.

The characteristic roots of an idempotent matrix are either zero or unity. For

$$\mathbf{Ax} = \lambda\mathbf{x}$$

Therefore

$$\mathbf{A}^2\mathbf{x} = \lambda\mathbf{Ax} = \lambda^2\mathbf{x}$$

But

$$\mathbf{A}^2\mathbf{x} = \mathbf{Ax} = \lambda\mathbf{x}$$

Hence

$$\lambda^2\mathbf{x} = \lambda\mathbf{x}$$

But

$$\mathbf{x} \neq \mathbf{0}$$

Hence

$$\lambda^2 - \lambda = 0 \quad \text{and} \quad \lambda = 0 \quad \text{or} \quad \lambda = 1$$

It then follows from (4-71) that when an idempotent matrix of order n and of rank $n - k$ $(0 \leq k < n)$ is diagonalized, there will be $n - k$ units in the principal diagonal, and k zeros for the rank of the matrix on the right-hand side must be $n - k$, since the multiplication of $\mathbf{A}$ by nonsingular matrices cannot change the rank. We thus have the important result that if $\mathbf{x}'\mathbf{A}\mathbf{x}$ is a quadratic form in n independent normal variables with zero mean and common variance σ^2, and if $\mathbf{A}$ is idempotent of rank $n - k$, then

$$\mathbf{x}'\mathbf{A}\mathbf{x} = y_1^2 + \cdots + y_{n-k}^2 \tag{4-79}$$

where the y's are also independent normal variables with zero mean and variance σ^2.

Example The following rather lengthy example should be worked through carefully since it illustrates many points of importance for Chap. 5. Consider

$$\mathbf{Z} = \begin{bmatrix} 1 & 1 \\ 1 & 2 \\ 1 & 3 \end{bmatrix}$$

Then

$$(\mathbf{Z}'\mathbf{Z}) = \begin{bmatrix} 3 & 6 \\ 6 & 14 \end{bmatrix} \quad \text{and} \quad |\mathbf{Z}'\mathbf{Z}| = 6$$

$$(\mathbf{Z}'\mathbf{Z})^{-1} = \begin{bmatrix} \frac{14}{6} & -1 \\ -1 & \frac{3}{6} \end{bmatrix}$$

and

$$\mathbf{Z}(\mathbf{Z}'\mathbf{Z})^{-1}\mathbf{Z}' = \begin{bmatrix} \frac{5}{6} & \frac{2}{6} & -\frac{1}{6} \\ \frac{2}{6} & \frac{2}{6} & \frac{2}{6} \\ -\frac{1}{6} & \frac{2}{6} & \frac{5}{6} \end{bmatrix}$$

Define a new matrix $\mathbf{A}$ as

$$\mathbf{A} = \mathbf{I}_3 - \mathbf{Z}(\mathbf{Z}'\mathbf{Z})^{-1}\mathbf{Z}' = \begin{bmatrix} \frac{1}{6} & -\frac{2}{6} & \frac{1}{6} \\ -\frac{2}{6} & \frac{4}{6} & -\frac{2}{6} \\ \frac{1}{6} & -\frac{2}{6} & \frac{1}{6} \end{bmatrix}$$

$\mathbf{A}$ is seen to be a symmetric matrix. It is also an idempotent matrix, for $\mathbf{A}^2 = \mathbf{A}$. We notice also that $\mathbf{A}$ has rank 1.

We now wish to find the characteristic roots and vectors of $\mathbf{A}$. The characteristic equation

$$|\mathbf{A} - \lambda\mathbf{I}| = 0$$

gives, on expansion by the first row (or column) of $(\mathbf{A} - \lambda\mathbf{I})$,

$$(\tfrac{1}{6} - \lambda)[(\tfrac{4}{6} - \lambda)(\tfrac{1}{6} - \lambda) - \tfrac{4}{36}] + \tfrac{2}{6}[-\tfrac{2}{6}(\tfrac{1}{6} - \lambda) + \tfrac{2}{36}]$$
$$+ \tfrac{1}{6}[\tfrac{4}{36} - \tfrac{1}{6}(\tfrac{4}{6} - \lambda)] = 0$$

that is,

$$\lambda^3 - \lambda^2 = 0 \tag{4-80}$$

Equation (4-80) has roots $\lambda_1 = 1$ and $\lambda_2 = 0$ with multiplicity 2, which illustrate the result that the characteristic roots of an idempotent matrix are either zero or unity and that the number of unit roots is equal to the rank of the matrix. Corresponding to $\lambda_1 = 1$,

$$(\mathbf{A} - \lambda\mathbf{I}) = \begin{bmatrix} -\frac{5}{6} & -\frac{2}{6} & \frac{1}{6} \\ -\frac{2}{6} & -\frac{2}{6} & -\frac{2}{6} \\ \frac{1}{6} & -\frac{2}{6} & -\frac{5}{6} \end{bmatrix}$$

and the matrix equation $(\mathbf{A} - \lambda\mathbf{I})\mathbf{x} = \mathbf{0}$ gives

$$\begin{aligned} -5x_1 - 2x_2 + x_3 &= 0 \\ -2x_1 - 2x_2 - 2x_3 &= 0 \\ x_1 - 2x_2 - 5x_3 &= 0 \end{aligned} \tag{4-81}$$

To these three equations we append

$$x_1^2 + x_2^2 + x_3^2 = 1 \tag{4-82}$$

in order to normalize the $\mathbf{x}$ vector.

Equations (4-81) and (4-82) yield the $\mathbf{x}$ vector

$$\mathbf{x} = \left\{\frac{1}{\sqrt{6}} \quad \frac{-2}{\sqrt{6}} \quad \frac{1}{\sqrt{6}}\right\} \tag{4-83}$$

For $\lambda = 0$ the equation $(\mathbf{A} - \lambda\mathbf{I})\mathbf{x} = \mathbf{0}$ gives only a single independent equation,

$$x_1 - 2x_2 + x_3 = 0 \tag{4-84}$$

which, with the normalization equation (4-82) means that one of the x's can be set at an arbitrary value. For example, let $x_3 = 0$: then (4-82) and (4-84) give

$$\mathbf{x}^* = \left\{\frac{2}{\sqrt{5}} \quad \frac{1}{\sqrt{5}} \quad 0\right\} \tag{4-85}$$

which is one characteristic vector associated with the root $\lambda = 0$. Since this root has multiplicity 2, we expect another characteristic vector $\mathbf{x}^{**}$ associated with the root and orthogonal to $\mathbf{x}^*$. The orthogonality condition $(\mathbf{x}^*)'\mathbf{x}^{**} = 0$ implies

$$2x_1^{**} + x_2^{**} = 0 \tag{4-86}$$

Since $\mathbf{x}^{**}$ is associated with $\lambda = 0$, it must also satisfy (4-84) and, of course, the normalization condition (4-82). These three equations give

$$\mathbf{x}^{**} = \left\{ \frac{1}{\sqrt{30}} \quad \frac{-2}{\sqrt{30}} \quad \frac{-5}{\sqrt{30}} \right\} \tag{4-87}$$

Now define the matrix $\mathbf{X}$ whose columns consist of the three characteristic vectors (4-83), (4-85), and (4-87)

$$\mathbf{X} = \begin{bmatrix} \frac{1}{\sqrt{6}} & \frac{2}{\sqrt{5}} & \frac{1}{\sqrt{30}} \\ \frac{-2}{\sqrt{6}} & \frac{1}{\sqrt{5}} & \frac{-2}{\sqrt{30}} \\ \frac{1}{\sqrt{6}} & 0 & \frac{-5}{\sqrt{30}} \end{bmatrix} \tag{4-88}$$

Letting $\mathbf{x}_i$ denote the ith column of $\mathbf{X}$, we see that

$$\mathbf{x}_i'\mathbf{x}_j = \begin{cases} 0 & \text{for } i \neq j \\ 1 & \text{for } i = j \end{cases}$$

that is, $\mathbf{X}$ is an orthogonal matrix and $\mathbf{X}' = \mathbf{X}^{-1}$.

If the reader now forms the product $\mathbf{X}'\mathbf{A}\mathbf{X}$ he will find

$$\mathbf{X}'\mathbf{A}\mathbf{X} = \begin{bmatrix} 1 & 0 & 0 \\ 0 & 0 & 0 \\ 0 & 0 & 0 \end{bmatrix} \tag{4-89}$$

as is to be expected from (4-71) above.

If we consider a three element column vector $\mathbf{z}$ and the orthogonal transformation $\mathbf{y} = \mathbf{X}'\mathbf{z}$ then

$$\begin{aligned} \mathbf{z}'\mathbf{A}\mathbf{z} &= \mathbf{y}'\mathbf{X}'\mathbf{A}\mathbf{X}\mathbf{y} \\ &= y_1^2 \quad \text{using (4-89)} \end{aligned}$$

The original quadratic form involved terms in z_1^2, z_2^2, z_3^2 and the cross-product terms in z_iz_j. However, for a case where the matrix $\mathbf{A}$ of the form is idempotent of rank 1, we have seen that it is possible to define an orthogonal transformation, $\mathbf{y} = \mathbf{X}'\mathbf{z}$, such that $\mathbf{z}'\mathbf{A}\mathbf{z} = y_1^2$.

4-7 DIFFERENTIAL CALCULUS IN MATRIX NOTATION

In subsequent chapters we will have to differentiate some simple expressions involving vectors and matrices, and we now establish a few basic results. Consider first

$$\begin{aligned}\mathbf{a}'\mathbf{x} &= [a_1\, a_2 \cdots a_n]\{x_1 \cdots x_n\} \\ &= a_1x_1 + a_2x_2 + \cdots + a_nx_n\end{aligned}$$

If we take the partial derivatives of $\mathbf{a}'\mathbf{x}$ with respect to the scalar x_i, we have

$$\frac{\partial(\mathbf{a}'\mathbf{x})}{\partial x_1} = a_1$$

$$\frac{\partial(\mathbf{a}'\mathbf{x})}{\partial x_2} = a_2$$

$$\vdots$$

$$\frac{\partial(\mathbf{a}'\mathbf{x})}{\partial x_n} = a_n$$

and see that the partial derivatives are simply the elements of the vector $\mathbf{a}$. Thus if we form the n partial derivatives in turn and then arrange these as a vector $\mathbf{a}$, we may consider the process to be one of vector differentiation, defined by

$$\frac{\partial(\mathbf{a}'\mathbf{x})}{\partial \mathbf{x}} = \mathbf{a} \tag{4-90}$$

where the left-hand side (LHS) indicates the operation of differentiating with respect to the elements of the $\mathbf{x}$ vector.

Consider now the quadratic form

$$\begin{aligned}\mathbf{x}'\mathbf{A}\mathbf{x} &= [x_1\, x_2 \cdots x_n]\begin{bmatrix} a_{11} & a_{12} & \cdots & a_{1n} \\ a_{12} & a_{22} & \cdots & a_{2n} \\ \vdots & \vdots & & \vdots \\ a_{1n} & a_{2n} & \cdots & a_{nn} \end{bmatrix}\begin{bmatrix} x_1 \\ x_2 \\ \vdots \\ x_n \end{bmatrix} \\ &= a_{11}x_1^2 + 2a_{12}x_1x_2 + 2a_{13}x_1x_3 + \cdots + 2a_{1n}x_1x_n \\ &\quad + a_{22}x_2^2 + 2a_{23}x_2x_3 + \cdots + 2a_{2n}x_2x_n \\ &\quad \ddots \\ &\quad + a_{nn}x_n^2\end{aligned}$$

Taking partial derivatives with respect to the elements of **x** gives

$$\frac{\partial}{\partial x_1}(\mathbf{x}'\mathbf{A}\mathbf{x}) = 2(a_{11}x_1 + a_{12}x_2 + a_{13}x_3 + \cdots + a_{1n}x_n)$$

$$\frac{\partial}{\partial x_2}(\mathbf{x}'\mathbf{A}\mathbf{x}) = 2(a_{12}x_1 + a_{22}x_2 + a_{23}x_3 + \cdots + a_{2n}x_n)$$

$$\vdots \qquad\qquad\qquad\qquad \vdots$$

$$\frac{\partial}{\partial x_n}(\mathbf{x}'\mathbf{A}\mathbf{x}) = 2(a_{1n}x_1 + a_{2n}x_2 + a_{3n}x_3 + \cdots + a_{nn}x_n)$$

Apart from the multiplying factor 2, the right-hand sides (RHS) of the above equations contain the elements of the matrix product **Ax**, which give a *column* vector of n elements. Alternatively, we may regard the RHS of the above equations as the elements of the matrix product **x'A** a *row* vector of n elements. Thus

$$\frac{\partial}{\partial \mathbf{x}}(\mathbf{x}'\mathbf{A}\mathbf{x}) = 2\mathbf{A}\mathbf{x} \tag{4-91}$$

$$\frac{\partial}{\partial \mathbf{x}}(\mathbf{x}'\mathbf{A}\mathbf{x}) = 2\mathbf{x}'\mathbf{A} \tag{4-92}$$

The choice between (4-91) and (4-92) is usually determined by the context in which differentiation takes place, for in matrix equations we can equate only matrices of the same order, and we cannot set a row vector equal to a column vector.

Consider next the case where **y** denotes a column vector of n elements, each of which is a function of the m elements of **x**, that is,

$$y_i = f_i(x_1, x_2, \ldots, x_m) \qquad i = 1, \ldots, n$$

Each y_i may be differentiated partially with respect to each x_j giving mn partial derivatives in all. If these partial derivatives are arranged in an $m \times n$ matrix the result is indicated by

$$\frac{\partial \mathbf{y}}{\partial \mathbf{x}} = \begin{bmatrix} \dfrac{\partial y_1}{\partial x_1} & \dfrac{\partial y_2}{\partial x_1} & \cdots & \dfrac{\partial y_n}{\partial x_1} \\ \dfrac{\partial y_1}{\partial x_2} & \dfrac{\partial y_2}{\partial x_2} & \cdots & \dfrac{\partial y_n}{\partial x_2} \\ \vdots & \vdots & & \vdots \\ \dfrac{\partial y_1}{\partial x_m} & \dfrac{\partial y_2}{\partial x_m} & \cdots & \dfrac{\partial y_n}{\partial x_m} \end{bmatrix} \tag{4-93}$$

Expressions of the form (4-93) occur in the transformations considered in Chaps. 12 and 13.

First-order derivatives can be used to locate stationary values. To distinguish between maximum and minimum positions we need to look at second-order derivatives. Thus if

$$y = f(x_1, x_2, \ldots, x_n)$$

setting

$$\frac{\partial y}{\partial \mathbf{x}} = \mathbf{0} \tag{4-94}$$

gives a solution vector $\mathbf{x}^0$ at which y is stationary. The stationary value will be a minimum if

$$\sum_{i=1}^{n} \sum_{j=1}^{n} \frac{\partial^2 y}{\partial x_i \partial x_j} dx_i\, dx_j > 0 \tag{4-95}$$

for every set of dx's not all of which are zero, the derivatives being evaluated at $\mathbf{x}^0$. The stationary value will be a maximum if the inequality sign in (4-95) is reversed. To express (4-95) in matrix form we define

$$\frac{\partial^2 y}{\partial \mathbf{x}^2} = \frac{\partial(\partial y/\partial \mathbf{x})}{\partial \mathbf{x}} = \begin{bmatrix} \dfrac{\partial^2 y}{\partial x_1^2} & \dfrac{\partial^2 y}{\partial x_1 \partial x_2} & \cdots & \dfrac{\partial^2 y}{\partial x_1 \partial x_n} \\ \dfrac{\partial^2 y}{\partial x_2 \partial x_1} & \dfrac{\partial^2 y}{\partial x_2^2} & \cdots & \dfrac{\partial^2 y}{\partial x_2 \partial x_n} \\ \vdots & \vdots & & \vdots \\ \dfrac{\partial^2 y}{\partial x_n \partial x_1} & \dfrac{\partial^2 y}{\partial x_n \partial x_2} & \cdots & \dfrac{\partial^2 y}{\partial x_n^2} \end{bmatrix} \tag{4-96}$$

The left-hand side of (4-95) is thus seen to be a quadratic form in $\mathbf{dx} = \{dx_1 \quad dx_2 \quad \cdots \quad dx_n\}$ with the matrix defined in (4-96) and condition (4-95) is that the matrix $\partial^2 y/\partial \mathbf{x}^2$ should be positive definite.

REFERENCES

There are many introductory books on matrix algebra available, but one of the best for social science students is

1. G. Hadley: *Linear Algebra*, Addison-Wesley, Reading, Mass., 1961.

A very useful summary of matrix results, though mostly without proofs is contained in the first chapter of

2. Franklin A. Graybill: *An Introduction to Linear Statistical Models*, McGraw-Hill, New York, 1961, vol. 1.

EXERCISES

4-1. Expand $(\mathbf{A}+\mathbf{B})(\mathbf{A}-\mathbf{B})$ and $(\mathbf{A}-\mathbf{B})(\mathbf{A}+\mathbf{B})$. Are these expansions the same? If not, why not? How many terms in each?

4-2. Given

$$\mathbf{A}=\begin{bmatrix}1 & 0 & 3\\ 2 & -1 & 1\end{bmatrix}$$

$$\mathbf{B}=\begin{bmatrix}3 & 4 & 1\\ 0 & -1 & 5\\ 1 & 2 & -2\end{bmatrix} \qquad \mathbf{C}=\begin{bmatrix}2\\ -1\\ 4\end{bmatrix}$$

Calculate $(\mathbf{AB})'$, $\mathbf{B}'\mathbf{A}'$, $(\mathbf{AC})'$, and $\mathbf{C}'\mathbf{A}'$.

4-3. Find all matrices $\mathbf{B}$ obeying the equation

$$\begin{bmatrix}0 & 1\\ 0 & 2\end{bmatrix}\mathbf{B}=\begin{bmatrix}0 & 0 & 1\\ 0 & 0 & 2\end{bmatrix}$$

4-4. Find all matrices $\mathbf{B}$ which commute with

$$\mathbf{A}=\begin{bmatrix}0 & 1\\ 0 & 2\end{bmatrix}$$

to give $\mathbf{AB}=\mathbf{BA}$.

4-5. Write down a few matrices of order 3×3 with numerical elements. Find first their squares and then their cubes, checking the latter by using the two processes $\mathbf{A}(\mathbf{A}^2)$ and $\mathbf{A}^2(\mathbf{A})$.

4-6. Prove that diagonal matrices of the same order are commutative in multiplication with each other.

4-7. Let

$$\mathbf{J}=\begin{bmatrix}0 & 0 & 1\\ 0 & 1 & 0\\ 1 & 0 & 0\end{bmatrix}$$

Write out in full some products $\mathbf{JA}$, where $\mathbf{A}$ is a rectangular matrix. Describe in words the effect on $\mathbf{A}$. Do the same with products of type $\mathbf{AJ}$. Find $\mathbf{J}^2$.

4-8. If

$$\mathbf{V}=\begin{bmatrix}0 & 1 & 0\\ 0 & 0 & 1\\ 0 & 0 & 0\end{bmatrix}$$

find $\mathbf{V}^2$ and $\mathbf{V}^3$. Examine some products of type $\mathbf{VA}$, $\mathbf{V}^2\mathbf{A}$, and $\mathbf{V}'\mathbf{A}$.

4-9. Prove that if $\mathbf{A}$ and $\mathbf{B}$ are such that $\mathbf{AB}$ and $\mathbf{BA}$ coexist, then $\mathbf{AB}$ and $\mathbf{BA}$ have the same sum of diagonal elements $[\operatorname{tr}(\mathbf{AB})=\operatorname{tr}(\mathbf{BA})]$.

4-10. Given

$$\mathbf{A}=\begin{bmatrix}1 & 3 & 2\\ 2 & 6 & 9\\ 7 & 6 & 1\end{bmatrix} \quad \text{and} \quad \mathbf{E}=\begin{bmatrix}0 & 1 & 0\\ 1 & 0 & 0\\ 0 & 0 & 1\end{bmatrix}$$

Calculate $|\mathbf{A}|$, $|\mathbf{E}|$, and $|\mathbf{B}|$, where $\mathbf{B}=\mathbf{EA}$.
Verify that $|\mathbf{B}|=|\mathbf{E}||\mathbf{A}|$.

4-11. Show that

$$\begin{vmatrix} 1 & 1 & 1 \\ a & b & c \\ a^2 & b^2 & c^2 \end{vmatrix} = (c-b)(c-a)(b-a)$$

4-12. If (x_1, y_1) and (x_2, y_2) are points on the x, y plane, show that the equation

$$\begin{vmatrix} x & y & 1 \\ x_1 & y_1 & 1 \\ x_2 & y_2 & 1 \end{vmatrix} = 0$$

represents a straight line through these two points.

4-13. Prove that

$$\begin{vmatrix} a_{11} & a_{12} & \cdots & a_{1n} \\ 0 & a_{22} & \cdots & a_{2n} \\ \vdots & \vdots & & \vdots \\ 0 & 0 & \cdots & a_{nn} \end{vmatrix} = a_{11}a_{22}\cdots a_{nn}$$

4-14. Prove that the determinant of a skew-symmetric matrix of odd order vanishes identically. (If $\mathbf{A}$ is a skew-symmetric matrix, then $\mathbf{A}' = -\mathbf{A}$.)

4-15. Show that the matrix

$$\mathbf{Q} = \begin{bmatrix} \frac{1}{\sqrt{6}} & \frac{2}{\sqrt{5}} & \frac{1}{\sqrt{30}} \\ \frac{-2}{\sqrt{6}} & \frac{1}{\sqrt{5}} & \frac{-2}{\sqrt{30}} \\ \frac{1}{\sqrt{6}} & 0 & \frac{-5}{\sqrt{30}} \end{bmatrix}$$

is orthogonal, i.e., that $\mathbf{Q}' = \mathbf{Q}^{-1}$.

4-16. If the u_i are normal variables with

$$E(u_i) = 0 \qquad i = 1, \ldots, n$$
$$E(u_i^2) = \sigma^2 \qquad i = 1, \ldots, n$$
$$E(u_i u_j) = 0 \qquad i \neq j$$

show that $E(\mathbf{u}'\mathbf{A}\mathbf{u}) = \sigma^2 \operatorname{tr}(\mathbf{A})$.

4-17. Given

$$\mathbf{X} = \begin{bmatrix} 1 & 1 \\ 1 & 2 \\ 1 & 1 \\ 1 & 3 \end{bmatrix}$$

Compute

$$\mathbf{A} = (\mathbf{I}_4 - \mathbf{X}(\mathbf{X}'\mathbf{X})^{-1}\mathbf{X}')$$

Show that **A** is idempotent and determine its rank. Find the characteristic roots and associated characteristic vectors of **A**, and hence obtain the orthogonal matrix which diagonalizes **A**.

4-18. Extend the result of Exercise 4–9 to show that

$$\text{tr}(\mathbf{ABC}) = \text{tr}(\mathbf{BCA}) = \text{tr}(\mathbf{CAB})$$

provided the matrices are conformable for multiplication.

4-19. Let **B** be a matrix of order $n \times s$ with $s \leq n$ and rank s. It has already been shown in (4-69) that

$$\rho(\mathbf{B}'\mathbf{B}) = s$$

Show also that

$$\rho(\mathbf{B}\mathbf{B}') = s$$

4-20. **A** and **B** are nonsingular matrices of the same order. Prove that **AB** and **BA** possess identical characteristic roots. Show also that no such matrices can be found to satisfy the equation

$$\mathbf{AB} - \mathbf{BA} = \mathbf{I}$$

(Cambridge Economics Tripos 1968)

4-21. Evaluate the characteristic roots and vectors of

$$\mathbf{A} = \begin{bmatrix} 5 & -6 & -6 \\ -1 & 4 & 2 \\ 3 & -6 & -4 \end{bmatrix}$$

4-22. Examine the following quadratic forms for positive definiteness.

(a) $6x_1^2 + 49x_2^2 + 51x_3^2 - 82x_2x_3 + 20x_1x_3 - 4x_1x_2$

(b) $4x_1^2 + 9x_2^2 + 2x_3^2 + 8x_2x_3 + 6x_3x_1 + 6x_1x_2$

(Cambridge Economics Tripos 1967)

4-23. (a) Find the characteristic roots of the following matrix

$$\begin{bmatrix} 3 & 1 & 1 \\ 0 & -2 & 1 \\ 0 & 0 & 2 \end{bmatrix}$$

(b) Prove that if the characteristic vectors $\mathbf{x}_1, \mathbf{x}_2, \ldots, \mathbf{x}_m$ of a matrix **A** correspond to distinct characteristic roots, then the $\mathbf{x}_1, \mathbf{x}_2, \ldots, \mathbf{x}_m$ are linearly independent.

(c) If **x** is a characteristic vector of the nonsingular matrix **A**, prove that it is also a characteristic vector of $\mathbf{A}^{-1}$.

(Cambridge Economics Tripos 1969)

4-24. (a) Given that

$$\mathbf{A} = \begin{bmatrix} 2 & 2 & 2 \\ 2 & 2 & 2 \\ 2 & 2 & 2 \end{bmatrix} \qquad \mathbf{B} = \begin{bmatrix} 1 & 0 & 1 \\ 0 & -1 & 0 \\ 1 & 0 & 1 \end{bmatrix}$$

find $\mathbf{A}^n$ for $n \geq 1$ and $\mathbf{B}^n$ for $n > 1$.

(b) If **A** is defined as

$$\mathbf{A} = \begin{bmatrix} \frac{1}{3} & \frac{2}{3} & \frac{2}{3} \\ \frac{2}{3} & \frac{1}{3} & -\frac{2}{3} \\ \frac{2}{3} & -\frac{2}{3} & \frac{1}{3} \end{bmatrix}$$

show that **A** is orthogonal.

Prove that the product of two orthogonal matrices of the same order is also an orthogonal matrix. (L.S.E. 1967)

5
The General Linear Model

We now set out as compactly as possible the general linear model in k variables. To do so we shall use the matrix notation developed in Chap. 4 and also make use of many of the results obtained in that chapter.

5-1 ASSUMPTIONS

Let us assume that a linear relationship exists between a variable Y and $k - 1$ explanatory variables $X_2, X_3, \ldots, X_k$ and a disturbance term u. If we have a sample of n observations on Y and the X's we can write

$$Y_i = \beta_1 + \beta_2 X_{2i} + \cdots + \beta_k X_{ki} + u_i \qquad i = 1, 2, \ldots, n \tag{5-1}$$

The β coefficients and the parameters of the u distribution are unknown, and our problem is to obtain estimates of these unknowns. The n equations in (5-1) can be set out compactly in matrix notation as

$$\mathbf{y} = \mathbf{X}\boldsymbol{\beta} + \mathbf{u} \tag{5-2}$$

where

$$\mathbf{y} = \begin{bmatrix} Y_1 \\ Y_2 \\ \vdots \\ Y_n \end{bmatrix} \qquad \mathbf{X} = \begin{bmatrix} 1 & X_{21} & \cdots & X_{k1} \\ 1 & X_{22} & \cdots & X_{k2} \\ \vdots & \vdots & & \vdots \\ 1 & X_{2n} & \cdots & X_{kn} \end{bmatrix}$$
$$\boldsymbol{\beta} = \begin{bmatrix} \beta_1 \\ \beta_2 \\ \vdots \\ \beta_k \end{bmatrix} \qquad \mathbf{u} = \begin{bmatrix} u_1 \\ u_2 \\ \vdots \\ u_n \end{bmatrix} \tag{5-3}$$

The intercept β_1 requires the insertion of a column of units in the **X** matrix. The convention of using X_{ki} to denote the ith observation on the variable X_k means that the subscripts in the **X** matrix follow the reverse of the normal pattern, where the first subscript usually indicates the row, and the second the column, of the matrix.

To make any progress with the estimation of the vector of coefficients, **β**, we must make some further assumptions about how the observations in (5-1) have been generated. These assumptions are crucial for the estimation process, and we commence with the simplest set, leaving for later chapters a detailed treatment of the cases where one or more of these assumptions is not fulfilled. The simplest set of crucial assumptions is

$$E(\mathbf{u}) = \mathbf{0} \tag{5-4a}$$

$$E(\mathbf{uu}') = \sigma^2\mathbf{I}_n \tag{5-4b}$$

X is a set of fixed numbers (5-4c)

X has rank $k < n$ (5-4d)

The first assumption states that $E(u_i) = 0$ for all i, that is, that the u_i are variables with zero expectation. Assumption (5–4b) is a compact way of writing a very important double assumption. Since **u** is an $n \times 1$ column vector and **u**′ a row vector, the product **uu**′ is a symmetric matrix of order n and, since the operation of taking expected values is to be applied to each element of the matrix, we have

$$E(\mathbf{uu}') = \begin{bmatrix} E(u_1^2) & E(u_1u_2) & \cdots & E(u_1u_n) \\ E(u_2u_1) & E(u_2^2) & \cdots & E(u_2u_n) \\ \vdots & \vdots & & \vdots \\ E(u_nu_1) & E(u_nu_2) & \cdots & E(u_n^2) \end{bmatrix} = \begin{bmatrix} \sigma^2 & 0 & \cdots & 0 \\ 0 & \sigma^2 & \cdots & 0 \\ \vdots & \vdots & & \vdots \\ 0 & 0 & \cdots & \sigma^2 \end{bmatrix}$$

The terms on the main diagonal show that $E(u_i^2) = \sigma^2$ for all i; that is, the u_i have constant variance σ^2, which property is referred to as homoscedasticity. The off-diagonal terms give $E(u_t u_{t+s}) = 0$ for $s \neq 0$, that is, the u_i values are pairwise uncorrelated. Assumption (5–4c) that the **X** matrix denotes a set of fixed numbers parallels that made in Chap. 2. This means that in repeated sampling the sole source of variation in the **y** vector is variation in the **u** vector and the properties of our estimators and tests are *conditional* upon **X**. But as in Chap. 2, we shall examine how these properties hold up when this assumption is relaxed. The final assumption about **X** is that the number of observations exceeds the number of parameters to be estimated and that no exact linear relations exist between any of the X variables, where it is convenient to extend the list of X variables to include X_1, whose value is always unity, corresponding to the first column in **X**. If, for example, one explanatory variable were a multiple of another, or one were an exact linear function of several others, then the rank of **X** would be less than k, and likewise the rank of **X′X** would be less than k. (See 4-69). Since **X′X** is a symmetric matrix of order k, this would mean that its inverse did not exist, and as we shall see, this inverse $(\mathbf{X}'\mathbf{X})^{-1}$ plays a crucial role in the estimation procedure.

5-2 LEAST-SQUARES ESTIMATION

Taking (5-1) and (5-4a) to (5-4d), we now apply the least-squares principle to estimate the parameters of (5-1). Let

$$\hat{\boldsymbol{\beta}} = \{\hat{\beta}_1 \quad \hat{\beta}_2 \quad \dots \quad \hat{\beta}_k\}$$

denote a column vector of estimates of $\boldsymbol{\beta}$. Then we may write

$$\mathbf{y} = \mathbf{X}\hat{\boldsymbol{\beta}} + \mathbf{e} \tag{5-5}$$

where **e** denotes the column vector of n residuals $(\mathbf{y} - \mathbf{X}\hat{\boldsymbol{\beta}})$. Notice carefully the distinction between (5-2) and (5-5). In the former the unknown coefficients $\boldsymbol{\beta}$ and the unknown disturbances **u** appear, while in the latter we have some set of estimates $\hat{\boldsymbol{\beta}}$ and the corresponding set of residuals **e**. From (5-5) the sum of squared residuals is

$$\begin{aligned}\sum_{i=1}^{n} e_i^2 &= \mathbf{e}'\mathbf{e} \\ &= (\mathbf{y} - \mathbf{X}\hat{\boldsymbol{\beta}})'(\mathbf{y} - \mathbf{X}\hat{\boldsymbol{\beta}}) \\ &= \mathbf{y}'\mathbf{y} - 2\hat{\boldsymbol{\beta}}'\mathbf{X}'\mathbf{y} + \hat{\boldsymbol{\beta}}'\mathbf{X}'\mathbf{X}\hat{\boldsymbol{\beta}} \end{aligned} \tag{5-6}$$

which follows from noting that $\hat{\boldsymbol{\beta}}'\mathbf{X}'\mathbf{y}$ is a scalar and thus equal to its transpose $\mathbf{y}'\mathbf{X}\hat{\boldsymbol{\beta}}$. To find the value of $\hat{\boldsymbol{\beta}}$ which minimizes the sum of squared residuals we differentiate (5-6).

$$\frac{\partial}{\partial \hat{\boldsymbol{\beta}}}(\mathbf{e}'\mathbf{e}) = -2\mathbf{X}'\mathbf{y} + 2\mathbf{X}'\mathbf{X}\hat{\boldsymbol{\beta}}$$

Equating to zero gives

$$\mathbf{X}'\mathbf{X}\hat{\boldsymbol{\beta}} = \mathbf{X}'\mathbf{y}$$

and from assumption (5-4d)

$$\hat{\boldsymbol{\beta}} = (\mathbf{X}'\mathbf{X})^{-1}\mathbf{X}'\mathbf{y} \tag{5-7}$$

This is the fundamental result for the least-squares estimators. As an illustration of this result consider the two-variable case. Here

$$\mathbf{X}'\mathbf{X} = \begin{bmatrix} n & \Sigma X \\ \Sigma X & \Sigma X^2 \end{bmatrix} \quad \text{and} \quad \mathbf{X}'\mathbf{y} = \begin{bmatrix} \Sigma Y \\ \Sigma XY \end{bmatrix}$$

so that writing (5-7) in the alternative form

$$(\mathbf{X}'\mathbf{X})\hat{\boldsymbol{\beta}} = \mathbf{X}'\mathbf{y}$$

and substituting gives

$$\Sigma Y = n\hat{\beta}_1 + \hat{\beta}_2 \Sigma X$$
$$\Sigma XY = \hat{\beta}_1 \Sigma X + \hat{\beta}_2 \Sigma X^2$$

which are the two normal equations already derived in (2-7). For the three variable case (5-7) gives

$$\Sigma Y = n\hat{\beta}_1 + \hat{\beta}_2 \Sigma X_2 + \hat{\beta}_3 \Sigma X_3$$
$$\Sigma X_2 Y = \hat{\beta}_1 \Sigma X_2 + \hat{\beta}_2 \Sigma X_2^2 + \hat{\beta}_3 \Sigma X_2 X_3$$
$$\Sigma X_3 Y = \hat{\beta}_1 \Sigma X_3 + \hat{\beta}_2 \Sigma X_2 X_3 + \hat{\beta}_3 \Sigma X_3^2$$

and it is clear from the symmetry how these equations can be built up for higher order cases.

Equation (5-7) gives $\hat{\boldsymbol{\beta}}$ as a column vector. Alternatively, we might have written

$$\frac{\partial}{\partial \hat{\boldsymbol{\beta}}}(\mathbf{e}'\mathbf{e}) = -2\mathbf{y}'\mathbf{X} + 2\hat{\boldsymbol{\beta}}'\mathbf{X}'\mathbf{X}$$

which would give

$$\hat{\boldsymbol{\beta}}' = \mathbf{y}'\mathbf{X}(\mathbf{X}'\mathbf{X})^{-1}$$

Transposing both sides of this last result takes us back directly to (5-7).

To establish the mean and variance of $\hat{\boldsymbol{\beta}}$, we substitute (5-2) into (5-7), which gives

$$\begin{aligned}\hat{\boldsymbol{\beta}} &= (\mathbf{X}'\mathbf{X})^{-1}\mathbf{X}'(\mathbf{X}\boldsymbol{\beta} + \mathbf{u}) \\ &= \boldsymbol{\beta} + (\mathbf{X}'\mathbf{X})^{-1}\mathbf{X}'\mathbf{u} \qquad (5\text{-}8)\end{aligned}$$

since $(\mathbf{X}'\mathbf{X})^{-1}(\mathbf{X}'\mathbf{X}) = \mathbf{I}_k$. This expresses $\hat{\boldsymbol{\beta}}$ as a linear function of the true but unknown $\boldsymbol{\beta}$ and the disturbance values $u_1, u_2, \ldots, u_n$. If we consider the sampling process to be repeated, then the X values remain fixed from sample to sample by assumption (5-4c), but each sample will give a different set of u's and hence a different vector $\hat{\boldsymbol{\beta}}$. Taking expected values of both sides of (5-8) gives

$$\begin{aligned}E(\hat{\boldsymbol{\beta}}) &= E(\boldsymbol{\beta}) + E[(\mathbf{X}'\mathbf{X})^{-1}\mathbf{X}'\mathbf{u}] \\ &= \boldsymbol{\beta} + (\mathbf{X}'\mathbf{X})^{-1}\mathbf{X}'E(\mathbf{u})\end{aligned}$$

since $\mathbf{X}$ remains fixed. Thus

$$E(\hat{\boldsymbol{\beta}}) = \boldsymbol{\beta} \qquad (5\text{-}9)$$

since $E(\mathbf{u}) = \mathbf{0}$ by assumption (5-4a). Thus the least-squares estimators are unbiased.

Now consider

$$E[(\hat{\boldsymbol{\beta}} - \boldsymbol{\beta})(\hat{\boldsymbol{\beta}} - \boldsymbol{\beta})']$$

$$= \begin{bmatrix} E(\hat{\beta}_1 - \beta_1)^2 & E(\hat{\beta}_1 - \beta_1)(\hat{\beta}_2 - \beta_2) & \ldots & E(\hat{\beta}_1 - \beta_1)(\hat{\beta}_k - \beta_k) \\ E(\hat{\beta}_2 - \beta_2)(\hat{\beta}_1 - \beta_1) & E(\hat{\beta}_2 - \beta_2)^2 & \ldots & E(\hat{\beta}_2 - \beta_2)(\hat{\beta}_k - \beta_k) \\ \vdots & \vdots & & \vdots \\ E(\hat{\beta}_k - \beta_k)(\hat{\beta}_1 - \beta_1) & E(\hat{\beta}_k - \beta_k)(\hat{\beta}_2 - \beta_2) & \ldots & E(\hat{\beta}_k - \beta_k)^2 \end{bmatrix} \qquad (5\text{-}10)$$

Since (5-9) shows that $E(\hat{\beta}_i) = \beta_i$ for $i = 1, 2, \ldots, k$, it follows that $E(\hat{\beta}_i - \beta_i)^2$ is the variance of $\hat{\beta}_i$ and $E(\hat{\beta}_i - \beta_i)(\hat{\beta}_j - \beta_j)$ is the covariance of $\hat{\beta}_i$ and $\hat{\beta}_j$. Thus the symmetric matrix in (5-10) contains variances along its main diagonal and covariances everywhere else. We refer to it as the variance-covariance or dispersion matrix of the $\hat{\beta}$'s and denote it by var $(\hat{\boldsymbol{\beta}})$.

From (5-8)

$$(\hat{\boldsymbol{\beta}} - \boldsymbol{\beta}) = (\mathbf{X}'\mathbf{X})^{-1}\mathbf{X}'\mathbf{u}$$

Thus

$$\begin{aligned}\text{var}(\hat{\boldsymbol{\beta}}) &= E[(\hat{\boldsymbol{\beta}} - \boldsymbol{\beta})(\hat{\boldsymbol{\beta}} - \boldsymbol{\beta})'] \\ &= E[(\mathbf{X}'\mathbf{X})^{-1}\mathbf{X}'\mathbf{u}\mathbf{u}'\mathbf{X}(\mathbf{X}'\mathbf{X})^{-1}]\end{aligned}$$

using the rule that $(\mathbf{ABC})' = \mathbf{C'B'A'}$ and noting that $(\mathbf{X'X})^{-1}$ is a symmetric matrix, for $(\mathbf{X'X})$ is a symmetric matrix. Thus

$$\begin{aligned}\text{var}(\hat{\boldsymbol{\beta}}) &= (\mathbf{X'X})^{-1}\mathbf{X'}E(\mathbf{uu'})\mathbf{X}(\mathbf{X'X})^{-1} \\ &= (\mathbf{X'X})^{-1}\mathbf{X'}\sigma^2\mathbf{I}_n\mathbf{X}(\mathbf{X'X})^{-1} \quad \text{by assumption (5-4b)} \\ &= \sigma^2(\mathbf{X'X})^{-1}\end{aligned}$$

since σ^2, a scalar, can be moved from in front of a matrix to behind, or vice versa, and $\mathbf{I}_n$ can be suppressed. So

$$\text{var}(\hat{\boldsymbol{\beta}}) = \sigma^2(\mathbf{X'X})^{-1} \tag{5-11}$$

and the variance of $\hat{\beta}_i$ may be obtained by taking the ith term from the principal diagonal of $(\mathbf{X'X})^{-1}$ and multiplying by σ^2, the variance of u_i, while the covariance of any pair of estimates, $\hat{\beta}_i$ and $\hat{\beta}_j$, is found by multiplying σ^2 by the i, jth term in $(\mathbf{X'X})^{-1}$.

We have shown that the least-squares estimators are linear unbiased, the linearity property indicating here that the estimators are linear functions of $\mathbf{y}$, as is shown by (5–7). It can also be shown, as in Chap. 2, that they possess a smaller variance than any other linear unbiased estimators and hence are best linear unbiased.

We shall do this by proving a more general result, of which this is a special case. The more general result also has applications in prediction problems. Consider a linear parametric function $\mathbf{c'\boldsymbol{\beta}}$ where $\mathbf{c}$ is a $k \times 1$ column vector of known constants. A possible estimator of $\mathbf{c'\boldsymbol{\beta}}$ is $\mathbf{c'}\hat{\boldsymbol{\beta}}$, where

$$\hat{\boldsymbol{\beta}} = (\mathbf{X'X})^{-1}\mathbf{X'y}$$

This estimator is unbiased for

$$E(\mathbf{c'}\hat{\boldsymbol{\beta}}) = \mathbf{c'}\boldsymbol{\beta}$$

and its variance is

$$\begin{aligned}\text{var}(\mathbf{c'}\hat{\boldsymbol{\beta}}) &= E\{[\mathbf{c'}(\hat{\boldsymbol{\beta}} - \boldsymbol{\beta})]^2\} \\ &= E\{\mathbf{c'}(\hat{\boldsymbol{\beta}} - \boldsymbol{\beta})(\hat{\boldsymbol{\beta}} - \boldsymbol{\beta})'\mathbf{c}\} \\ &= \sigma^2\, \mathbf{c'}(\mathbf{X'X})^{-1}\mathbf{c}\end{aligned} \tag{5-12}$$

Let

$$\text{b} = \mathbf{a'y}$$

be any other linear unbiased estimator of $\mathbf{c'}\boldsymbol{\beta}$

$$\begin{aligned}E(\text{b}) &= E(\mathbf{a'X}\boldsymbol{\beta} + \mathbf{a'u}) \\ &= \mathbf{a'X}\boldsymbol{\beta} \quad \text{since } E(\mathbf{u}) = \mathbf{0} \\ &= \mathbf{c'}\boldsymbol{\beta}\end{aligned}$$

if and only if

$$\mathbf{a}'\mathbf{X} = \mathbf{c}' \tag{5-13}$$

Provided (5-13) is satisfied

$$\text{b} = \mathbf{c}'\boldsymbol{\beta} + \mathbf{a}'\mathbf{u}$$

Thus

$$\text{var (b)} = E\{(\text{b} - \mathbf{c}'\boldsymbol{\beta})^2\}$$

$$= E\{\mathbf{a}'\mathbf{u}\mathbf{u}'\mathbf{a}\}$$

$$= \sigma^2\mathbf{a}'\mathbf{a}$$

Using (5-13) we can also write

$$\text{var }(\mathbf{c}'\hat{\boldsymbol{\beta}}) = \sigma^2\mathbf{a}'\mathbf{X}(\mathbf{X}'\mathbf{X})^{-1}\mathbf{X}'\mathbf{a}$$

Thus

$$\text{var (b)} - \text{var }(\mathbf{c}'\hat{\boldsymbol{\beta}}) = \sigma^2\mathbf{a}'[\mathbf{I} - \mathbf{X}(\mathbf{X}'\mathbf{X})^{-1}\mathbf{X}']\mathbf{a}$$

$$= \sigma^2\mathbf{a}'\mathbf{M}\mathbf{a} \tag{5-14}$$

where

$$\mathbf{M} = \mathbf{I} - \mathbf{X}(\mathbf{X}'\mathbf{X})^{-1}\mathbf{X}' \tag{5-15}$$

It is easily seen that **M** is a symmetric, idempotent matrix. It is, moreover, positive semi-definite for, as shown in (5-19) below, $\mathbf{e}'\mathbf{e} = \mathbf{u}'\mathbf{M}\mathbf{u}$. But $\mathbf{e}'\mathbf{e} \geq \mathbf{0}$. Hence **M** is positive semi-definite and so

$$\text{var (b)} - \text{var }(\mathbf{c}'\hat{\boldsymbol{\beta}}) \geq \mathbf{0} \tag{5-16}$$

that is, the least-squares estimator of $\mathbf{c}'\boldsymbol{\beta}$ has at least as small a sampling variance as any other linear unbiased estimator. Considering the vectors

$$\mathbf{c}_i' = [0 \quad \cdots \quad 0 \quad 1 \quad 0 \quad \cdots \quad 0]$$

with unity in the ith position and zeros everywhere else (5-16) gives

$$\text{var }(\hat{\beta}_i) \leq \text{var }(b_i) \qquad i = 1, \ldots, k. \tag{5-17}$$

so that the least-squares estimators $\hat{\beta}_i$ $(i = 1, \ldots, k)$ are best linear unbiased estimators of the unknown parameters β_i $(i = 1, \ldots, k)$.

Turning now to the residual sum of squares, we have from (5-5)

$$\begin{aligned}\mathbf{e} &= \mathbf{y} - \mathbf{X}\hat{\boldsymbol{\beta}} \\ &= \mathbf{X}\boldsymbol{\beta} + \mathbf{u} - \mathbf{X}[(\mathbf{X}'\mathbf{X})^{-1}\mathbf{X}'(\mathbf{X}\boldsymbol{\beta} + \mathbf{u})] \quad \text{using (5-2) and (5-7)} \\ &= \mathbf{u} - \mathbf{X}(\mathbf{X}'\mathbf{X})^{-1}\mathbf{X}'\mathbf{u} \\ &= [\mathbf{I}_n - \mathbf{X}(\mathbf{X}'\mathbf{X})^{-1}\mathbf{X}']\mathbf{u} \\ &= \mathbf{M}\mathbf{u} \quad \text{using (5-15)} \end{aligned} \tag{5-18}$$

which expresses the observed residuals as a linear function of the unknown disturbances.

Thus the sum of squared residuals is

$$\begin{aligned}\mathbf{e}'\mathbf{e} &= \mathbf{u}'\mathbf{M}'\mathbf{M}\mathbf{u} \\ &= \mathbf{u}'\mathbf{M}\mathbf{u} \quad \text{since } \mathbf{M} \text{ is symmetric idempotent} \\ &= \mathbf{u}'[\mathbf{I}_n - \mathbf{X}(\mathbf{X}'\mathbf{X})^{-1}\mathbf{X}']\mathbf{u} \end{aligned} \tag{5-19}$$

Taking expected values of both sides,

$$\begin{aligned}E(\mathbf{e}'\mathbf{e}) &= \sigma^2 \operatorname{tr}[\mathbf{I}_n - \mathbf{X}(\mathbf{X}'\mathbf{X})^{-1}\mathbf{X}'] \quad \text{see Exercise (4-16)} \\ &= \sigma^2\{\operatorname{tr}\mathbf{I}_n - \operatorname{tr}[\mathbf{X}(\mathbf{X}'\mathbf{X})^{-1}\mathbf{X}']\} \\ &= \sigma^2\{n - \operatorname{tr}[(\mathbf{X}'\mathbf{X})^{-1}(\mathbf{X}'\mathbf{X})]\} \quad \text{see Exercise (4-18)} \\ &= (n-k)\sigma^2 \end{aligned} \tag{5-20}$$

since $(\mathbf{X}'\mathbf{X})$ is of order k so that $(\mathbf{X}'\mathbf{X})^{-1}(\mathbf{X}'\mathbf{X}) = \mathbf{I}_k$. Thus

$$s^2 = \frac{\mathbf{e}'\mathbf{e}}{n-k} \tag{5-21}$$

provides us with an unbiased estimator of the disturbance variance.

The calculation of s^2 is easily achieved by using

$$\begin{aligned}\mathbf{e}'\mathbf{e} &= \mathbf{y}'\mathbf{y} - 2\hat{\boldsymbol{\beta}}'\mathbf{X}'\mathbf{y} + \hat{\boldsymbol{\beta}}'\mathbf{X}'\mathbf{X}\hat{\boldsymbol{\beta}} \quad \text{from (5-6)} \\ &= \mathbf{y}'\mathbf{y} - \hat{\boldsymbol{\beta}}'\mathbf{X}'\mathbf{y} \end{aligned} \tag{5-22}$$

since $(\mathbf{X}'\mathbf{X})\hat{\boldsymbol{\beta}} = \mathbf{X}'\mathbf{y}$ from the least-squares derivation of $\hat{\boldsymbol{\beta}}$. Using small letters to denote deviations from arithmetic means,

$$\begin{aligned}\sum_{i=1}^{n} y_i^2 &= \sum_{i=1}^{n} Y_i^2 - \frac{1}{n}\left(\sum_{i=1}^{n} Y_i\right)^2 \\ &= \mathbf{y}'\mathbf{y} - \frac{1}{n}(\Sigma Y)^2 \end{aligned}$$

$$\sum_{i=1}^{n} e_i^2 = \mathbf{e}'\mathbf{e}$$

Notice that a property of the least-squares fit is that $\bar{e} = 0$.[1] Partitioning the total sum of squares in Y in the manner of Chaps. 2 and 3 into the "explained" sum of squares, due to the linear influence of the explanatory variables, and the residual sum of squares, we have

$$\begin{aligned}\text{"Explained" SS} &= \Sigma y_i^2 - \Sigma e_i^2 \\ &= \mathbf{y}'\mathbf{y} - \mathbf{e}'\mathbf{e} - \frac{1}{n}(\Sigma Y)^2 \\ &= \hat{\boldsymbol{\beta}}'\mathbf{X}'\mathbf{y} - \frac{1}{n}(\Sigma Y)^2 \quad \text{using (5-22)}\end{aligned}$$

The coefficient of multiple correlation ($\mathbf{R}_{1\cdot 23\ldots k}$) is then defined by

$$R^2_{1\cdot 23\ldots k} = \frac{\hat{\boldsymbol{\beta}}'\mathbf{X}'\mathbf{y} - (1/n)(\Sigma Y)^2}{\mathbf{y}'\mathbf{y} - (1/n)(\Sigma Y)^2} \tag{5-23}$$

It is customary to compute a correlation coefficient only for random variables which possess some joint distribution. We have introduced it here for two reasons. First, even in the case of fixed $\mathbf{X}$, it is a useful summary statistic for the analysis-of-variance tables that will be given later, and second, the assumption of fixed $\mathbf{X}$ can be relaxed later. In any case, a summary statistic measuring the proportion of the total variance accounted for by the linear relation fitted often serves a useful descriptive purpose.

It is sometimes useful to compute an R^2 adjusted for degrees of freedom, especially when comparing the explanatory power of different sets of explanatory variables. The rationale of the adjustment is to note that R^2 may be expressed as

$$R^2_{1\cdot 23\ldots k} = 1 - \frac{s_e^2}{s_y^2}$$

where $s_e^2 = \Sigma e^2/n$ and $s_y^2 = \Sigma y^2/n$, that is both the unexplained and the total sums of squares are divided by n. Unbiased estimators of these variances, however, are given respectively by $\Sigma e^2/(n-k)$ and $\Sigma y^2/(n-1)$. The adjusted

[1] This may be seen by differentiating the sum of squares partially with respect to $\hat{\beta}_1$ and setting the result equal to zero.

$$\begin{aligned}\frac{\partial}{\partial \hat{\beta}_1}\Sigma e_i^2 &= \frac{\partial}{\partial \hat{\beta}_1}\Sigma(Y_i - \hat{\beta}_1 - \hat{\beta}_2 X_{2i} - \cdots - \hat{\beta}_k X_{ki})^2 \\ &= -2\Sigma(Y_i - \hat{\beta}_1 - \hat{\beta}_2 X_{2i} - \cdots - \hat{\beta}_k X_{ki}) = 0\end{aligned}$$

that is,

$$\Sigma e_i = 0 \quad \text{therefore } \bar{e} = 0$$

R^2 is thus defined as

$$\bar{R}^2_{1\cdot 23\ldots k} = 1 - \frac{\Sigma e^2/(n-k)}{\Sigma y^2/(n-1)}$$

and the relation between the two coefficients may be expressed as

$$\bar{R}^2_{1\cdot 23\ldots k} = 1 - \frac{n-1}{n-k}(1 - R^2_{1\cdot 23\ldots k})$$

or

$$\bar{R}^2_{1\cdot 23\ldots k} = \frac{1-k}{n-k} + \frac{n-1}{n-k}R^2_{1\cdot 23\ldots k}$$

The unadjusted coefficient will never decrease as additional explanatory variables are added to a regression, but it is possible for the adjusted coefficient to decline if an additional variable produces too small a reduction in $(1 - R^2)$ to compensate for the increase in $(n-1)/(n-k)$.

Collecting results so far we have

$$\mathbf{y} = \mathbf{X}\boldsymbol{\beta} + \mathbf{u} = \mathbf{X}\hat{\boldsymbol{\beta}} + \mathbf{e}$$

$$\hat{\boldsymbol{\beta}} = (\mathbf{X}'\mathbf{X})^{-1}\mathbf{X}'\mathbf{y}$$

$$E(\hat{\boldsymbol{\beta}}) = \boldsymbol{\beta}$$

$$\text{var}(\hat{\boldsymbol{\beta}}) = \sigma^2(\mathbf{X}'\mathbf{X})^{-1}$$

$$E(\mathbf{e}'\mathbf{e}) = (n-k)\sigma^2$$

$$R^2 = \frac{\hat{\boldsymbol{\beta}}\mathbf{X}'\mathbf{y} - (1/n)(\Sigma Y)^2}{\mathbf{y}'\mathbf{y} - (1/n)(\Sigma Y)^2}$$

These formulae have all been developed from the initial relation (5-1), where the variables are measured from zero origin. Averaging (5-1) and (5-5) over the n sample observations gives

$$\bar{Y} = \beta_1 + \beta_2\bar{X}_2 + \cdots + \beta_k\bar{X}_k + \bar{u} = \hat{\beta}_1 + \hat{\beta}_2\bar{X}_2 + \cdots + \hat{\beta}_k\bar{X}_k$$

since $\bar{u}$ will not, in general, disappear, but, as shown above, a consequence of the least-squares fit is that $\bar{e}$ is identically zero.

Subtracting from the original relations and using lowercase letters to denote deviations from arithmetic means gives

$$y_i = \beta_2 x_{2i} + \cdots + \beta_k x_{ki} + u_i - \bar{u} = \hat{\beta}_2 x_{2i} + \cdots + \hat{\beta}_k x_{ki} + e_i \qquad i = 1, \ldots, n$$

or in matrix notation

$$\mathbf{y} = \mathbf{X}\boldsymbol{\beta} + \mathbf{u} - \bar{\mathbf{u}} = \mathbf{X}\hat{\boldsymbol{\beta}} + \mathbf{e} \tag{5-24}$$

where now

$$\mathbf{y} = \begin{bmatrix} y_1 \\ y_2 \\ \vdots \\ y_n \end{bmatrix} \qquad \mathbf{X} = \begin{bmatrix} x_{21} & x_{31} & \cdots & x_{k1} \\ x_{22} & x_{32} & \cdots & x_{k2} \\ \vdots & \vdots & & \vdots \\ x_{2n} & x_{3n} & \cdots & x_{kn} \end{bmatrix} \qquad \boldsymbol{\beta} = \begin{bmatrix} \beta_2 \\ \beta_3 \\ \vdots \\ \beta_k \end{bmatrix}$$

$$\hat{\boldsymbol{\beta}} = \begin{bmatrix} \hat{\beta}_2 \\ \hat{\beta}_3 \\ \vdots \\ \hat{\beta}_k \end{bmatrix} \qquad \mathbf{u} = \begin{bmatrix} u_1 \\ u_2 \\ \vdots \\ u_n \end{bmatrix} \qquad \bar{\mathbf{u}} = \begin{bmatrix} \bar{u} \\ \bar{u} \\ \vdots \\ \bar{u} \end{bmatrix} \qquad \mathbf{e} = \begin{bmatrix} e_1 \\ e_2 \\ \vdots \\ e_n \end{bmatrix} \tag{5-25}$$

The contrast between (5-25) and the original formulation (5-3) is that now the elements of $\mathbf{y}$ and $\mathbf{X}$ are in deviation form, the column of units no longer appears in the $\mathbf{X}$ matrix, and the $\boldsymbol{\beta}$, $\hat{\boldsymbol{\beta}}$ vectors contain $k - 1$ elements rather than k because the intercept term disappears in the new formulation.

It is clear from (5-24) that we could proceed exactly as in the development of (5-7) to derive the formula

$$\hat{\boldsymbol{\beta}} = (\mathbf{X}'\mathbf{X})^{-1}\mathbf{X}'\mathbf{y}$$

so that this result still holds when $\mathbf{X}$ and $\mathbf{y}$ are in deviation form. In obtaining the results $E(\hat{\boldsymbol{\beta}}) = \boldsymbol{\beta}$ and $\text{var}(\hat{\boldsymbol{\beta}}) = \sigma^2(\mathbf{X}'\mathbf{X})^{-1}$, we made the substitution $\mathbf{y} = \mathbf{X}\boldsymbol{\beta} + \mathbf{u}$. Now we have to substitute $\mathbf{y} = \mathbf{X}\boldsymbol{\beta} + \mathbf{u} - \bar{\mathbf{u}}$. For example,

$$\begin{aligned} \hat{\boldsymbol{\beta}} &= (\mathbf{X}'\mathbf{X})^{-1}\mathbf{X}'\mathbf{y} \\ &= (\mathbf{X}'\mathbf{X})^{-1}\mathbf{X}'(\mathbf{X}\boldsymbol{\beta} + \mathbf{u} - \bar{\mathbf{u}}) \\ &= \boldsymbol{\beta} + (\mathbf{X}'\mathbf{X})^{-1}\mathbf{X}'\mathbf{u} - (\mathbf{X}'\mathbf{X})^{-1}\mathbf{X}'\bar{\mathbf{u}} \end{aligned}$$

This gives an additional term $(\mathbf{X}'\mathbf{X})^{-1}\mathbf{X}'\bar{\mathbf{u}}$, which, however, is zero, for

$$\begin{aligned} \mathbf{X}'\bar{\mathbf{u}} &= \{\bar{u}\Sigma x_{2i} \quad \bar{u}\Sigma x_{3i} \quad \cdots \quad \bar{u}\Sigma x_{ki}\} \\ &= \mathbf{0} \end{aligned}$$

since the sum of deviations about the mean is identically zero. Thus, $E(\hat{\boldsymbol{\beta}}) = \boldsymbol{\beta}$ and $\text{var}(\hat{\boldsymbol{\beta}}) = \sigma^2(\mathbf{X}'\mathbf{X})^{-1}$ also hold for the formulation in terms of deviations. The residuals $\mathbf{e}$ are exactly the same as before, so that $E(\mathbf{e}'\mathbf{e}) = (n - k)\sigma^2$ and $\mathbf{e}'\mathbf{e} = \mathbf{y}'\mathbf{y} - \hat{\boldsymbol{\beta}}'\mathbf{X}'\mathbf{y}$. The one change is in the formula for R^2, which now becomes

$$R^2 = \frac{\hat{\boldsymbol{\beta}}'\mathbf{X}'\mathbf{y}}{\mathbf{y}'\mathbf{y}} \tag{5-26}$$

and the sum of squares due to the linear influence of the explanatory variables is

$$\hat{\boldsymbol{\beta}}'\mathbf{X}'\mathbf{y} = \hat{\beta}_2 \sum_{i=1}^{n} x_{2i}y_i + \cdots + \hat{\beta}_k \sum_{i=1}^{n} x_{ki}y_i \tag{5-27}$$

5-3 THE CORRELATION MATRIX, PARTIAL CORRELATION COEFFICIENTS, AND REGRESSION COEFFICIENTS

In econometric applications of the general linear model interest usually centres on the least-squares estimator $\hat{\boldsymbol{\beta}}$ and all the normal problems of statistical inference can be handled by use of the sampling distribution of the $\hat{\beta}_i$. However, we have seen in Chap. 2 the connection between simple correlation and regression coefficients. Similar relations hold in the general case and we will give a brief development of them in this section before continuing in subsequent sections with the inference problems of the general linear model, for interest sometimes centres on the correlation coefficients, or occasionally, the only data we have on a problem are already expressed in terms of correlation coefficients.

If we compute all the simple (zero-order) correlations between the variables $Y, X_2, X_3, \ldots, X_k$ and arrange them in matrix form, we have the correlation matrix

$$\mathbf{R} = \begin{bmatrix} r_{11} & r_{12} & r_{13} & \cdots & r_{1k} \\ r_{21} & r_{22} & r_{23} & \cdots & r_{2k} \\ \vdots & \vdots & \vdots & & \vdots \\ r_{k1} & r_{k2} & r_{k3} & \cdots & r_{kk} \end{bmatrix} \tag{5-28}$$

where r_{1j} $(j = 2, \ldots, k)$ denotes the correlation between Y and X_j and $r_{ii} = 1$ $(i = 1, 2, \ldots, k)$. The least-squares regression coefficients and the partial correlation coefficients can all be expressed in terms of co-factors of this correlation matrix. Writing the variables in deviation form the least-squares regression is

$$\hat{y} = \hat{\beta}_2 x_2 + \cdots + \hat{\beta}_k x_k \tag{5-29}$$

where the $\hat{\beta}_i$ are obtained by minimizing $\sum_{i=1}^{n} (y_i - \hat{y}_i)^2$, which gives the normal equations

$$\begin{aligned} \hat{\beta}_2\Sigma x_2^2 + \hat{\beta}_3\Sigma x_2x_3 + \cdots + \hat{\beta}_k\Sigma x_2x_k &= \Sigma yx_2 \\ \hat{\beta}_2\Sigma x_2x_3 + \hat{\beta}_3\Sigma x_3^2 + \cdots + \hat{\beta}_k\Sigma x_3x_k &= \Sigma yx_3 \\ \vdots \qquad\qquad \vdots \qquad\qquad\qquad \vdots \qquad & \quad \vdots \\ \hat{\beta}_2\Sigma x_2x_k + \hat{\beta}_3\Sigma x_3x_k + \cdots + \hat{\beta}_k\Sigma x_k^2 &= \Sigma yx_k \end{aligned}$$

This set of equations may be re-written as

$$
\begin{aligned}
\hat{\beta}_2 r_{22} s_2 + \hat{\beta}_3 r_{23} s_3 + \cdots + \hat{\beta}_k r_{2k} s_k &= r_{21} s_1 \\
\hat{\beta}_2 r_{32} s_2 + \hat{\beta}_3 r_{33} s_3 + \cdots + \hat{\beta}_k r_{3k} s_k &= r_{31} s_1 \\
\vdots \qquad\quad \vdots \qquad\qquad\qquad \vdots \quad & \quad \vdots \\
\hat{\beta}_2 r_{k2} s_2 + \hat{\beta}_3 r_{k3} s_3 + \cdots + \hat{\beta}_k r_{kk} s_k &= r_{k1} s_1
\end{aligned}
\tag{5-30}
$$

where $s_i = \sqrt{\Sigma x_i^2/n}$ denotes the sample standard deviation of X_i, s_1 the sample standard deviation of Y, and we have divided through the first equation by ns_2, the second by ns_3 and so forth. Solving for $\hat{\beta}_2$ gives

$$
\hat{\beta}_2 = \frac{s_1 s_3 s_4 \cdots s_k \begin{vmatrix} r_{21} & r_{23} & \cdots & r_{2k} \\ r_{31} & r_{33} & \cdots & r_{3k} \\ \vdots & \vdots & & \vdots \\ r_{k1} & r_{k3} & \cdots & r_{kk} \end{vmatrix}}{s_2 s_3 s_4 \cdots s_k \begin{vmatrix} r_{22} & r_{23} & \cdots & r_{2k} \\ r_{32} & r_{33} & \cdots & r_{3k} \\ \vdots & \vdots & & \vdots \\ r_{k2} & r_{k3} & \cdots & r_{kk} \end{vmatrix}}
$$

$$
= -\frac{s_1}{s_2}\frac{\mathscr{R}_{12}}{\mathscr{R}_{11}}
$$

where $\mathscr{R}_{ij}$ denotes the co-factor of r_{ij} in the matrix **R**. In general

$$
\hat{\beta}_i = -\frac{s_1}{s_i}\frac{\mathscr{R}_{1i}}{\mathscr{R}_{11}} \tag{5-31}
$$

Substituting these coefficients in (5-29) gives an alternative expression for the least-squares regression, namely

$$
\frac{\mathscr{R}_{11}}{s_1}\hat{y} + \frac{\mathscr{R}_{12}}{s_2}x_2 + \frac{\mathscr{R}_{13}}{s_3}x_3 + \ldots + \frac{\mathscr{R}_{1k}}{s_k}x_k = 0 \tag{5-32}
$$

The residual sum of squares may also be expressed in terms of determinants formed from **R**

$$
\Sigma e^2 = \Sigma(y - \hat{y})^2
$$

$$
= \Sigma\left(y + \frac{s_1}{s_2}\frac{\mathscr{R}_{12}}{\mathscr{R}_{11}}x_2 + \frac{s_1}{s_3}\frac{\mathscr{R}_{13}}{\mathscr{R}_{11}}x_3 + \cdots + \frac{s_1}{s_k}\frac{\mathscr{R}_{1k}}{\mathscr{R}_{11}}x_k\right)^2
$$

which after some tedious but simple algebraic reduction gives

$$\Sigma e^2 = \frac{ns_1^2 \mathscr{R}}{\mathscr{R}_{11}} \tag{5-33}$$

where $\mathscr{R} = |\mathbf{R}|$, the determinant of the correlation matrix. This in turn yields an alternative expression for the multiple correlation coefficient

$$\begin{aligned} R^2_{1\cdot 23,\ldots k} &= 1 - \frac{\Sigma e^2}{\Sigma y^2} \\ &= 1 - \frac{\mathscr{R}}{\mathscr{R}_{11}} \end{aligned} \tag{5-34}$$

remembering that $\Sigma y^2 = ns_1^2$.

The derivation of corresponding expressions for partial correlation coefficients is simplified if we first of all present a slightly different way of looking at partial correlation coefficients. In the simple two-variable case

$$\begin{aligned} r^2 &= \frac{(\Sigma xy)^2}{(\Sigma x^2)(\Sigma y^2)} \\ &= b_{yx} b_{xy} \end{aligned}$$

where b_{yx} denotes the coefficient of X in the regression of Y on X and b_{xy} denotes the coefficient of Y in the regression of X on Y. Thus the square of the simple correlation coefficient is given as the product of two regression coefficients. A partial correlation coefficient may be similarly defined. For example, to obtain $r_{12\cdot 3}$ in the three-variable case, suppose that we compute the two multiple regressions:

regression of Y on X_2 and X_3

regression of X_2 on Y and X_3

If we set X_3 equal to some arbitrary level (c) in these regressions, the X_3 term merges with the intercept term and we have two simple regressions showing the joint variation of Y and X_2 in the plane $X_3 = c$. The partial correlation between Y and X_2 with X_3 held constant may then be defined by saying that its square is equal to the product of the regression coefficients of X_2 and Y in these multiple regressions. Because of the linear nature of the model these regression coefficients do not change for different values of c. Using (5-32) the two multiple regressions may be written

$$\hat{y} = -\frac{s_1}{s_2}\frac{\mathscr{R}_{12}}{\mathscr{R}_{11}}x_2 - \frac{s_1}{s_3}\frac{\mathscr{R}_{13}}{\mathscr{R}_{11}}x_3$$

$$\hat{x}_2 = -\frac{s_2}{s_1}\frac{\mathscr{R}_{21}}{\mathscr{R}_{22}}y - \frac{s_2}{s_3}\frac{\mathscr{R}_{23}}{\mathscr{R}_{22}}x_3$$

Thus

$$r^2_{12\cdot 3} = \frac{\mathscr{R}^2_{12}}{\mathscr{R}_{11}\mathscr{R}_{22}} \tag{5-35}$$

It only remains to settle whether to choose the positive or negative sign on taking the square root of (5-35). The sign of $r_{12\cdot 3}$ must be the same as that of the coefficients of x_2 and y in the multiple regressions. Since $\mathscr{R}_{11}$, $\mathscr{R}_{22}$ and the standard deviations are necessarily positive the sign of

$$-\frac{s_1}{s_2}\frac{\mathscr{R}_{12}}{\mathscr{R}_{11}} \quad \text{and} \quad -\frac{s_2}{s_1}\frac{\mathscr{R}_{21}}{\mathscr{R}_{22}}$$

is -1 times the sign of $\mathscr{R}_{12}$. Thus

$$r_{12\cdot 3} = -\frac{\mathscr{R}_{12}}{\sqrt{\mathscr{R}_{11}\mathscr{R}_{22}}} \tag{5-36}$$

and, similarly,

$$r_{13\cdot 2} = -\frac{\mathscr{R}_{13}}{\sqrt{\mathscr{R}_{11}\mathscr{R}_{33}}} \tag{5-37}$$

The extension to more than three variables is simple since it merely involves additional terms in the two regressions, but all the additional terms are held constant just as x_3. The only difference is that the $\mathscr{R}_{ij}$ now denote the co-factors of the elements in a larger correlation matrix. Thus the general result for partial correlation coefficients is

$$r_{1i\cdot 23\ldots i-1,i+1,\ldots k} = -\frac{\mathscr{R}_{1i}}{\sqrt{\mathscr{R}_{11}\mathscr{R}_{ii}}} \tag{5-38}$$

Comparing (5-31) with (5-38) and using (5-33) it is easy to obtain

$$\hat{\beta}_i = r_{1i\cdot 23\ldots i-1,i+1,\ldots,k}\frac{s_{1\cdot 2\ldots k}}{s_{i\cdot 2\ldots k}} \tag{5-39}$$

where $s_{1\cdot 2\ldots k}$ and $s_{i\cdot 2\ldots k}$ are the standard deviations of the residuals when Y and X_i are each in turn regressed on the variables $X_2,\ldots,X_{i-1},X_{i+1},\ldots,X_k$.

5-4 SIGNIFICANCE TESTS AND CONFIDENCE INTERVALS

So far no assumption has been made about the form of the distribution of the u_i. To derive significance tests and confidence intervals for the $\hat{\beta}_i$, we may proceed either by assuming the u_i to be normally distributed, in which case the following results will hold exactly, or by making no explicit assumption about the form of the distribution and appealing to the Central Limit

Theorem to justify our regarding the tests as approximately correct.[1] To derive the tests we shall add to assumptions (5-4a) to (5-4d) the assumption

$$u_i \text{ has a normal distribution} \quad i = 1, 2, \ldots, n \tag{5-4e}$$

Assumptions (5-4a), (5-4b), and (5-4e) may now be compactly written

$$\mathbf{u} \text{ is } N(\mathbf{0}, \sigma^2\mathbf{I}_n) \tag{5-40}$$

It follows from (5-40) that the likelihood for the sample values is

$$L = \frac{1}{(2\pi\sigma^2)^{n/2}} \exp\left(\frac{-\mathbf{u}'\mathbf{u}}{2\sigma^2}\right)$$

$$= \frac{1}{(2\pi\sigma^2)^{n/2}} \exp\left[-\frac{(\mathbf{y} - \mathbf{X}\boldsymbol{\beta})'(\mathbf{y} - \mathbf{X}\boldsymbol{\beta})}{2\sigma^2}\right]$$

Maximizing the likelihood with respect to $\boldsymbol{\beta}$ is equivalent to choosing $\boldsymbol{\beta}$ to minimize the sum of squares $(\mathbf{y} - \mathbf{X}\boldsymbol{\beta})'(\mathbf{y} - \mathbf{X}\boldsymbol{\beta})$. This is exactly the least-squares criterion already set up in (5-6), and so the maximum-likelihood estimator of $\boldsymbol{\beta}$ is simply the least-squares estimator $\hat{\boldsymbol{\beta}} = (\mathbf{X}'\mathbf{X})^{-1}\mathbf{X}'\mathbf{y}$.

From (5-8) it is seen that any estimate $\hat{\beta}_i$ is equal to β_i plus a linear function of $\mathbf{u}$, which has a multivariate normal distribution. Thus $\hat{\beta}_i$ has a normal distribution.[2] Its mean and variance are already known from (5-9) and (5-11) as β_i and $a_{ii}\sigma^2$, where a_{ii} is the ith element in the principal diagonal of $(\mathbf{X}'\mathbf{X})^{-1}$. In fact, (5-8), (5-9), and (5-11), together with assumption (5-40), mean that $\hat{\boldsymbol{\beta}}$ has a multivariate normal distribution specified by

$$\hat{\boldsymbol{\beta}} \text{ is } N[\boldsymbol{\beta}, \sigma^2(\mathbf{X}'\mathbf{X})^{-1}] \tag{5-41}$$

If σ^2 were known, this result would enable us to carry out tests of significance and estimate confidence intervals for $\boldsymbol{\beta}$ in the usual way. However, σ^2 is unknown, and we require one further step to obtain a practical procedure.

We have shown in (5-19) that the residual sum of squares, $\mathbf{e}'\mathbf{e}$, is a quadratic form in $\mathbf{u}$.

$$\mathbf{e}'\mathbf{e} = \mathbf{u}'\mathbf{M}\mathbf{u} = \mathbf{u}'[\mathbf{I}_n - \mathbf{X}(\mathbf{X}'\mathbf{X})^{-1}\mathbf{X}']\mathbf{u}$$

We have further shown that $\mathbf{M}$ is a symmetric idempotent matrix and, in (5-20), that its trace is $n - k$. Thus it follows that the rank of $\mathbf{M}$ is $n - k$, and it is possible to find an orthogonal matrix $\mathbf{P}$ such that $\mathbf{P}'\mathbf{M}\mathbf{P} = \mathbf{E}_{n-k}$, where $\mathbf{E}_{n-k}$ is a diagonal matrix with $n - k$ units and k zeros in the main

[1] See W. Feller, *An Introduction to Probability Theory and Its Applications*, 2nd ed., Wiley, New York, 1957, vol. I, pp. 229, 238–241.

[2] See, for example, Franklin A. Graybill, *An Introduction to Linear Statistical Models*, McGraw-Hill, New York, 1961, vol. I, pp. 56–57.

diagonal.[1] This orthogonal matrix $\mathbf{P}$ may also be used to define a transformation from the $\mathbf{u}$ vector to a $\mathbf{v}$ vector, namely,

$$\mathbf{u} = \mathbf{P}\mathbf{v} \quad \text{or} \quad \mathbf{v} = \mathbf{P}'\mathbf{u} \quad \text{since} \quad \mathbf{P}^{-1} = \mathbf{P}' \tag{5-42}$$

Substituting in (5-19) gives

$$\begin{aligned} \mathbf{e}'\mathbf{e} &= \mathbf{u}'\mathbf{M}\mathbf{u} \\ &= \mathbf{v}'\mathbf{P}'\mathbf{M}\mathbf{P}\mathbf{v} \\ &= \mathbf{v}'\mathbf{E}_{n-k}\mathbf{v} \\ &= v_1^2 + v_2^2 + \cdots + v_{n-k}^2 \end{aligned} \tag{5-43}$$

where, without any loss of generality we have taken the $n - k$ unit elements to occupy the first $n - k$ places in the main diagonal of $\mathbf{E}_{n-k}$. It follows from the properties of orthogonal matrices that if the u_i are normally and independently distributed with zero mean and constant variance σ^2, then so are the v_i.[2] Thus (5-43) expresses the residual sum of squares as the sum of the squares of $n - k$ independent normal variates with zero mean and variance σ^2. Hence $\mathbf{e}'\mathbf{e}/\sigma^2$ has a χ^2 distribution with $n - k$ degrees of freedom.[3]

It remains finally to show that $\mathbf{e}'\mathbf{e}$ is distributed independently of $\hat{\boldsymbol{\beta}}$. This may be done by showing that $\mathbf{e}$ is distributed independently of $\hat{\boldsymbol{\beta}}$. Consider the matrix

$$E[\mathbf{e}(\hat{\boldsymbol{\beta}} - \boldsymbol{\beta})'] = \begin{bmatrix} E[e_1(\hat{\beta}_1 - \beta_1)] & E[e_1(\hat{\beta}_2 - \beta_2)] & \cdots & E[e_1(\hat{\beta}_k - \beta_k)] \\ E[e_2(\hat{\beta}_1 - \beta_1)] & E[e_2(\hat{\beta}_2 - \beta_2)] & \cdots & E[e_2(\hat{\beta}_k - \beta_k)] \\ \vdots & \vdots & & \vdots \\ E[e_n(\hat{\beta}_1 - \beta_1)] & E[e_n(\hat{\beta}_2 - \beta_2)] & \cdots & E[e_n(\hat{\beta}_k - \beta_k)] \end{bmatrix}$$

This represents all possible covariances between the e_i and the $\hat{\beta}_j$, since $E(\mathbf{e}) = \mathbf{0}$. We have shown in (5-18) that

$$\mathbf{e} = [\mathbf{I}_n - \mathbf{X}(\mathbf{X}'\mathbf{X})^{-1}\mathbf{X}']\mathbf{u}$$

and in (5-8) that $(\hat{\boldsymbol{\beta}} - \boldsymbol{\beta}) = (\mathbf{X}'\mathbf{X})^{-1}\mathbf{X}'\mathbf{u}$. Substituting these values gives

$$\begin{aligned} E[\mathbf{e}(\boldsymbol{\beta} - \hat{\boldsymbol{\beta}})'] &= E\{[\mathbf{I}_n - \mathbf{X}(\mathbf{X}'\mathbf{X})^{-1}\mathbf{X}']\mathbf{u}\mathbf{u}'\mathbf{X}(\mathbf{X}'\mathbf{X})^{-1}\} \\ &= \sigma^2\mathbf{X}(\mathbf{X}'\mathbf{X})^{-1} - \sigma^2\mathbf{X}(\mathbf{X}'\mathbf{X})^{-1} \\ &= \mathbf{0} \end{aligned} \tag{5-44}$$

[1] This follows from the results on idempotent matrices in Chap. 4. See pp. 110–111.

[2] See pp. 109–110.

[3] See P. G. Hoel, *Introduction to Mathematical Statistics*, 3rd ed., Wiley, New York, 1962, pp. 152–155.

Since $\mathbf{e}$ and $\hat{\boldsymbol{\beta}}$ are each linear functions of normal variates, they are also normally distributed, and since we have shown their covariances to be zero, it follows that they are independently distributed.[1]

This final result enables us to use the "t" distribution to derive tests for individual regression coefficients:

$\hat{\beta}_i$ is $N(\beta_i, a_{ii}\sigma^2)$

$\sum_{i=1}^{n} e_i^2/\sigma^2$ has an independent χ^2 distribution with $n - k$ degrees of freedom.
Hence, from the definition of the t distribution,

$$t = \frac{\hat{\beta}_i - \beta_i}{\sqrt{\sum_{i=1}^{n} e_i^2/(n-k)}\sqrt{a_{ii}}} \tag{5-45}$$

has the t distribution with $n - k$ degrees of freedom, where a_{ii} is the ith diagonal element in $(\mathbf{X}'\mathbf{X})^{-1}$. To test any particular hypothesis about β_i, we substitute the hypothetical value of β_i in (5-45), and if the resultant value of t lies in an appropriate critical region, we reject the hypothesis under test. For example, to test the hypothesis that $\beta_i = 0$, that is, that X_i has no linear influence on Y, we compute the test statistic

$$t = \frac{\hat{\beta}_i}{\sqrt{\Sigma e_i^2/(n-k)}\sqrt{a_{ii}}} \tag{5-46}$$

It also follows from (5-45) that a $100(1 - \varepsilon)$ per cent confidence interval for β_i is given by

$$\hat{\beta}_i \pm t_{\varepsilon/2}\sqrt{\frac{\Sigma e_i^2}{n-k}}\sqrt{a_{ii}} \tag{5-47}$$

To obtain a joint test for several or all β_i, we need one further theoretical development. This may be fairly simply obtained by a further use of orthogonal variables. Define $k - 1$ new variables $z_2, \ldots, z_k$ in terms of the deviations $x_2, \ldots, x_k$.

$$\begin{aligned} z_{2i} &= w_{22}x_{2i} \\ z_{3i} &= w_{32}x_{2i} + w_{33}x_{3i} \qquad i = 1, 2, \ldots, n \\ &\vdots \\ z_{ki} &= w_{k2}x_{2i} + \cdots + w_{kk}x_{ki} \end{aligned} \tag{5-48}$$

[1] See Graybill, *op. cit.*, pp. 57–58.

where the w's are chosen so as to make

$$\sum_{i=1}^{n} z_{ji}^2 = 1 \qquad j = 2, 3, \ldots, k$$

$$\sum_{i=1}^{n} z_{ji}z_{li} = 0 \qquad j, l = 2, \ldots, k; \; j \neq l \tag{5-49}$$

that is, the z's are orthogonal variables, and condition (5-49) may be written

$$\mathbf{Z}'\mathbf{Z} = \mathbf{I}_{k-1} \tag{5-50}$$

The relations (5-48) may be set in matrix form as

$$\mathbf{Z} = \mathbf{XW} \tag{5-51}$$

that is,

$$\begin{bmatrix} z_{21} & z_{31} & \cdots & z_{k1} \\ z_{22} & z_{32} & \cdots & z_{k2} \\ \vdots & \vdots & & \vdots \\ z_{2n} & z_{3n} & \cdots & z_{kn} \end{bmatrix} = \begin{bmatrix} x_{21} & x_{31} & \cdots & x_{k1} \\ x_{22} & x_{32} & \cdots & x_{k2} \\ \vdots & \vdots & & \vdots \\ x_{2n} & x_{3n} & \cdots & x_{kn} \end{bmatrix} \begin{bmatrix} w_{22} & w_{32} & \cdots & w_{k2} \\ 0 & w_{33} & \cdots & w_{k3} \\ \vdots & \vdots & & \vdots \\ 0 & 0 & \cdots & w_{kk} \end{bmatrix} \tag{5-52}$$

To illustrate how the w's might be computed consider first of all the case of a single explanatory variable X_2. We then just have the single condition $\Sigma z_2^2 = 1$, which gives

$$w_{22}^2 = 1/\Sigma x_2^2$$

and we may take either square root. For two explanatory variables w_{22} is the same as in the previous case and we have the two additional conditions

$$\Sigma z_2 z_3 = 0 \quad \text{and} \quad \Sigma z_3^2 = 1$$

to determine w_{32} and w_{33}. These conditions give

$$w_{32}\Sigma x_2^2 + w_{33}\Sigma x_2 x_3 = 0$$

$$w_{32}^2\Sigma x_2^2 + w_{33}^2\Sigma x_3^2 + 2w_{32}w_{33}\Sigma x_2 x_3 = 1$$

which solve to give

$$w_{33}^2 = \Sigma x_2^2/[\Sigma x_2^2 \Sigma x_3^2 - (\Sigma x_2 x_3)^2]$$

and

$$w_{32} = -w_{33}\Sigma x_2 x_3/\Sigma x_2^2$$

When we introduce a third variable the w's already obtained remain unchanged and three new conditions

$$\Sigma z_2 z_4 = 0 \qquad \Sigma z_3 z_4 = 0 \qquad \Sigma z_4^2 = 1$$

are available for the determination of w_{42}, w_{43}, and w_{44}. The set of w's is not unique but clearly exists so long as there are no perfect correlations among the X variables. In general, from (5-50) and (5-51), we have

$$\mathbf{Z'Z} = \mathbf{W'X'XW} = \mathbf{I}$$

giving

$$\mathbf{WW'} = (\mathbf{X'X})^{-1}$$

We leave it as an exercise for the reader to show that this general result specializes for the two-variable case to the values obtained above.

Recalling from (5-24) the equations in deviation form,

$$\mathbf{y} = \mathbf{X\beta} + \mathbf{u} - \bar{\mathbf{u}} = \mathbf{X\hat{\beta}} + \mathbf{e}$$

and substituting $\mathbf{ZW}^{-1}$ for $\mathbf{X}$ gives

$$\mathbf{y} = \mathbf{ZW}^{-1}\boldsymbol{\beta} + \mathbf{u} - \bar{\mathbf{u}} = \mathbf{ZW}^{-1}\hat{\boldsymbol{\beta}} + \mathbf{e} \tag{5-53}$$

Defining

$$\boldsymbol{\beta}^* = \mathbf{W}^{-1}\boldsymbol{\beta} \quad \text{and} \quad \hat{\boldsymbol{\beta}}^* = \mathbf{W}^{-1}\hat{\boldsymbol{\beta}} \tag{5-54}$$

gives

$$\mathbf{y} = \mathbf{Z}\boldsymbol{\beta}^* + \mathbf{u} - \bar{\mathbf{u}} = \mathbf{Z}\hat{\boldsymbol{\beta}}^* + \mathbf{e} \tag{5-55}$$

From (5-55) we see that $\mathbf{y}$ has now been expressed as a linear function of the orthogonal variables $\mathbf{Z}$, with coefficients $\boldsymbol{\beta}^*$, and the disturbances or, alternatively, $\mathbf{y}$ may be written as the sum of a linear function of the orthogonal variables, with coefficients $\hat{\boldsymbol{\beta}}^*$, and the residuals $\mathbf{e}$, which are exactly the residuals of the original least-squares relation $\mathbf{y} = \mathbf{X}\hat{\boldsymbol{\beta}} + \mathbf{e}$. It is intuitively clear from (5-55) that $\hat{\boldsymbol{\beta}}^*$ is the least-squares estimator of $\boldsymbol{\beta}^*$, but it may be proved as follows:

$$\hat{\boldsymbol{\beta}} = (\mathbf{X'X})^{-1}\mathbf{X'y}$$

Therefore

$$\begin{aligned}\hat{\boldsymbol{\beta}}^* &= \mathbf{W}^{-1}(\mathbf{X'X})^{-1}\mathbf{X'y} \qquad \text{using (5-54)} \\ &= \mathbf{W}^{-1}(\mathbf{X'X})^{-1}(\mathbf{W}^{-1})'\mathbf{Z'y} \qquad \text{using (5-51)}\end{aligned}$$

But from $\mathbf{Z} = \mathbf{XW}$ we have

$$\mathbf{Z'Z} = \mathbf{W'X'XW}$$

Therefore

$$(\mathbf{Z}'\mathbf{Z})^{-1} = \mathbf{W}^{-1}(\mathbf{X}'\mathbf{X})^{-1}(\mathbf{W}')^{-1} \qquad \text{using } (\mathbf{ABC})^{-1} = \mathbf{C}^{-1}\mathbf{B}^{-1}\mathbf{A}^{-1}$$
$$= \mathbf{W}^{-1}(\mathbf{X}'\mathbf{X})^{-1}(\mathbf{W}^{-1})'$$

using the result that the inverse of the transpose is equal to the transpose of the inverse. Hence

$$\hat{\boldsymbol{\beta}}^* = (\mathbf{Z}'\mathbf{Z})^{-1}\mathbf{Z}'\mathbf{y}$$

which is the least-squares estimator of $\boldsymbol{\beta}^*$ in (5-55).

As we have seen in (5-50), $\mathbf{Z}'\mathbf{Z} = \mathbf{I}_{k-1}$, and so $(\mathbf{Z}'\mathbf{Z})^{-1} = \mathbf{I}_{k-1}$, which on substitution in the formula for $\hat{\boldsymbol{\beta}}^*$ gives the very simple result

$$\hat{\boldsymbol{\beta}}^* = \mathbf{Z}'\mathbf{y} \tag{5-56}$$

that is,

$$\hat{\beta}_2^* = \sum_{i=1}^{n} z_{2i}y_i$$

$$\hat{\beta}_3^* = \sum_{i=1}^{n} z_{3i}y_i$$

$$\vdots$$

$$\hat{\beta}_k^* = \sum_{i=1}^{n} z_{ki}y_i$$

It is very important to notice that (5-48) and (5-56) mean that $\hat{\beta}_i^*$ is independent of whether z_i is the last orthogonal variable included in the relation or whether z_{i+1}, z_{i+2}, etc., also appear, for in

$$z_{it} = w_{i2}x_{2t} + w_{i3}x_{3t} + \cdots + w_{ii}x_{it}$$

the weights w_{ij} depend only on $x_2 \ldots x_i$ as we have seen above and remain unchanged if we then introduce

$$z_{i+1,t} = w_{i+1,2}x_{2t} + w_{i+1,3}x_{3t} + \cdots + w_{i+1,i+1}x_{i+1,t}$$

etc.

From (5-11) we have directly

$$\operatorname{var}(\hat{\boldsymbol{\beta}}^*) = \sigma^2(\mathbf{Z}'\mathbf{Z})^{-1}$$
$$= \sigma^2\mathbf{I}_{k-1} \tag{5-57}$$

Thus the $\hat{\beta}_i^*$ are normally and *independently* distributed about β_i^* with variance σ^2, for all the covariance terms in (5-57) are zero. Thus

$$\frac{\hat{\beta}_i^* - \beta_i^*}{\sigma} \text{ is } N(0, 1)$$

and from the property of independence, $\sum_{i=2}^{k} (\hat{\beta}_i^* - \beta_i^*)^2/\sigma^2$ has a χ^2 distribution with $k - 1$ degrees of freedom. Since $\sum_{i=1}^{n} e_i^2/\sigma^2$ has an independent χ^2 distribution, the quantity

$$F = \frac{\sum_{i=2}^{k} (\hat{\beta}_i^* - \beta_i^*)^2/(k-1)}{\sum_{i=1}^{n} e_i^2/(n-k)} \tag{5-58}$$

has the F distribution with $k - 1$ and $n - k$ degrees of freedom.

Consider the hypothesis $\beta_2^* = \beta_3^* = \cdots = \beta_k^* = 0$. From (5-54) we have $\boldsymbol{\beta} = \mathbf{W}\boldsymbol{\beta}^*$, and so this hypothesis is equivalent to the hypothesis $\beta_2 = \beta_3 = \cdots = \beta_k = 0$. The initial hypothesis $\boldsymbol{\beta}^* = 0$ thus provides a test of the overall relation, that is, a test of whether $X_2, X_3, \ldots, X_k$ exercise any influence upon Y. The appropriate test statistic then becomes:

$$F = \frac{\sum_{i=2}^{k} \hat{\beta}_i^{*2}/(k-1)}{\sum_{i=1}^{n} e_i^2/(n-k)} \tag{5-59}$$

One way of computing this test statistic would be first to compute the values of the orthogonal variables $\mathbf{Z}$, then to fit a least-squares regression to them, and finally to sum the squared coefficients of this regression to obtain the term $\sum_{i=2}^{k} \hat{\beta}_i^{*2}$. Fortunately there is no need to follow such an arduous course, for

$$\begin{aligned}
\sum_{i=2}^{k} \hat{\beta}_i^{*2} &= \hat{\boldsymbol{\beta}}^{*\prime}\hat{\boldsymbol{\beta}}^* \\
&= (\mathbf{W}^{-1}\hat{\boldsymbol{\beta}})'\mathbf{Z}'\mathbf{y} \qquad \text{since } \hat{\boldsymbol{\beta}}^* = \mathbf{W}^{-1}\hat{\boldsymbol{\beta}} = \mathbf{Z}'\mathbf{y} \\
&= \hat{\boldsymbol{\beta}}'(\mathbf{W}^{-1})'\mathbf{W}'\mathbf{X}'\mathbf{y} \qquad \text{since } \mathbf{Z} = \mathbf{X}\mathbf{W} \\
&= \hat{\boldsymbol{\beta}}'(\mathbf{W}')^{-1}\mathbf{W}'\mathbf{X}'\mathbf{y} \\
&= \hat{\boldsymbol{\beta}}'\mathbf{X}'\mathbf{y}
\end{aligned}$$

Thus the required quantity is expressed in terms of the least-squares coefficients of the regression on the original X_i variables. Moreover, as shown in the development of (5-27) above, $\hat{\boldsymbol{\beta}}'\mathbf{X}'\mathbf{y}$ measures the reduction in the sum of squares due to the explanatory variables. Also, using (5-22) and (5-26), we may write

$$\hat{\boldsymbol{\beta}}'\mathbf{X}'\mathbf{y} = \mathbf{y}'\mathbf{y} \cdot R^2$$

$$\mathbf{e}'\mathbf{e} = \mathbf{y}'\mathbf{y}(1 - R^2)$$

which yield the following alternative form for the test statistic

$$F = \frac{R^2/(k-1)}{(1-R^2)/(n-k)} \tag{5-60}$$

These results provide the basis for the conventional analysis-of-variance treatment outlined in Table 5-1. The ratio of the first mean square to the second gives (5-59) or (5-60), and an appropriate critical region is selected from the F distribution with $k - 1$ and $n - k$ degrees of freedom.

Table 5-1 Analysis of variance

Source of variation	*Sum of squares*	*Degrees of freedom*	*Mean square*
$X_2, X_3, \ldots, X_k$	$\hat{\boldsymbol{\beta}}'\mathbf{X}'\mathbf{y} = \mathbf{y}'\mathbf{y} \cdot R^2$	$k - 1$	$\hat{\boldsymbol{\beta}}'\mathbf{X}'\mathbf{y}/(k-1)$
Residual	$\mathbf{e}'\mathbf{e} = \mathbf{y}'\mathbf{y}(1 - R^2)$	$n - k$	$\mathbf{e}'\mathbf{e}/(n-k)$
Total	$\mathbf{y}'\mathbf{y} = \sum_{i=1}^{n} y_i^2$	$n - 1$	

An alternative procedure for testing a single coefficient may also be developed in an analysis-of-work framework. We shall show that it is equivalent to the test already developed in (5-46), but the analysis-of-variance approach can also be extended to cover any subgroup of several coefficients. From (5-54) we have $\boldsymbol{\beta}^* = \mathbf{W}^{-1}\boldsymbol{\beta}$. Since the $\mathbf{W}$ matrix is triangular, with zeros everywhere below the main diagonal, its inverse is of the same form, and thus

$$\beta_2^* = f_2(\beta_2, \beta_3, \ldots, \beta_k)$$

$$\beta_3^* = f_3(\beta_3, \ldots, \beta_k)$$

$$\vdots$$

$$\beta_{k-1}^* = f_{k-1}(\beta_{k-1}, \beta_k)$$

$$\beta_k^* = f_k(\beta_k)$$

where the f_i are linear homogeneous functions of the β_i. Thus $\beta_k = 0$ implies and is implied by $\beta_k^* = 0$. To test the hypothesis that $\beta_k^* = 0$, we have $\hat{\beta}_k^{*2}/\sigma^2$

has the χ^2 distribution with 1 degree of freedom and $\sum_{i=1}^{n} e_i^2/\sigma^2$ has an independent χ^2 distribution with $n - k$ degrees of freedom. Hence

$$F = \frac{\hat{\beta}_k^{*2}}{\Sigma e^2/(n-k)} \tag{5-61}$$

has the F distribution with $(1, n-k)$ degrees of freedom. Now $\sum_{i=2}^{k-1} \hat{\beta}_i^{*2}$ measures the explained sum of squares when the variables $z_2, \ldots, z_{k-1}$ (or equivalently $X_2, \ldots, X_{k-1}$) have been included. $\sum_{i=2}^{k} \hat{\beta}_i^{*2}$ measures the sum of squares when all variables $X_2, \ldots, X_{k-1}, X_k$ have been included. Thus $\hat{\beta}_k^{*2}$ measures the *increment* in the explained sum of squares due to the addition of X_k to the list of variables. The analysis-of-variance setup is given in Table 5-2, and the test of the net X_k effect is made by computing the two indicated mean squares and comparing the resultant F value with a preselected point on the F distribution with $(1, n-k)$ degrees of freedom.

Table 5-2

	Sum of squares	*Degrees of freedom*	*Mean square*
$X_2, \ldots, X_{k-1}$	$\sum_{i=2}^{k-1} \hat{\beta}_i^{*2}$	$k-2$	
X_k	$\hat{\beta}_k^{*2}$	1	$\hat{\beta}_k^{*2}$
Total due to $X_2, \ldots, X_k$	$\sum_{i=2}^{k} \hat{\beta}_i^{*2}$	$k-1$	
Residual	$\sum_{i=2}^{n} e_i^2$	$n-k$	$\sum_{i=1}^{n} e_i^2/(n-k)$
Total	$\sum_{i=1}^{n} y_i^2$	$n-1$	

This test, however, is formally equivalent to the one developed earlier. In (5-46) the test quantity suggested for the hypothesis $\beta_k = 0$ is

$$t = \frac{\hat{\beta}_k}{\sqrt{\sum_{i=1}^{n} e_i^2/(n-k)}\sqrt{a_{kk}}}$$

with $n - k$ degrees of freedom, where a_{kk} is the kth element in the main diagonal of $(\mathbf{X}'\mathbf{X})^{-1}$. But since a t quantity is the ratio of a standard normal variable to the square root of a χ^2 variable, which has been divided by its degrees of freedom r, squaring a t quantity gives an F quantity with $(1, r)$ degrees of freedom. Thus our earlier test gives rise to the test statistic

$$F = \frac{\hat{\beta}_k^2}{\left[\sum_{i=1}^{n} e_i^2/(n-k)\right] a_{kk}}$$

The analysis-of-variance statistic in (5-61) is

$$F = \frac{\hat{\beta}_k^{*2}}{\Sigma e_i^2/(n-k)}$$

Thus the two are equivalent if

$$\hat{\beta}_k^2 = a_{kk}\hat{\beta}_k^{*2}$$

From

$$\hat{\boldsymbol{\beta}}^* = \mathbf{W}^{-1}\hat{\boldsymbol{\beta}}$$

$$\hat{\boldsymbol{\beta}} = \mathbf{W}\hat{\boldsymbol{\beta}}^*$$

therefore

$$\hat{\beta}_k = w_{kk}\hat{\beta}_k^*$$

Thus we simply have to show that $w_{kk}^2 = a_{kk}$. We have already shown on page 140 above that

$$(\mathbf{X}'\mathbf{X})^{-1} = \mathbf{W}\mathbf{W}'$$

and from the definition of $\mathbf{W}$ in (5-52), we see that the bottom element in the principal diagonal of $\mathbf{W}\mathbf{W}'$ is w_{kk}^2. Hence $w_{kk}^2 = a_{kk}$, and the two tests are identical. The above exposition has been in terms of X_k, the last variable to be included in the set, but clearly the net contribution of any variable can be assessed in this way. Thus the conventional t test of a regression coefficient is equivalent to asking whether the addition to the explained sum of squares due to adding X_i to the set $X_2, X_3, \ldots, X_{i-1}, X_{i+1}, \ldots, X_k$ is significantly large in relation to the residual sum of squares. The calculations for Table 5-2 can be carried out by using the formulae of Table 5-1. The expression $\hat{\boldsymbol{\beta}}'\mathbf{X}'\mathbf{y}$ or $\mathbf{y}'\mathbf{y}R^2$ gives the explained sum of squares for the set of variables included in $\mathbf{X}$. Thus this quantity is found first of all for the set of variables *excluding* the one under test and then for the complete set. Differencing gives the increment in the explained sum of squares due to the variable under test.

The analysis-of-variance treatment exemplified in Table 5-2 may be extended to test the contribution to the explained sum of squares of a subgroup of variables, say, $X_{r+1}, \ldots, X_k$. Since the $\hat{\beta}_i^*$ are normally and independently distributed about β_i^* with variance σ^2, the ratio

$$F = \frac{\sum_{i=r+1}^{k} (\hat{\beta}_i^* - \beta_i^*)^2/(k-r)}{\sum_{i=1}^{n} e_i^2/(n-k)}$$

has the F distribution with $(k - r, n - k)$ degrees of freedom. The hypothesis $\beta_{r+1} = \cdots = \beta_k = 0$ implies from (5-54) that

$$\beta_{r+1}^* = \cdots = \beta_k^* = 0$$

and this latter hypothesis is tested by computing

$$F = \frac{\sum_{i=r+1}^{k} \hat{\beta}_i^{*2}/(k-r)}{\sum_{i=1}^{n} e_i^2/(n-k)}$$

This is the basis of the analysis of variance shown in Table 5-3. The test of the hypothesis $\beta_{r+1} = \cdots = \beta_k = 0$ is then made by taking the ratio of the

Table 5-3

Source of variation	*Sum of squares*	*Degrees of freedom*	*Mean square*
$X_2, X_3, \ldots, X_r$	$\sum_{i=2}^{r} \hat{\beta}_i^{*2}$	$r - 1$	
$X_{r+1}, \ldots, X_k$	$\sum_{i=r+1}^{k} \hat{\beta}_i^{*2}$	$k - r$	$\sum_{i=r+1}^{k} \hat{\beta}_i^{*2}/(k-r)$
$X_2, \ldots, X_k$	$\sum_{i=2}^{k} \hat{\beta}_i^{*2}$	$k - 1$	
Residual	$\sum_{i=1}^{n} e_i^2$	$n - k$	$\sum_{i=1}^{n} e_i^2/(n-k)$
Total	$\sum_{i=1}^{n} y_i^2$	$n - 1$	

first to the second mean square in the last column of Table 5-3 and referring to the F distribution with $(k - r, n - k)$ degrees of freedom. In implementing Table 5-3 one needs to compute the explained sum of squares for lines 1 and 3 of the table. This is most simply done by the formulae already displayed in Table 5-1, namely, that if we are working in deviation terms,

$$\text{Explained Sum of Squares} = \hat{\boldsymbol{\beta}}'\mathbf{X}'\mathbf{y} = \mathbf{y}'\mathbf{y}R^2$$

where $\hat{\boldsymbol{\beta}}$, $\mathbf{X}$, and R^2 refer to the appropriate set of explanatory variables. For example, in the first line of Table 5-3 the computations are based on the multiple regression of Y on the sub-set $X_2, \ldots, X_r$ while in the third line the complete set of explanatory variables $X_2, \ldots, X_r, \ldots, X_k$ is used. The other sums of squares then follow easily by subtraction.

As an illustration of practical computations, consider the data in Table 5-4, where Y = index of imports of goods and services to United Kingdom at constant (1948) prices

X_2 = index of gross United Kingdom product at 1948 prices

X_3 = ratio of indices of prices of imports and general United Kingdom output, respectively

Table 5-4

Year	Y	X_2	X_3
1948	100	100	100
1949	106	104	99
1950	107	106	110
1951	120	111	126
1952	110	111	113
1953	116	115	103
1954	123	120	102
1955	133	124	103
1956	137	126	98

We first of all compute

$$n = 9 \qquad \Sigma Y = 1{,}052 \qquad \Sigma X_2 = 1{,}017 \qquad \Sigma X_3 = 954$$

$$\bar{Y} = 116.9 \qquad \bar{X}_2 = 113 \qquad \bar{X}_3 = 106$$

$$\Sigma Y^2 = 124{,}228 \qquad \Sigma X_2^2 = 115{,}571 \qquad \Sigma X_3^2 = 101{,}772$$

$$\Sigma Y X_2 = 119{,}750 \qquad \Sigma Y X_3 = 111{,}433 \qquad \Sigma X_2 X_3 = 107{,}690$$

From these we construct the following quantities in terms of deviations around the means:

$$\Sigma y^2 = 124{,}228 - \tfrac{1}{9}(1{,}052)^2 = 1{,}260.89$$

$$\Sigma x_2^2 = 115{,}571 - \tfrac{1}{9}(1{,}017)^2 = 650$$

$$\Sigma x_3^2 = 101{,}772 - \tfrac{1}{9}(954)^2 = 648$$

$$\Sigma yx_2 = 119{,}750 - \tfrac{1}{9}(1{,}052)(1{,}017) = 874$$

$$\Sigma yx_3 = 111{,}433 - \tfrac{1}{9}(1{,}052)(954) = -79$$

$$\Sigma x_2x_3 = 107{,}690 - \tfrac{1}{9}(1{,}017)(954) = -112$$

Hence we have

$$\mathbf{X}'\mathbf{X} = \begin{bmatrix} 650 & -112 \\ -112 & 648 \end{bmatrix} \qquad \mathbf{X}'\mathbf{y} = \begin{bmatrix} 874 \\ -79 \end{bmatrix}$$

$$|\mathbf{X}'\mathbf{X}| = 408{,}656$$

$$(\mathbf{X}'\mathbf{X})^{-1} = \frac{1}{408{,}656}\begin{bmatrix} 648 & 112 \\ 112 & 650 \end{bmatrix} = \begin{bmatrix} 0.001{,}585{,}68 & 0.000{,}274{,}07 \\ 0.000{,}274{,}07 & 0.001{,}590{,}58 \end{bmatrix}$$

From (5-7) we have

$$\begin{bmatrix} \hat{\beta}_2 \\ \hat{\beta}_3 \end{bmatrix} = \hat{\boldsymbol{\beta}} = (\mathbf{X}'\mathbf{X})^{-1}\mathbf{X}'\mathbf{y} = \begin{bmatrix} 1.364{,}232{,}79 \\ 0.113{,}881{,}40 \end{bmatrix}$$

and from the footnote on page 129 above

$$\hat{\beta}_1 = \bar{Y} - \hat{\beta}_2\bar{X}_2 - \hat{\beta}_3\bar{X}_3$$

$$= 116.9 - (1.364{,}232{,}79)(113) - (0.113{,}881{,}4)(106)$$

$$= -49.3297$$

giving the estimated relation

$$\hat{Y} = -49.3297 + 1.3642X_2 + 0.1139X_3$$

From (5-27) the explained sum of squares is

$$\hat{\boldsymbol{\beta}}'\mathbf{X}'\mathbf{y} = 1183.3428$$

which gives the analysis of variance shown in Table 5-5. The resultant F value is

$$F = 591.67/12.93 = 45.76$$

with (2, 6) degrees of freedom. $F_{0.01} = 10.925$, so that a highly significant association exists between these three variables.

Table 5-5

Source of variation	*Sum of squares*	*Degrees of freedom*	*Mean square*
X_2 and X_3	1,183.34	2	591.67
Residual	77.55	6	12.93
Total	1,260.89	8	

The analysis may also be conducted in a stepwise fashion, and the separate contributions of each variable analyzed. Let

b_2 = coefficient of X_2 in the simple regression of Y on X_2

b_3 = coefficient of X_3 in the simple regression of Y on X_3

Then

$$b_2 = \frac{\Sigma yx_2}{\Sigma x_2^2} = \frac{874}{650} = 1.344{,}615$$

$$b_3 = \frac{\Sigma yx_3}{\Sigma x_3^2} = \frac{-79}{648} = -0.121{,}914$$

The explained sum of squares due to X_2 alone is

$$b_2\Sigma yx_2 = (1.344{,}615)(874) = 1{,}175.19$$

and the explained sum of squares due to X_3 alone is

$$b_3\Sigma yx_3 = (-0.121{,}914)(-79) = 9.63$$

From these quantities we may set up Tables 5-6 and 5-7.

Table 5-6

Source of variation	*Sum of squares*	*Degrees of freedom*	*Mean square*
X_2	1,175.19	1	1,175.19
Addition of X_3	8.15	1	8.15
X_2 and X_3	1,183.34	2	
Residual	77.55	6	12.93
Total	1,260.89	8	

Table 5-7

Source of variation	*Sum of squares*	*Degrees of freedom*	*Mean square*
X_3	9.63	1	9.63
Addition of X_2	1,173.71	1	1,173.71
X_2 and X_3	1,183.34	2	
Residual	77.55	6	12.93
Total	1,260.89	8	

The total sum of squares due to X_2 *and* X_3 is known from Table 5-5 as 1,183.34. The X_2 sum of squares is 1,175.19, and the *additional* effect due to the inclusion of X_3 as well as X_2 is found by subtraction to be 8.15. The additional X_3 effect is then tested by the F ratio,

$$F = 8.15/12.93 = 0.63$$

with (1, 6) degrees of freedom, which is evidently insignificant. The significance of X_2 alone can be tested by computing the residual sum of squares after X_2 as 1,260.89 − 1,175.19 = 85.70 with 7 degrees of freedom, giving a mean square of 12.24. The appropriate F ratio is then

$$F = 1{,}175.19/12.24 = 96.01$$

with (1, 7) degrees of freedom, which is highly significant.

Alternatively, we may construct Table 5-7. The direct effect of X_3 is clearly insignificant, and the additional effect of X_2 highly significant.

The net (additional) effect of X_2 or X_3 might, alternatively, have been tested by using (5-45).

$$t = \frac{\hat{\beta}_i - \beta_i}{\sqrt{\sum_{i=1}^{n} e_i^2/(n-k)}\sqrt{a_{ii}}}$$

where a_{ii} is the appropriate diagonal element from $(\mathbf{X}'\mathbf{X})^{-1}$. For $\hat{\beta}_2$ we have, on the hypothesis that $\beta_2 = 0$,

$$t = \frac{1.364{,}232{,}79}{\sqrt{12.93}\sqrt{0.001{,}585{,}68}}$$

since $\Sigma e^2/(n-k) = 12.93$, as shown in Table 5-5, and 0.001,585,68 is the first element, and hence the element corresponding to X_2, in the principal diagonal of $(\mathbf{X}'\mathbf{X})^{-1}$. On squaring,

$$t^2 = 90.8$$

The additional effect of X_2 from Table 5-7 is given by

$$F = 1{,}173.71/12.93 = 90.8$$

and the tests are exactly equivalent.

Applying (5-47), we compute a 95 per cent confidence interval for β_2 as

$$1.364{,}232{,}8 \pm 2.4469\sqrt{12.93}\sqrt{0.001{,}585{,}68}$$

that is,

$$1.0143 \text{ to } 1.7141$$

As an alternative to the above, one might have started with the calculation from zero origin and written the $\mathbf{X'X}$ matrix as

$$\mathbf{X'X} = \begin{bmatrix} 9 & 1{,}017 & 954 \\ 1{,}017 & 115{,}571 & 107{,}690 \\ 954 & 107{,}690 & 101{,}772 \end{bmatrix}$$

One disadvantage of this approach, at any rate for work on desk calculators, is that the matrix to be inverted is of order 3 rather than 2 and also the elements in the first row and column are usually much smaller in absolute value than those in the rest of the matrix, thus making it difficult to retain sufficient significant figures in subsequent calculations. When this latter difficulty exists it is advisable to scale the variables initially by multiplying by constants in order to make the various sums of squares approximately the same magnitude. At the end of the calculations appropriate adjustments must be made to the estimated coefficients and standard errors. For example, if we wish to estimate the relation

$$Y = \beta_1 + \beta_2 X_2 + \beta_3 X_3 + u$$

but actually fit

$$Y = b_1 + b_2 W_2 + b_3 W_3 + e$$

where $W_2 = \frac{1}{10}X_2$ and $W_3 = \frac{1}{100}X_3$ b_2 is then an estimate of $10\beta_2$ and b_3 an estimate of $100\beta_3$ so these coefficients and their standard errors must be divided by 10 and 100 respectively to give estimates of the coefficients in the original relation.

The development that has produced tests of subsets of the β_i coefficients may also be used to derive joint confidence regions for groups of β_i coefficients. We have already given in (5-47) the confidence interval for any single β coefficient, but since the $\hat{\beta}_i$ are not in general independently distributed we are sometimes interested in obtaining joint confidence regions. In (5-58) above we derived the basic result that

$$F = \frac{\sum_{i=2}^{k} (\hat{\beta}_i^* - \beta_i^*)^2/(k-1)}{\sum_{i=1}^{n} e_i^2/(n-k)}$$

has the F distribution with $k - 1$ and $n - k$ degrees of freedom. The β_i^* and $\hat{\beta}_i^*$ are the true and estimated coefficients of the orthogonal variables so we must transform this statement into one in terms of the β_i and $\hat{\beta}_i$.

$$\begin{aligned}\sum_{i=2}^{k} (\hat{\beta}_i^* - \beta_i^*)^2 &= (\hat{\boldsymbol{\beta}}^* - \boldsymbol{\beta}^*)'(\hat{\boldsymbol{\beta}}^* - \boldsymbol{\beta}^*) \\ &= [\mathbf{W}^{-1}(\hat{\boldsymbol{\beta}} - \boldsymbol{\beta})]'[\mathbf{W}^{-1}(\hat{\boldsymbol{\beta}} - \boldsymbol{\beta})] \quad \text{from} \quad (5\text{-}54) \\ &= (\hat{\boldsymbol{\beta}} - \boldsymbol{\beta})'(\mathbf{W}^{-1})'\mathbf{W}^{-1}(\hat{\boldsymbol{\beta}} - \boldsymbol{\beta}) \\ &= (\hat{\boldsymbol{\beta}} - \boldsymbol{\beta})'\mathbf{X}'\mathbf{X}(\hat{\boldsymbol{\beta}} - \boldsymbol{\beta}) \quad \text{from p. 140 above.}\end{aligned}$$

Thus we have the alternative statement that

$$F = \frac{(\hat{\boldsymbol{\beta}} - \boldsymbol{\beta})'\mathbf{X}'\mathbf{X}(\hat{\boldsymbol{\beta}} - \boldsymbol{\beta})/(k-1)}{\mathbf{e}'\mathbf{e}/(n-k)}$$

has the F distribution with $k - 1$ and $n - k$ degrees of freedom, which means that

$$(\hat{\boldsymbol{\beta}} - \boldsymbol{\beta})'\mathbf{X}'\mathbf{X}(\hat{\boldsymbol{\beta}} - \boldsymbol{\beta}) \leq (k-1)s^2F_{0.05}$$

provides a 95 per cent confidence region for the elements of $\boldsymbol{\beta}$.

Applications of this result are difficult and tedious for anything beyond two or three variables. If we have two explanatory variables X_2 and X_3, working in terms of deviations from means gives

$$\begin{aligned}(\hat{\boldsymbol{\beta}} - \boldsymbol{\beta})'\mathbf{X}'\mathbf{X}(\hat{\boldsymbol{\beta}} - \boldsymbol{\beta}) &= (\hat{\beta}_2 - \beta_2)^2\Sigma x_2^2 + 2(\hat{\beta}_2 - \beta_2)(\hat{\beta}_3 - \beta_3)\Sigma x_2x_3 \\ &\quad + (\hat{\beta}_3 - \beta_3)^2\Sigma x_3^2\end{aligned}$$

Setting this expression equal to $(k-1)s^2F_{0.05}$ traces out a 95 per cent elliptical confidence region in the β_2, β_3 plane.

5-5 PREDICTION[1]

Often one of the main purposes of estimating a relation such as (5-1) is to enable one to make predictions of the expected value of Y associated with

[1] In preparing this section on prediction problems I have benefited from correspondence with R. Bodkin.

some set of X values not observed in the sample. Suppose, for example, that we expect the X values in period $(n + 1)$ to be given by the column vector

$$\mathbf{c} = \{1 \quad X_{2,n+1} \quad X_{3,n+1} \quad \cdots \quad X_{k,n+1}\}$$

and that our problem is to predict the expected value of Y_{n+1}, namely

$$E(Y_{n+1}) = E(\mathbf{c}'\boldsymbol{\beta} + u_{n+1}) = \mathbf{c}'\boldsymbol{\beta}$$

As in Chap. 2 we make a point prediction or an interval prediction. The former is quite straightforward since we have already shown on pages 126 to 127 above that $\mathbf{c}'\hat{\boldsymbol{\beta}}$ is a best linear unbiased predictor of $\mathbf{c}'\boldsymbol{\beta}$. Thus our point predictor is

$$\hat{Y}_{n+1} = \mathbf{c}'\hat{\boldsymbol{\beta}} = \hat{\beta}_1 + \hat{\beta}_2 X_{2,n+1} + \cdots + \hat{\beta}_k X_{k,n+1} \tag{5-62}$$

To obtain an interval predictor we need to establish the sampling distribution of the point predictor $\mathbf{c}'\hat{\boldsymbol{\beta}}$.

$$E(\mathbf{c}'\hat{\boldsymbol{\beta}}) = \mathbf{c}'\boldsymbol{\beta} \quad \text{since } E(\hat{\boldsymbol{\beta}}) = \boldsymbol{\beta}$$

and, as we have already shown in (5-12)

$$\text{var}\,(\mathbf{c}'\hat{\boldsymbol{\beta}}) = \sigma^2\mathbf{c}'(\mathbf{X}'\mathbf{X})^{-1}\mathbf{c}$$

Since the $\hat{\beta}_i$ have a multivariate normal distribution, $\mathbf{c}'\hat{\boldsymbol{\beta}}$ is a normal variate; that is

$$\mathbf{c}'\hat{\boldsymbol{\beta}} \text{ is } N(\mathbf{c}'\boldsymbol{\beta}, \sigma^2\mathbf{c}'(\mathbf{X}'\mathbf{X})^{-1}\mathbf{c}) \tag{5-63}$$

Shifting to the t distribution in the usual way

$$t = \frac{\mathbf{c}'\hat{\boldsymbol{\beta}} - \mathbf{c}'\boldsymbol{\beta}}{s\sqrt{\mathbf{c}'(\mathbf{X}'\mathbf{X})^{-1}\mathbf{c}}} \tag{5-64}$$

where

$$s = \sqrt{\sum_{i=1}^{n} e_i^2/(n-k)}$$

has the t distribution with $(n - k)$ degrees of freedom. Hence a $100(1 - \varepsilon)$ per cent confidence interval for $E(Y_{n+1}|\mathbf{c})$ is given by

$$\mathbf{c}'\hat{\boldsymbol{\beta}} \pm t_{\varepsilon/2}s\sqrt{\mathbf{c}'(\mathbf{X}'\mathbf{X})^{-1}\mathbf{c}} \tag{5-65}$$

As an illustration of this result consider the problem of predicting the mean value of Y, conditional on X_0, for the model $Y = \alpha + \beta X + u$. In this case

$$(\mathbf{X}'\mathbf{X}) = \begin{bmatrix} n & \Sigma X \\ \Sigma X & \Sigma X^2 \end{bmatrix}$$

and

$$\mathbf{c} = \{1 \quad X_0\}$$

Hence

$$\mathbf{c}'(\mathbf{X}'\mathbf{X})^{-1}\mathbf{c} = \frac{\Sigma X^2 - 2X_0\Sigma X + nX_0^2}{n\Sigma X^2 - (\Sigma X)^2}$$

which simplifies to

$$\mathbf{c}'(\mathbf{X}'\mathbf{X})^{-1}\mathbf{c} = \frac{1}{n} + \frac{(X_0 - \bar{X})^2}{\Sigma x^2}$$

Thus a $100(1 - \varepsilon)$ confidence interval for $E(Y_0|X_0)$ is

$$(\hat{\alpha} + \hat{\beta}X_0) \pm t_{\varepsilon/2}s\sqrt{\frac{1}{n} + \frac{(X_0 - \bar{X})^2}{\Sigma x^2}} \tag{5-66}$$

in agreement with the result previously obtained in (2-50).

Again, as in Chap. 2, we may sometimes be more interested in setting a confidence interval for the individual Y value associated with $\mathbf{c} = \{1 \quad X_{2,n+1} \ldots X_{k,n+1}\}$. This merely requires a slight extension of the previous analysis. The forecast value, as before, is

$$\hat{Y}_{n+1} = \mathbf{c}'\hat{\boldsymbol{\beta}}$$

The actual value is

$$Y_{n+1} = \mathbf{c}'\boldsymbol{\beta} + u_{n+1}$$

where u_{n+1} indicates the actual value of the stochastic disturbance term in the forecast period. The discrepancy between the forecast and actual values is

$$\begin{aligned} d &= \hat{Y}_{n+1} - Y_{n+1} \\ &= \mathbf{c}'(\hat{\boldsymbol{\beta}} - \boldsymbol{\beta}) - u_{n+1} \end{aligned}$$

We have

$$E(d) = 0$$

since $E(\hat{\boldsymbol{\beta}}) = \boldsymbol{\beta}$ and $E(u_{n+1}) = 0$. From the assumption of independence for the u's and from (5-12) we then have

$$\operatorname{var}(d) = \sigma^2[1 + \mathbf{c}'(\mathbf{X}'\mathbf{X})^{-1}\mathbf{c}] \tag{5-67}$$

and

$$t = \frac{\hat{Y}_{n+1} - Y_{n+1}}{s[1 + \mathbf{c}'(\mathbf{X}'\mathbf{X})^{-1}\mathbf{c}]^{1/2}} \tag{5-68}$$

has the t distribution with $(n - k)$ degrees of freedom. This yields a $100(1 - \varepsilon)$ confidence interval for Y_{n+1} as

$$\mathbf{c}'\hat{\boldsymbol{\beta}} \pm t_{\varepsilon/2}s[1 + \mathbf{c}'(\mathbf{X}'\mathbf{X})^{-1}\mathbf{c}]^{1/2} \tag{5-69}$$

Again, as in Chap. 2 for the two-variable case, (5-68) may be used to test the hypothesis that a new observation $(Y_{n+1}, X_{2,n+1}, \ldots, X_{k,n+1})$ comes from the same population or structure as that presumed to have generated the n sample observations. To carry out the test use $X_{2,n+1}, \ldots, X_{k,n+1}$ to compute

$$\hat{Y}_{n+1} = \hat{\beta}_1 + \hat{\beta}_2 X_{2,n+1} + \cdots + \hat{\beta}_k X_{k,n+1}$$

and hence compute the t value defined in (5-68). If the calculated t value exceeds a pre-selected critical value we would infer that the new observation comes from a different structure. When more than one new observation is available the same test can be carried out by the covariance methods described in section 3 of Chap. 6 below.

5-6 LINEAR RESTRICTIONS

Economic theory often suggests that the coefficients of a relation should obey a linear restriction; for example, constant returns to scale imply that the exponents in a Cobb-Douglas production function should sum to unity, and the absence of the money illusion on the part of consumers implies that the sum of the money income and price elasticities in a demand function should be zero. These restrictions may be dealt with in two ways. One is to fit the function free of any restrictions and then test whether the estimated coefficients come sufficiently close to satisfying the restriction. The appropriate theory for the test has already been developed in the previous section. The hypothesis is that the true coefficients obey the condition $\mathbf{c}'\boldsymbol{\beta} = r$, where $\mathbf{c}$ is an appropriately specified vector of constants and r is a known constant. From the estimated coefficients we can compute $\mathbf{c}'\hat{\boldsymbol{\beta}}$, and as we have seen above

$$t = \frac{\mathbf{c}'\hat{\boldsymbol{\beta}} - \mathbf{c}'\boldsymbol{\beta}}{s\sqrt{\mathbf{c}'(\mathbf{X}'\mathbf{X})^{-1}\mathbf{c}}} \tag{5-70}$$

where

$$s = \sqrt{\sum_{i=1}^{n} e_i^2/(n - k)}$$

has the t distribution with $(n - k)$ degrees of freedom. The test of the hypothesis that $\mathbf{c}'\boldsymbol{\beta} = r$ is then carried out by replacing $\mathbf{c}'\boldsymbol{\beta}$ in (5-70) by r and referring the resultant t value to the appropriate critical points of the t distribution.

As an illustration, consider a three-variable relationship.

$$Y = \beta_1 + \beta_2 X_2 + \beta_3 X_3 + u$$

and suppose we wish to test the hypothesis $\beta_2 = \beta_3$. Working with *deviations*, let us suppose that data from 23 sample observations yield

$$\mathbf{X}'\mathbf{X} = \begin{bmatrix} 21.5 & 0 \\ 0 & 43.6 \end{bmatrix} \qquad \mathbf{X}'\mathbf{y} = \begin{bmatrix} 17.3 \\ 25.4 \end{bmatrix} \qquad \Sigma y^2 = 49.2$$

The hypothesis under test is then

$$\mathbf{c}'\boldsymbol{\beta} = 0$$

where

$$\mathbf{c} = \begin{bmatrix} 1 \\ -1 \end{bmatrix} \quad \text{and} \quad \boldsymbol{\beta} = \begin{bmatrix} \beta_2 \\ \beta_3 \end{bmatrix}$$

We require to compute the quantities entering into (5-70). Thus

$$(\mathbf{X}'\mathbf{X})^{-1} = \begin{bmatrix} 0.046{,}512 & 0 \\ 0 & 0.022{,}936 \end{bmatrix}$$

$$\hat{\boldsymbol{\beta}} = \begin{bmatrix} 0.804{,}658 \\ 0.582{,}574 \end{bmatrix} \qquad \hat{\boldsymbol{\beta}}'\mathbf{X}'\mathbf{y} = 28.7$$

$$\mathbf{e}'\mathbf{e} = 49.2 - 28.7 = 20.5$$

$$s = \sqrt{20.5/20} = 1.012 \qquad \mathbf{c}'(\mathbf{X}'\mathbf{X})^{-1}\mathbf{c} = 0.069{,}448$$

Substitution in (5-70) gives

$$t = \frac{0.222{,}084}{1.012\sqrt{0.069{,}448}} = 0.83$$

with 20 degrees of freedom. This low value does not lead to the rejection of the hypothesis $\beta_2 = \beta_3$.

An alternative way of dealing with the problem is to incorporate the restriction in the fitting process so that the estimated coefficients satisfy the restriction exactly. In some cases this is most simply done by working out directly the special form of the estimating equations for the problem in hand. As an illustration consider the conventional Cobb-Douglas production function

$$Y = AL^{\alpha}K^{\beta}$$

where Y denotes output, L labor input, K capital input, and α and β are the output-labor and output-capital elasticities. Taking logarithms of both sides and adding a disturbance term

$$y = a + \alpha x_2 + \beta x_3 + u \qquad \text{(5-71)}$$

where $y = \log Y$, $x_2 = \log L$ and $x_3 = \text{Log } K$. To incorporate the restriction $(\alpha + \beta) = 1$ we rewrite (5-71) as

$$y = a + \alpha x_2 + (1 - \alpha)x_3 + u$$

and so we must find the $\hat{a}$ and $\hat{\alpha}$ which minimize

$$\sum_{i=1}^{n} [y_i - \hat{a} - \hat{\alpha}x_{2i} - (1 - \hat{\alpha})x_{3i}]^2$$

A straightforward differentiation gives the estimating equations

$$n\hat{a} + \hat{\alpha}\Sigma(x_{2i} - x_{3i}) = \Sigma(y_i - x_{3i}) \tag{5-72}$$

$$\hat{a}\Sigma(x_{2i} - x_{3i}) + \hat{\alpha}\Sigma(x_{2i} - x_{3i})^2 = \Sigma(y_i - x_{3i})(x_{2i} - x_{3i})$$

Alternatively, a general formula may be developed.[1] Linear restrictions may be expressed in the form

$$\mathbf{r} = \mathbf{R}\boldsymbol{\beta}$$

where $\mathbf{r}$ is a known column vector of $g < k$ elements, g being the number of restrictions, and $\mathbf{R}$ is a known matrix of order $g \times k$. For example, if we wish to incorporate two restrictions, namely, $\beta_2 = \beta_4$ and $\beta_3 + 2\beta_4 + \beta_5 = 1$ we would set

$$\mathbf{r} = \begin{bmatrix} 0 \\ 1 \end{bmatrix} \quad \text{and} \quad \mathbf{R} = \begin{bmatrix} 0 & 1 & 0 & -1 & 0 & 0 & \dots \\ 0 & 0 & 1 & 2 & 1 & 0 & \dots \end{bmatrix}$$

We now require the estimated coefficient vector, $\mathbf{b}$, to satisfy the restrictions, so we must choose $\mathbf{b}$ to minimize $(\mathbf{y} - \mathbf{Xb})'(\mathbf{y} - \mathbf{Xb})$ subject to $\mathbf{Rb} = \mathbf{r}$. Define

$$\varphi = (\mathbf{y} - \mathbf{Xb})'(\mathbf{y} - \mathbf{Xb}) - \boldsymbol{\mu}'(\mathbf{Rb} - \mathbf{r})$$

where $\boldsymbol{\mu}$ is a column vector of g Lagrange multipliers. Differentiating

$$\frac{\partial\varphi}{\partial\mathbf{b}} = -2\mathbf{X}'\mathbf{y} + 2(\mathbf{X}'\mathbf{X})\mathbf{b} - \mathbf{R}'\boldsymbol{\mu} = \mathbf{0} \tag{5-73}$$

$$\frac{\partial\varphi}{\partial\boldsymbol{\mu}} = \mathbf{Rb} - \mathbf{r} = \mathbf{0} \tag{5-74}$$

Premultiplying the first equation by $\mathbf{R}(\mathbf{X}'\mathbf{X})^{-1}$ gives

$$-2\mathbf{R}(\mathbf{X}'\mathbf{X})^{-1}\mathbf{X}'\mathbf{y} + 2\mathbf{R}(\mathbf{X}'\mathbf{X})^{-1}(\mathbf{X}'\mathbf{X})\mathbf{b} - \mathbf{R}(\mathbf{X}'\mathbf{X})^{-1}\mathbf{R}'\boldsymbol{\mu} = \mathbf{0}$$

i.e.,

$$-2\mathbf{R}\hat{\boldsymbol{\beta}} + 2\mathbf{Rb} - \mathbf{R}(\mathbf{X}'\mathbf{X})^{-1}\mathbf{R}'\boldsymbol{\mu} = \mathbf{0}$$

[1] See H. Theil, *Economic Forecasts and Policy*, second revised edition, North-Holland, 1961, pp. 331–2, on which this section is based.

where $\hat{\boldsymbol{\beta}} = (\mathbf{X}'\mathbf{X})^{-1}\mathbf{X}'\mathbf{y}$ is the unrestricted O.L.S. estimator. Hence $\boldsymbol{\mu} = 2[\mathbf{R}(\mathbf{X}'\mathbf{X})^{-1}\mathbf{R}']^{-1}(\mathbf{r} - \mathbf{R}\hat{\boldsymbol{\beta}})$ since $\mathbf{Rb} = \mathbf{r}$. Substituting for $\boldsymbol{\mu}$ in (5-73) then gives

$$\mathbf{b} = (\mathbf{X}'\mathbf{X})^{-1}\mathbf{X}'\mathbf{y} + (\mathbf{X}'\mathbf{X})^{-1}\mathbf{R}'[\mathbf{R}(\mathbf{X}'\mathbf{X})^{-1}\mathbf{R}']^{-1}(\mathbf{r} - \mathbf{R}\hat{\boldsymbol{\beta}})$$

or

$$\mathbf{b} = \hat{\boldsymbol{\beta}} + (\mathbf{X}'\mathbf{X})^{-1}\mathbf{R}'[\mathbf{R}(\mathbf{X}'\mathbf{X})^{-1}\mathbf{R}']^{-1}(\mathbf{r} - \mathbf{R}\hat{\boldsymbol{\beta}}) \tag{5-75}$$

Substituting $\mathbf{X}\boldsymbol{\beta} + \mathbf{u}$ for $\mathbf{y}$ on the right-hand side of (5-75) then gives

$$\mathbf{b} = (\mathbf{X}'\mathbf{X})^{-1}\mathbf{X}'(\mathbf{X}\boldsymbol{\beta} + \mathbf{u}) + (\mathbf{X}'\mathbf{X})^{-1}\mathbf{R}'[\mathbf{R}(\mathbf{X}'\mathbf{X})^{-1}\mathbf{R}']^{-1}$$
$$\times [\mathbf{r} - \mathbf{R}(\boldsymbol{\beta} + (\mathbf{X}'\mathbf{X})^{-1}\mathbf{X}'\mathbf{u})]$$

that is

$$\mathbf{b} - \boldsymbol{\beta} = \mathbf{A}(\mathbf{X}'\mathbf{X})^{-1}\mathbf{X}'\mathbf{u} \tag{5-76}$$

where

$$\mathbf{A} = \mathbf{I} - (\mathbf{X}'\mathbf{X})^{-1}\mathbf{R}'[\mathbf{R}(\mathbf{X}'\mathbf{X})^{-1}\mathbf{R}']^{-1}\mathbf{R} \tag{5-77}$$

It follows immediately from (5-76) that

$$E(\mathbf{b}) = \boldsymbol{\beta}$$

and

$$\text{var}(\mathbf{b}) = \sigma^2\mathbf{A}(\mathbf{X}'\mathbf{X})^{-1}\mathbf{A}' \tag{5-78}$$

From the definition of $\mathbf{A}$ in (5-77) this last result for the variance-covariance matrix may be simplified still further to

$$\text{var}(\mathbf{b}) = \sigma^2\mathbf{A}(\mathbf{X}'\mathbf{X})^{-1} \tag{5-79}$$

Thus (5-75) defines the restricted estimator **b**, which is unbiased and which has the variance-covariance matrix given by (5-79).

A special case of linear restrictions arises when the value of one or more parameters is known exactly. Suppose in a problem with just two explanatory variables we know $\beta_2 = c$. Working with the relation in deviation form we could then express this knowledge by setting

$$\mathbf{r} = c \quad \text{and} \quad \mathbf{R} = [1 \quad 0]$$

so that the condition $\mathbf{R}\boldsymbol{\beta} = \mathbf{r}$ gives simply $\beta_2 = c$. With this specification of **R** and **r** we could then substitute directly in (5-75) to obtain the restricted estimator **b**. In this case

$$(\mathbf{X}'\mathbf{X}) = \begin{bmatrix} \Sigma x_2^2 & \Sigma x_2 x_3 \\ \Sigma x_2 x_3 & \Sigma x_3^2 \end{bmatrix}$$

where the lowercase letters denote deviations from sample means. Thus $\mathbf{R}(\mathbf{X}'\mathbf{X})^{-1}\mathbf{R}' = \Sigma x_3^2/D$, where D denotes the determinant of $(\mathbf{X}'\mathbf{X})$, and we then have

$$\mathbf{b} = \begin{bmatrix} b_2 \\ b_3 \end{bmatrix} = \begin{bmatrix} \hat{\beta}_2 \\ \hat{\beta}_3 \end{bmatrix} + \frac{1}{D}\begin{bmatrix} \Sigma x_3^2 & -\Sigma x_2 x_3 \\ -\Sigma x_2 x_3 & \Sigma x_2^2 \end{bmatrix}\begin{bmatrix} 1 \\ 0 \end{bmatrix}\frac{D}{\Sigma x_3^2}(c - \hat{\beta}_2)$$

where $\hat{\beta}_2$ and $\hat{\beta}_3$ are the unrestricted OLS coefficients. On simplification, this equation reduces to

$$\begin{bmatrix} b_2 \\ b_3 \end{bmatrix} = \begin{bmatrix} c \\ \hat{\beta}_3 - \dfrac{\Sigma x_2 x_3}{\Sigma x_3^2}(c - \hat{\beta}_2) \end{bmatrix} \tag{5-80}$$

The restricted estimator sets b_2 at the known value c as required. It is possible, however, to obtain an illuminating interpretation of b_3. Developing (5-80) further

$$\begin{aligned} b_3 &= \frac{1}{\Sigma x_3^2}[\hat{\beta}_3 \Sigma x_3^2 + \hat{\beta}_2 \Sigma x_2 x_3 - c\Sigma x_2 x_3] \\ &= \frac{1}{\Sigma x_3^2}[\Sigma x_3(\hat{\beta}_3 x_3 + \hat{\beta}_2 x_2) - c\Sigma x_2 x_3] \end{aligned}$$

From the unrestricted OLS regression we have $y = \hat{\beta}_2 x_2 + \hat{\beta}_3 x_3 + e$ so that $\Sigma x_3(\hat{\beta}_2 x_2 + \hat{\beta}_3 x_3) = \Sigma x_3(y - e) = \Sigma y x_3$ since $\Sigma x_3 e = 0$ as an automatic consequence of the least-squares fit. Thus

$$\begin{aligned} b_3 &= \frac{\Sigma y x_3 - c\Sigma x_2 x_3}{\Sigma x_3^2} \\ &= \frac{\Sigma(y - c x_2)x_3}{\Sigma x_3^2} \end{aligned} \tag{5-81}$$

but (5-81) indicates the slope of the regression line when $(y - cx_2)$ is regressed on x_3. Thus in the case of exact knowledge of a coefficient the intuitive procedure of "correcting" the dependent variable for the variations in the variable associated with that coefficient and then regressing the "corrected" variable on the remaining explanatory variables will give identical results to (5-75) and will in most cases be a simpler computational procedure.

5-7 MULTICOLLINEARITY

The general linear model set out in the previous section of this chapter is an extremely powerful and widely used statistical tool. As in all statistical applications, however, the power of the method depends on the underlying assumptions being fulfilled for the particular application in question. The rest of the book is basically concerned with developing alternative procedures for cases where one or more of the assumptions underlying the general linear model breaks down. As we shall see, some assumptions turn out to be much more crucial than others, but in all cases we should ideally like to know what consequences to expect from nonfulfillment of various assumptions, how to test whether an assumption is satisfied or not, and what alternative statistical methods to employ when the classical least-squares model is inappropriate.

One of the basic assumptions of the general linear model is that the data matrix $\mathbf{X}$, which is of order $n \times k$, has rank k, that is, that no linear dependence exists between the explanatory variables. The reason for this assumption is that the least-squares estimator $\hat{\boldsymbol{\beta}} = (\mathbf{X}'\mathbf{X})^{-1}\mathbf{X}'\mathbf{y}$ requires the inversion of $\mathbf{X}'\mathbf{X}$, which is impossible if the rank of $\mathbf{X}$, and hence the rank of $\mathbf{X}'\mathbf{X}$, is less than k. This is the case of extreme multicollinearity which exists when some or all of the explanatory variables are perfectly collinear. A less extreme but still very serious case arises when the assumption is only just satisfied, that is when some or all of the explanatory variables are highly but not perfectly collinear.

The main consequences of multicollinearity are the following:

1. The precision of estimation falls so that it becomes very difficult, if not impossible, to disentangle the relative influences of the various X variables. This loss of precision has three aspects: specific estimates may have very large errors; these errors may be highly correlated, one with another; and the sampling variances of the coefficients will be very large.

2. Investigators are sometimes led to drop variables incorrectly from an analysis because their coefficients are not significantly different from zero, but the true situation may be not that a variable has no effect but simply that the set of sample data has not enabled us to pick it up.

3. Estimates of coefficients become very sensitive to particular sets of sample data, and the addition of a few more observations can sometimes produce dramatic shifts in some of the coefficients.[1]

The fall in precision may be demonstrated for a very simple model. Consider

$$Y_t = \beta_1 + \beta_2 X_{2t} + \beta_3 X_{3t} + u_t$$

which we shall write in deviation form as

$$y_t = \beta_2 x_{2t} + \beta_3 x_{3t} + (u_t - \bar{u}) \tag{5-82}$$

[1] For an example of this see J. Johnston, "An Econometric Model of the United Kingdom," *Rev. Econ. Studies*, vol. XXIX, pp. 29–39, 1961.

Since the x's are deviations $\sum_t x_{2t} = \sum_t x_{3t} = 0$. The x's are fixed variables at our disposal so let us set

$$\begin{aligned} x_{3t} &= \alpha x_{2t} + v_t, \qquad t = 1, \ldots, n \\ \sum_t x_{2t}^2 &= \sum_t x_{3t}^2 = 1 \\ \sum_t v_t &= 0, \qquad \sum_t v_t x_{2t} = 0. \end{aligned} \tag{5-83}$$

The effect of these conditions is to make the correlation between X_2 and $X_3(r_{23})$ simply α and to give $(\mathbf{X}'\mathbf{X})$ a particularly simple form, namely,

$$(\mathbf{X}'\mathbf{X}) = \begin{bmatrix} 1 & \alpha \\ \alpha & 1 \end{bmatrix}$$

The O.L.S. estimator then has a sampling variance–covariance matrix given by

$$\text{var}(\hat{\boldsymbol{\beta}}) = \frac{\sigma_u^2}{(1 - \alpha^2)} \begin{bmatrix} 1 & -\alpha \\ -\alpha & 1 \end{bmatrix}$$

so that

$$\text{var}(\hat{\beta}_2) = \text{var}(\hat{\beta}_3) = \frac{\sigma_u^2}{(1 - \alpha^2)} \tag{5-84}$$

and

$$\text{cov}(\hat{\beta}_2, \hat{\beta}_3) = \frac{-\alpha\sigma_u^2}{(1 - \alpha^2)} \tag{5-85}$$

As multicollinearity, here measured by α, increases it is immediately clear from (5-84) that the sampling variances of the estimated coefficients increase. For example, as α increases from 0.5 to 0.9 the sampling variance increases by over 300 per cent, while a rise to 0.95 gives an increase of 750 per cent. When α is positive we see from (5-85) that there will be a negative covariance between the two regression coefficients and that this covariance also increases dramatically with increasing multicollinearity.

Formulae (5-84) and (5-85) indicate what to expect in repeated applications of the least-squares estimating technique. It is instructive, however, to analyze the errors in any specific application of the method. From (5-8) we have

$$\hat{\boldsymbol{\beta}} = \boldsymbol{\beta} + (\mathbf{X}'\mathbf{X})^{-1}\mathbf{X}'\mathbf{u}$$

which, on application to this case, gives

$$(\hat{\beta}_2 - \beta_2) = \Sigma u x_2 - \frac{\alpha}{1-\alpha^2}\Sigma uv$$
$$(\hat{\beta}_3 - \beta_3) = \frac{1}{1-\alpha^2}\Sigma uv \tag{5-86}$$

These two expressions show how the covariance between $\hat{\beta}_2$ and $\hat{\beta}_3$ arises, since Σuv appears in each error term. A large positive α is thus likely to produce large and opposite errors in $\hat{\beta}_2$ and $\hat{\beta}_3$; if $\hat{\beta}_2$ underestimates β_2, then $\hat{\beta}_3$ is likely to overestimate β_3 and vice versa. It is thus very important that the standard errors should alert one for the presence of multicollinearity. Formula (5-84) shows that the *true* standard error does increase with α, but the formula contains σ_u^2 which is unknown. The *estimated* standard error replaces σ_u^2 by $\Sigma e^2/(n-k)$, where Σe^2 is the sum of the squared residuals from the fitted regression. As shown in (5-19)

$$\mathbf{e'e} = \mathbf{u'u} - \mathbf{u'X(X'X)^{-1}X'u}$$

Working in terms of deviations we have

$$\mathbf{u'X(X'X)^{-1}X'u} = \frac{1}{(1-\alpha^2)}[\Sigma u x_2 \quad \Sigma u x_3]\begin{bmatrix} 1 & -\alpha \\ -\alpha & 1 \end{bmatrix}\begin{bmatrix} \Sigma u x_2 \\ \Sigma u x_3 \end{bmatrix}$$

which, by using the conditions expressed in (5-83), may be reduced to

$$\mathbf{u'X(X'X)^{-1}X'u} = (\Sigma u x_2)^2 + \frac{1}{1-\alpha^2}(\Sigma uv)^2$$

So

$$\mathbf{e'e} = \Sigma u^2 - (\Sigma u x_2)^2 - \frac{1}{1-\alpha^2}(\Sigma uv)^2 \tag{5-87}$$

The crucial question is whether the calculated sum of squared residuals ($\mathbf{e'e}$) will be affected by increasing collinearity between X_2 and X_3. For this purpose we can keep u and x_2 fixed. However, as we increase α, Σuv also changes as a consequence of the conditions imposed in (5-83). As α increases from α_1 to α_2 the residuals v must decrease. Let the new residuals (v_2) be defined in terms of the old residuals (v_1) as

$$v_{2t} = k v_{1t} \qquad 0 < k < 1 \qquad (t = 1, \ldots, n)$$

Hence

$$(\Sigma u v_2)^2 = k^2 (\Sigma u v_1)^2$$

From (5-83)

$$\begin{aligned} 1 - \alpha_2^2 &= \Sigma v_2^2 \\ &= k^2 \Sigma v_1^2 \\ &= k^2(1 - \alpha_1^2) \end{aligned}$$

Thus

$$\frac{1}{1 - \alpha_2^2}(\Sigma uv_2)^2 = \frac{1}{1 - \alpha_1^2}(\Sigma uv_1)^2$$

so that the residual sum of squares from the fitted regression will in fact be unchanged if the increased collinearity still satisfies conditions (5-83). This result will still hold approximately in the more general case

$$v_{2t} = kv_{1t} + \varepsilon_t$$

where

$$\Sigma \varepsilon = 0$$

and

$$\Sigma \varepsilon x_2 = 0$$

Thus there is no reason why collinearity should seriously bias the estimate of σ_u^2 and so we expect the standard errors to give adequate warning of collinearity. The effect of an explanatory variable may be sufficiently strong for the estimated coefficient to be statistically different from zero in spite of the effect of collinearity in increasing the standard error, but such collinearity may obscure the presence of less strong effects.

Tests for the presence of multicollinearity require the judicious use of various correlation coefficients. For the case of two explanatory variables, as in the above example, the simple correlation coefficient suffices. When there are more than two explanatory variables both zero-order and partial correlation coefficients should be examined, but even these may not be sufficient indicators, for as we will see in Chap. 6 it is possible to have a set of dummy variables which may have very low pair-wise correlations among themselves and yet form a perfectly collinear set. A more generally reliable guide therefore may be obtained by considering the coefficient of multiple determination, R_i^2, between each X_i and the remaining $(k - 1)$ variables in $\mathbf{X}$.[1]

The F statistic already defined in (5-60) may then be computed for each R_i^2, replacing k by $(k - 1)$ since we have excluded Y and are looking only at

[1] This is essentially the suggestion of D. E. Farrar and R. R. Glauber, "Multicollinearity in Regression Analysis: The Problem Re-visited," *Rev. of Economics and Statistics*, vol. 49, pp. 92–107, 1967.

the relationship between the X's. This gives

$$F_i = \frac{R_i^2/(k-2)}{(1-R_i^2)/(n-k+1)} \qquad (i = 2, \ldots, k) \tag{5-88}$$

Most, if not all, of the F_i in any econometric analysis will be statistically significant, that is the hypothesis of orthogonality among the explanatory variables will be rejected, but Farrar and Glauber suggest that inspection of the F_i will show which explanatory variables are most affected by multicollinearity and will thus indicate the area in which the search for better and more fruitful data should be concentrated.[1]

If multicollinearity proves serious in the sense that estimated parameters have an unsatisfactorily low degree of precision, we are in the statistical position of not being able to make bricks without straw. The remedy lies essentially in the acquisition, if possible, of new data or information, which will break the multicollinearity deadlock. Early demand studies, for example, which were based on time-series data, often ran into difficulties because of the correlation between the explanatory variables, income and prices, plus the inadequate variation in the income series. The use of cross-section budget data, however, gives a wide range of income variation, thus permitting a fairly precise determination of the income coefficient, which can then be employed in the time-series analysis. The combined use of time-series and cross-section data is now conventional practice in demand studies.[2] There are, however, difficulties of specification and interpretation.[3]

If estimates of some parameters are available they may be incorporated into the analysis as follows. Suppose that for the usual model, $\mathbf{y} = \mathbf{X}\boldsymbol{\beta} + \mathbf{u}$, we have estimates of $(k - r)$ of the k elements of $\boldsymbol{\beta}$. Without loss of generality we may, if necessary, renumber the X variables so that the estimated coefficients refer to the last $(k - r)$ variables in the $\mathbf{X}$ matrix. This leaves the coefficients of the first r variables in the $\mathbf{X}$ matrix to be estimated and one method of doing so is to "correct" the Y variable for the influence of $X_{r+1}, \ldots, X_k$ by estimating

$$Y_t^* = Y_t - b_{r+1}X_{r+1,t} - \cdots - b_kX_{kt} \qquad t = 1, \ldots, n$$

[1] A different, though now little used, method of searching for multicollinearity is the bunch map analysis developed by Ragnar Frisch. A full account is given in R. Frisch, *Statistical Confluence Analysis by Means of Complete Regression Systems*, University Economics Institute, Oslo, 1934. A useful short summary of the method is contained in E. Malinvaud, *Statistical Methods of Econometrics*, Rand McNally, Chicago, 1966, pp. 32–36, and an extensive practical application is described in J. R. N. Stone, *The Measurement of Consumers' Expenditure and Behaviour in the United Kingdom*, 1920–1938, Cambridge, London, 1954.

[2] See J. Tobin, "A Statistical Demand Function for Food in the U.S.A.", *J. Royal Statist. Soc.*, Series A, vol. 113, pp. 113–141, 1950, and J. R. N. Stone, *op. cit.*

[3] See J. Meyer and E. Kuh, "How Extraneous are Extraneous Estimates?" *Rev. Economics and Statistics*, vol. 39, pp. 380–393, 1957.

where $b_{r+1}, \ldots, b_k$ are the given estimates, and then regressing Y^* on $X_1, \ldots X_r$ to obtain estimates $b_1, \ldots, b_r$.

Let us partition **X**, **β**, and **b** as follows

$$\mathbf{X} = [\mathbf{X}_r \quad \mathbf{X}_{k-r}] \qquad \boldsymbol{\beta} = \begin{bmatrix} \boldsymbol{\beta}_r \\ \boldsymbol{\beta}_{k-r} \end{bmatrix} \qquad \mathbf{b} = \begin{bmatrix} \mathbf{b}_r \\ \mathbf{b}_{k-r} \end{bmatrix}$$

where $\mathbf{X}_r$ is the $n \times r$ sub-matrix consisting of the first r columns of $\mathbf{X}$, $\mathbf{X}_{k-r}$ the sub-matrix of the remaining $k - r$ columns, and $\boldsymbol{\beta}$ and $\mathbf{b}$ are each partitioned into two sub-vectors consisting of the first r and the remaining $k - r$ elements. Let us suppose that $\mathbf{b}_{k-r}$ is an unbiased estimate of $\boldsymbol{\beta}_{k-r}$, that its sampling variance-covariance matrix is known, say, $E(\mathbf{b}_{k-r} - \boldsymbol{\beta}_{k-r})(\mathbf{b}_{k-r} - \boldsymbol{\beta}_{k-r})' = \mathbf{V}$, and that these estimates are independent of the set of data that we are now using to estimate $\mathbf{b}_r$. The estimation process described above is

$$\mathbf{b}_r = (\mathbf{X}_r'\mathbf{X}_r)^{-1}\mathbf{X}_r'\mathbf{y}^* \tag{5-89}$$

where

$$\mathbf{y}^* = \mathbf{y} - \mathbf{X}_{k-r}\mathbf{b}_{k-r} \tag{5-90}$$

Combining (5-89) and (5-90) we obtain

$$\mathbf{b}_r = (\mathbf{X}_r'\mathbf{X}_r)^{-1}[\mathbf{X}_r'\mathbf{y} - \mathbf{X}_r'\mathbf{X}_{k-r}\mathbf{b}_{k-r}]$$

Replacing $\mathbf{y}$ by $\mathbf{X}_r\boldsymbol{\beta}_r + \mathbf{X}_{k-r}\boldsymbol{\beta}_{k-r} + \mathbf{u}$ we then have

$$\mathbf{b}_r = \boldsymbol{\beta}_r + (\mathbf{X}_r'\mathbf{X}_r)^{-1}\mathbf{X}_r'\mathbf{u} - (\mathbf{X}_r'\mathbf{X}_r)^{-1}\mathbf{X}_r'\mathbf{X}_{k-r}(\mathbf{b}_{k-r} - \boldsymbol{\beta}_{k-r})$$

Since $E(\mathbf{u}) = \mathbf{0}$ and $E(\mathbf{b}_{k-r}) = \boldsymbol{\beta}_{k-r}$ we have immediately $E(\mathbf{b}_r) = \boldsymbol{\beta}_r$ and from the assumption of independence of the two sets of data the variance-covariance matrix for $\mathbf{b}_r$ is

$$\begin{aligned} \text{var}\,(\mathbf{b}_r) &= E\{(\mathbf{b}_r - \boldsymbol{\beta}_r)(\mathbf{b}_r - \boldsymbol{\beta}_r)'\} \\ &= \sigma_u^2(\mathbf{X}_r'\mathbf{X}_r)^{-1} + (\mathbf{X}_r'\mathbf{X}_r)^{-1}\mathbf{X}_r'\mathbf{X}_{k-r}\mathbf{V}\mathbf{X}_{k-r}'\mathbf{X}_r(\mathbf{X}_r'\mathbf{X}_r)^{-1} \end{aligned} \tag{5-91}$$

The first term on the right-hand side of (5-91) is the conventional expression for the variance–covariance matrix of a least-squares estimator and the second shows the elements by which this must be adjusted because of the uncertainty attaching to the coefficients used in the adjustment of Y. The only remaining practical problem is the estimation of σ_u^2. This should be estimated as $\mathbf{e}'\mathbf{e}/(n - k)$, where $\mathbf{e} = \mathbf{y}^* - \mathbf{X}_r\mathbf{b}_r = \mathbf{y} - \mathbf{X}_r\mathbf{b}_r - \mathbf{X}_{k-r}\mathbf{b}_{k-r}$, and we note that we divide by $(n - k)$ rather than $(n - r)$ since $\mathbf{e}$ depends on k estimated parameters.[1]

In many situations the econometrician has no control over his data and must make the best estimates he can from the data available. In the fortunate cases where new data can be obtained the Farrar–Glauber analysis

[1] Other methods of incorporating prior information are discussed in 7-4 below.

does not give a very precise indication of exactly what data will best break the multicollinearity deadlock, but the problem has recently been solved by Silvey, whose work also contains an illuminating approach to the nature and causes of multicollinearity.[1] Silvey concentrates directly on standard errors and asks the question: What additional data would best reduce any specific standard error?

Under the assumptions of the linear model, $(\mathbf{X}'\mathbf{X})$ is a $k \times k$, symmetric, positive definite matrix. Thus it possesses k positive latent roots $\lambda_1, \lambda_2, \ldots, \lambda_k$. Let $\mathbf{V} = [\mathbf{v}_1\ \mathbf{v}_2 \ldots \mathbf{v}_k]$ be the associated matrix of latent vectors where $\mathbf{v}_i$ denotes the column vector associated with λ_i, that is,

$$(\mathbf{X}'\mathbf{X})\mathbf{v}_i = \lambda_i \mathbf{v}_i \tag{5-92}$$

and we also have

$$\mathbf{V}'\mathbf{V} = \mathbf{V}\mathbf{V}' = \mathbf{I}_k$$

Any linear combination of estimated coefficients can be written $\mathbf{c}'\boldsymbol{\beta}$ where $\mathbf{c}$ is a $k \times 1$ vector of known elements. Since $\mathbf{c}$ contains k elements it can be expressed as a linear combination of the k orthogonal latent vectors, that is,

$$\mathbf{c} = \mathbf{V}\boldsymbol{\alpha} \tag{5-93}$$

where

$$\boldsymbol{\alpha} = \{\alpha_1 \quad \alpha_2 \quad \cdots \quad \alpha_k\}$$

Using (5-93) it is simple to derive

$$\begin{aligned} \operatorname{var}(\mathbf{c}'\hat{\boldsymbol{\beta}}) &= \sigma_u^2 \boldsymbol{\alpha}'\mathbf{V}'(\mathbf{X}'\mathbf{X})^{-1}\mathbf{V}\boldsymbol{\alpha} \\ &= \sigma_u^2 \boldsymbol{\alpha}'\boldsymbol{\Lambda}^{-1}\boldsymbol{\alpha} \end{aligned} \tag{5-94}$$

where

$$\boldsymbol{\Lambda} = \begin{bmatrix} \lambda_1 & 0 & \ldots & 0 \\ 0 & \lambda_2 & \ldots & 0 \\ \vdots & \vdots & & \vdots \\ 0 & 0 & \ldots & \lambda_k \end{bmatrix}$$

that is,

$$\operatorname{var}(\mathbf{c}'\hat{\boldsymbol{\beta}}) = \sigma_u^2\left(\frac{\alpha_1^2}{\lambda_1} + \frac{\alpha_2^2}{\lambda_2} + \cdots + \frac{\alpha_k^2}{\lambda_k}\right) \tag{5-95}$$

[1] S. D. Silvey, "Multicollinearity and Imprecise Estimation," *J. Royal Statist. Soc.*, Series B, vol. 31, pp. 539–552, 1969.

The variance of $(\mathbf{c}'\hat{\boldsymbol{\beta}})$ thus depends inversely on the latent roots of $(\mathbf{X}'\mathbf{X})$, the smaller any λ_i the greater is its contribution to the variance.

If we are interested in a particular coefficient, $\hat{\beta}_i$, then $\mathbf{c}$ has unity in the ith position and zeros elsewhere. From $\mathbf{c} = \mathbf{V}\boldsymbol{\alpha}$ we then have

$$\boldsymbol{\alpha} = \mathbf{V}'\mathbf{c} = \begin{bmatrix} v_{i1} \\ v_{i2} \\ \vdots \\ v_{ik} \end{bmatrix}$$

where $v_{i1}, v_{i2}, \ldots, v_{ik}$ are the elements of the ith *row* of $\mathbf{V}$. Thus

$$\text{var}(\hat{\beta}_i) = \sigma_u^2\left(\frac{v_{i1}^2}{\lambda_1} + \frac{v_{i2}^2}{\lambda_2} + \cdots + \frac{v_{ik}^2}{\lambda_k}\right) \qquad i = 1, \ldots, k \tag{5-96}$$

If new data can be added to the existing sample to give an augmented data matrix $\mathbf{X}_*$ such that $\mathbf{X}_*'\mathbf{X}_*$ has latent roots none of which are less than those of $\mathbf{X}'\mathbf{X}$ and at least one of which is greater then the standard errors of the regression coefficients will be reduced. Clearly also it will, in general, be beneficial to increase smaller latent roots rather than those which are already large.

The root λ_i can be increased by additional data in the $\mathbf{v}_i$ direction, leaving the latent vectors and all other latent roots unchanged. Suppose $\mathbf{X}$ is augmented by another row of the form $d\mathbf{v}_i'$, where d is some nonzero number, to give

$$\mathbf{X}_* = \begin{bmatrix} \mathbf{X} \\ d\mathbf{v}_i' \end{bmatrix}$$

Then

$$\mathbf{X}_*'\mathbf{X}_* = \mathbf{X}'\mathbf{X} + d^2\mathbf{v}_i\mathbf{v}_i'$$

$$\begin{aligned}\mathbf{X}_*'\mathbf{X}_*\mathbf{v}_i &= \mathbf{X}'\mathbf{X}\mathbf{v}_i + d^2\mathbf{v}_i\mathbf{v}_i'\mathbf{v}_i \\ &= (\lambda_i + d^2)\mathbf{v}_i \qquad \text{since } \mathbf{v}_i'\mathbf{v}_i = 1\end{aligned}$$

So $\mathbf{v}_i$ is a latent vector of $\mathbf{X}_*'\mathbf{X}_*$, corresponding to the root $(\lambda_i + d^2)$. Further

$$\begin{aligned}\mathbf{X}_*'\mathbf{X}_*\mathbf{v}_j &= \mathbf{X}'\mathbf{X}\mathbf{v}_j + d^2\mathbf{v}_i\mathbf{v}_i'\mathbf{v}_j \\ &= \lambda_j\mathbf{v}_j \qquad \text{since } \mathbf{v}_i'\mathbf{v}_j = 0\end{aligned}$$

So $\mathbf{v}_j$ is a latent vector of $\mathbf{X}_*'\mathbf{X}_*$ corresponding to root λ_j. Thus the latent vectors of $\mathbf{X}_*'\mathbf{X}_*$ are those of $\mathbf{X}'\mathbf{X}$ and all the latent roots are the same except λ_i which is increased to $(\lambda_i + d^2)$. This merely shows in what direction a new observation should be taken in order to increase a specific latent root. The more important question is what is the optimum direction for improving the precision of estimation of β_i, or more generally, of $\mathbf{c}'\boldsymbol{\beta}$. Silvey's main result is that for improving the precision of estimation of $\mathbf{c}'\boldsymbol{\beta}$ the optimum direction of the new observation is that of the vector

$$(\mathbf{I} + \mathbf{X}'\mathbf{X})^{-1}\mathbf{c}$$

Interested readers are referred to the article for details of the proof.

5-8 SPECIFICATION ERROR

Strictly speaking the term specification error covers any type of error in the specification of the model being estimated, but it has come to be used particularly for errors in specifying the data matrix $\mathbf{X}$.[1] Suppose, as usual, that the true model is

$$\mathbf{y} = \mathbf{X}\boldsymbol{\beta} + \mathbf{u} \tag{5-97}$$

where $\mathbf{X}$ is a data matrix of order $n \times k$. However, instead of using $\mathbf{X}$, the investigator mistakenly employs a data matrix $\overline{\mathbf{X}}$ of order $n \times \bar{k}$. The matrices $\overline{\mathbf{X}}$ and $\mathbf{X}$, will usually have certain columns in common, that is the investigator does include at least some of the correct variables, but they may differ in the exclusion of some relevant variables from $\overline{\mathbf{X}}$ or in the inclusion of irrelevant variables or in incorrect specification of the form in which relevant variables should appear. The investigator would then obtain the least-squares estimator

$$\bar{\mathbf{b}} = (\overline{\mathbf{X}}'\overline{\mathbf{X}})^{-1}\overline{\mathbf{X}}'\mathbf{y} \tag{5-98}$$

Substituting (5-97) in (5-98) we obtain

$$\bar{\mathbf{b}} = (\overline{\mathbf{X}}'\overline{\mathbf{X}})^{-1}\overline{\mathbf{X}}'\mathbf{X}\boldsymbol{\beta} + (\overline{\mathbf{X}}'\overline{\mathbf{X}})^{-1}\overline{\mathbf{X}}'\mathbf{u}$$

so that

$$E(\bar{\mathbf{b}}) = \mathbf{P}\boldsymbol{\beta} \tag{5-99}$$

where

$$\mathbf{P} = (\overline{\mathbf{X}}'\overline{\mathbf{X}})^{-1}\overline{\mathbf{X}}'\mathbf{X} \tag{5-100}$$

If we regress each of the relevant variables $X_1, X_2, \ldots, X_k$ in turn on the set $\overline{\mathbf{X}}$ and arrange the estimated coefficients as column vectors then the result is the matrix $\mathbf{P}$ defined in (5-100).

To illustrate the meaning of (5-99) suppose that $\overline{\mathbf{X}}$ differs from $\mathbf{X}$ merely in the exclusion of $(k - r)$ relevant variables $X_{r+1}, X_{r+2}, \ldots, X_k$.

[1] See H. Theil, "Specification Errors and the Estimation of Economic Relationships," *Rev. Intern. Statist. Inst.*, vol. 25, pp. 41–51, 1957, on which this section is based.

Thus

$$\mathbf{X} = [\mathbf{x}_1 \ldots \mathbf{x}_r \mathbf{x}_{r+1} \ldots \mathbf{x}_k]$$

and

$$\bar{\mathbf{X}} = [\mathbf{x}_1 \ldots \mathbf{x}_r]$$

where $\mathbf{x}_i$ denotes the column vector of sample observations on the variable X_i. In this case $\mathbf{P}$ is the $(r \times k)$ matrix

$$\mathbf{P} = \begin{bmatrix} 1 & 0 & \ldots & 0 & p_{1,r+1} & \cdots & p_{1k} \\ 0 & 1 & \ldots & 0 & p_{2,r+1} & \cdots & p_{2k} \\ \vdots & \vdots & & \vdots & \vdots & & \vdots \\ 0 & 0 & \ldots & 1 & p_{r,r+1} & \cdots & p_{rk} \end{bmatrix} \tag{5-101}$$

for if X_i belongs to $\bar{\mathbf{X}}$, regressing X_i on $\bar{\mathbf{X}}$ gives a regression coefficient of unity for X_i and zero for all the remaining explanatory variables. The last $(k - r)$ columns of $\mathbf{P}$ show the regression coefficients when $X_{r+1}, \ldots, X_k$ are each regressed on $\bar{\mathbf{X}}$. Combining (5-99) and (5-101) the bias in any estimated coefficient can be obtained as

$$E(\bar{b}_i) = \beta_i + p_{i,r+1}\beta_{r+1} + \cdots + p_{ik}\beta_k \tag{5-102}$$

so that the estimated regression coefficients will be biased estimates of the true coefficients, the extent of the biases depending on the correlations between the included and excluded variables and the β_j of the excluded variables. On the other hand, if $\bar{\mathbf{X}}$ is of order $n \times s$ $(s > k)$ and differs from $\mathbf{X}$ merely on the inclusion of $(s - k)$ irrelevant variables, then $\mathbf{P}$ is the $(s \times k)$ matrix

$$\mathbf{P} = \begin{bmatrix} \mathbf{I} \\ \mathbf{0} \end{bmatrix} \tag{5-103}$$

where $\mathbf{I}$ is the unit matrix of order k and $\mathbf{0}$ the null matrix of order $(s - k) \times k$. The estimated coefficients will here be unbiased estimates of the true coefficients. The contrast between (5-101) and (5-103) shows clearly that the *exclusion* of relevant variables from the regression may be a very serious error: not only may the estimated coefficients be seriously biased, but inferences based on them will also be inaccurate since the estimate of the residual variance will be biased upwards. Data and degrees of freedom permitting, one should err on the side of including variables in the regression analysis rather than excluding them. Formula (5-102) should also serve as a warning against concluding naïvely that least-squares automatically gives best linear unbiased estimates: it does if the assumptions (5-2) and (5-4a) to (5-4d) are fulfilled. This section has examined just one situation in which the least-squares estimates will be biased; succeeding sections and chapters will demonstrate the great variety of other things that can go wrong.

REFERENCES

The most comprehensive treatment of the topics covered in this chapter is available in

1. Franklin A. Graybill: *An Introduction to Linear Statistical Models*, McGraw-Hill, New York, 1961, vol. I, Chaps. 5–10.
2. R. L. Anderson and T. A. Bancroft: *Statistical Theory in Research*, McGraw-Hill, New York, 1952, Chaps. 14-16.
3. Oscar Kempthorne: *The Design and Analysis of Experiments*, Wiley, New York, 1952, Chap. 5.

EXERCISES

5-1. A study of the demand for a particular commodity, based on annual data for 21 years, yields the following results:

Means	*Standard deviations*	*Correlation coefficients*
$\bar{X} = 51.843$ $\bar{Y} = 8.313$ $\bar{T} = 0$	$s_X = 9.205$ $s_Y = 1.780$ $s_T = 6.057$	$r_{XY} = -0.9158$ $r_{YT} = -0.8696$ $r_{XT} = 0.9304$

where X = per capita consumption, lb
Y = deflated price, cents per lb
T = time, years

(a) Compute the coefficient of time in the estimated relationship between Y and X and T.
(b) Test whether this coefficient differs significantly from zero.
(c) Explain briefly the economic significance of the inclusion of time as an explanatory variable. (Manchester, 1960)

5-2.

Year	*Production of sugar beet,* 1,000 tons	*Mean July temperature,* °F	*Mean rainfall,* in.
1945	470	62	33
1946	520	62	42
1947	560	63	32
1948	510	61	38
1949	500	64	31
1950	550	61	40
1951	630	62	44
1952	640	63	36
1953	650	61	30
1954	620	58	43

Find the partial correlations of the production of sugar beet on the other two variables. Discuss the meaning of your results. (Cambridge, Economics Tripos, Part II, 1956)

5-3. All the variables of a set X are standardized, and their matrix of correlations **R** is known. Find formulae for the set of regression equations and for the partial correlations in terms of matrices and determinants derived from **R**. (Cambridge, Economics Tripos, Part II, 1956) (*Note*: Standardization is the expression of a variable in standard deviation units so that the standard deviation of the transformed variables is unity. This transformation affects the regression coefficients, but not the partial correlation coefficients. For example, if in the two-variable case we define $Y' = Y/s_Y$ and X/s_X, the relation

$$Y = \hat{\alpha} + \hat{\beta}X$$

becomes

$$Y' = \frac{\hat{\alpha}}{s_Y} + \left(\hat{\beta}\frac{s_X}{s_Y}\right)X'$$

As shown in (2-41), $\hat{\beta} = rs_Y/s_X$; hence the coefficient of X' is simply r.)

5-4. It is desired to investigate the effect of climate, to be measured either by direct meteorological observation or by its secondary effects, such as plant development, on the incidence of a disease of bees.

X_1	X_2	X_3	Y
35	53	200	49
35	53	212	40
38	50	211	41
40	64	212	46
40	70	203	52
42	68	194	59
44	59	194	53
46	73	188	61
50	59	196	55
50	71	190	64

where X_1 = mean January temperature, °F
X_2 = mean June temperature, °F
X_3 = date of flowering of a particular summer-flowering species (days from January 1)
Y = percentage of hives affected by disease

Investigate the regression of Y on X_1, X_2, and X_3. (Oxford, Diploma, 1955)

5-5. Commenting on the British demand for imported potatoes, Stone finds that "the own-price (substitution) elasticity is greater than unity—and is matched by a substitution elasticity of the same order of magnitude with respect to the price of home produced potatoes. A large negative trend is found ...." Assuming the two elasticities to be of equal magnitude, estimate that magnitude and also the percentage trend in the demand per annum from the figures given in the table.

Quantities and prices of potatoes purchased in Great Britain, 1920–1938

Year	*Imports purchased for final consumption or by producers*		*Home produce, pence per 7 lb*
	1000 tons Q	*Pence per 7 lb* P	P'
1920	307	26.8	13.1
1922	155	26.6	7.8
1924	363	16.3	10.8
1926	273	14.5	7.4
1928	383	13.9	8.0
1930	232	12.5	5.7
1932	626	10.0	8.0
1934	124	18.4	6.2
1936	255	13.2	7.5
1938	117	19.0	6.8

Source: J. R. N. Stone, *The Measurement of Consumers' Expenditure and Behaviour in the United Kingdom, 1920–1938*, Cambridge, London, 1953, vol. 1. (Oxford Diploma, 1955)
(*Note*: Stone's procedure is to fit functions linear in the logarithms of the variables, that is, constant elasticity functions.)

5-6. The table below shows the forecasts F_{1t} and F_{2t} made by two different forecasting techniques of the volume of United Kingdom imports of iron ore in a series of years, and also Y_t, the figure afterward published. Which would you consider the better technique? If you were to use a weighted average of the forecasts to obtain a better forecast, what weighted average would you use? It has been suggested that a useful standard by which to judge a technique of forecasting is to compare its performance with a "naive" forecast, $F_{3t} = Y_{t-1}$. Do you consider such a comparison useful?

United Kingdom imports of iron ore, million tons

	1946	1947	1948	1949	1950	1951	1952	1953	1954
Y_t	6.5	6.8	8.7	8.7	8.4	8.8	9.7	11.0	11.6
F_{1t}	5.0	6.3	8.0	8.6	8.7	8.9	9.4	9.9	11.0
F_{2t}	6.2	6.7	8.5	9.0	9.0	9.2	9.9	11.1	12.0

(Oxford Diploma, 1957)

5-7. The following weight measurements on a pig were taken at weekly intervals. Fit a polynomial growth curve up to the third degree, testing the necessity of the cubic term.

Week	Weight, lb	Week	Weight, lb	Week	Weight, lb
1	48	7	94	13	158
2	54	8	104	14	170
3	60	9	112	15	181
4	67	10	124	16	192
5	76	11	134	17	204
6	86	12	144		

(Oxford Diploma, 1959)

5-8. In a certain chemical process the impurity Y present in the product varies considerably from day to day, and this is thought to be associated with the strength X_1 of one of the ingredients. From 67 pairs of values of Y and X_1 the following quantities are calculated:

$$\Sigma(Y-\bar{Y})^2 = 1.16 \qquad \Sigma(Y-\bar{Y})(X_1-\bar{X}_1) = -8 \qquad \Sigma(X_1-\bar{X}_1)^2 = 100$$

(a) Find the least-squares coefficient b, of Y on X_1, and estimate its standard error.

It is observed that the time X_2 for which the mixture has to be heated to complete the reaction also varies. For the same set of data,

$$\Sigma(X_2-\bar{X}_2)^2 = 100 \qquad \Sigma(X_1-\bar{X}_1)(X_2-\bar{X}_2) = -80 \qquad \Sigma(Y-\bar{Y})(X_2-\bar{X}_2) = 10$$

(b) Find the coefficients of X_1 and X_2 in the least-squares relationship of Y on X_1 and X_2 and estimate their standard errors.

(c) Why does the coefficient of X_1 in part (b) differ from that in part (a), and what conclusions about the process do you draw from your calculations in parts (a) and (b)?

(R.S.S. Diploma, 1955)

5-9. In a study of 89 firms, the dependent variable was total cost (X_1) with explanatory variables, rate of output (X_2), and rate of absenteeism (X_3). The means were

$$\bar{X}_1 = 5.8 \qquad \bar{X}_2 = 2.9 \qquad \bar{X}_3 = 3.9$$

and the matrix showing sums of squares and cross products adjusted for means is

$$\begin{array}{c} \\ X_1 \\ X_2 \\ X_3 \end{array}\begin{array}{c} \begin{array}{ccc} X_1 & X_2 & X_3 \end{array} \\ \begin{bmatrix} 113.6 & 36.8 & 39.1 \\ & 50.5 & -66.2 \\ & & 967.1 \end{bmatrix}\end{array}$$

Estimate the relationship between X_1 and the other two variables. Set up an analysis-of-variance table to show the reduction in the total sum of squares due to fitting X_2, the additional reduction due to fitting X_3, and the total reduction due to X_2 and X_3 together. Test the overall effect and the partial X_3 effect, given X_2. (Manchester, 1960)

5-10. The following matrix gives the variances and covariances of the three variables:

X_1 = log food consumption per capita

X_2 = log food price

X_3 = log disposable income per capita

$$\begin{array}{c} \\ X_1 \\ X_2 \\ X_3 \end{array}\begin{array}{c} \begin{array}{ccc} X_1 & X_2 & X_3 \end{array} \\ \begin{bmatrix} 7.59 & 3.12 & 26.99 \\ & 29.16 & 30.80 \\ & & 133.00 \end{bmatrix}\end{array}$$

On the assumption that the demand relationship may be adequately represented by a function of the form $Y_1 = AY_2^{\alpha}Y_3^{\beta}$ (where $X_i = \log Y_i$), estimate the income elasticity of demand and compute a 95 per cent confidence interval for this coefficient, based on a sample of 20 observations.

5-11. In a study of production costs at 62 coal mines, data were obtained on costs per ton (X_1), degrees of mechanization (X_2), a measure of geological difficulty (X_3), and percentage of absenteeism (X_4). Defining

$$Z_i = \log X_i \qquad i = 1, 2, 3$$
$$Z_4 = X_4$$

the matrix of zero-order correlations for the Z's were

$$\begin{array}{c} \\ Z_1 \\ Z_2 \\ Z_3 \\ Z_4 \end{array} \begin{array}{c} \begin{array}{cccc} Z_1 & Z_2 & Z_3 & Z_4 \end{array} \\ \begin{bmatrix} 1.0000 & 0.3597 & 0.5749 & 0.4109 \\ & 1.0000 & 0.4630 & 0.3050 \\ & & 1.0000 & 0.2702 \\ & & & 1.0000 \end{bmatrix} \end{array}$$

Discuss the influence of these variables on production costs, performing any calculations or tests you consider desirable.

5-12. Derive equations (5-72).

5-13. Derive (5-79) from (5-77) and (5-78).

5-14. Estimate the coefficients of the relation

$$Y = \beta_1 + \beta_2 X_2 + \beta_3 X_3 + u$$

subject to the restriction $\hat{\beta}_2 = \hat{\beta}_3$, where data from 23 observations in deviation form yield

$$\mathbf{X'X} = \begin{bmatrix} 20 & 0 \\ 0 & 40 \end{bmatrix} \qquad \mathbf{X'y} = \begin{bmatrix} 15 \\ 25 \end{bmatrix}$$

5-15. Consider the model

$$Y_t = \beta_1 + \beta_2 x_{2t} + \beta_3 x_{3t} + u_t \qquad (t = 1, \ldots, n)$$

with

$$\begin{aligned} E(u_t) &= 0 && \text{for all } t \\ E(u_t u_s) &= \sigma^2 && \text{if } t = s \\ &= 0 && \text{if } t \neq s \end{aligned}$$

and x_2 and x_3 are such that $\sum_t x_{2t} = \sum x_{3t} = 0$. From independent data an unbiased estimate b_3 of β_3 is available with var $(b_3) = v^2$. Show that the regression coefficient of the ordinary least-squares regression of $(Y - b_3 x_3)$ on x_2 has variance

$$\frac{\sigma^2}{\Sigma x_2^2} + v^2 b_{32}^2$$

where b_{32} is the slope in the regression of x_3 on x_2. (This is a simple illustration of (5-79) but the reader should also work it out from first principles.)

5-16. Derive (5-33).

5-17. Derive (5-39).

5-18. Show that (5-36) and (5-37) are equivalent to (3-26) and (3-27).

5-19. Given

$$(\mathbf{X}'\mathbf{X}) = \begin{bmatrix} 2 & 0 & \frac{1}{2} \\ 0 & 2 & \sqrt{\frac{3}{2}} \\ \frac{1}{2} & \sqrt{\frac{3}{2}} & 2 \end{bmatrix}$$

find the latent roots of $(\mathbf{X}'\mathbf{X})$ and by the methods of section 5-7 compute the sampling variances of $\hat{\beta}_2$, $\hat{\beta}_3$, and $\hat{\beta}_4$ (taking $\sigma_u^2 = 1$) in the linear model $Y = \beta_2 X_2 + \beta_3 X_3 + \beta_4 X_4 + u$ and check by the conventional formula. In what direction should a new observation be obtained to increase λ_1?

5-20. The true model is $\mathbf{y} = \mathbf{X}\boldsymbol{\beta} + \mathbf{u}$ but an investigator mistakenly postulates $\mathbf{y} = \mathbf{X}\boldsymbol{\beta} + \mathbf{Z}\boldsymbol{\gamma} + \mathbf{u}$ where $\mathbf{Z}$ is a matrix of erroneously included variables. Letting $\mathbf{b}$ denote the estimate of $\boldsymbol{\beta}$ obtained by applying least-squares to the incorrectly specified model, derive the variance–covariance matrix for $\mathbf{b}$. What can be said about the efficiency of these estimates compared with the estimates obtained by applying least-squares to the true model?

5-21. From a set of 20 observations on the four variables $x_i (i = 0, 1, 2, 3)$ the following covariance matrix is calculated

$$[\text{cov}(x_i, x_j)] = \begin{bmatrix} 13 & 12 & 15 & 27 \\ 12 & 14 & 10 & 24 \\ 15 & 10 & 16 & 26 \\ 27 & 24 & 26 & 50 \end{bmatrix}$$

By considering the regression of x_0 on x_1, x_2, and x_3, predict the effect on x_0 of the following changes:

(a) $\Delta x_1 = 1 \qquad \Delta x_2 = -1 \qquad \Delta x_3 = 0$

(b) $\Delta x_1 = 1 \qquad \Delta x_2 = -1 \qquad \Delta x_3 = 2$

(Cambridge Economics Tripos, 1968)

5-22. "In the general linear regression model $\mathbf{y} = \mathbf{X}\boldsymbol{\beta} + \mathbf{u}$ the X-variables are often called the *independent* variables, the columns of $\mathbf{X}$ are assumed to be *linearly independent*, and the elements of $\mathbf{u}$ are assumed to be *independently distributed* random variables."

Explain what is meant by "independent" in each of those three uses and the role which each concept of independence plays in the theory of estimating the elements of $\boldsymbol{\beta}$.

(Cambridge Economics Tripos, 1967)

6
Extensions of the General Linear Model

6-1 DUMMY VARIABLES

In the general linear equation $\mathbf{y} = \mathbf{X}\boldsymbol{\beta} + \mathbf{u}$ we have assumed so far that the X variables are cardinal variables given by economic theory. Some or all of the X's may be nonlinear functions of other variables, for example, $X_i = \sqrt{Z_i}$, $X_j = \log Z_j$, $X_k = 1/Z_k$ and so forth, but the model is still linear in the β's and the properties of ordinary least-squares (OLS) apply. However, we can substantially extend the range and usefulness of the linear model by, on occasion, expanding the X matrix to include dummy variables. These are specially constructed variables which may be used to represent various factors such as

— temporal effects

— spatial effects

— qualitative variables

— broad groupings of quantitative variables.

Under the heading of temporal effects we sometimes postulate that a behavioral relation shifts between one period and another; for example, the consumption function might be expected to show a downward shift in wartime compared with its peacetime position, or a wage-determination equation might shift with a change of political regime or many relations may be expected to show seasonal shifts, if we are dealing with quarterly or monthly data. Spatially we sometimes expect shifts in economic functions between one region of a country and another as a consequence of regional differences in economic structure and prospects. Then qualitative variables such as sex, marital status, social or occupational class will often play an important role in determining economic behavior and must be incorporated in the estimation process. Finally, we may sometimes have fully cardinal variables such as income or age but a broad grouping may be sufficient for the purpose in hand. All of these cases may be handled by the specification of appropriate dummy variables.

To illustrate the detailed working let us consider the very simple example of a wartime and peacetime consumption function. We postulate

$$C = \alpha_1 + \beta Y + u \qquad \text{(wartime)} \tag{6-1a}$$

$$C = \alpha_2 + \beta Y + u \qquad \text{(peacetime)} \tag{6-1b}$$

with $\alpha_2 > \alpha_1$. Notice that the model postulates a common marginal propensity to consume in both periods. If β is not common to both there is nothing to be gained by using dummy variables; one merely fits (6-1a) to wartime data and (6-1b) to peacetime data. However, if we do assume a common β then it is sensible to use *all* the data to obtain as efficient an estimate as possible of this coefficient. This may be done by combining (6-1a) and (6-1b) into a single relationship

$$C = \alpha_1 X_1 + \alpha_2 X_2 + \beta Y + u \tag{6-2}$$

where the X's are dummy variables such that

$$X_1 = 1 \text{ in each wartime year}$$

$$= 0 \text{ in each peacetime year}$$

$$X_2 = 0 \text{ in each wartime year}$$

$$= 1 \text{ in each peacetime year}$$

A single regression is then run with C as the dependent variable and data matrix

$$\begin{bmatrix} 0 & 1 & Y_1 \\ 0 & 1 & Y_2 \\ 1 & 0 & Y_3 \\ 1 & 0 & Y_4 \\ 1 & 0 & Y_5 \\ 0 & 1 & Y_6 \\ 0 & 1 & Y_7 \\ \vdots & \vdots & \vdots \\ 0 & 1 & Y_n \end{bmatrix} \tag{6-3}$$

where we assume that the sample period consisted of two years of peace followed by three of war followed again by peace. Taking conditional expectations with respect to war- and peacetime years gives

$$E(C|X_2 = 0) = \alpha_1 + \beta Y$$

$$E(C|X_2 = 1) = \alpha_2 + \beta Y$$

so that the first coefficient in (6-2) estimates the wartime intercept, the second the peacetime intercept and the third the common marginal propensity to consume. Notice that the distinction between war and peace may be given unambiguously in terms of either dummy variable.

The dummy variable trap At this stage we must warn the reader of the dummy variable trap. If explanatory variables such as those on the right-hand side of Eq. (6-2) are used in conjunction with a regression program that automatically produces an intercept term, then the estimating procedure breaks down, for this is equivalent to using an expanded data matrix with four columns in which the first is a column of units and the remaining three columns are those specified in (6-3). A linear dependence then exists between the columns, that is,

$$\text{col}\,(1) - \text{col}\,(2) - \text{col}\,(3) + 0 \cdot \text{col}\,(4) = \mathbf{0}$$

so that $(\mathbf{X}'\mathbf{X})$ is singular. However, when other explanatory variables are combined with the dummy variables it can sometimes happen that rounding errors in the machine can produce a computed $(\mathbf{X}'\mathbf{X})$ matrix, which is nearly but not quite singular, so that the computation proceeds and estimated coefficients and other statistics such as R^2 are produced which may not violate any *a priori* constraints and the unwary investigator may not realize that anything is wrong.

If the computer program does produce an intercept then one way to deal with it is to write (6-2) as

$$C = \gamma_1 + \gamma_2 X_2 + \beta Y + u \tag{6-4}$$

where

$$X_2 = 0 \text{ in each wartime year}$$
$$= 1 \text{ in each peacetime year}$$

Again taking conditional expectations of (6-4)

$$E(C|X_2 = 0) = \gamma_1 + \beta Y$$
$$E(C|X_2 = 1) = \gamma_1 + \gamma_2 + \beta Y$$

so we see by comparison with the previous relation that

$$\gamma_1 = \alpha_1 = \text{wartime intercept}$$
$$\gamma_1 + \gamma_2 = \alpha_2 = \text{peacetime intercept}$$

and

$$\gamma_2 = \alpha_2 - \alpha_1 = \text{difference between the peacetime and wartime intercepts}$$

Care must be exercised in carrying out significance tests on the coefficients of dummy variables. If (6-4) has been fitted the conventional test of significance on γ_1 is testing whether the wartime intercept is significantly different from zero. The same test on γ_2 is testing whether there is any significant difference between the wartime and peacetime intercepts. If we wish to test whether the peacetime intercept is significantly different from zero, the hypothesis is $(\gamma_1 + \gamma_2) = 0$ so we add the estimated coefficients to obtain $(\hat{\gamma}_1 + \hat{\gamma}_2)$ and compare this sum with the estimated standard error

$$\sqrt{\text{var}(\hat{\gamma}_1) + \text{var}(\hat{\gamma}_2) + 2\,\text{cov}(\hat{\gamma}_1, \hat{\gamma}_2)}$$

where the three terms in the standard error are obtained from the variance–covariance matrix.

Many examples of this use of dummy variables can be found in econometric studies. In Stone's analysis of prewar U.K. budget data for a sample of civil servants and manual workers a dummy variable was inserted to allow the civil servant's expenditure function to have a higher intercept than that of the manual workers.[1] The Oxford Econometric Model of the U.K. contained a dummy variable in several equations to allow for a possible difference in wage behavior under the postwar Labour government.[2] The

[1] J. R. N. Stone: *The Measurement of Consumers' Expenditure and Behaviour in the United Kingdom, 1920–1938*. Cambridge, London, 1954.

[2] L. R. Klein, *et al.*: *An Econometric Model of the United Kingdom*, Blackwell, Oxford, 1961.

Klein–Shinkai Econometric Model of Japan takes the years 1930–1936, 1951–1958 as a single sample period but a dummy variable is inserted in each relation to allow for the possibility of a structural shift between the first sub-period and the second.[1] In cases of this kind it can sometimes happen that the structural shift plays a major role in determining the explained sum of squares, which means that the economic variables are playing a minor role *within* each sub-period. As a consequence the predictive power of various relations may be almost totally uncorrelated with the R^2's in the sample period, and the investigator may incorrectly conclude that he has achieved a satisfactory *economic* explanation of the variable under study.[2]

Two or more sets of dummy variables Sometimes we wish to incorporate two or more sets of dummy variables in a regression. For example, suppose that we have cross-sectional budget data for a number of quarters and we postulate that the consumption (q) of some commodity is given by

$q = f$ (Seasonal Dummies, Social Class Factors, Other Economic Variables)

If there are four seasons and three social classes then one way to set up this relation is

$$q = \alpha_1 + \alpha_2 Q_2 + \alpha_3 Q_3 + \alpha_4 Q_4 + \beta_2 S_2 + \beta_3 S_3 + \gamma_1 X_1 + \cdots + \gamma_k X_k + u \tag{6-5}$$

where

$$Q_i = 1 \text{ if the observation relates to Quarter } i \qquad i = 2, 3, 4$$
$$= 0 \text{ otherwise}$$
$$S_j = 1 \text{ if the observation relates to Social Class } j \qquad j = 2, 3$$
$$= 0 \text{ otherwise}$$

and $X_1, \ldots, X_k$ denote the set of economic variables, such as income and relative prices. It is important to notice here that we must drop one dummy variable from *each* set if we are using an intercept term, otherwise we would once again produce a linear dependence in the data matrix. Care must be taken in the interpretation of the α and β coefficients. If an observation relates to a household from Social Class I in the first quarter all dummy variables are zero and the intercept term is simply α_1. For Social Class I and the second quarter the intercept is $(\alpha_1 + \alpha_2)$; for Social Class III and the

[1] L. R. Klein and Y. Shinkai, "An Econometric Model of Japan, 1930–59," *Intern. Econ. Rev.*, vol. 4, pp. 1–28, 1963.

[2] This point has been brought out in T. Blumenthal, "A Test of the Klein–Shinkai Econometric Model of Japan," *Intern. Econ. Rev.*, vol. 6, pp. 211–228, 1965.

fourth quarter it is $(\alpha_1 + \alpha_4 + \beta_3)$ and so forth. Thus α_2, α_3 and α_4 represent differential seasonal effects compared with the first quarter and β_2, β_3 differential class effects compared with the first class. The differential effect of, say, the fourth quarter contrasted with the second quarter is given by $(\alpha_4 - \alpha_2)$ and the differential effect of Social Class III compared with Social Class II is given by $(\beta_3 - \beta_2)$.

Another common application of this type occurs in the estimation of production functions. Suppose we have data on output (Y) and inputs (X) for m firms over n years and we wish to estimate a production function. In doing so we might allow specifically for "year effects" and "firm effects" by fitting

$$Y_{ij} = \alpha_1 + \alpha_2 T_2 + \cdots + \alpha_n T_n + \beta_2 F_2 + \cdots + \beta_m F_m + \mathbf{x}_{ij}\gamma + u_{ij} \quad (6\text{-}6)$$

where Y_{ij} indicates the output of the jth firm in year i, the $\mathbf{x}_{ij}$ the row vector of input variables for the jth firm in year i, γ the common set of coefficients for inputs and

$$T_i = 1 \text{ for all firms in year } i \qquad i = 2, \ldots, n$$
$$= 0 \text{ otherwise}$$

$$F_j = 1 \text{ for firm } j \text{ in all years} \qquad j = 2, \ldots, m$$
$$= 0 \text{ otherwise}$$

Equation (6-6) postulates that all firms react in the same way to the economic inputs and that in addition there can be differential shifts in the function between firms and between years.

Interaction Neither Eq. (6-5) nor (6-6) allows for any interaction between the different sets of dummy variables; the effect of any pair of values of dummy variables is assumed to be the sum of the two separate effects. Interaction, however, can be allowed for by introducing additional dummy variables. For example, suppose we distinguish three educational levels and two sex categories. Without interaction we would need three dummy variables in addition to the intercept term. Two more dummy variables adequately cater for possible interactions. This is shown in Table 6-1. X_1 is the usual intercept variable, X_2 and X_3 the two educational level variables and X_4 the sex variable: X_5 and X_6 allow the differential sex effect to be different at all three educational levels, where X_5 and X_6 have been obtained by multiplying X_2 and X_3 respectively by X_4.

Table 6-1

Educational level	*Sex*	*Dummy variables*					
		X_1	X_2	X_3	X_4	X_5	X_6
1	1	1	0	0	0	0	0
1	2	1	0	0	1	0	0
2	1	1	1	0	0	0	0
2	2	1	1	0	1	1	0
3	1	1	0	1	0	0	0
3	2	1	0	1	1	0	1

Suppose, for example, that we regard a dependent variable Y, the number of hours in a year spent in reading nonfiction, as dependent on the two qualitative variables, sex and educational attainment as defined in Table 6-1. Our postulated relationship is then

$$Y = \beta_1 X_1 + \beta_2 X_2 + \cdots + \beta_6 X_6 + u$$

If we use the symbol $E(Y|\text{II}, \text{I})$ to indicate the expected value of Y, given educational level II and sex classification I, we see from Table 6-1 and the postulated relation that

$$E(Y|\text{I}, \text{I}) = \beta_1$$

$$E(Y|\text{I}, \text{II}) = \beta_1 + \beta_4$$

$$E(Y|\text{II}, \text{I}) = \beta_1 + \beta_2$$

$$E(Y|\text{II}, \text{II}) = \beta_1 + \beta_2 + \beta_4 + \beta_5$$

$$E(Y|\text{III}, \text{I}) = \beta_1 + \beta_3$$

$$E(Y|\text{III}, \text{II}) = \beta_1 + \beta_3 + \beta_4 + \beta_6$$

This scheme allows for interaction effects. Thus the difference between the sexes for people of educational level I is β_4; for people of educational level II, it is $\beta_4 + \beta_5$; and for people at level III, it is $\beta_4 + \beta_6$. Similarly, for people of sex I, the differential effect of educational level II compared with I is β_2; of III compared with I, β_3; and of III compared with II, $\beta_3 - \beta_2$. For people of sex II, these same three differential effects are, respectively,

$$\beta_2 + \beta_5, \beta_3 + \beta_6, \quad \text{and} \quad \beta_3 + \beta_6 - \beta_2 - \beta_5$$

So far our dummy variables, taking on values of zero and unity, have been confined to the right-hand side of the relationship, but there is no reason why the dependent variable itself might not have this form. For example, a person owns a car or does not, he has a mortgage on his home or he does not, and so forth. In all such cases the dependent variable takes on only two values, so that we may use unity to indicate the occurrence of the event and zero to indicate its nonoccurrence. If we run a multiple regression of such a dependent variable Y on several explanatory variables X, then we may interpret the calculated value of Y, for any given X, as an estimate of the *conditional* probability of Y, given X. The most extensive application of this approach in econometrics is due to Guy H. Orcutt and his associates at the Social Systems Research Institute of the University of Wisconsin.[1] The work of the Institute is concerned with the integration of sociological and other variables with the more orthodox economic variables in the study of the dynamics of socioeconomic systems, and since many of these variables, whether explanatory or dependent, are of qualitative form, the use of dummy variables with conventional regression analysis is a natural development.

In a study of the mortgage-debt holdings of United States spending units, Orcutt and Rivlin have split the problem into two parts. First they develop a prediction equation for the *probability* that a spending unit has mortgage debt, and then for spending units with a nonzero mortgage debt they develop a prediction equation for the *amount* of mortgage debt.[2] The first equation, based on data from the Survey of Consumer Finances, is

$$\hat{Y}_1 = -0.08 + F_{1\cdot 1} + F_{1\cdot 2} + F_{1\cdot 3} + F_{1\cdot 4}$$

where $\hat{Y}_1$ is the predicted probability that a spending unit will hold mortgage debt, and the values of functions $F_{1\cdot 1}$, $F_{1\cdot 2}$, etc., are obtained from the following tables.

$F_{1\cdot 1}$ (*marital status*)		$F_{1\cdot 2}$ (*age of head*)	
Marital status	$F_{1\cdot 1}$	*Age of head*	$F_{1\cdot 2}$
Unmarried	0	18–20	0
1 year	0.07	21–24	−0.02
2 years	0.15	25–29	0.09
3 years	0.19	30–34	0.16
4 years	0.27	35–39	0.25
5–9 years	0.31	40–44	0.22
10–20 years	0.25	45–49	0.24
Over 20 years	0.14	50–54	0.16
		55–59	0.15
		60–64	0.12
		65+	0.07

[1] See Guy H. Orcutt, Martin Greenberger, John Korbel, and Alice M. Rivlin, *Microanalysis of Socioeconomic Systems: A Simulation Study*, Harper and Row, New York, 1961.
[2] *Ibid.*, Chap. 12.

$F_{1\cdot 3}$ (*education*)		$F_{1\cdot 4}$ (*race*)	
Education of head	$F_{1\cdot 3}$	*Race of head*	$F_{1\cdot 4}$
None	0	White	0
Grammar	0.02	Negro	−0.10
Some high school	0.05	Other	−0.14
High school degree	0.08		
Some college	0.12		
College degree	0.13		

Thus the estimated probability that a spending unit headed by a 32-year-old Negro with some high school education and married for 3 years will have mortgage debt is

$$\hat{Y}_1 = -0.08 + 0.19 + 0.16 + 0.05 - 0.10$$

$$= 0.22$$

For units with a nonzero mortgage debt, the prediction equation for the amount of mortgage debt is

$$\hat{Y}_2 = 3{,}040 + F_{2\cdot 1} + F_{2\cdot 2} + F_{2\cdot 3} + F_{2\cdot 4}$$

where the F functions are now obtained from the following tables.

$F_{2\cdot 1}$ (*marital status*)		$F_{2\cdot 2}$ (*age of head*)	
Marital status	$F_{2\cdot 1}$	*Age of head*	$F_{2\cdot 2}$
Unmarried	0	18–20	0
1 year	4,550	21–24	526
2 years	1,380	25–29	1,290
3 years	1,530	30–34	1,560
4 years	167	35–39	1,200
5–9 years	49	40–44	964
10–20 years	744	45–49	134
Over 20 years	215	50–54	166
		55–59	−1,270
		60–64	−1,140
		65+	−1,000

$F_{2\cdot 3}$ (*education*)		$F_{2\cdot 4}$ (*race*)	
Education	$F_{2\cdot 3}$	*Race*	$F_{2\cdot 4}$
None	0	White	0
Grammar	835	Negro	−1,040
Some high school	1,190	Other	−1,010
High school degree	1,980		
Some college	3,610		
College degree	4,930		

Thus the expected amount of mortgage debt for the same unit as before is

$$\hat{Y}_2 = 3{,}040 + 1{,}530 + 1{,}560 + 1{,}190 - 1{,}040$$

$$= \$6{,}280$$

The basic feature of the second step in this analysis is the absence of any assumption about a precise functional form for the relationship. In both steps the application of least-squares regression corresponds to the estimation of cell means, where the cells are defined by the specified steps in the explanatory variables. For example, for the marital-status variable they use seven dummy variables,

$$X_1 = \begin{cases} 1 & \text{if duration is 1 year} \\ 0 & \text{if duration is not 1 year} \end{cases}$$

$$X_2 = \begin{cases} 1 & \text{if duration is 2 years} \\ 0 & \text{if duration is not 2 years} \end{cases}$$

$$\vdots$$

$$X_7 = \begin{cases} 1 & \text{if duration is over 20 years} \\ 0 & \text{if duration is not over 20 years} \end{cases}$$

Dummy variables are also used to represent the other explanatory variables, and when a regression of Y on all dummy variables is run, the least-squares coefficients of the dummy variables are simply the cell means, which are tabulated in the above functions. The above schemes assume additivity. This is not, of course, necessary, since the dummy-variable approach can be extended to incorporate interaction effects, but the approach does require extensive survey observations if sufficiently fine subdivisions are to be made for the explanatory variables and still leave sufficient observations in each cell to provide reliable estimates of the mean values.[1]

6-2 SEASONAL ADJUSTMENT

Dummy variables play an important role in problems of seasonal adjustment. These problems are of two kinds: first there is the conventional and long-standing problem of deseasonalizing a given quarterly or monthly time series and secondly there is the problem of estimating econometric relationships between variables that are available in both unadjusted and deseasonalized form. Many of the formulae needed in the discussion of the second problem are easily developed in the context of the first and it is to that which we now turn.

Deseasonalization of a single series Suppose we have $4n$ quarterly observations on Y so that Y_{ij} indicates the observation on Y in the jth quarter of the ith year ($i = 1, \ldots, n; j = 1, \ldots, 4$).
Define a ($4n \times 4$) matrix $\mathbf{D}$

$$\mathbf{D} = \begin{bmatrix} 1 & 0 & 0 & 0 \\ 0 & 1 & 0 & 0 \\ 0 & 0 & 1 & 0 \\ 0 & 0 & 0 & 1 \\ 1 & 0 & 0 & 0 \\ 0 & 1 & 0 & 0 \\ \vdots & \vdots & \vdots & \vdots \\ 0 & 0 & 0 & 1 \end{bmatrix} \tag{6-7}$$

and regress $\mathbf{y}$ on $\mathbf{D}$ to obtain

$$\mathbf{y} = \mathbf{Db} + \mathbf{y}^\alpha \tag{6-8}$$

where $\mathbf{b}$ is the vector of least-squares coefficients and $\mathbf{y}^\alpha$ the vector of residuals. Since

$$\mathbf{b} = (\mathbf{D}'\mathbf{D})^{-1}\mathbf{D}'\mathbf{y}$$

$$\mathbf{y}^\alpha = \mathbf{y} - \mathbf{D}(\mathbf{D}'\mathbf{D})^{-1}\mathbf{D}'\mathbf{y}$$

or

$$\mathbf{y}^\alpha = \mathbf{Ay} \tag{6-9}$$

[1] Goldberger has shown that one difficulty with applying classical least squares where Y is dichotomous is that the assumption of homoscedastic disturbances is untenable. See A. S. Goldberger, *Econometric Theory*, Wiley, New York, 1964, pp. 249-250.

where

$$\mathbf{A} = \mathbf{I} - \mathbf{D}(\mathbf{D}'\mathbf{D})^{-1}\mathbf{D}' \tag{6-10}$$

giving $\mathbf{y}^\alpha$ as a linear transformation of $\mathbf{y}$. It is easily seen that $\mathbf{A}$ is symmetric idempotent and that

$$\mathbf{AD} = \mathbf{0} \tag{6-11}$$

The series $\mathbf{y}^\alpha$ cannot serve directly as a deseasonalized series for two reasons. First of all it sums to zero, whereas it would seem plausible to require a deseasonalized series to have the same sum as the uncorrected, original series. Secondly, it can easily be seen from the nature of $\mathbf{D}$ that

$$\mathbf{b} = \begin{bmatrix} \frac{1}{n}\sum_{i=1}^{n} Y_{i1} \\ \frac{1}{n}\sum_{i=1}^{n} Y_{i2} \\ \frac{1}{n}\sum_{i=1}^{n} Y_{i3} \\ \frac{1}{n}\sum_{i=1}^{n} Y_{i4} \end{bmatrix}$$

so that $\mathbf{y}^\alpha$ merely consists of the deviations of the Y values from the quarterly means. If the original series contains trend and cyclical elements these will affect the quarterly means and thus in turn the deseasonalized series.

The first point can be dealt with simply by adding $\bar{Y}$ to $\mathbf{y}^\alpha$, but the second requires a major adjustment. We now postulate that $\mathbf{y}$ is composed of trend, cyclical components, a seasonal component, and a disturbance. Thus $\mathbf{y}$ is now regressed on an expanded matrix $[\mathbf{P} \quad \mathbf{D}]$ where $\mathbf{P}$ is an appropriate set of powers of time, that is,

$$[\mathbf{P} \quad \mathbf{D}] = \left[\begin{array}{cccc|cccc} 1 & 1^2 & \cdots & 1^p & 1 & 0 & 0 & 0 \\ 2 & 2^2 & & 2^p & 0 & 1 & 0 & 0 \\ 3 & 3^2 & & 3^p & 0 & 0 & 1 & 0 \\ 4 & 4^2 & & 4^p & 0 & 0 & 0 & 1 \\ \vdots & \vdots & & \vdots & \vdots & \vdots & \vdots & \vdots \\ 4n & (4n)^2 & \cdots & (4n)^p & 0 & 0 & 0 & 1 \end{array}\right] \tag{6-12}$$

The regression may be written

$$\mathbf{y} = \mathbf{Pa} + \mathbf{Db} + \mathbf{e} \tag{6-13}$$

and the deseasonalized series would be

$$\mathbf{y}^s = \mathbf{y} - \mathbf{Db} \tag{6-14}$$

Jorgenson has argued that if the **P** and **D** matrices are properly specified then **a** and **b** will be best linear unbiased estimates of the systematic and seasonal components since (6-13) is then a straightforward example of ordinary least squares.[1]

The estimates **a** and **b** are given by

$$\begin{bmatrix} \mathbf{a} \\ \mathbf{b} \end{bmatrix} = \begin{bmatrix} \mathbf{P'P} & \mathbf{P'D} \\ \mathbf{D'P} & \mathbf{D'D} \end{bmatrix}^{-1} \begin{bmatrix} \mathbf{P'y} \\ \mathbf{D'y} \end{bmatrix} \tag{6-15}$$

Applying the formula for the inverse of a partitioned matrix one finds

$$\mathbf{b} = (\mathbf{D'MD})^{-1}\mathbf{D'My} \tag{6-16}$$

where

$$\mathbf{M} = \mathbf{I} - \mathbf{P}(\mathbf{P'P})^{-1}\mathbf{P'} \tag{6-17}$$

Substituting in (6-14) gives

$$\mathbf{y}^s = \mathbf{A^*y} \tag{6-18}$$

where

$$\mathbf{A}^* = \mathbf{I} - \mathbf{D}(\mathbf{D'MD})^{-1}\mathbf{D'M} \tag{6-19}$$

so that the deseasonalized series can still be expressed as a linear transformation of **y**. However, in contrast with the **A** matrix defined in (6-10) above $\mathbf{A}^*$ is not symmetric, though it is idempotent and does satisfy the condition $\mathbf{A^*D} = \mathbf{0}$.

As a numerical illustration of these methods we made several estimates of the quarterly seasonal component in the United Kingdom Index of Industrial Production for the period 1948–1957. The results are shown in Table 6-2. The centered four-quarter moving average is a flexible method of removing trend and cycle, and we can take the estimates of the seasonal component in the first row of Table 6-2 as the standard by which to judge the various regressions. It is seen that the simple regression on seasonal dummies alone gives misleading estimates of the seasonal component, apart from the pronounced dip in the third quarter, and it is only when we use a sixth-degree polynomial in time that the results agree fairly closely with those obtained from the moving average method.

[1] D. W. Jorgenson, "Minimum Variance, Linear, Unbiased Seasonal Adjustment of Economic Time Series," *J. Am. Statist. Assoc.*, vol. 59, pp. 681–724, 1964.

Table 6-2 Quarterly seasonal component of the U.K. Index of Industrial Production, 1948–1957

Methods	*Seasonal component*			
	b_1	b_2	b_3	b_4
Moving average (additive)	3.28	0.77	−7.13	3.08
Regression on **D**	1.85	0.35	−7.15	4.95
Regression on [**P** **D**]($p = 4$)	4.87	0.36	−7.17	2.95
Regression on [**P** **D**]($p = 6$)	3.35	0.95	−7.54	3.25

Estimation of econometric relationships When we turn to the estimation of relationships between variables where the data are in quarterly or monthly form the first basic question to decide is whether economic theory gives any indication of the form (that is, unadjusted or deseasonalized) in which each variable should appear in the relation. For example, a salaried worker may have an income which shows no seasonal pattern but his consumption expenditures do show a seasonal pattern, with, say, a major peak in the third quarter due to vacation expenditures. In this case deseasonalized quarterly expenditure might be taken as a function of income and actual expenditure equal to deseasonalized expenditure plus a seasonal component. The appropriate regression would then be actual consumption on income plus a suitable set of seasonal dummies. On the other hand, income itself may contain a seasonal pattern and one which may be different from the seasonal pattern of consumption, as in the case of a worker with income peaks in the winter quarters and expenditure peaks in the summer quarters. The appropriate regression would then be actual consumption on deseasonalized income plus seasonal dummies. In the study of production decisions it is often found that firms attempt to base production rates on "smoothed" or averaged sales figures so that the regression would be actual production as a function of deseasonalized sales. In many cases and especially with macro-variables theory may give no clear guide and as the data are often available in both unadjusted and deseasonalized form it is sometimes difficult to decide in which form to incorporate variables in the regression. In practice, however, the problem of specification turns out to be less important than might have been expected because of an important set of results due to Lovell.[1] To illustrate one of Lovell's basic results, consider two least-squares regressions

$$\mathbf{y} = \mathbf{X}\mathbf{c}_1 + \mathbf{D}\mathbf{b}_1 + \mathbf{e}_1 \tag{6-20}$$

$$\mathbf{y}^{\alpha} = \mathbf{X}^{\alpha}\mathbf{c}_2 + \mathbf{e}_2 \tag{6-21}$$

[1] M. C. Lovell, "Seasonal Adjustment of Economic Time Series," *J. Am. Statist. Assoc.*, vol. 58, pp. 993–1010, 1963.

where

$$\mathbf{y}^{\alpha} = \mathbf{A}\mathbf{y} \quad \text{and} \quad \mathbf{X}^{\alpha} = \mathbf{A}\mathbf{X} \tag{6-22}$$

and

$$\mathbf{A} = \mathbf{I} - \mathbf{D}(\mathbf{D}'\mathbf{D})^{-1}\mathbf{D}' \tag{6-23}$$

Lovell proves that $\mathbf{c}_1 = \mathbf{c}_2$, that is that regressions (6-20) and (6-21) yield exactly the same estimates of the coefficients of the X variables. Notice that Eqs. (6-22) and (6-23) say nothing about the elements of the **D** matrix: all that those equations say is that **y** and **X** have been "adjusted" by means of least-squares regressions on a common data matrix **D**, so that $\mathbf{y}^{\alpha}$ and $\mathbf{X}^{\alpha}$ are the residuals from those regressions. However, it is clear that what Lovell has in mind is that **D** should be the matrix of seasonal dummies defined in (6-7) above.

A simple proof that $\mathbf{c}_1 = \mathbf{c}_2$ is as follows.[1] Since (6-20) is a least-squares regression the coefficients satisfy the usual normal equations[2]

$$\begin{aligned} \mathbf{X}'(\mathbf{y} - \mathbf{X}\mathbf{c}_1 - \mathbf{D}\mathbf{b}_1) &= \mathbf{0} \\ \mathbf{D}'(\mathbf{y} - \mathbf{X}\mathbf{c}_1 - \mathbf{D}\mathbf{b}_1) &= \mathbf{0} \end{aligned} \tag{6-24}$$

Similarly since (6-21) is a least-squares regression

$$(\mathbf{X}^{\alpha})'(\mathbf{y}^{\alpha} - \mathbf{X}^{\alpha}\mathbf{c}_2) = \mathbf{0}$$

that is

$$\mathbf{X}'\mathbf{A}'(\mathbf{A}\mathbf{y} - \mathbf{A}\mathbf{X}\mathbf{c}_2) = \mathbf{0} \tag{6-25}$$

[1] I am indebted to S. D. Silvey for this proof.

[2] For the simple least-squares model, $\mathbf{y} = \mathbf{X}\mathbf{b} + \mathbf{e}$, the normal equation may be written

$$\mathbf{X}'\mathbf{y} = \mathbf{X}'\mathbf{X}\mathbf{b}$$

But premultiplying through $\mathbf{y} = \mathbf{X}\mathbf{b} + \mathbf{e}$ by $\mathbf{X}'$ gives

$$\mathbf{X}'\mathbf{y} = \mathbf{X}'\mathbf{X}\mathbf{b} + \mathbf{X}'\mathbf{e}$$

Thus it is a consequence of the least-squares fit that

$$\mathbf{X}'\mathbf{e} = \mathbf{0}$$

In (6-20) the data matrix is $[\mathbf{X}\ \mathbf{D}]$ and so the condition of zero correlation between the explanatory variables and the residual becomes

$$\begin{bmatrix} \mathbf{X}' \\ \mathbf{D}' \end{bmatrix}(\mathbf{y} - \mathbf{X}\mathbf{c}_1 - \mathbf{D}\mathbf{b}_1) = \mathbf{0}$$

that is

$$\mathbf{X}'(\mathbf{y} - \mathbf{X}\mathbf{c}_1 - \mathbf{D}\mathbf{b}_1) = \mathbf{0}$$

$$\mathbf{D}'(\mathbf{y} - \mathbf{X}\mathbf{c}_1 - \mathbf{D}\mathbf{b}_1) = \mathbf{0}$$

Least-squares estimates are unique, so if $\mathbf{c}_1$ were to satisfy (6-25) $\mathbf{c}_1$ would be equal to $\mathbf{c}_2$. Substitute $\mathbf{c}_1$, therefore, in the left-hand side of (6-25) giving

$$\begin{aligned}\mathbf{X}'\mathbf{A}'(\mathbf{Ay} - \mathbf{AXc}_1) &= \mathbf{X}'\mathbf{A}'(\mathbf{Ay} - \mathbf{AXc}_1 - \mathbf{ADb}_1) \qquad \text{since } \mathbf{AD} = \mathbf{0} \\ &= \mathbf{X}'\mathbf{A}(\mathbf{y} - \mathbf{Xc}_1 - \mathbf{Db}_1) \qquad \text{since } \mathbf{A} \text{ is symmetric idempotent} \\ &= \mathbf{X}'(\mathbf{y} - \mathbf{Xc}_1 - \mathbf{Db}_1) - \mathbf{X}'\mathbf{D}(\mathbf{D}'\mathbf{D})^{-1} \\ &\quad \times \mathbf{D}'(\mathbf{y} - \mathbf{Xc}_1 - \mathbf{Db}_1) \qquad \text{using (6-10)} \\ &= \mathbf{0} \qquad \text{using (6-24)}\end{aligned}$$

so

$$\mathbf{c}_1 = \mathbf{c}_2$$

Two other basic results from Lovell are that the regressions

$$\mathbf{y} = \mathbf{X}^\alpha \mathbf{c}_3 + \mathbf{e}_3 \tag{6-26}$$

$$\mathbf{y} = \mathbf{X}^\alpha \mathbf{c}_4 + \mathbf{Db}_4 + \mathbf{e}_4 \tag{6-27}$$

also yield identical vectors of coefficients for the X variables, that is,

$$\mathbf{c}_1 = \mathbf{c}_2 = \mathbf{c}_3 = \mathbf{c}_4 \tag{6-28}$$

Thus regressing $\mathbf{y}$ on (i) $\mathbf{X}$ and $\mathbf{D}$, (ii) $\mathbf{X}^\alpha$, or (iii) $\mathbf{X}^\alpha$ and $\mathbf{D}$ will in all cases yield identical estimates of the vector of X coefficients, as will regressing $\mathbf{y}^\alpha$ on $\mathbf{X}^\alpha$.

These results raise some further questions. We have already seen that if $\mathbf{D}$ is merely a matrix of seasonal dummies then $\mathbf{y}^\alpha$ and $\mathbf{X}^\alpha$, defined in (6-22), are not, in any meaningful sense, properly deseasonalized series. On the other hand, if properly deseasonalized series are obtained using the transformation matrix, $\mathbf{A}^*$, defined in (6-19), this matrix, though idempotent, does not have the property of symmetry required to prove the equality of $\mathbf{c}_1$ and $\mathbf{c}_2$. One wonders therefore how much difference will appear between $\mathbf{c}_1$ and $\mathbf{c}_2$ when properly deseasonalized series are used in regression (6-21). Secondly, many official series are not deseasonalized by least-squares methods at all, but by moving average or other methods. If such series are used in regression (6-21), for example, will the coefficients differ much from those of regression (6-20)? Some experimental calculations with various equations from the Oxford Econometric Model of the United Kingdom indicate agreement to several decimal places between estimated coefficients whether the regression has been run with uncorrected data and dummy variables or with deseasonalized variables produced by moving average methods or by least-squares regressions on $\mathbf{D}$ or on $[\mathbf{P} \quad \mathbf{D}]$.[1] The years

[1] Athena Georgopoulou and J. Johnston, "Seasonal Adjustment of Economic Time Series," unpublished manuscript.

covered by the model showed fairly steady growth and negligible cyclical oscillations. One would not expect such close agreement if the cyclical effects were very strong, but the results do suggest that Lovell's results probably hold approximately in a fairly wide range of cases. In practical work one should not, however, allow this theorem to be a substitute for careful thought about the proper specification of the relationship, of which variables react to which.

6-3 COVARIANCE ANALYSIS

In Chap. 5 we introduced the analysis of variance table as a method of showing the decomposition of the total sum of squares about the mean of Y into the explained sum of squares due to the complete set of explanatory variables and the unexplained or residual sum of squares; it was also shown that the explained sum of squares could be further decomposed into that attributable to any subset of explanatory variables and the incremental sum of squares due to the remaining explanatory variables. A similar decomposition of sums of squares is used in simple analysis of variance problems to answer rather different questions. Suppose we have sample data

$$Y_{ij} \qquad i = 1, \ldots, p; j = 1, \ldots, m$$

where p denotes the number of classes and m the number of observations per class. For example, the data might refer to incomes in samples of m households taken in p different regions or to the yields of p different varieties of wheat, each variety being grown on m sample plots. The class means

$$\bar{Y}_i = \frac{1}{m} \sum_{j=1}^{m} Y_{ij} \qquad i = 1, \ldots, p$$

may then be computed and the basic question is whether the sample means indicate a significant variation in the Y variable between classes. Clearly the variation observed in Y within classes is an indicator of the inherent stochastic component in Y and thus it can serve as a base against which the variation of the class means can be assessed. It is very easy to show that the total variation in Y can be expressed as the sum of the variation *between* classes and the variation *within* classes, that is,

$$\sum_{ij} (Y_{ij} - \bar{Y})^2 = \sum_{i} m(\bar{Y}_i - \bar{Y})^2 + \sum_{ij} (Y_{ij} - \bar{Y}_i)^2 \tag{6-29}$$

where

$$\bar{Y} = \frac{1}{mp} \sum_{ij} Y_{ij} \text{ is the overall mean}$$

and the appropriate F test for the significance of the variation between class means is

$$F = \frac{\sum_i m(\bar{Y}_i - \bar{Y})^2/(p-1)}{\sum_{ij} (Y_{ij} - \bar{Y}_i)^2/p(m-1)}$$

The validity of this F test, however, depends among other things upon the use of the within-class sum of squares as an indicator of the inherent stochastic component of Y against which significant effects are to be established. Suppose, however, that Y is affected by other variables, which we are not able to control and standardize within classes. For example, different varieties of wheat may have been sown on plots that experienced different rainfalls, or regions may differ markedly in household size and in the opportunities for gainfull employment by married women. In such cases the simple within-class sum of squares will be an overestimate of the stochastic component in Y and also the differences between class means will now reflect not only any class effect but also the effect of any differences in the values assumed by the uncontrolled variables in different classes. For the case of just one uncontrolled (or intervening) variable and two classes the problem is indicated in Fig. 6-1. The ellipses indicate the two scatters and the parallel dotted lines the common regression slope of Y on X. Class II has experienced, on the whole, higher X values than Class I. Consequently, the crude difference between the class means $(\bar{Y}_2 - \bar{Y}_1)$ is an overestimate of the class effect, shown on the diagram by the distance d between the parallel regression lines. If the two classes had experienced the same X values the ellipses would lie vertically beneath one another and $(\bar{Y}_2 - \bar{Y}_1)$ would approximate to d. We notice that the class effect is estimated simply by the difference between the regression intercepts.

It was for this kind of problem that the analysis of covariance was first developed and it essentially consists of correcting statistically for the effects

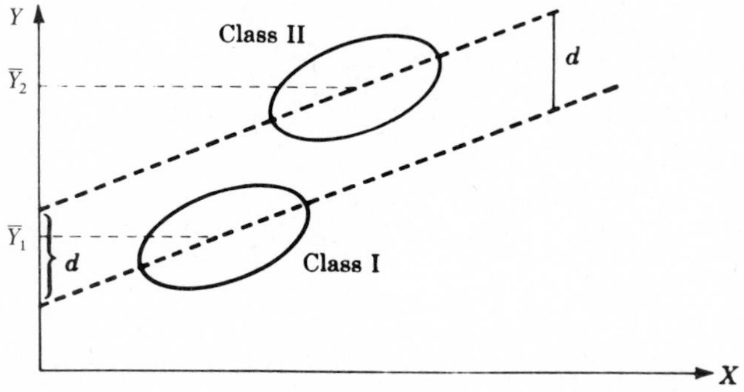

Fig. 6-1.

of uncontrolled variables that could not be properly standardized between classes. In making such statistical corrections it is plausible to assume that the X variable has the same effect on Y (that is, the same regression coefficient) in the various classes. Econometricians, however, are often much more interested in testing this very assumption of common regression coefficients for all classes. For example, do production functions for a given industry have the same coefficients in different regions, do demand functions show the same coefficients for different social groups, or does some economic function remain unchanged in different time periods? This type of question can also be answered by the techniques of covariance analysis. We can in fact use covariance analysis

(a) to test differences in intercepts (slopes assumed constant for all classes)
(b) to test differences in slopes between classes
(c) to test differences in the complete relationship between classes that is, ignoring the distinction between intercepts and slopes and considering the relation as a whole).

Let our sample data be

$$Y_{ij}, X_{rij} \qquad r = 2, \ldots, k; i = 1, \ldots, p; j = 1, \ldots, m$$

that is we are postulating one dependent variable (Y), $(k - 1)$ uncontrolled (intervening, explanatory) variables $X_2, \ldots, X_k$, a single factor of classification, which is the basis for sub-division of the data into p groups or classes, and m observations on the variables in each group, so that there are $n = mp$ sample points.

The simplest possible model that we might apply to this data is

$$\mathbf{y} = \mathbf{X\beta} + \mathbf{u} \tag{6-30}$$

Here $\mathbf{y}$ is an $(n \times 1)$ column vector made up of p sub-vectors, which are the sample observations on Y for each of the p classes. $\mathbf{X}$ is an $(n \times k)$ matrix and $\boldsymbol{\beta}$ a $(k \times 1)$ vector of coefficients; that is, $\mathbf{X}$ contains a first column of ones in the usual way to allow for a single intercept term. Equation (6-30) says, in effect, that the grouping of the data into p classes has no relevance or significance, that the variation in Y is effectively explained by the variation in the $\mathbf{X}$ variables.

If, however, we wish to investigate the possible existence of a class effect in the form of different intercepts we would postulate a more general model

$$\mathbf{y} = \mathbf{D\alpha} + \mathbf{X\beta} + \mathbf{u} \tag{6-31}$$

where $\mathbf{y}$, $\mathbf{X}$, and $\boldsymbol{\beta}$ are as before, $\boldsymbol{\alpha}$ is a $(p - 1)$ element column vector,

$$\boldsymbol{\alpha} = \{\alpha_2 \quad \alpha_3 \ldots \alpha_p\}$$

and $\mathbf{D}$ is an $(mp \times (p-1))$ matrix of dummy variables

$$\mathbf{D} = [\mathbf{D}_2 \quad \mathbf{D}_3 \quad \cdots \quad \mathbf{D}_p] = \begin{bmatrix} \left.\begin{matrix}0\\ \vdots\\ 0\end{matrix}\right\} \begin{matrix} m \\ \text{elements}\end{matrix} & \left.\begin{matrix}0\\ \vdots\\ 0\end{matrix}\right\} & \cdots & \left.\begin{matrix}0\\ \vdots\\ 0\end{matrix}\right\} \\ \left.\begin{matrix}1\\ \vdots\\ 1\end{matrix}\right\} m & \left.\begin{matrix}0\\ \vdots\\ 0\end{matrix}\right\} & \cdots & \left.\begin{matrix}0\\ \vdots\\ 0\end{matrix}\right\} \\ \left.\begin{matrix}0\\ \vdots\\ 0\end{matrix}\right\} m & \left.\begin{matrix}1\\ \vdots\\ 1\end{matrix}\right\} & \cdots & \left.\begin{matrix}0\\ \vdots\\ 0\end{matrix}\right\} \\ \vdots & \vdots & & \vdots \\ \left.\begin{matrix}0\\ \vdots\\ 0\end{matrix}\right\} m & \left.\begin{matrix}0\\ \vdots\\ 0\end{matrix}\right\} & \cdots & \left.\begin{matrix}1\\ \vdots\\ 1\end{matrix}\right\}. \end{bmatrix} \tag{6-32}$$

Each column of $\mathbf{D}$ contains p sub-vectors, each of m elements. Model (6-31) implies the following relationships for the various classes,

$$\textit{Class 1} \quad Y_{1j} = \beta_1 + \beta_2 X_{21j} + \cdots + \beta_k X_{k1j} + u_{1j} \qquad (j = 1, \ldots, m)$$

$$\textit{Class 2} \quad Y_{2j} = (\alpha_2 + \beta_1) + \beta_2 X_{22j} + \cdots + \beta_k X_{k2j} + u_{2j} \qquad (j = 1, \ldots, m)$$

$$\vdots \qquad \vdots \qquad \vdots$$

$$\textit{Class p} \quad Y_{pj} = (\alpha_p + \beta_1) + \beta_2 X_{2pj} + \cdots + \beta_k X_{kpj} + u_{pj} \qquad (j = 1, \ldots, m)$$

so that the intercepts vary from class to class but we still postulate a common set of slope coefficients $\beta_2, \ldots, \beta_k$ over all classes. If there is no differential class (intercept) effect then $\alpha_2 = \cdots = \alpha_p = 0$. Thus we merely need to test the hypothesis $\boldsymbol{\alpha} = \mathbf{0}$ and this can be done by applying the test for the significance of a subset of coefficients developed in Chap. 5. It amounts to asking if (6-31) gives a significant increase in the explained sum of squares over (6-30), or equivalently whether the residual sum of squares associated with (6-31) is significantly less than the residual sum of squares associated with (6-30).

Let us indicate the result of applying least-squares to (6-30) as

$$\mathbf{y} = \mathbf{X}\hat{\boldsymbol{\beta}} + \mathbf{s}$$

where $\hat{\boldsymbol{\beta}} = (\mathbf{X}'\mathbf{X})^{-1}\mathbf{X}'\mathbf{y}$ as usual and $\mathbf{s}$ indicates the vector of least-squares residuals. We then have

$$\mathbf{y}'\mathbf{y} = \hat{\boldsymbol{\beta}}'\mathbf{X}'\mathbf{X}\hat{\boldsymbol{\beta}} + \mathbf{s}'\mathbf{s} + 2\hat{\boldsymbol{\beta}}'\mathbf{X}'\mathbf{s}$$

or more simply

$$\mathbf{y}'\mathbf{y} = \hat{\boldsymbol{\beta}}'\mathbf{X}'\mathbf{y} + \mathbf{s}'\mathbf{s} \tag{6-33}$$

since

$$\begin{aligned}\mathbf{X}'\mathbf{s} &= \mathbf{X}'\mathbf{y} - \mathbf{X}'\mathbf{X}\hat{\boldsymbol{\beta}} \\ &= \mathbf{0} \qquad \text{from the definition of } \hat{\boldsymbol{\beta}}\end{aligned}$$

Likewise if we indicate the result of applying least-squares to (6-31) by

$$\mathbf{y} = \mathbf{D}\hat{\hat{\boldsymbol{\alpha}}} + \mathbf{X}\hat{\hat{\boldsymbol{\beta}}} + \mathbf{e}$$

where

$$\begin{bmatrix}\hat{\hat{\boldsymbol{\alpha}}} \\ \hat{\hat{\boldsymbol{\beta}}}\end{bmatrix} = \begin{bmatrix}\mathbf{D}'\mathbf{D} & \mathbf{D}'\mathbf{X} \\ \mathbf{X}'\mathbf{D} & \mathbf{X}'\mathbf{X}\end{bmatrix}^{-1}\begin{bmatrix}\mathbf{D}'\mathbf{y} \\ \mathbf{X}'\mathbf{y}\end{bmatrix}$$

a similar partitioning to (6-33) gives

$$\mathbf{y}'\mathbf{y} = \hat{\hat{\boldsymbol{\alpha}}}'\mathbf{D}'\mathbf{y} + \hat{\hat{\boldsymbol{\beta}}}'\mathbf{X}'\mathbf{y} + \mathbf{e}'\mathbf{e}$$

The reduction in the residual sum of squares in moving from (6-30) to (6-31) is thus

$$\mathbf{s}'\mathbf{s} - \mathbf{e}'\mathbf{e} = \hat{\hat{\boldsymbol{\alpha}}}'\mathbf{D}'\mathbf{y} + \hat{\hat{\boldsymbol{\beta}}}'\mathbf{X}'\mathbf{y} - \hat{\boldsymbol{\beta}}'\mathbf{X}'\mathbf{y}$$

and the structure of the test of the hypothesis $\boldsymbol{\alpha} = \mathbf{0}$ is shown in Table 6-3, where the sum of squares and degrees of freedom in the second line of the table are given by subtracting the first line from the third.

Table 6-3 Analysis of covariance for differential intercepts

Source	*Sum of squares*	*df*	*Mean square*
X and **D**	Residual: $\mathbf{e}'\mathbf{e} = \mathbf{y}'\mathbf{y} - \hat{\hat{\boldsymbol{\alpha}}}'\mathbf{D}'\mathbf{y} - \hat{\hat{\boldsymbol{\beta}}}'\mathbf{X}'\mathbf{y} = S_2$	$mp - p - k + 1$	$S_2/(mp - p - k + 1)$
D	Incremental: $\mathbf{s}'\mathbf{s} - \mathbf{e}'\mathbf{e} = \hat{\hat{\boldsymbol{\alpha}}}'\mathbf{D}'\mathbf{y} + \hat{\hat{\boldsymbol{\beta}}}'\mathbf{X}'\mathbf{y} - \hat{\boldsymbol{\beta}}'\mathbf{X}'\mathbf{y} = S_1$	$p - 1$	$S_1/(p - 1)$
X	Residual: $\mathbf{s}'\mathbf{s} = \mathbf{y}'\mathbf{y} - \hat{\boldsymbol{\beta}}'\mathbf{X}'\mathbf{y}$	$mp - k$	

The test of the hypothesis $\alpha_2 = \cdots = \alpha_p = 0$ is then given by the F statistic

$$F_{(1)} = \frac{S_1/(p-1)}{S_2/(mp-p-k+1)} \tag{6-34}$$

with $(p-1, mp-p-k+1)$ degrees of freedom.

This test is conditional on the assumption of a common set of slope coefficients $\beta_2, \ldots, \beta_k$ over all the p classes, so that this assumption requires testing and it is often, in any case, of direct interest in itself. The appropriate test is developed by a further extension of the above approach. In using the data matrix $[\mathbf{D} \quad \mathbf{X}]$ we have allowed the intercepts to vary but imposed a single set of slope coefficients on all classes. Now we must allow the slope coefficients to vary from class to class as well as the intercepts. This amounts simply to running separate regressions for each class. Let

$$\mathbf{y}_i = \begin{bmatrix} Y_{i1} \\ Y_{i2} \\ \vdots \\ Y_{im} \end{bmatrix} \quad \text{and } \mathbf{X}_i = \begin{bmatrix} 1 & X_{i21} & \cdots & X_{ik1} \\ 1 & X_{i22} & \cdots & X_{ik2} \\ \vdots & \vdots & & \vdots \\ 1 & X_{i2m} & \cdots & X_{ikm} \end{bmatrix} \qquad i = 1, \ldots, p$$

indicate the sample data on Y and the X's in the ith class, but notice that we include a column of ones in $\mathbf{X}_i$. The least-squares regression of $\mathbf{y}_i$ on $\mathbf{X}_i$ may then be written

$$\mathbf{y}_i = \mathbf{X}_i\mathbf{b}_i + \mathbf{r}_i \qquad i = 1, \ldots, p \tag{6-35}$$

where $\mathbf{b}_i$ is the estimated vector of k coefficients (intercept and slopes) for the ith class and $\mathbf{r}_i$ is the vector of least-squares residuals. If we define a block-diagonal matrix $\mathbf{Z}$ as

$$\mathbf{Z} = \begin{bmatrix} \mathbf{X}_1 & \mathbf{0} & \cdots & \mathbf{0} \\ \mathbf{0} & \mathbf{X}_2 & \cdots & \mathbf{0} \\ \vdots & \vdots & & \vdots \\ \mathbf{0} & \mathbf{0} & \cdots & \mathbf{X}_p \end{bmatrix} \tag{6-36}$$

then the set of p regressions in (6-35) may be written

$$\mathbf{y} = \mathbf{Z}\mathbf{b} + \mathbf{r} \tag{6-37}$$

where $\mathbf{b}$ is the $(pk \times 1)$ column vector consisting of the $\mathbf{b}_i$ as sub-vectors and $\mathbf{r}$ is the $(mp \times 1)$ column vector with the $\mathbf{r}_i$ as sub-vectors. From the form of $\mathbf{Z}$ and the definition of least-squares coefficients

$$\mathbf{b} = (\mathbf{Z}'\mathbf{Z})^{-1}\mathbf{Z}'\mathbf{y} = \begin{bmatrix} (\mathbf{X}_1'\mathbf{X}_1)^{-1}\mathbf{X}_1'\mathbf{y}_1 \\ (\mathbf{X}_2'\mathbf{X}_2)^{-1}\mathbf{X}_2'\mathbf{y}_2 \\ \vdots \\ (\mathbf{X}_p'\mathbf{X}_p)^{-1}\mathbf{X}_p'\mathbf{y}_p \end{bmatrix} = \begin{bmatrix} \mathbf{b}_1 \\ \mathbf{b}_2 \\ \vdots \\ \mathbf{b}_p \end{bmatrix}$$

The residual sum of squares from (6-37) is $\mathbf{r}'\mathbf{r}$. This will be less than the residual $(\mathbf{e}'\mathbf{e})$ of Table 6-3 since we have introduced additional parameters; the reduction in the residual sum of squares, or equivalently the increment in the explained sum of squares indicates what has been achieved by allowing the slope coefficients to vary over classes and this increment can be tested for significance against the final residual $\mathbf{r}'\mathbf{r}$. The complete analysis of covariance is now indicated in Table 6-4, with the F tests listed after the table.

Table 6-4 Complete analysis of covariance table

Source	*Sum of squares*	*df*	*Mean square*
$\mathbf{Z}$	Residual: $\mathbf{r}'\mathbf{r} = \mathbf{y}'\mathbf{y} - \mathbf{b}'\mathbf{Z}'\mathbf{y} = S_4$	$p(m-k)$	$S_4/p(m-k)$
	Incremental (Differential slope vectors) $\mathbf{e}'\mathbf{e} - \mathbf{r}'\mathbf{r} = \mathbf{b}'\mathbf{Z}'\mathbf{y} - \hat{\boldsymbol{\alpha}}'\mathbf{D}'\mathbf{y} - \hat{\hat{\boldsymbol{\beta}}}'\mathbf{X}'\mathbf{y} = S_3$	$pk - p - k + 1$	$S_3/(pk - p - k + 1)$
$\mathbf{X}$ and $\mathbf{D}$	Residual: $\mathbf{e}'\mathbf{e} = \mathbf{y}'\mathbf{y} - \hat{\boldsymbol{\alpha}}'\mathbf{D}'\mathbf{y} - \hat{\hat{\boldsymbol{\beta}}}'\mathbf{X}'\mathbf{y}$ $= S_2 = S_3 + S_4$	$mp - p - k + 1$	$S_2/(mp - p - k + 1)$
	Incremental (Differential intercepts) $\mathbf{s}'\mathbf{s} - \mathbf{e}'\mathbf{e} = \hat{\boldsymbol{\alpha}}'\mathbf{D}'\mathbf{y} + \hat{\hat{\boldsymbol{\beta}}}'\mathbf{X}'\mathbf{y} - \hat{\boldsymbol{\beta}}'\mathbf{X}'\mathbf{y} = S_1$	$p - 1$	$S_1/(p-1)$
$\mathbf{X}$	Residual: $\mathbf{s}'\mathbf{s} = \mathbf{y}'\mathbf{y} - \hat{\boldsymbol{\beta}}'\mathbf{X}'\mathbf{y}$	$mp - k$	

Test of differential intercepts

$$F_{(1)} = \frac{S_1/(p-1)}{S_2/(mp - p - k + 1)}$$

Test of differential slope vectors

$$F_{(2)} = \frac{S_3/(pk - p - k + 1)}{S_4/p(m-k)}$$

Test of overall homogeneity

$$F_{(3)} = \frac{(S_1 + S_3)/k(p - 1)}{S_4/p(m - k)}$$

The degrees of freedom in the table follow directly from the number of observations and the number of parameters used, but the reader should derive them as an exercise.

The test for the homogeneity of the slope coefficients is given by

$$F_{(2)} = \frac{S_3/(pk - p - k + 1)}{S_4/p(m - k)} \tag{6-38}$$

with $(pk - p - k + 1, p(m - k))$ degrees of freedom. If the hypothesis of homogeneous slopes is not rejected then the test for differential intercepts may be made.

Finally a test of the homogeneity of the complete relationship (intercepts and slopes) over the p classes may be derived. This is done simply by contrasting the reduction in the residual sum of squares from $\mathbf{s's}$ to $\mathbf{r'r}$ with $\mathbf{r'r}$, each corrected for the appropriate degrees of freedom. From the structure of Table 6-4 it is easily seen that

$$\mathbf{s's} - \mathbf{r'r} = \mathbf{b'Z'y} - \hat{\boldsymbol{\beta}}'\mathbf{X'y} = S_1 + S_3$$

with $(pk - p - k + 1) + (p - 1) = k(p - 1)$ degrees of freedom. Thus the appropriate F test is

$$F_{(3)} = \frac{(S_1 + S_3)/k(p - 1)}{S_4/p(m - k)} \tag{6-39}$$

These three F tests are summarized at the bottom of Table 6-4.

The principle of these tests may also be applied to test the equality of any *subset* of coefficients over the p classes. The practical procedure is to fit the restricted model in which the hypothetical equality is imposed, all other coefficients being allowed to vary from class to class, and calculate the corresponding residual sum of squares. Then the unrestricted model is fitted in which this subset of coefficients is also allowed to vary from class to class and the resultant sum of squares is calculated. The equality of the subsets is tested by contrasting the reduction in the residual sum of squares in going from the restricted to the unrestricted model against the unrestricted sum of squares. If there are c coefficients in the subset and p classes the numerator in the F test will have $c(p - 1)$ degrees of freedom.

Example

$$(k = 2, m = 5, p = 4, n = mp = 20)$$

Table 6-5

	Class									
	1		2		3		4			
Observation	*Y*	*X*	*Y*	*X*	*Y*	*X*	*Y*	*X*		
1	22	29	30	15	12	16	23	5		
2	22	20	32	9	8	31	25	25		
3	20	14	26	1	13	26	28	16		
4	24	21	25	6	25	35	26	10		
5	12	6	37	19	7	12	23	24	*Y*	*X*
Sums	100	90	150	50	65	120	125	80	440	340
Means	20	18	30	10	13	24	25	16	22	17

Let us test the homogeneity of the slope coefficients for this data, and then, if the null hypothesis is not rejected, test the variation in the intercepts. We will thus build up the numerical equivalent of Table 6-4. Beginning with the bottom line

$$\mathbf{y}'\mathbf{y} - \hat{\boldsymbol{\beta}}'\mathbf{X}'\mathbf{y} = \mathbf{y}'\mathbf{y} - \mathbf{y}'\mathbf{X}(\mathbf{X}'\mathbf{X})^{-1}\mathbf{X}'\mathbf{y}$$

$$= \Sigma Y^2 - [\Sigma Y \ \ \Sigma XY]\begin{bmatrix} n & \Sigma X \\ \Sigma X & \Sigma X^2 \end{bmatrix}^{-1}\begin{bmatrix} \Sigma Y \\ \Sigma XY \end{bmatrix}$$

where the summations are over all 20 sample observations

$$= 10876 - [440 \quad 7288]\begin{bmatrix} 20 & 340 \\ 340 & 7462 \end{bmatrix}^{-1}\begin{bmatrix} 440 \\ 7288 \end{bmatrix}$$

$$= 10876 - [440 \quad 7288]\frac{1}{33640}\begin{bmatrix} 7462 & -340 \\ -340 & 20 \end{bmatrix}\begin{bmatrix} 440 \\ 7288 \end{bmatrix}$$

$$= 1174.1$$

Now going to the first line of Table 6-4 the residual sum of squares from **y** on **Z** is most simply obtained by running the four separate class regressions, obtaining the residual sum of squares for each and summing. For the first class the residual sum is

$$\sum_j Y_{1j}^2 - \begin{bmatrix} \sum_j Y_{1j} & \sum_j X_{1j}Y_{1j} \end{bmatrix} \begin{bmatrix} m & \sum_j X_{1j} \\ \sum_j X_{1j} & \sum_j X_{1j}^2 \end{bmatrix}^{-1} \begin{bmatrix} \sum_j Y_{1j} \\ \sum_j X_{1j}Y_{1j} \end{bmatrix}$$

$$= 2088 - [100 \quad 1934] \begin{bmatrix} 5 & 90 \\ 90 & 1914 \end{bmatrix}^{-1} \begin{bmatrix} 100 \\ 1934 \end{bmatrix}$$

$$= 2088 - [100 \quad 1934] \frac{1}{1470} \begin{bmatrix} 1914 & -90 \\ -90 & 5 \end{bmatrix} \begin{bmatrix} 100 \\ 1934 \end{bmatrix}$$

$$= 26.9$$

For the other three classes the residual sums are 26.9, 124.0, and 18.0. Thus $\mathbf{r'r} = 195.8$.

Finally we need to compute the residual from the regression of $\mathbf{y}$ on $[\mathbf{D} \quad \mathbf{X}]$ for the third line of the table. This is given by

$$\mathbf{e'e} = \mathbf{y'y} - [\mathbf{y'D} \quad \mathbf{y'X}] \begin{bmatrix} \mathbf{D'D} & \mathbf{D'X} \\ \mathbf{X'D} & \mathbf{X'X} \end{bmatrix}^{-1} \begin{bmatrix} \mathbf{D'y} \\ \mathbf{X'y} \end{bmatrix}$$

where the structure of $\mathbf{D}$ is specified in general terms in (6-32) so that for this example

$$\begin{bmatrix} \mathbf{D'D} & \mathbf{D'X} \\ \mathbf{X'D} & \mathbf{X'X} \end{bmatrix} = \left[\begin{array}{ccc|cc} 5 & 0 & 0 & 5 & \sum_j X_{2j} \\ 0 & 5 & 0 & 5 & \sum_j X_{3j} \\ 0 & 0 & 5 & 5 & \sum_j X_{4j} \\ \hline 5 & 5 & 5 & 20 & \sum_{ij} X_{ij} \\ \sum_j X_{2j} & \sum_j X_{3j} & \sum_j X_{4j} & \sum_{ij} X_{ij} & \sum_{ij} X_{ij}^2 \end{array}\right]$$

and

$$\begin{bmatrix} \mathbf{D}'\mathbf{y} \\ \mathbf{X}'\mathbf{y} \end{bmatrix} = \begin{bmatrix} \sum_j Y_{2j} \\ \sum_j Y_{3j} \\ \sum_j Y_{4j} \\ \sum_{ij} Y_{ij} \\ \sum_{ij} X_{ij} Y_{ij} \end{bmatrix}$$

So

$$\mathbf{e}'\mathbf{e} = 10{,}876 - [150 \quad 65 \quad 125 \quad 440 \quad 7{,}288] \frac{1}{106{,}380}$$

$$\times \begin{bmatrix} 48{,}312 & 16{,}956 & 22{,}716 & -34{,}236 & 720 \\ 16{,}956 & 45{,}792 & 20{,}196 & -11{,}556 & -540 \\ 22{,}716 & 20{,}196 & 42{,}912 & -24{,}516 & 180 \\ -34{,}236 & -11{,}556 & -24{,}516 & 50{,}436 & -1{,}620 \\ 720 & -540 & 180 & -1{,}620 & 90 \end{bmatrix} \begin{bmatrix} 150 \\ 65 \\ 125 \\ 440 \\ 7{,}288 \end{bmatrix}$$

$$= 10{,}876 - \frac{1}{106{,}380} [150 \quad 65 \quad 125 \quad 440 \quad 7{,}288] \begin{bmatrix} 1{,}371{,}960 \\ -975{,}780 \\ 608{,}940 \\ 1{,}434{,}240 \\ 38{,}520 \end{bmatrix}$$

$$= 10{,}876 - \frac{1}{106{,}380} [1{,}130{,}285{,}160]$$

$$= 251.0$$

Having obtained the three residual sums of squares the differential effects in Table 6-4 may then be obtained by subtraction. See Table 6-6. For the differences between regression slopes

$$F_{(2)} = \frac{18.4}{16.3} = 1.13$$

Table 6-6

Sum of squares	*df*	*Mean square*
$S_4 = 195.8$	12	16.3
$S_3 = 55.2$	3	18.4
$S_2 = S_3 + S_4 = 251.0$	15	16.7
$S_1 = 923.1$	3	307.7
1174.1	18	

while $F_{0.05}(3, 12) = 3.49$, so we do not reject the hypothesis of a common regression slope. The test for differences in intercepts is then

$$F_{(1)} = \frac{307.7}{16.7} = 18.4$$

while $F_{0.01}(3, 15) = 5.42$, so that the intercept effect is highly significant.

The numerical calculations for this type of example are much easier if one works throughout in terms of deviations. This is especially true of the calculation of $\mathbf{e}'\mathbf{e}$, which may also be calculated by first expressing Y and X in terms of deviations from *class means*, pooling all the sample data, fitting a single regression slope and computing the residual sum of squares from this regression. For work with a computer, however, the direct regression expressions given in Table 6-4 are preferable in that they clearly indicate the structure of the problem and no preliminary manipulation of the data is required, apart from the specification of an appropriate $\mathbf{D}$ matrix. Three crucial residual sums of squares are required and the other items follow directly by subtraction.

To illustrate the alternative calculation Table 6-7 shows the data of Table 6-5 expressed as deviations from class means. The residual sum of squares from a single regression fitted to these 20 observations is then

$$\sum_{ij}(Y_{ij} - \bar{Y}_i)^2 - \left[\sum_{ij}(Y_{ij} - \bar{Y}_i)(X_{ij} - \bar{X}_i)\right]^2 \Big/ \sum_{ij}(X_{ij} - \bar{X}_i)^2$$

$$= (88 + 94 + 206 + 18)$$

$$- (134 + 117 + 177 + 0)^2/(294 + 204 + 382 + 302)$$

$$= 251.0$$

which agrees with the value obtained for $\mathbf{e}'\mathbf{e}$ on page 202 above. The elements of $\mathbf{r}'\mathbf{r}$ may also be obtained quite simply from Table 6-7. For example, the residual sum of squares from the first class regression is

$$88 - (134)^2/294 = 26.9$$

and so forth.

To summarize the practical procedures, all covariance tests are based on comparisons between pairs of three basic regressions, namely,

1. Regress $\mathbf{y}$ on the $(n \times k)$ data matrix $\mathbf{X}$ consisting of a column of ones and the observations on the explanatory variables $X_2, \ldots, X_k$. This yields the estimated vector $\hat{\boldsymbol{\beta}}$ and residual sum of squares $\mathbf{y}'\mathbf{y} - \hat{\boldsymbol{\beta}}'\mathbf{X}'\mathbf{y}$.
2. Regress $\mathbf{y}$ on $[\mathbf{D} \quad \mathbf{X}]$ where $\mathbf{D}$ is the $n \times (p-1)$ matrix of class dummies specified in (6-32). This allows each class to have a different intercept but imposes a common vector of slope coefficients on all classes. The residual sum of squares from this regression has been denoted by $\mathbf{e}'\mathbf{e}$.
3. Fit a separate regression to the data for each class and sum the residual sum of squares over all classes to obtain $\mathbf{r}'\mathbf{r}$.

The test of the homogeneity of regressions (slopes and intercepts) between classes is then achieved by contrasting the reduction in the residual sum of squares from (1) to (3) with the residual $\mathbf{r}'\mathbf{r}$ at Stage 3 ($F_{(3)}$ of Table 6-4). The test of the homogeneity of vectors of slope coefficients is based on the reduction in the residual sum of squares from (2) to (3), again contrasted with $\mathbf{r}'\mathbf{r}$ ($F_{(2)}$ of Table 6-4), and the test for differential intercepts is found by comparing the reduction in the residual sum of squares from (1) to (2) with the residual at Stage 2 ($F_{(1)}$ of Table 6-4).

The F tests described above are tests for the significance of groups of coefficients. Should an F value prove significant it is often the case that certain variables have made a much greater contribution to that level of significance than others and it is of interest to identify them. This may be done by setting up the basic regressions in a slightly different way and examining the standard errors of particular coefficients. As an illustration of the principle consider again the data in Table 6-5. With four classes and one uncontrolled variable the Stage 3 regression may be written

$$\begin{aligned} Y = a_1 + a_2D_2 + a_3D_3 + a_4D_4 + b_1X + b_2(D_2X) + b_3(D_3X) \\ + b_4(D_4X) + e \end{aligned} \tag{6-40}$$

where

$$\begin{aligned} D_i &= 1 \text{ for an observation in class } i \qquad i = 2, 3, 4 \\ &= 0 \text{ otherwise} \end{aligned}$$

Table 6-7

Observation	*Class*							
	1		2		3		4	
j	$(Y_{1j} - \overline{Y}_1)$	$(X_{1j} - \overline{X}_1)$	$(Y_{2j} - \overline{Y}_2)$	$(X_{2j} - \overline{X}_2)$	$(Y_{3j} - \overline{Y}_3)$	$(X_{3j} - \overline{X}_3)$	$(Y_{4j} - \overline{Y}_4)$	$(X_{4j} - \overline{X}_4)$
1	2	11	0	5	−1	−8	−2	−11
2	2	2	2	−1	−5	7	0	9
3	0	−4	−4	−9	0	2	3	0
4	4	3	−5	−4	12	11	1	−6
5	−8	−12	7	9	−6	−12	−2	8
$\sum_j (Y_{ij} - \overline{Y}_i)^2$	88		94		206		18	
$\sum_j (X_{ij} - \overline{X}_i)^2$		294		204		382		302
$\sum_j (Y_{ij} - \overline{Y}_i)(X_{ij} - \overline{X}_i)$	134		117		177		0	

This allows both intercepts and slopes to vary from class to class. Notice that the dummy variables have been used in both additive and multiplicative fashion, in the former case to allow for differential intercepts and in the latter case for differential slopes: (D_3X), for example, represents in this case a column of twenty numbers of which the first ten and the last five are zero and the remaining five are the values of the X variable in the third class. The resultant regression for the third class is

$$Y = (a_1 + a_3) + (b_1 + b_3)X$$

In fitting (6-40) X itself is taken as the twenty values of the X variable in all four classes. This means that the coefficient of X is the regression slope *in the first class* and the coefficient of D_iX the difference between the slope in the ith class and that in the first class. Alternatively, one might have replaced X by D_1X_1 where D_1 equals one in the first class and zero elsewhere, in which case the coefficients of the (D_iX) variables ($i = 1, 2, 3, 4$) are direct estimates of the regression slopes in each of the four classes: the disadvantage of this formulation, however, is that we no longer have such a direct and simple test of the *differences* in regression slopes as in the first formulation.

Fitting (6-40) to the data of Table 6-5 yields[1]

$$\begin{aligned} Y = {} & \underset{(2.5591)}{11.7959} + \underset{(2.1869)}{12.4688\, D_2} - \underset{(-1.4150)}{9.9163\, D_3} + \underset{(2.1324)}{13.2041\, D_4} + \underset{(1.1947)}{0.4558\, X} \\ & + \underset{(0.3198)}{0.1177\, D_2X} + \underset{(0.0241)}{0.0076\, D_3X} - \underset{(-1.3772)}{0.4558\, D_4X} \end{aligned}$$

with $R^2 = 0.7468$ and 12 degrees of freedom. The figures in parentheses are "t" ratios and we see that none of the coefficients of the (D_iX) variables are significantly different from zero. This, of course, confirms the homogeneity of regression slopes established earlier by the F test. Imposing the assumption of a common regression slope gives the revised regression

$$Y = \underset{(4.7864)}{13.4882} + \underset{(4.6782)}{12.8968\, D_2} - \underset{(-3.4176)}{9.1726\, D_3} + \underset{(2.2032)}{5.7242\, D_4} + \underset{(3.0432)}{0.3621\, X}$$

with $R^2 = 0.7341$ and 15 degrees of freedom. All three dummies have significant coefficients, thus establishing that they are significantly different from the intercept for the first class, again in agreement with the earlier F test on intercepts.

In many practical applications of the above technique we often have just two classes ($p = 2$). For example, one may be interested in whether a structural shift has taken place in some relation between two time periods or in whether a production function, say, is different in two industries or a consumption function significantly different in two countries. So long as the

[1] I am indebted to D. Gujarati for discussions of this point and also for the calculations.

number of observations in each class exceeds the number of parameters to be estimated the above techniques apply directly. A special case arises, however, when the number of observations in one class is less than the number of parameters. For example, we may have a sample of $n(>k)$ observations on the variables $Y, X_2, \ldots, X_k$. An additional sample of $m(<k)$ observations on these variables becomes available and the question is whether they may be considered to come from the same population. G. C. Chow, and alternatively F. M. Fisher, have shown that the appropriate test is as follows.[1] To the first n observations fit the least-squares regression

$$\mathbf{y}_1 = \mathbf{X}_1\mathbf{b}_1 + \mathbf{e}_1$$

and compute the residual sum of squares $\mathbf{e}_1'\mathbf{e}_1$. Pool the $n + m$ sample observations to give $\mathbf{y}$ and $\mathbf{X}$ and fit the least-squares regression

$$\mathbf{y} = \mathbf{X}\mathbf{b} + \mathbf{e}$$

again computing the residual sum of squares $\mathbf{e}'\mathbf{e}$. The test of the null hypothesis that the m additional observations obey the same relation as the first is given by

$$F = \frac{(\mathbf{e}'\mathbf{e} - \mathbf{e}_1'\mathbf{e}_1)/m}{\mathbf{e}_1'\mathbf{e}_1/(n-k)}$$

which is distributed as F with $(m, n - k)$ degrees of freedom.

EXERCISES

6-1. Derive Eq. (6-16) from (6-15).

6-2. Prove the last two equalities in (6-28) by the method used to prove the first.

6-3. Prove formula (6-29).

6-4. Derive and explain the degrees of freedom in Tables 6-3 and 6-4.

6-5. When

$$\mathbf{y} = \begin{bmatrix} y_1 \\ \vdots \\ y_m \\ \\ y_{m+1} \\ \vdots \\ y_n \end{bmatrix} \qquad \mathbf{X} = \begin{bmatrix} x_1 & 0 \\ \vdots & \vdots \\ x_m & 0 \\ \\ x_{m+1} & x_{m+1} \\ \vdots & \vdots \\ x_n & x_n \end{bmatrix}$$

show that the least-squares regression of $\mathbf{y}$ on $\mathbf{X}$ yields coefficients b_1 and b_2 with the properties $b_1 = \Sigma_1 xy/\Sigma_1 x^2$ and $b_1 + b_2 = \Sigma_2 xy/\Sigma_2 x^2$ where Σ_1 indicates summation over the first m observations and Σ_2 over the remaining $(n - m)$ observations.

[1] G. C. Chow, "Tests of Equality between Sets of Coefficients in Two Linear Regressions," *Econometrica*, vol. 28, pp. 591–605, 1960, and F. M. Fisher, "Tests of Equality between Sets of Coefficients in Two Linear Regressions: An Expository Note," *Econometrica*, vol. 38, pp. 361–366, 1970.

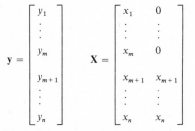

7
Generalized Least-squares

7-1 THE GENERALIZED LEAST-SQUARES (AITKEN) ESTIMATOR

We saw in the development of the model $\mathbf{y} = \mathbf{X}\boldsymbol{\beta} + \mathbf{u}$ in Chap. 5 that $E(\mathbf{uu}') = \sigma^2\mathbf{I}$ is a compact way of writing the double assumption that the disturbance term has constant variance and is not autocorrelated. Let us retain the assumption that

$$E(\mathbf{u}) = \mathbf{0}$$

but now add to it

$$E(\mathbf{uu}') = \sigma^2\boldsymbol{\Omega} \tag{7-1}$$

where σ^2 is unknown but $\boldsymbol{\Omega}$ is a known symmetric positive definite matrix of order n. Assumption (7-1) states that the variances and covariances of the disturbance $\mathbf{u}$ are known up to a scale factor.

Before discussing the problem of estimating $\boldsymbol{\beta}$ under assumption (7-1) let us explore the meaning of the assumption that $\boldsymbol{\Omega}$ is positive definite. As stated in Chap. 4, every principal minor of a positive definite matrix is positive. Thus for $\mathbf{\Omega}$ of order 2×2, we may write

$$\sigma^2\mathbf{\Omega} = \begin{bmatrix} \sigma_{11} & \sigma_{12} \\ \sigma_{12} & \sigma_{22} \end{bmatrix}$$

where σ_{ii} denotes the variance of u_i and σ_{ij} the covariance of u_i and u_j.

So the condition gives $\sigma_{11} > 0$, $\sigma_{22} > 0$ and

$$\sigma_{11}\sigma_{22} - \sigma_{12}^2 = \sigma_{11}\sigma_{22}(1 - \rho_{12}^2) > 0$$

where ρ_{12} denotes the population correlation between u_1 and u_2. Thus each disturbance must have a positive variance and the two disturbances must not be perfectly correlated. For $\mathbf{\Omega}$ of order 3×3 the above condition must hold for each pair of disturbances and also the determinant of $\mathbf{\Omega}$ must be positive. It is easy to show that

$$\begin{aligned} |\sigma^2\mathbf{\Omega}| &= \sigma_{11}\sigma_{22}\sigma_{23}(1 - \rho_{12}^2 - \rho_{13}^2 - \rho_{23}^2 + 2\rho_{12}\rho_{13}\rho_{23}) \\ &= \sigma_{11}\sigma_{22}\sigma_{33}(1 - \rho_{23}^2)(1 - \rho_{1\cdot 23}^2) \end{aligned}$$

where $\rho_{1\cdot 23}^2$ is the population coefficient of multiple determination between u_1 and u_2 and u_3, so that the condition that $\mathbf{\Omega}$ should be positive definite means that as well as no perfect correlation between any pair of u's there must be no perfect correlation between the set of all u's.

Apart from these restrictions on the u's assumption (7-1) is a very general one. It can allow in particular for heteroscedasticity and for autocorrelated error terms, and as we shall see below it can also cater for a number of other problems. The problem now is how to estimate $\boldsymbol{\beta}$ in

$$\mathbf{y} = \mathbf{X}\boldsymbol{\beta} + \mathbf{u} \tag{7-2}$$

when

$$E(\mathbf{uu'}) = \sigma^2\mathbf{\Omega}$$

This estimation problem may be approached in a number of equivalent ways, but one of the simplest is the following.

We saw in Chap. 4 that a positive definite matrix can be expressed in the form $\mathbf{PP'}$, where $\mathbf{P}$ is nonsingular. Thus let us write

$$\mathbf{\Omega} = \mathbf{PP'} \tag{7-3}$$

so that

$$\mathbf{P}^{-1}\mathbf{\Omega}\mathbf{P}^{-1'} = \mathbf{I} \tag{7-4}$$

and

$$\mathbf{P}^{-1'}\mathbf{P}^{-1} = \mathbf{\Omega}^{-1} \tag{7-5}$$

Pre-multiply the model $\mathbf{y} = \mathbf{X}\boldsymbol{\beta} + \mathbf{u}$ by $\mathbf{P}^{-1}$ to give

$$\mathbf{y}_* = \mathbf{X}_*\boldsymbol{\beta} + \mathbf{u}_* \tag{7-6}$$

where

$$\mathbf{y}_* = \mathbf{P}^{-1}\mathbf{y}, \qquad \mathbf{X}_* = \mathbf{P}^{-1}\mathbf{X}, \quad \text{and} \quad \mathbf{u}_* = \mathbf{P}^{-1}\mathbf{u} \tag{7-7}$$

Using (7-4) it is easily seen that

$$E(\mathbf{u}_*\mathbf{u}'_*) = \sigma^2\mathbf{I}$$

so that (7-6) satisfies all the assumptions required for the simple least-squares model of Chap 5. In particular

$$\begin{aligned}\mathbf{b} &= (\mathbf{X}'_*\mathbf{X}_*)^{-1}\mathbf{X}'_*\mathbf{y}_* \\ &= (\mathbf{X}'\boldsymbol{\Omega}^{-1}\mathbf{X})^{-1}\mathbf{X}'\boldsymbol{\Omega}^{-1}\mathbf{y} \quad \text{using (7-5)}\end{aligned} \tag{7-8}$$

is a minimum variance unbiased linear estimator of $\boldsymbol{\beta}$, with variance-covariance matrix

$$\begin{aligned}\operatorname{var}(\mathbf{b}) &= \sigma^2(\mathbf{X}'_*\mathbf{X}_*)^{-1} \\ &= \sigma^2(\mathbf{X}'\boldsymbol{\Omega}^{-1}\mathbf{X})^{-1}\end{aligned} \tag{7-9}$$

An unbiased estimate of σ^2 is provided by

$$\begin{aligned}\frac{1}{n-k}(\mathbf{y}_* - \mathbf{X}_*\mathbf{b})'(\mathbf{y}_* - \mathbf{X}_*\mathbf{b}) &= \frac{1}{n-k}(\mathbf{y} - \mathbf{X}\mathbf{b})'\boldsymbol{\Omega}^{-1}(\mathbf{y} - \mathbf{X}\mathbf{b}) \\ &= \frac{1}{n-k}\mathbf{e}'\boldsymbol{\Omega}^{-1}\mathbf{e}\end{aligned} \tag{7-10}$$

Further, if $\mathbf{u}$ is assumed to be normally distributed then so is $\mathbf{u}_*$. Thus $\mathbf{b}$ is a maximum-likelihood estimator and has minimum variance in the class of all unbiased estimators.

The estimator $\mathbf{b}$ defined in (7-8) is the generalized least-sqares (Aitken) estimator.[1] Notice carefully that if we had applied simple (ordinary) least-squares to (7-2) the resultant estimator $\hat{\boldsymbol{\beta}} = (\mathbf{X}'\mathbf{X})^{-1}\mathbf{X}'\mathbf{y}$ would be unbiased linear but it would not be minimum variance unbiased linear. The presence of assumption (7-1) rather than the simple $E(\mathbf{uu}') = \sigma^2\mathbf{I}$ destroys the minimum variance property of ordinary least-squares.

Given $\boldsymbol{\Omega}$, the generalized least-squares (GLS) estimator can be computed from (7-8) and standard errors from (7-9) so that the usual significance tests and confidence intervals for the β_i can be constructed. Alternatively one can work in an analysis of variance framework by establishing the

[1] A. C. Aitken, "On Least-squares and Linear Combinations of Observations," *Proc. Royal Soc.*, Edinburgh, vol. 55, pp. 42–48, 1934.

appropriate sums of squares from (7-6). Defining

$$\mathbf{e} = \mathbf{y} - \mathbf{X}\mathbf{b}$$

and premultiplying by $\mathbf{P}^{-1}$

$$\mathbf{P}^{-1}\mathbf{e} = \mathbf{y}_* - \mathbf{X}_*\mathbf{b}$$

Thus

$$\begin{aligned}\mathbf{y}_*'\mathbf{y}_* &= (\mathbf{X}_*\mathbf{b} + \mathbf{P}^{-1}\mathbf{e})'(\mathbf{X}_*\mathbf{b} + \mathbf{P}^{-1}(\mathbf{e})\\ &= \mathbf{b}'\mathbf{X}'\mathbf{\Omega}^{-1}\mathbf{X}\mathbf{b} + \mathbf{e}'\mathbf{\Omega}^{-1}\mathbf{e}\end{aligned}$$

or

$$\mathbf{y}'\mathbf{\Omega}^{-1}\mathbf{y} = \mathbf{b}'\mathbf{X}'\mathbf{\Omega}^{-1}\mathbf{y} + \mathbf{e}'\mathbf{\Omega}^{-1}\mathbf{e} \tag{7-11}$$

which is a decomposition of the total sum of squares from (7–6) into an explained sum of squares and a residual sum of squares. Equation (7-11) can serve as a basis for the usual analysis of variance table but since the analysis is derived from the transformed variables $\mathbf{y}_*$ and $\mathbf{X}_*$ we see that we are weighting sums of squares in the original variables $\mathbf{y}$ and $\mathbf{X}$ by the matrix $\mathbf{\Omega}^{-1}$. Moreover, if $\mathbf{y}_* = \mathbf{P}^{-1}\mathbf{y}$ has been measured from zero origin, then the mean of the transformed variable must be computed and applied in the usual correction for the mean to the total and explained sum of squares.

The generalized least-squares model is sometimes specified in the form

$$\mathbf{y} = \mathbf{X}\boldsymbol{\beta} + \mathbf{u}$$

with

$$E(\mathbf{u}) = \mathbf{0}$$

and

$$E(\mathbf{u}\mathbf{u}') = \mathbf{V} \tag{7-12}$$

where $\mathbf{V}$ is assumed to be a known, symmetric, positive-definite matrix. The contrast with (7-1) is that $\sigma^2\mathbf{\Omega}$ has been replaced by $\mathbf{V}$. Making this substitution in (7-8) and (7-9) gives

$$\mathbf{b} = (\mathbf{X}'\mathbf{V}^{-1}\mathbf{X})^{-1}\mathbf{X}'\mathbf{V}^{-1}\mathbf{y} \tag{7-13}$$

and

$$\text{var}(\mathbf{b}) = (\mathbf{X}'\mathbf{V}^{-1}\mathbf{X})^{-1} \tag{7-14}$$

as the corresponding expressions for the GLS estimator and its variance–covariance matrix.

7-2 PREDICTION

Prediction problems require special treatment in the generalized least-squares model.[1] Let us assume

$$\mathbf{y} = \mathbf{X}\boldsymbol{\beta} + \mathbf{u}$$

with

$$E(\mathbf{u}) = \mathbf{0} \quad \text{and} \quad E(\mathbf{uu}') = \mathbf{V}$$

The problem is to predict a single value of the regressand y_0 given the row vector of prediction regressors $\mathbf{x}_0$. We can write

$$y_0 = \mathbf{x}_0\boldsymbol{\beta} + u_0 \tag{7-15}$$

where u_0 is the true but unknown value of the prediction disturbance. We assume

$$Eu_0 = 0 \tag{7-16}$$

$$Eu_0^2 = \sigma_0^2 \tag{7-17}$$

$$Eu_0\,\mathbf{u} = \begin{bmatrix} Eu_1u_0 \\ Eu_2u_0 \\ \vdots \\ Eu_nu_0 \end{bmatrix} = \mathbf{w} \tag{7-18}$$

where $\mathbf{w}$ is the $n \times 1$ vector of covariances of the prediction disturbance with the vector of sample disturbances. Define a linear predictor

$$p = \mathbf{c}'\mathbf{y} \tag{7-19}$$

where $\mathbf{c}$ is a vector of n constants. If p is to be a best linear unbiased predictor we must then choose $\mathbf{c}$ to minimize the prediction variance

$$\sigma_p^2 = E\{(p - y_0)^2\} \tag{7-20}$$

subject to $E(p - y_0) = 0$. From (7-15) and (7-19) we have

$$p - y_0 = (\mathbf{c}'\mathbf{X} - \mathbf{x}_0)\boldsymbol{\beta} + \mathbf{c}'\mathbf{u} - u_0$$

The condition for an unbiased predictor thus requires that $\mathbf{c}$ must satisfy

$$\mathbf{c}'\mathbf{X} - \mathbf{x}_0 = \mathbf{0} \tag{7-21}$$

The prediction error is then

$$p - y_0 = \mathbf{c}'\mathbf{u} - u_0$$

[1] See A. S. Goldberger, "Best Linear Unbiased Prediction in the Generalized Linear Regression Model," *J. Am. Statis. Assoc.*, vol. 57, 369–375, 1962, on which this section is based.

and the prediction variance is

$$\begin{aligned}\sigma_p^2 &= E\{(p-y_0)^2\} \\ &= E\{(p-y_0)(p-y_0)'\} \qquad \text{since } (p-y_0) \text{ is a scalar} \\ &= E\{(\mathbf{c}'\mathbf{u}-u_0)(\mathbf{c}'\mathbf{u}-u_0)'\} \\ &= E\{\mathbf{c}'\mathbf{u}\mathbf{u}'\mathbf{c}+u_0^2-2\mathbf{c}'\mathbf{u}u_0\} \\ &= \mathbf{c}'\mathbf{V}\mathbf{c}+\sigma_0^2-2\mathbf{c}'\mathbf{w} \end{aligned} \tag{7-22}$$

To minimize (7-22) subject to (7-21) we minimize

$$\varphi = \mathbf{c}'\mathbf{V}\mathbf{c} - 2\mathbf{c}'\mathbf{w} - 2(\mathbf{c}'\mathbf{X} - \mathbf{x}_0)\boldsymbol{\lambda}$$

where $\boldsymbol{\lambda}$ is a $k \times 1$ vector of Lagrange multipliers. Differentiating φ with respect to $\mathbf{c}$ and $\boldsymbol{\lambda}$ and setting the results equal to zero vectors gives the equations

$$\begin{bmatrix}\mathbf{V} & \mathbf{X} \\ \mathbf{X}' & \mathbf{0}\end{bmatrix}\begin{bmatrix}\hat{\mathbf{c}} \\ -\hat{\boldsymbol{\lambda}}\end{bmatrix} = \begin{bmatrix}\mathbf{w} \\ \mathbf{x}_0'\end{bmatrix}$$

or

$$\begin{bmatrix}\hat{\mathbf{c}} \\ -\hat{\boldsymbol{\lambda}}\end{bmatrix} = \begin{bmatrix}\mathbf{V} & \mathbf{X} \\ \mathbf{X}' & \mathbf{0}\end{bmatrix}^{-1}\begin{bmatrix}\mathbf{w} \\ \mathbf{x}_0'\end{bmatrix}$$

Applying the rule for the inverse of a partitioned matrix then gives

$$\hat{\mathbf{c}} = \mathbf{V}^{-1}[\mathbf{I} - \mathbf{X}(\mathbf{X}'\mathbf{V}^{-1}\mathbf{X})^{-1}\mathbf{X}'\mathbf{V}^{-1}]\mathbf{w} + \mathbf{V}^{-1}\mathbf{X}(\mathbf{X}'\mathbf{V}^{-1}\mathbf{X})^{-1}\mathbf{x}_0'$$

so that the best linear unbiased predictor is

$$\begin{aligned}\hat{p} &= \hat{\mathbf{c}}'\mathbf{y} \\ &= \mathbf{x}_0(\mathbf{X}'\mathbf{V}^{-1}\mathbf{X})^{-1}\mathbf{X}'\mathbf{V}^{-1}\mathbf{y} + \mathbf{w}'\mathbf{V}^{-1}\mathbf{y} - \mathbf{w}'\mathbf{V}^{-1}\mathbf{X}(\mathbf{X}'\mathbf{V}^{-1}\mathbf{X})^{-1}\mathbf{X}'\mathbf{V}^{-1}\mathbf{y} \\ &= \mathbf{x}_0\mathbf{b} + \mathbf{w}'\mathbf{V}^{-1}(\mathbf{y} - \mathbf{X}\mathbf{b}) \qquad \text{since } \mathbf{b} = (\mathbf{X}'\mathbf{V}^{-1}\mathbf{X})^{-1}\mathbf{X}'\mathbf{V}^{-1}\mathbf{y}\end{aligned}$$

that is

$$\hat{p} = \mathbf{x}_0\mathbf{b} + \mathbf{w}'\mathbf{V}^{-1}\mathbf{e} \tag{7-23}$$

where $\mathbf{e} = \mathbf{y} - \mathbf{X}\mathbf{b}$ is the vector of generalized least-squares residuals. This is the basic result, due to Goldberger, for prediction in the generalized least-squares model. We see that it has two essential features: first of all the vector of prediction regressors is multiplied by the GLS estimator **b**, and secondly our *a priori* knowledge of the interdependence of the disturbances, embodied in **V**, is used along with the sample residuals to estimate the unknown prediction disturbance u_0. A special application of (7-23) to the case where disturbances are autocorrelated is given in Chap. 8.

7-3 HETEROSCEDASTIC DISTURBANCES

In the many econometric studies, especially those based on cross-section data, the assumption of a constant variance for the disturbance term is unrealistic. In consumer budget studies the residual variance about the regression function very likely increases with income and likewise in cross-section studies of firms the residual variance probably increases with size of firm.

Suppose we postulate $\mathbf{y} = \mathbf{X}\boldsymbol{\beta} + \mathbf{u}$ in the usual way and

$$E(\mathbf{uu}') = \sigma^2\boldsymbol{\Omega} = \sigma^2 \begin{bmatrix} 1/\lambda_1 & 0 & \cdots & 0 \\ 0 & 1/\lambda_2 & \cdots & 0 \\ \vdots & \vdots & & \vdots \\ 0 & 0 & \cdots & 1/\lambda_n \end{bmatrix} \tag{7-24}$$

where the λ's are assumed to be known positive numbers but σ^2 is unknown. If we then define a matrix $\mathbf{P}^{-1}$

$$\mathbf{P}^{-1} = \begin{bmatrix} \sqrt{\lambda_1} & 0 & \cdots & 0 \\ 0 & \sqrt{\lambda_2} & \cdots & 0 \\ \vdots & \vdots & & \vdots \\ 0 & 0 & \cdots & \sqrt{\lambda_n} \end{bmatrix} \tag{7-25}$$

then clearly

$$\mathbf{P}^{-1'}\mathbf{P}^{-1} = \boldsymbol{\Omega}^{-1}$$

and in accordance with (7-6) and (7-8) above

$$\mathbf{b} = (\mathbf{X}'\boldsymbol{\Omega}^{-1}\mathbf{X})^{-1}\mathbf{X}'\boldsymbol{\Omega}^{-1}\mathbf{y} \tag{7-26}$$

is a best linear unbiased estimator of $\boldsymbol{\beta}$ with variance–covariance matrix

$$\text{var}(\mathbf{b}) = \sigma^2(\mathbf{X}'\boldsymbol{\Omega}^{-1}\mathbf{X})^{-1} \tag{7-27}$$

For the case of a single explanatory variable

$$\mathbf{X}'\boldsymbol{\Omega}^{-1}\mathbf{X} = \begin{bmatrix} \sum_{i=1}^{n} \lambda_i & \sum_{i=1}^{n} \lambda_i X_i \\ \sum_{i=1}^{n} \lambda_i X_i & \sum_{i=1}^{n} \lambda_i X_i^2 \end{bmatrix}$$

and (7-26) gives the two simultaneous equations

$$\begin{aligned} b_1\Sigma\lambda + b_2\Sigma\lambda X &= \Sigma\lambda Y \\ b_1\Sigma\lambda X + b_2\Sigma\lambda X^2 &= \Sigma\lambda XY \end{aligned} \tag{7-28}$$

and from (7-27) the sampling variance of the regression slope b_2 is

$$\operatorname{var}(b_2) = \frac{\sigma^2\Sigma\lambda}{(\Sigma\lambda)(\Sigma\lambda X^2) - (\Sigma\lambda X)^2} \tag{7-29}$$

If we applied simple least-squares directly to $\mathbf{y} = \mathbf{X}\boldsymbol{\beta} + \mathbf{u}$ the estimator would be

$$\hat{\boldsymbol{\beta}} = (\mathbf{X}'\mathbf{X})^{-1}\mathbf{X}'\mathbf{y} \tag{7-30}$$

which would be unbiased. Its variance-covariance matrix would be

$$\begin{aligned} E[(\hat{\boldsymbol{\beta}} - \boldsymbol{\beta})(\hat{\boldsymbol{\beta}} - \boldsymbol{\beta})'] &= (\mathbf{X}'\mathbf{X})^{-1}\mathbf{X}'E(\mathbf{uu}')\mathbf{X}(\mathbf{X}'\mathbf{X})^{-1} \\ &= \sigma^2(\mathbf{X}'\mathbf{X})^{-1}\mathbf{X}'\boldsymbol{\Omega}\mathbf{X}(\mathbf{X}'\mathbf{X})^{-1} \end{aligned} \tag{7-31}$$

In the case of a single explanatory variable (7-30) reduces to the usual normal equations

$$\begin{aligned} n\hat{\beta}_1 + \hat{\beta}_2\Sigma X &= \Sigma Y \\ \hat{\beta}_1\Sigma X + \hat{\beta}_2\Sigma X^2 &= \Sigma XY \end{aligned} \tag{7-32}$$

while (7-31) gives the sampling variance of the regression slope as

$$\operatorname{var}(\hat{\beta}_2) = \frac{\sigma^2\left[\left(\Sigma\frac{1}{\lambda_i}\right)(\Sigma X_i)^2 - 2n\left(\Sigma\frac{1}{\lambda_i}X_i\right)(\Sigma X_i) + n^2\left(\Sigma\frac{1}{\lambda_i}X_i^2\right)\right]}{[n\Sigma X_i^2 - (\Sigma X_i)^2]^2} \tag{7-33}$$

Provided the λ's are known it is preferable to estimate the $\mathbf{b}$ of (7-26) rather than the simple least-squares $\hat{\boldsymbol{\beta}}$ of (7-30) since the former is a best linear unbiased estimate. The loss of efficiency in using $\hat{\boldsymbol{\beta}}$ rather than $\mathbf{b}$ may be illustrated for the case of one explanatory variable by making various assumptions about the form of heteroscedasticity.

Suppose, for example, that the variance of the disturbance term is proportional to the square of X, that is,

$$E(u_i^2) = \sigma^2 X_i^2 \qquad i = 1, \ldots, n \tag{7-34}$$

where σ^2 denotes some unknown constant. This situation is pictured in Fig. 7-1.

Comparing (7-24) and (7-34) shows that we may write

$$\sqrt{\lambda_i} = \frac{1}{X_i} \tag{7-35}$$

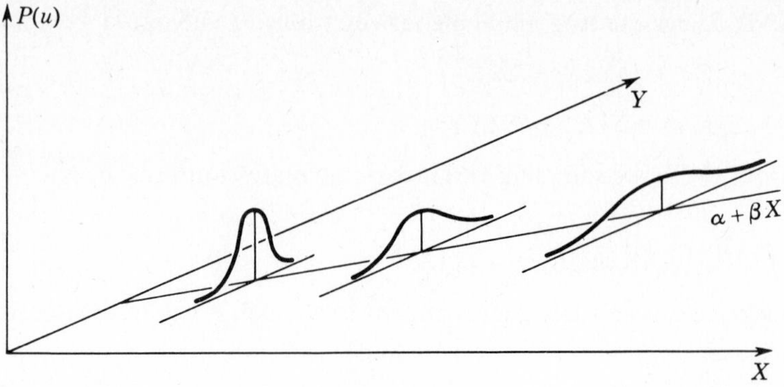

Fig. 7-1.

Making this substitution in (7-29) and (7-33) gives

$$\text{var}\,(b_2) = \frac{\sigma^2\Sigma(1/X_i^2)}{n\Sigma(1/X_i^2) - [\Sigma(1/X_i)]^2} \tag{7-36}$$

and

$$\text{var}\,(\hat{\beta}_2) = \frac{\sigma^2[(\Sigma X_i^2)(\Sigma X_i)^2 - 2n(\Sigma X_i^3)(\Sigma X_i) + n^2(\Sigma X_i^4)]}{[n\Sigma X_i^2 - (\Sigma X_i)^2]^2} \tag{7-37}$$

For a simple numerical comparison let us assume that X takes the values 1, 2, 3, 4, 5. We then find

$$\frac{\text{var}\,(b_2)}{\text{var}\,(\hat{\beta}_2)} = \frac{0.69}{1.24} = 0.56$$

so that the efficiency of the simple least-squares estimator is only about 56 per cent of that of the generalized least-squares estimator. Notice that if we apply the transformation $\mathbf{P}^{-1}$ as defined by (7-25) and (7-35) to

$$Y_i = \beta_1 + \beta_2 X_i + u_i \qquad i = 1, \ldots, n$$

we obtain

$$\frac{Y_i}{X_i} = \beta_1 \frac{1}{X_i} + \beta_2 + v_i \qquad i = 1, \ldots, n \tag{7-38}$$

where $v_i = u_i/X_i$. Since the generalized least-squares estimator is equivalent to applying simple least-squares to the *transformed* data we see from (7-38) that b_2, the generalized least-squares estimate of the coefficient of X in the original relation, is in fact the intercept in the regression of Y_i/X_i on $1/X_i$, and we note that (7-36) is the sampling variance of the intercept in a simple linear regression where $1/X_i$ has been used as the explanatory variable (cf. formula (2-19)). Thus if (7-34) is an appropriate assumption about the variance of the disturbance term in a two-variable, linear relation the simplest method of estimation is to divide through the relation by X_i, thus obtaining (7-38), and then apply simple least-squares to this transformed relation.

As a final example, suppose the variance of the disturbance term is proportional to X; that is

$$E(u_i^2) = \sigma^2 X_i.$$

Reference to (7-24) shows that we can now write

$$\lambda_i = \frac{1}{X_i}$$

Substitution in (7-29) and (7-33) now gives

$$\text{var}\,(b_2) = \frac{\sigma^2 \Sigma(1/X_i)}{\Sigma(1/X_i)\Sigma X_i - n^2}$$

and

$$\text{var}\,(\hat{\beta}_2) = \frac{\sigma^2[(\Sigma X_i)^3 - 2n(\Sigma X_i^2)(\Sigma X_i) + n^2(\Sigma X_i^3)]}{[n\Sigma X_i^2 - (\Sigma X_i)^2]^2}$$

For the above numerical example

$$\frac{\text{var}\,(b_2)}{\text{var}\,(\hat{\beta}_2)} = 0.83$$

which shows that the application of simple least-squares to the original data to be relatively more efficient than in the previous example, which is to be expected since the second example assumes a less radical departure from homoscedasticity than the first.

There is scant empirical evidence on the likely type of heteroscedasticity in economic relationships. A study of the residual variance around savings-income regressions found that "a good approximation states that the standard deviation of savings within each of several income classes is proportional to the average income of each class."[1] T. Lancaster has analyzed 200 observations of dividends (D) and profits (P) for 20 manufacturing companies over 10 consecutive years. He ordered the 200 observations by size of profits and divided them into 20 groups each containing 10 pairs of observations. He then computed the variance of dividends and the mean profit within each group and estimated the relationship

$$\text{var}\,(D_i) = \alpha \bar{P}_i^{\beta}$$

[1] G. Katona, *et al.*, *Contributions of Survey Methods to Econometrics*, Columbia University Press, 1954, p. 203.

or

$$\log \text{var}\,(D_i) = \log \alpha + \beta \log \bar{P}_i$$

obtaining a value of 1.47 for β and an r^2 of 0.88.[1] He appears to have computed the variance of dividends around the mean in each class rather than the variance about the regression function, but if the regression function is well specified the two estimates will not differ much. The two illustrative examples used earlier correspond to this type of relation with values of 2 and 1 for β, while the Katona example implies a value of 2 for β.

The possibility of testing the assumption of homoscedasticity depends on the nature of the sample data available. If we have, for example, plentiful cross-section data we might apply the standard test for homogeneous variances to the Y data. If we split the Y data into m classes according to the size of Y and compute

$$\lambda = \prod_{i=1}^{m} (s_i/n_i)^{n_i/2}/(\Sigma s_i/\Sigma n_i)^{\Sigma n_i/2}$$

where

$$s_i = \sum_{j=1}^{n_i} (Y_{ij} - \bar{Y}_i)^2$$

and n_i is the number of observations in the ith class, so that $\Sigma n_i = n$, then

$$\mu = -2 \log_e \lambda$$

will be distributed approximately as χ^2_{m-1} under the hypothesis of homogeneous variances.[2] This is a test based on the variation of the Y values around the sample means but if we have a well-specified regression function this will be very close to the variation about that function.

The more typical case of a smaller number of observations, which precludes this kind of grouping of the data, has been studied by Goldfield and Quandt.[3] They consider the linear model

$$\mathbf{y} = \mathbf{X}\boldsymbol{\beta} + \mathbf{u}$$

where the departure from homoscedasticity takes the form

$$E(u_i^2) = \sigma^2 X_{ji}^2$$

[1] T. Lancaster, "Grouping Estimators on Heteroscedastic Data," *J. Am. Statist. Assoc.*, vol. 63, p. 191, 1968.

[2] See, for example, A. M. Mood, *Introduction to the Theory of Statistics*, McGraw-Hill, New York, 1950, pp. 269–270.

[3] S. M. Goldfield and R. E. Quandt, "Some Tests for Homoscedasticity," *J. Am. Statist. Assoc.*, vol. 60, pp. 539–547, 1965.

that is, the disturbance variance increases with the square of one of the explanatory variables. They then proposed two alternative tests, one parametric and the other nonparametric.

In the parametric test the steps are as follows:

1. Order the observations in accordance with the size of X_j
2. Omit c central observations, the actual choice of c being discussed below
3. Fit separate regressions by ordinary least-squares to the first $(n - c)/2$ observations and to the last $(n - c)/2$ observations, provided, of course, that $(n - c)/2$ exceeds k, the number of parameters to be estimated
4. Let S_1 and S_2 denote the sum of the squared residuals from the two regressions (1 denoting that from the smaller X_j values and 2 that from the larger X_j values). Then

$$R = S_2/S_1$$

will, on the assumption of homoscedasticity, have the F distribution with $((n - c - 2k)/2, (n - c - 2k)/2)$ degrees of freedom. Under the alternative hypothesis R will tend to be large.

The power of the test clearly depends on the value of c. For very large values of c it will be small; on the other hand, as c is reduced the residual variances will likely move closer together and this will tend to offset the added power that comes from extra observations. Some experimental calculations by the authors for the case of one explanatory variable suggest an optimum value of about 8 for c when n is 30 and about 16 when n is 60.

The nonparametric test is based on the number of peaks in the ordered residuals; it is, of course, less powerful than the parametric test and interested readers should consult the original article for details. In an unpublished M.A. thesis at the University of Manchester, P. A. Gorringe has examined the power of an alternative nonparametric test. The suggested test is merely to compute the Spearman coefficient of rank correlation between the *absolute* values of the residuals and the X variable with which σ_i^2 might be associated.[1] Gorringe's sampling experiments suggest that this simple test is more powerful than the nonparametric test proposed by Goldfield and Quandt.

[1] If the values of two variables X and Y are replaced by their ranks X' and Y', which range over the values 1 to n, then the coefficient of rank correlation is the simple product-moment correlation coefficient computed from X' and Y'. Its value may be easily obtained from

$$r = 1 - \frac{6 \sum_{i=1}^{n} d_i^2}{n^3 - n}$$

where

$$d_i = X_i' - Y_i'$$

Yet another test for heteroscedasticity has recently been suggested by Glejser.[1] He proposes that the absolute values of the least-squares residuals $|e_i|$ should be regressed on some function of X_j, where X_j is thought to be the explanatory variable with which σ_i^2 might be associated. In practice this would mean considering fairly simple functions such as

$$\begin{aligned} &\text{(i)}\ |e| = a_0 + a_1 X_j \\ &\text{(ii)}\ |e| = a_0 + a_1 X_j^{-1} \\ &\text{(iii)}\ |e| = a_0 + a_1 X_j^{1/2} \quad \text{etc.} \end{aligned} \tag{7-39}$$

Glejser then suggests that decisions about homoscedasticity of the residuals should be taken on the basis of the statistical significance of the coefficients a_0 and a_1. An advantage of his approach is the possibility of distinguishing between cases of pure heteroscedasticity ($a_0 = 0$, $a_1 \neq 0$) and mixed heteroscedasticity ($a_0 \neq 0$, $a_1 \neq 0$). The relevance of the distinction is that different matrices would be used in the generalized least-squares estimation of $\boldsymbol{\beta}$. For example, case (i) above corresponds to the assumption that

$$u = v(\alpha_0 + \alpha_1 X_j)$$

where we may postulate $E(v) = 0$ and $E(v^2) = \sigma^2$. Then

$$E(\mathbf{uu}') = \sigma^2 \boldsymbol{\Omega}$$

$$= \sigma^2 \begin{bmatrix} (\alpha_0 + \alpha_1 X_{j1})^2 & 0 & \cdots & 0 \\ 0 & (\alpha_0 + \alpha_1 X_{j2})^2 & \cdots & 0 \\ \vdots & \vdots & & \vdots \\ 0 & 0 & \cdots & (\alpha_0 + \alpha_1 X_{jn})^2 \end{bmatrix}$$

Replacing α_0 and α_1 by their estimated values (if statistically significant) gives the appropriate $\hat{\boldsymbol{\Omega}}$ matrix for use in

$$\mathbf{b} = (\mathbf{X}'\hat{\boldsymbol{\Omega}}^{-1}\mathbf{X})^{-1}\mathbf{X}'\hat{\boldsymbol{\Omega}}^{-1}\mathbf{y}$$

Some sampling experiments by Glejser indicate that his test is slightly more powerful than the parametric test proposed by Goldfield and Quandt, except when the standard deviation of X_j is large ($\sigma_{X_j} = 30$ around a mean of 50). These comparisons, however, are based on the choice of the correct exponent for X_j in the Glejser regressions. This appears to be the main weakness of the Glejser approach for one does not know *a priori* the correct specification for the disturbance. An odd feature of the Glejser sampling experiments is that in those cases where the disturbance has been generated

[1] H. Glejser, "A New Test for Heteroscedasticity," *J. Am. Statist. Assoc.*, vol. 64, pp. 316–323, 1969.

by a *mixed* heteroscedastic pattern the test hardly ever picks this up and almost invariably indicates *pure* heteroscedasticity, which casts serious doubt on the claimed ability of the test to distinguish between the two cases. This together with the problems of specification suggest that the parametric test of Goldfield and Quandt or the Spearman rank test are preferable. If one of them rejects homoscedasticity the computation of a number of Glejser-type regressions might indicate the most suitable $\hat{\mathbf{\Omega}}$ matrix to use in obtaining the generalized least-squares estimates.

7-4 PURE AND MIXED ESTIMATION

It not infrequently happens that a regression equation yields results which are deemed surprising or unacceptable because they conflict with prior expectations held by the investigator. Such expectations may be derived from theoretical considerations in which case we may label them *a priori information*. Examples are that marginal productivities should be positive in a production function, or that own price has a negative sign in a demand function. Other expectations may be derived from previous statistical work which has yielded estimates of certain coefficients together with estimates of the sampling variances. We shall call such information *statistical prior information*. An example might be a prior estimate of the income elasticity in a demand function.

Theil and Goldberger have argued forcibly that the conventional approach of *pure* estimation in which neither of these types of information is incorporated in the formulation and estimation of the model is inadequate and that an attempt should be made to incorporate these types of information in the formal set-up of the model. Their work is based on that of Durbin, but their approach is slightly different and somewhat more general.[1] Their method begins with the fact that both *a priori* and statistical prior information may be expressed in the same way as

$$\mathbf{r} = \mathbf{R}\boldsymbol{\beta} + \mathbf{v} \tag{7–40}$$

where $\mathbf{r}$ is a known $g \times 1$ vector $(g \leq k)$, $\mathbf{R}$ a known $_{o} \times k$ matrix and $\mathbf{v}$ a $g \times 1$ vector of errors with

$$E(\mathbf{v}) = \mathbf{0} \quad \text{and} \quad E(\mathbf{v}\mathbf{v}') = \mathbf{\Psi} \tag{7-41}$$

$\mathbf{\Psi}$ likewise being assumed known. If, for example, prior information consists of unbiased estimates, b_1 and b_2, of the first two elements of $\boldsymbol{\beta}$, along with

[1] J. Durbin, "A Note on Regression when there is Extraneous Information about One of the Coefficients," *J. Am. Statist. Assoc.*, vol. 48, pp. 799–808, 1953; H. Theil and A. S. Goldberger, "On Pure and Mixed Statistical Estimation in Economics," *Intern. Econ. Rev.*, vol. 2, pp. 65–78, 1960; and H. Theil, "On the Use of Incomplete Prior Information in Regression Analysis," *J. Am. Statist. Assoc.*, vol. 58, 401–414, 1963.

their estimated sampling variances s_{11}, s_{22} and their covariance s_{12} we then have

$$\mathbf{r} = \begin{bmatrix} b_1 \\ b_2 \end{bmatrix} \qquad \mathbf{R} = \begin{bmatrix} 1 & 0 & 0 & \cdots & 0 \\ 0 & 1 & 0 & \cdots & 0 \end{bmatrix} \qquad \mathbf{\Psi} = \begin{bmatrix} s_{11} & s_{12} \\ s_{12} & s_{22} \end{bmatrix}$$

Or, to illustrate *a priori* information, suppose we feel reasonably sure that an income elasticity, β_3, lies between zero and one and probably between $\frac{1}{4}$ and $\frac{3}{4}$. We could express this as

$$\tfrac{1}{2} = \beta_3 + v \qquad Ev = 0 \qquad Ev^2 = \tfrac{1}{16}$$

so that

$$\beta_3 \pm \sigma_{\beta_3} \text{ gives a range from } \tfrac{1}{4} \text{ to } \tfrac{3}{4}$$

and

$$\beta_3 \pm 2\sigma_{\beta_3} \text{ gives a range from 0 to 1}$$

We can in this case set (7-40) as

$$\mathbf{r} = \tfrac{1}{2} \qquad \mathbf{R} = [0 \quad 0 \quad 1 \quad 0 \quad 0] \qquad \mathbf{\Psi} = \tfrac{1}{16}$$

Notice that (7-40) also covers the more general case of prior information relating to linear combinations of the elements of $\boldsymbol{\beta}$.

If (7-40) is combined with the basic model $\mathbf{y} = \mathbf{X}\boldsymbol{\beta} + \mathbf{u}$ we have

$$\begin{bmatrix} \mathbf{y} \\ \mathbf{r} \end{bmatrix} = \begin{bmatrix} \mathbf{X} \\ \mathbf{R} \end{bmatrix} \boldsymbol{\beta} + \begin{bmatrix} \mathbf{u} \\ \mathbf{v} \end{bmatrix} \tag{7-42}$$

where

$$E\begin{bmatrix} \mathbf{u} \\ \mathbf{v} \end{bmatrix} = \mathbf{0} \quad \text{and} \quad E\begin{bmatrix} \mathbf{u} \\ \mathbf{v} \end{bmatrix}[\mathbf{u}' \ \mathbf{v}'] = \begin{bmatrix} \sigma^2\mathbf{I}_n & 0 \\ 0 & \mathbf{\Psi} \end{bmatrix} \tag{7-43}$$

The off-diagonal sub-matrices in the second equation of (7-43) are set to zero on the assumption of independence between the sample and the prior information. Ordinary least-squares cannot be applied directly to estimate $\boldsymbol{\beta}$ in (7-42) since the variance–covariance matrix is not $\sigma^2\mathbf{I}_{n+g}$. Generalized least-squares, however, is an appropriate estimating procedure and yields

$$\mathbf{b} = \left[[\mathbf{X}' \ \mathbf{R}'] \begin{bmatrix} \sigma^2\mathbf{I}_n & \mathbf{0} \\ \mathbf{0} & \mathbf{\Psi} \end{bmatrix}^{-1} \begin{bmatrix} \mathbf{X} \\ \mathbf{R} \end{bmatrix} \right]^{-1} [\mathbf{X}' \ \mathbf{R}'] \begin{bmatrix} \sigma^2\mathbf{I}_n & \mathbf{0} \\ \mathbf{0} & \mathbf{\Psi} \end{bmatrix}^{-1} \begin{bmatrix} \mathbf{y} \\ \mathbf{r} \end{bmatrix}$$

$$= (\varphi\mathbf{X}'\mathbf{X} + \mathbf{R}'\mathbf{\Psi}^{-1}\mathbf{R})^{-1}(\varphi\mathbf{X}'\mathbf{y} + \mathbf{R}'\mathbf{\Psi}^{-1}\mathbf{r}) \tag{7-44}$$

where

$$\varphi = 1/\sigma^2 \tag{7-45}$$

The variance–covariance matrix of the estimate is given by

$$\text{var}(\mathbf{b}) = (\varphi\mathbf{X}'\mathbf{X} + \mathbf{R}'\mathbf{\Psi}^{-1}\mathbf{R})^{-1} \tag{7-46}$$

This suggested method raises a number of interesting questions. One may state formally that the **b** of (7-44) is a best linear unbiased estimator of the $\boldsymbol{\beta}$ of (7-42), where "best" refers to the sample and prior information taken together. At first sight this seems puzzling since the model (7-42) combines two qualitatively different types of data, namely, sample observations **y** and **X**, and arbitrary *a priori* numbers or statistical estimates in **r** and **R**. In a typical application the Y variable and hence the disturbance u might be measured in constant dollars per capita per annum, while v might refer to the error in an income elasticity and hence be dimensionless. However, the application of generalized least-squares means that it is a weighted sum of squares which is being minimized, namely

$$\frac{1}{\sigma^2}\mathbf{u}'\mathbf{u} + \mathbf{v}'\mathbf{\Psi}^{-1}\mathbf{v}$$

The correction of $\mathbf{u}'\mathbf{u}$ by the factor $(1/\sigma^2)$ and the use of $\mathbf{\Psi}^{-1}$ in the second term renders both terms dimensionless and obviates any problem in pooling the two types of data. In fact, Durbin's approach shows quite directly that the estimator (7-44) can be considered as a weighted average of two separate estimators.

Suppose, to use the notation of Durbin's article,

$$\mathbf{b}_1 = \text{vector of unbiased estimates of } \boldsymbol{\beta}_1 = \begin{bmatrix} \beta_1 \\ \beta_2 \\ \vdots \\ \beta_h \end{bmatrix}$$

with $\text{var}(\mathbf{b}_1) = \mathbf{V}_1$ and

$$\mathbf{b}_2 = \text{vector of unbiased estimates of } \boldsymbol{\beta} = \begin{bmatrix} \beta_1 \\ \beta_2 \\ \vdots \\ \beta_h \\ \vdots \\ \beta_k \end{bmatrix}$$

with $h \leq k$ and $\text{var}(\mathbf{b}_2) = \mathbf{V}_2$.

In the terminology of Theil–Goldberger $\mathbf{b}_1$ ($=\mathbf{r}$) is a vector of prior estimates of some or all of the components of $\boldsymbol{\beta}$, where we have numbered the elements of $\boldsymbol{\beta}$ so that the first h are those about which we have prior information. It follows then that $\mathbf{V}_1 = \boldsymbol{\Psi}$. The vector $\mathbf{b}_2$ is the vector of unbiased estimates of all the elements of $\boldsymbol{\beta}$, obtained from the current sample data. Thus

$$\mathbf{b}_2 = (\mathbf{X}'\mathbf{X})^{-1}\mathbf{X}'\mathbf{y}$$

and

$$\text{var}\,(\mathbf{b}_2) = \mathbf{V}_2 = \sigma^2(\mathbf{X}'\mathbf{X})^{-1}$$

We can then write

$$E\begin{bmatrix} \mathbf{b}_1 \\ \\ \mathbf{b}_2 \end{bmatrix} = \begin{bmatrix} \mathbf{I}_h & \mathbf{0} \\ \mathbf{I}_h & \mathbf{0} \\ \mathbf{0} & \mathbf{I}_{k-h} \end{bmatrix} \boldsymbol{\beta} = \mathbf{P}\boldsymbol{\beta} \tag{7-47}$$

where the subscripts indicate the order of the identity matrices. Also

$$\text{var}\begin{bmatrix} \mathbf{b}_1 \\ \mathbf{b}_2 \end{bmatrix} = \begin{bmatrix} \mathbf{V}_1 & \mathbf{0} \\ \mathbf{0} & \mathbf{V}_2 \end{bmatrix} = \mathbf{V} \tag{7-48}$$

The generalized least-squares model in which

$$\mathbf{y} = \mathbf{X}\boldsymbol{\beta} + \mathbf{u}$$

with

$$E(\mathbf{u}) = 0 \quad \text{and} \quad E(\mathbf{uu}') = \mathbf{V}$$

may be re-stated as

$$E(\mathbf{y}) = \mathbf{X}\boldsymbol{\beta} \quad \text{and} \quad \text{var}\,(\mathbf{y}) = \mathbf{V}$$

and it then follows directly from (7-47) and (7-48) that the best linear unbiased estimator of $\boldsymbol{\beta}$ is

$$\mathbf{b} = (\mathbf{P}'\mathbf{V}^{-1}\mathbf{P})^{-1}\mathbf{P}'\mathbf{V}^{-1}\begin{bmatrix} \mathbf{b}_1 \\ \mathbf{b}_2 \end{bmatrix} \tag{7-49}$$

or

$$(\mathbf{P}'\mathbf{V}^{-1}\mathbf{P})\mathbf{b} = \mathbf{P}'\mathbf{V}^{-1}\begin{bmatrix} \mathbf{b}_1 \\ \mathbf{b}_2 \end{bmatrix} \tag{7-50}$$

The $\mathbf{R}$ of the Theil–Goldberger formulation is in this case given by

$$\mathbf{R} = [\mathbf{I}_h \quad \mathbf{0}]$$

where $\mathbf{R}$ is the order $h \times k$, $\mathbf{I}_h$ is the identity matrix of order h and $\mathbf{0}$ is the null matrix of order $h \times (k - h)$. Using this result then gives

$$\mathbf{P}'\mathbf{V}^{-1} = [\mathbf{R}'\mathbf{V}_1^{-1} \quad \mathbf{V}_2^{-1}]$$

and

$$\mathbf{P}'\mathbf{V}^{-1}\mathbf{P} = (\mathbf{R}'\mathbf{V}_1^{-1}\mathbf{R} + \mathbf{V}_2^{-1})$$

so that (7-50) becomes

$$(\mathbf{R}'\mathbf{V}_1^{-1}\mathbf{R} + \mathbf{V}_2^{-1})\mathbf{b} = \mathbf{R}'\mathbf{V}_1^{-1}\mathbf{b}_1 + \mathbf{V}_2^{-1}\mathbf{b}_2$$

Finally, using

$$\mathbf{V}_2^{-1} = \frac{1}{\sigma^2}(\mathbf{X}'\mathbf{X}) = \varphi(\mathbf{X}'\mathbf{X})$$

and

$$\begin{aligned}\mathbf{V}_2^{-1}\mathbf{b}_2 &= \varphi(\mathbf{X}'\mathbf{X})(\mathbf{X}'\mathbf{X})^{-1}\mathbf{X}'\mathbf{y} \\ &= \varphi\mathbf{X}'\mathbf{y}\end{aligned}$$

the equation may be written

$$(\mathbf{R}'\mathbf{\Psi}^{-1}\mathbf{R} + \varphi\mathbf{X}'\mathbf{X})\mathbf{b} = \mathbf{R}'\mathbf{\Psi}^{-1}\mathbf{r} + \varphi\mathbf{X}'\mathbf{y} \tag{7-51}$$

which is the Theil–Goldberger equation (7-44).

Secondly, Theil and Goldberger developed the above procedure in their 1960 article in order to deal with apparent conflicts between prior information and sample information. As is clear from Durbin's approach the resultant mixed estimate **b** is a weighted average of the two sets of information. As an illustration Table 7-1 shows some estimates from their illustrative example.[1] The equation being estimated is a supply equation in which γ is expected to be positive and both β's to be negative. The pure

Table 7-1 Alternative estimates of the meat supply equation using *a priori* information on all elasticities

Coefficient	*Pure*	*Mixed*		**r**
		Initial	*5th Iteration*	
γ	−0.321	0.412	0.992	0.900
β_1	−0.278	−0.444	−0.620	−0.940
β_2	0.603	0.225	−0.253	−0.810
σ^2	21.13	74.39	166.44	

[1] Theil and Goldberger, *op. cit.*, 1960, p. 77.

estimates are two-stage least-squares estimates (see Chap. 13) and we see that γ and β_2 have signs contrary to expectation. The final column of the table shows the **r** vector containing arbitrarily specified values for all three coefficients and the two remaining columns show the initial mixed estimates and those obtained at the fifth iteration. The reason for the iteration is that $\varphi = 1/\sigma^2$ in (7-44) is unknown and one can iterate on s^2 and **b** as described below. It is clear that the initial mixed estimates lie roughly midway between the pure estimates and the *a priori* values, and that the final iteration mixed estimates are closer to the *a priori* values than to the pure estimates. But should one pool sample and prior information when there are such startling conflicts between them? The resultant mixed estimate will in effect be a compromise, but if the conflict is a real one an average of the two opposing positions is not necessarily the best solution. For example, there may have been a break in structure between the period yielding the statistical prior information and that yielding the sample information, in which case one wants pure estimates from the period of interest rather than mongrel estimates averaging two sets of parameters. Or the sample relationship may have been badly specified so that one was not really getting estimates of the elasticities or coefficients about which one had valid prior information. Or perhaps the prior information is suspect, coming either from a poor sample or poor theory.

In the second article Theil shows his awareness of these problems and in fact proposes a test for the compatibility of prior and sample information in the case of a single equation. The proposed compatibility statistic is

$$\gamma = (\mathbf{r} - \mathbf{R}\hat{\boldsymbol{\beta}})'[s^2\mathbf{R}(\mathbf{X}'\mathbf{X})^{-1}\mathbf{R}' + \boldsymbol{\Psi}]^{-1}(\mathbf{r} - \mathbf{R}\hat{\boldsymbol{\beta}})$$

where $\hat{\boldsymbol{\beta}} = (\mathbf{X}'\mathbf{X})^{-1}\mathbf{X}'\mathbf{y}$ is the estimated vector of coefficients obtained by applying ordinary least-squares to the sample data, and s^2 is the corresponding estimate of σ^2, that is,

$$s^2 = (\mathbf{y}'\mathbf{y} - \mathbf{y}'\mathbf{X}(\mathbf{X}'\mathbf{X})^{-1}\mathbf{X}'\mathbf{y})/(n - k) \tag{7-52}$$

Theil shows that for large samples γ will be distributed approximately as χ^2 with g degrees of freedom.[1] By implication if γ exceeds a preselected critical value the prior and sample information are incompatible and the mixed estimate should not be computed. For the data underlying Table 7-1 I have estimated the value of γ to 41.48. The test is not strictly applicable here,

[1] Theil, *op. cit.*, 1963, 406–407.

since it is a single equation test and this is a simultaneous equation problem, but the empirical γ so far exceeds the critical points of the χ^2 distribution ($\chi^2_{0.01} = 13.3$) that there does appear to be a real incompatibility here between the sample and the prior information.

This example illustrates the situation that arises in Bayesian methods of estimation where typically one pools prior and sample information to yield a mixed (posterior) estimator. If one has very strong *a priori* beliefs or very precise prior information the diagonal elements in $\mathbf{\Psi}$ will be correspondingly small and it would take a lot of new sample information to alter one's belief in the prior information; the mixed estimates will then be strongly influenced by the prior information. If the prior information is less strong it will exercise less influence on the final estimator. The crucial question, of course, is the validity of the prior information and its compatibility with the sample data.

A third problem is that the formula for the mixed estimator (7-44) involves $\varphi = 1/\sigma^2$ and σ^2 is in general unknown. If one starts with an initial estimate s_1^2 substitution in (7-44) will yield a mixed estimate, say, $\mathbf{b}_1$: application of this in the sample data will produce a new set of residuals, $\mathbf{y} - \mathbf{X}\mathbf{b}_1$, from which we can derive a new estimate s_2^2 of σ^2 and hence a new $\mathbf{b}_2$ vector and so on. In the original illustration Theil and Goldberger proceed to five iterations before the estimates stabilize at two significant figures, at which stage the residual variance in the sample data has risen to about eight times the initial value corresponding to the pure estimates. In the second paper Theil apparently recommends simply an initial mixed estimate based on s^2 as defined in (7-52) on the grounds that it is impossible to gain in asymptotic efficiency by iteration on s^2 and $\mathbf{b}$ as the $\mathbf{b}$ vectors will all have the same asymptotic distribution.[1]

An alternative approach to this problem has been developed by Judge and Takayama.[2] They deal with the case where prior knowledge on the coefficients comes in the form of inequality restrictions. Such restrictions could, of course, be handled in the Theil-Goldberger method by choosing a mean and variance for the prior distribution of the parameter which will only yield values outside the postulated upper and lower limits with arbitrarily low probabilities. Tackling it directly, however, gives a quadratic programming problem for we have to minimize $(\mathbf{y} - \mathbf{X}\mathbf{b})'(\mathbf{y} - \mathbf{X}\mathbf{b})$ subject to various inequality constraints. Judge and Takayama suggest that this should be done by use of the standard simplex version of the quadratic programming algorithm developed by Wolfe. Interested readers should consult their article for the details.

[1] If f_n represents the sampling distribution of an estimator based on a sample of n observations, the asymptotic distribution is the limiting value of f_n as n tends to infinity.

[2] G. C. Judge and T. Takayama, "Inequality Restrictions in Regression Analysis," *J. Am. Statist. Assoc.* vol. 61, pp. 166–181, 1966.

7-5 GROUPING OF OBSERVATIONS[1]

Grouping of observations is an important topic for several reasons. First of all most survey data are only published in group form so that estimation and hypothesis testing must be carried out on the grouped data rather than on the original observations. The same is true of much time series information which is published in highly aggregative rather than disaggregated form. And it is sometimes the case that an investigator faced with very large numbers of observations will undertake some prior grouping of the data in order to reduce the sheer bulk of the calculations, but this is a misguided practice.

To see what happens when grouping takes place let us suppose that the model,

$$\mathbf{y} = \mathbf{X}\boldsymbol{\beta} + \mathbf{u} \tag{7-53}$$

with $\mathbf{X}$ of order $n \times k$ and rank $k(<n)$, $E(\mathbf{u}) = \mathbf{0}$ and $E(\mathbf{uu}') = \sigma^2\mathbf{I}$, applies to the original observations. Instead of presenting the original data $\mathbf{y}$ and $\mathbf{X}$, the observations are arranged in m groups, where $k < m < n$, and only the group means are given for each of the variables. Let $\bar{\mathbf{y}}$, $\bar{\mathbf{X}}$, and $\bar{\mathbf{u}}$ denote the appropriate vectors and matrices of group means, where $\bar{\mathbf{y}}$ and $\bar{\mathbf{u}}$ are both $m \times 1$ column vectors and $\bar{\mathbf{X}}$ is an $m \times k$ matrix. Relation (7-53) then implies

$$\bar{\mathbf{y}} = \bar{\mathbf{X}}\boldsymbol{\beta} + \bar{\mathbf{u}} \tag{7-54}$$

The relation between the original and the grouped data may be written

$$\bar{\mathbf{y}} = \mathbf{Gy}, \qquad \bar{\mathbf{X}} = \mathbf{GX}, \qquad \bar{\mathbf{u}} = \mathbf{Gu} \tag{7-55}$$

where $\mathbf{G}$ is a grouping matrix of order $m \times n$. For example, if the first group consists of the first, second, and fourth observations, the second group consists of the third, fifth, sixth, and seventh observations and the mth group consists of the $(n - 1)$th and nth observation, $\mathbf{G}$ takes the form

$$\mathbf{G} = \begin{bmatrix} \frac{1}{3} & \frac{1}{3} & 0 & \frac{1}{3} & 0 & 0 & 0 & 0 & \cdots & 0 & 0 \\ 0 & 0 & \frac{1}{4} & 0 & \frac{1}{4} & \frac{1}{4} & \frac{1}{4} & 0 & \cdots & 0 & 0 \\ \vdots & & & & & & & & & \vdots & \vdots \\ 0 & 0 & 0 & 0 & 0 & 0 & 0 & 0 & \cdots & \frac{1}{2} & \frac{1}{2} \end{bmatrix} \tag{7-56}$$

[1] The basic references for this section are: S. J. Prais and J. Aitchison, "The Grouping of Observations in Regression Analysis," *Rev. Intern. Statist. Inst.*, vol. 1, pp. 1–22, 1954; J. S. Cramer, "Efficient Grouping, Regression and Correlation in Engel Curve Analysis," *J. Am. Statist. Assoc.*, vol. 59, pp. 233–250, 1964; Y. Haitovsky, "Unbiased Multiple Regression Coefficients Estimated from One-way-classification Tables when the Cross Classifications are Unknown," *J. Am. Statist. Assoc.*, vol. 61, pp. 720–728, 1966; Y. Haitovsky, "Regression Estimation from Grouped Observations," National Bureau of Economic Research, New York, October, 1967; G. H. Orcutt, H. W. Watts, and J. B. Edwards, "Data Aggregation and Information Loss," *Am. Econ. Rev.*, September, 1968.

From the properties of $\mathbf{u}$ it is clear that

$$E(\bar{\mathbf{u}}) = 0 \quad \text{and} \quad E\bar{\mathbf{u}}\bar{\mathbf{u}}' = \sigma^2\mathbf{GG}' \tag{7-57}$$

Thus the best linear unbiased estimator of $\boldsymbol{\beta}$, if we are restricted to the data $\bar{\mathbf{y}}$, $\bar{\mathbf{X}}$, is found by applying generalized least-squares to (7-54), that is,

$$\mathbf{b} = [\bar{\mathbf{X}}'(\mathbf{GG}')^{-1}\bar{\mathbf{X}}]^{-1}\bar{\mathbf{X}}'(\mathbf{GG}')^{-1}\bar{\mathbf{y}} \tag{7-58}$$

with variance–covariance matrix

$$\text{var}(\mathbf{b}) = \sigma^2[\bar{\mathbf{X}}'(\mathbf{GG}')^{-1}\bar{\mathbf{X}}]^{-1} \tag{7-59}$$

In effect, grouping has destroyed the homoscedastic properties assumed for $\mathbf{u}$ in the original model so that generalized least-squares has to be applied to the grouped data.

It is possible in this case to give a simple interpretation to the generalized least-squares estimator. From the grouping matrix defined in (7-56) we see that $\mathbf{GG}'$ is an $m \times m$ diagonal matrix

$$\mathbf{GG}' = \begin{bmatrix} \frac{1}{3} & 0 & \cdots & 0 \\ 0 & \frac{1}{4} & \cdots & 0 \\ \vdots & \vdots & & \vdots \\ 0 & 0 & \cdots & \frac{1}{2} \end{bmatrix}$$

so that

$$(\mathbf{GG}')^{-1} = \begin{bmatrix} 3 & 0 & \cdots & 0 \\ 0 & 4 & \cdots & 0 \\ \vdots & \vdots & & \vdots \\ 0 & 0 & \cdots & 2 \end{bmatrix}$$

and this acts as *weighting* matrix in which the weights are the numbers in the various groups. Clearly if the groups contained equal numbers of observations the grouped disturbances would be homoscedastic if the original disturbances were and ordinary least-squares could be applied to (7-54). If we work out (7-58) explicitly for the case of a single explanatory variable the generalized least-squares estimates of intercept (b_1) and slope (b_2) are given by

$$\begin{aligned} nb_1 + b_2 \sum_{i=1}^{m} n_i\bar{X}_i &= \sum_{i=1}^{m} n_i\bar{Y}_i \\ b_1 \sum_{i=1}^{m} n_i\bar{X}_i + b_2 \sum_{i=1}^{m} n_i\bar{X}_i^2 &= \sum_{i=1}^{m} n_i\bar{X}_i\bar{Y}_i \end{aligned} \tag{7-60}$$

where n_i denotes the number of observations in the ith group and $\sum_{i=1}^{m} n_i = n$. Comparing (7-60) with the normal equations for fitting a straight line by ordinary least-squares we see that the only difference is that each element in the summations in (7-60) is weighted by the appropriate cell frequency.

For any given grouping matrix, **G**, the generalized least-squares estimator **b** of (7-58) is best linear unbiased. The sampling variances of these coefficients are necessarily greater than those of the ordinary least-squares estimates from the original observations (should these be available). The loss of efficiency in moving from individual to grouped data depends on the manner of grouping, and finally we may note that the R^2 computed from grouped data can often be substantially greater than the R^2 for the individual data and may be quite a misleading indicator of the latter. These points may be illustrated by the two-variable model. Suppose we have

$$Y_{ij} = \alpha + \beta X_{ij} + u_{ij} \qquad i = 1, \ldots, m; \; j = 1, \ldots, n_i \tag{7-61}$$

the u_{ij} being independent random disturbances drawn from a normal population with zero mean and variance σ_u^2. The i subscript on each variable denotes the group and the j subscript position within the group, and the total sample size is $n = \sum_{i=1}^{m} n_i$. The group means are defined as

$$\bar{X}_i = \sum_{j=1}^{n_i} X_{ij}/n_i \qquad \bar{Y}_i = \sum_{j=1}^{n_i} Y_{ij}/n_i \qquad i = 1, \ldots, m$$

and the overall means as

$$\bar{\bar{X}} = \sum_{i=1}^{m} \sum_{j=1}^{n_i} X_{ij}/n = \sum_{i=1}^{m} n_i \bar{X}_i/n$$

$$\bar{\bar{Y}} = \sum_{i=1}^{m} \sum_{j=1}^{n_i} Y_{ij}/n = \sum_{i=1}^{m} n_i \bar{Y}_i/n$$

The estimate of the regression slope based on the individual data is

$$\hat{\beta} = \sum_{ij} (X_{ij} - \bar{\bar{X}})(Y_{ij} - \bar{\bar{Y}}) / \sum_{ij} (X_{ij} - \bar{\bar{X}})^2$$

with sampling variance

$$\text{var}(\hat{\beta}) = \sigma_u^2 / \sum_{ij} (X_{ij} - \bar{\bar{X}})^2 \tag{7-62}$$

The generalized least-squares estimate of the regression slope based on the grouped data is

$$b = \sum_i n_i(\bar{X}_i - \bar{\bar{X}})(\bar{Y}_i - \bar{\bar{Y}}) / \sum_i n_i(\bar{X}_i - \bar{\bar{X}})^2$$

with sampling variance

$$\operatorname{var}(b) = \sigma_u^2 / \sum_i n_i(\bar{X}_i - \bar{\bar{X}})^2 \tag{7-63}$$

Thus

$$\frac{\operatorname{var}(\hat{\beta})}{\operatorname{var}(b)} = \frac{\sum_i n_i(\bar{X}_i - \bar{\bar{X}})^2}{\sum_{ij} (X_{ij} - \bar{\bar{X}})^2} \tag{7-64}$$

which is necessarily less than one because of the identity

$$\sum_{ij} (X_{ij} - \bar{\bar{X}})^2 \equiv \sum_i n_i(\bar{X}_i - \bar{\bar{X}})^2 + \sum_{ij} (X_{ij} - \bar{X}_i)^2 \tag{7-65}$$

The last two formulae show that the drop in precision from individual to grouped data will be minimized if we can select a grouping which will maximize the *between* group variation of X in relation to the *within* group variation. This is a reason for the common practice of grouping by the size of the X variable.

The effect of grouping on R^2 may be illustrated by supposing that we are fitting the model

$$Y_{ij} = \alpha + \beta X_{ij} + u_{ij} \qquad i = 1, \ldots, m;\ j = 1, \ldots, r$$

where for simplicity we are now assuming an equal number of observations in each group. The R^2 that results from the fitting to all $n = mr$ original observations is approximately

$$R_1^2 = 1 - \frac{mr\sigma_u^2}{\sum_{ij} (Y_{ij} - \bar{\bar{Y}})^2}$$

If we work with group means the relationship is

$$\bar{Y}_i = \alpha + \beta \bar{X}_i + \bar{u}_i$$

and the assumption of equal numbers in each class means that this relation can be fitted by ordinary least-squares, giving

$$R_2^2 = 1 - \frac{m\sigma_{\bar{u}}^2}{\sum_i (\bar{Y}_i - \bar{\bar{Y}})^2}$$

$$= 1 - \frac{m\sigma_u^2}{r\Sigma(\bar{Y}_i - \bar{\bar{Y}})^2} \qquad \text{since } \sigma_{\bar{u}}^2 = \sigma_u^2/r$$

From the basic identity

$$\sum_{ij} (Y_{ij} - \bar{\bar{Y}})^2 \equiv \sum_{ij} (Y_{ij} - \bar{Y}_i)^2 + r \sum_i (\bar{Y}_i - \bar{\bar{Y}})^2$$

it follows that if the grouping procedure is random then

$$\sum_{ij} (Y_{ij} - \bar{\bar{Y}})^2/(mr - 1) \quad \text{and} \quad r\sum_{i} (\bar{Y}_i - \bar{\bar{Y}})^2/(m - 1)$$

are essentially unbiased estimates of the *same* variance. In that case R_1^2 and R_2^2 will be approximately the same. However, if we have a purposive grouping in which we have attempted to maximize the between-group variation compared with the within-group variation, then $\sum_i (\bar{Y}_i - \bar{\bar{Y}})^2$ will be much greater than in the case of a random grouping and so R_2^2 will exceed R_1^2. Some empirical confirmations of this result are given in Table 7-5 below and others may be found in Cramer's article.

The model in (7-54) and (7-55) allows for more than one explanatory variable but so far has not been explicit about how the grouping matrix **G** has been derived. For the case of two or more explanatory variables there are two distinct possibilities.

1. A complete cross-classification tabulation is available. For example, if we have two explanatory variables (X_2 and X_3) subdivided into m_2 and m_3 classes respectively, there are then $m_2 m_3$ possible cells and a complete cross-classification means having the frequencies and the means of the Y, X_2, and X_3 observations *for each cell.*
2. Only one-way classifications are available. For the previous example this would imply classifying the data first of all by the m_2 classes of X_2 and giving the frequencies and means of Y, X_2, and X_3 for each group and then doing the same for the m_3 classes of X_3.

As a numerical illustration consider the data in Table 7-2 which are those already given in a previous example in Table 5-4. Suppose we set up three groups based on X_2, namely, $X_2 < 110$, $110 \le X_2 < 120$, $X_2 \ge 120$,

Table 7-2

No. of observation	Y	X_2	X_3
1	100	100	100
2	106	104	99
3	107	106	110
4	120	111	126
5	110	111	113
6	116	115	103
7	123	120	102
8	133	124	103
9	137	126	98

and two groups based on X_3, namely, $X_3 < 110$, $X_3 \geq 110$.[1] This then gives six possible pairs of groups for X_2 and X_3 taken together and the reader can easily verify that the complete cross-classification of this data is shown in Table 7-3.

Table 7-3 Complete cross-classification

Definition of group	*Members of group*	*Group frequency*	*Group means*		
			$\bar{Y}_i$	$\bar{X}_{2i}$	$\bar{X}_{3i}$
$X_2 < 110, X_3 < 110$	1, 2	2	103	102	99.5
$X_2 < 110, X_3 \geq 110$	3	1	107	106	110
$110 \leq X_2 < 120, X_3 < 110$	6	1	116	115	103
$110 \leq X_2 < 120, X_3 \geq 110$	4, 5	2	115	111	119.5
$X_2 \geq 120, X_3 < 110$	7, 8, 9	3	131	$123\frac{1}{3}$	101
$X_2 \geq 120, X_3 \geq 110$		0			

The grouping matrix that would yield Table 7-3 is thus

$$\mathbf{G} = \begin{bmatrix} \frac{1}{2} & \frac{1}{2} & 0 & 0 & 0 & 0 & 0 & 0 & 0 \\ 0 & 0 & 1 & 0 & 0 & 0 & 0 & 0 & 0 \\ 0 & 0 & 0 & 0 & 0 & 1 & 0 & 0 & 0 \\ 0 & 0 & 0 & \frac{1}{2} & \frac{1}{2} & 0 & 0 & 0 & 0 \\ 0 & 0 & 0 & 0 & 0 & 0 & \frac{1}{3} & \frac{1}{3} & \frac{1}{3} \end{bmatrix} \tag{7-66}$$

and we see that

$$(\mathbf{GG}')^{-1} = \begin{bmatrix} 2 & 0 & 0 & 0 & 0 \\ 0 & 1 & 0 & 0 & 0 \\ 0 & 0 & 1 & 0 & 0 \\ 0 & 0 & 0 & 2 & 0 \\ 0 & 0 & 0 & 0 & 3 \end{bmatrix}$$

is a diagonal matrix with the cell frequencies displayed on the diagonal. On the other hand, if only one-way classifications are prepared from Table 7-2 the data presented would be as shown in Table 7-4. This data is equivalent

[1] Both groupings break the rule given above for a single variable that the number of groups should exceed the number of parameters to be estimated. When we have more than one explanatory variable some estimation methods involve a pooling of groups so that the requirement will be satisfied for all variables taken together; other methods do require the condition to be satisfied for each variable. Our main purpose here is to keep the illustration as simple as possible.

to pooling the grouping matrices corresponding to the X_2 and the X_3 classifications, giving,

$$\mathbf{G}^* = \begin{bmatrix} \frac{1}{3} & \frac{1}{3} & \frac{1}{3} & 0 & 0 & 0 & 0 & 0 & 0 \\ 0 & 0 & 0 & \frac{1}{3} & \frac{1}{3} & \frac{1}{3} & 0 & 0 & 0 \\ 0 & 0 & 0 & 0 & 0 & 0 & \frac{1}{3} & \frac{1}{3} & \frac{1}{3} \\ \frac{1}{6} & \frac{1}{6} & 0 & 0 & 0 & \frac{1}{6} & \frac{1}{6} & \frac{1}{6} & \frac{1}{6} \\ 0 & 0 & \frac{1}{3} & \frac{1}{3} & \frac{1}{3} & 0 & 0 & 0 & 0 \end{bmatrix} \tag{7-67}$$

Table 7-4 One-way classification

Definition of group	*Members of group*	*Group means*		
		$\bar{Y}_i$	$\bar{X}_{2i}$	$\bar{X}_{3i}$
$X_2 < 100$	1, 2, 3	104	103	103
$110 \leq X_2 < 120$	4, 5, 6	115	112	114
$X_2 \geq 120$	7, 8, 9	131	123	101
$X_3 < 110$	1, 2, 6, 7, 8, 9	119	114	100
$X_3 \geq 110$	3, 4, 5	112	109	116

As far as estimation is concerned, if the complete cross-classification is available, formulae (7-58) and (7-59) can be applied directly to the cell means with $(\mathbf{GG}')^{-1}$ being a diagonal matrix with the cell frequencies on the principal diagonal. This is equivalent to weighting the cell means with the corresponding cell frequencies. If only single classifications are available there are three possible approaches. One is to estimate $\boldsymbol{\beta}$ using the cell means provided by the classification based on X_2, repeat the estimation with the data from the X_3 classification and so on, provided of course that the number of groups in each classification exceeds the number of parameters to be estimated. This procedure is unsatisfactory as it yields in general $(k - 1)$ different estimates of $\boldsymbol{\beta}$, which often display very substantial variation. A second method due to H. S. Houthakkar is to pool the separate grouping matrices to form $\mathbf{G}^*$, as in (7-67), and then to use $\mathbf{G}^*$ in place of $\mathbf{G}$ in formulae (7-58) and (7-59).[1] One difficulty is that pooled matrices of the type $\mathbf{G}^*$ do not have full rank. It is, for example, easy to see that the $\mathbf{G}^*$ in (7-67) has rank four. Thus $(\mathbf{G}^*\mathbf{G}^{*\prime})$ will have rank four and will be singular so that $(\mathbf{G}^*\mathbf{G}^{*\prime})^{-1}$ does not exist. If the pooled matrix is based on $(k - 1)$ separate classifications there will in general be $(k - 2)$ redundant rows in $\mathbf{G}^*$. Haitovsky suggests omitting the last row of all but one of the separate

[1] See Haitovsky, *op. cit.*, 1966 and 1967 for a description of the Houthakker method, which has not been published.

grouping matrices that go to form **G*** thus producing an amended **G*** of full rank. The corresponding rows must also be deleted from the data matrices.

The third method, due to Haitovsky, may be illustrated with a two-variable model

$$Y = \beta_1 + \beta_2 X_2 + \beta_3 X_3 + u \tag{7-68}$$

which may be written in terms of deviations from overall means (that is, means taken over the complete sample of n observations)

$$y = \beta_2 x_2 + \beta_3 x_3 + (u - \bar{u}) \tag{7-69}$$

Form an estimate $\tilde{b}_2$ of β_2 by the simple regression of y on x_2 from the table based on the X_2 classification, and likewise an estimate $\tilde{b}_3$ of β_3 by the simple regression of y on x_3 from the table based on the X_3 classification. Both estimates will be biased since we have in each case committed a specification error by leaving out a relevant variable. Thus

$$\begin{aligned} E(\tilde{b}_2) &= \beta_2 + \beta_3 \frac{\Sigma_2 x_2 x_3}{\Sigma_2 x_2^2} \\ E(\tilde{b}_3) &= \beta_2 \frac{\Sigma_3 x_2 x_3}{\Sigma_3 x_3^2} + \beta_3 \end{aligned} \tag{7-70}$$

where the subscript on the summation sign indicates the table used for the computation. Unbiased estimators, b_2 and b_3, may then be obtained by solving the equations

$$\begin{aligned} \tilde{b}_2 &= b_2 + b_3 \frac{\Sigma_2 x_2 x_3}{\Sigma_2 x_2^2} \\ \tilde{b}_3 &= b_2 \frac{\Sigma_3 x_3 x_2}{\Sigma_3 x_3^2} + b_3 \end{aligned} \tag{7-71}$$

and the intercept estimated as

$$b_1 = \bar{Y} - b_2 \bar{X}_2 - b_3 \bar{X}_3$$

Table 7-5 shows the results of applying these various methods to sample data collected by H. S. Houthakker on 1218 households in order to estimate the model

$$Y = \beta_1 + \beta_2 X_2 + \beta_3 X_3 + u$$

where

Y = net purchase of automobiles

X_2 = income

X_3 = value of automobile inventory held at the beginning of the year

Table 7-5[1]

Model	β_1	β_2	β_3	R^2
1218	17.10 (7.30)	0.75781 (0.1398)	−0.17778 (0.0367)	0.03465
56	16.47 (10.32)	0.74734 (0.1203)	−0.16242 (0.0323)	0.49694
Houthakker	18.08	0.72633 (0.1259)	−0.17186 (0.0338)	0.81390
X_2 Table	10.86	0.55051 (1.6139)	0.03819 (1.8752)	0.72841
X_3 Table	73.74	−0.65315 (2.5391)	−0.09312 (0.1572)	0.90981
Haitovsky	18.03	0.72713 (0.1033)	−0.17177 (0.0282)	0.77045

[1] Haitovsky, *op. cit.*, 1967, p. IV-9.

The figures in parentheses are estimated standard errors, and it is a little puzzling that those in lines 2, 3, and 6 are with one exception all less than those in line 1. The true standard errors increase with grouping but the estimated ones depend on the estimated residual variances in grouped and ungrouped data and may not always reflect small increases. There are several very interesting features about this table. The first row refers to the estimates based on all 1218 individual observations; the coefficients have the expected signs and are reasonably well determined, but R^2 is quite low. The data were grouped by 7 income classes and 8 stock classes: the second row shows the estimates from the complete cross-classification by 56 cells; the estimated coefficients are quite close to those from the first row, but R^2 is much higher. The Houthakker and Haitovsky methods yield very similar coefficients with slightly smaller standard errors for Haitovsky. The estimates derived from either the X_2 table or the X_3 table, however, are very imprecise and wholly misleading.

Orcutt and his associates are concerned with analyzing the extent of the information loss when various degrees of data aggregation take place. For this purpose they construct a very simple micro-analytic model consisting of n spending units governed by the equation

$$E_{it} = \sigma + \alpha Y_{i,t-1} + \beta M_{i,t-1} + u_{it} \qquad (7\text{-}72)$$

$$M_{it} = M_{i,t-1} + Y_{it} - E_{it} \qquad (7\text{-}73)$$

$$Y_{it} = (1 - R_t)(E_t + G_t)(I_{it}/I_t) \qquad (7\text{-}74)$$

$$I_{it} = a_0 + a_1 I_{i,t-1} + v_{it} \qquad (7\text{-}75)$$

where for the ith unit at time t

E_{it} = expenditures

M_{it} = net financial assets

Y_{it} = disposable income

I_{it} = index for distributing income

u_{it}, v_{it} = stochastic terms for expenditures and income distribution respectively

The variables relating to government activities at time t are G_t = government expenditure and R_t = tax rate on aggregate income of the spending units. Since the parameters σ, α, and β are assumed to be the same for all spending units Eq. (7-72) holds at the "national accounts" level of aggregation over all spending units

$$E_t = n\sigma + \alpha Y_{t-1} + \beta M_{t-1} + u_t \tag{7-76}$$

or indeed at any intermediate level of aggregation, where variables without the i subscript indicate aggregate values. The authors postulate 16 spending units, assign numerical values to the parameters of the equations, and then generate sets of observations over 20 and 80 year periods by drawing u_{it} and v_{it} values at random from the specified distributions. The observations on the 16 primary units are aggregated (apparently on a random basis) into sets of four for each year to give semi-aggregated series, and these in turn are summed each year to give fully aggregated series. Equation (7-76) is then estimated for each set of data at each level of aggregation and the sampling distribution of the estimates studied.[1] The interested reader should consult the original article for details but the following main points emerge:

1. The dispersion of the sampling distributions for the coefficients increases with the degree of aggregation: the rate of increase, however, is greater than would be expected from the simple loss of degrees of freedom. The authors feel that this is due to the fact that the explanatory variables Y and M are much more highly correlated at the fully-aggregated level than at the micro-level owing to the existence of the macro-identities for each variable, and this increasing collinearity, of course, increases the sampling variances.

2. There is some suggestion that with increasing aggregation the estimated standard errors tend to underestimate the true values.

3. Government policies to stabilize aggregate income, Y_t, will, if successful, make it impossible to estimate α from the macro-data, while it is

[1] This is an example of a Monte Carlo sampling approach which can be used to study the characteristics of sampling distributions which may be difficult or impossible to derive analytically.

still possible to derive good estimates of this parameter from the micro-data.

4. Various mis-specifications of (7-76) were tried and in general the micro-data had greater discriminating power than the macro-data.

7-6 GROUPING OF EQUATIONS

Another application of generalized least-squares occurs in the estimation of a group of equations.[1] For example, suppose one is estimating demand equations for a number of different consumption (or investment) goods: it is then possible that two conditions may be fulfilled; namely, that the set of explanatory variables will not be identical for each commodity and there may be nonzero correlations between the disturbance terms in two or more equations. If these conditions do hold, then the generalized least-squares estimators, proposed by Zellner, will be asymptotically more efficient than those obtained by the application of ordinary least-squares to each equation in turn.

Suppose the ith equation in a set of m equations is

$$\mathbf{y}_i = \mathbf{X}_i\boldsymbol{\beta}_i + \mathbf{u}_i \qquad i = 1, \ldots, m \tag{7-77}$$

where $\mathbf{y}_i$ is an $n \times 1$ vector, $\mathbf{X}_i$ an $n \times k_i$ matrix, $\boldsymbol{\beta}_i$ a $k_i \times 1$ vector and $\mathbf{u}_i$ an $n \times 1$ vector. The set of equations may be written as

$$\begin{bmatrix} \mathbf{y}_1 \\ \mathbf{y}_2 \\ \vdots \\ \mathbf{y}_m \end{bmatrix} = \begin{bmatrix} \mathbf{X}_1 & \mathbf{0} & \cdots & \mathbf{0} \\ \mathbf{0} & \mathbf{X}_2 & \cdots & \mathbf{0} \\ \vdots & \vdots & & \vdots \\ \mathbf{0} & \mathbf{0} & \cdots & \mathbf{X}_m \end{bmatrix} \begin{bmatrix} \boldsymbol{\beta}_1 \\ \boldsymbol{\beta}_2 \\ \vdots \\ \boldsymbol{\beta}_m \end{bmatrix} + \begin{bmatrix} \mathbf{u}_1 \\ \mathbf{u}_2 \\ \vdots \\ \mathbf{u}_m \end{bmatrix} \tag{7-78}$$

or

$$\mathbf{y} = \mathbf{X}\boldsymbol{\beta} + \mathbf{u} \tag{7-79}$$

By definition the variance–covariance matrix for $\mathbf{u}$ is

$$\boldsymbol{\Sigma} = E(\mathbf{uu}') = \begin{bmatrix} E(\mathbf{u}_1\mathbf{u}_1') & E(\mathbf{u}_1\mathbf{u}_2') & \cdots & E(\mathbf{u}_1\mathbf{u}_m') \\ E(\mathbf{u}_2\mathbf{u}_1') & E(\mathbf{u}_2\mathbf{u}_2') & \cdots & E(\mathbf{u}_2\mathbf{u}_m') \\ \vdots & \vdots & & \vdots \\ E(\mathbf{u}_m\mathbf{u}_1') & E(\mathbf{u}_m\mathbf{u}_2') & \cdots & E(\mathbf{u}_m\mathbf{u}_m') \end{bmatrix}$$

[1] A. Zellner, "An Efficient Method of Estimating Seemingly Unrelated Regressions and Tests for Aggregation Bias," *J. Am. Statist. Assoc.*, vol. 57, pp. 348–368, 1962; A. Zellner and D. S. Huang, "Further Properties of Efficient Estimators for Seemingly Unrelated Regression Equations," *Intern. Econ. Rev.*, vol. 3, pp. 300–313, 1962; A. Zellner, "Estimates for Seemingly Unrelated Regression Equations: Some Exact Finite Sample Results," *J. Am. Statist. Assoc.*, vol. 58, pp. 977–992, 1963.

Each term in the principal diagonal of $\mathbf{\Sigma}$ is an $n \times n$ variance–covariance matrix. Thus $E(\mathbf{u}_i\mathbf{u}_i')$ is the variance–covariance matrix for the disturbance in the ith equation. Each off diagonal term in $\mathbf{\Sigma}$ represents an $n \times n$ matrix whose elements are the contemporaneous and lagged covariances between disturbances from a pair of equations. By assumption

$$E(\mathbf{u}_i\mathbf{u}_j') = \sigma_{ij}\mathbf{I} \qquad (i, j = 1, \ldots, m) \tag{7-80}$$

Setting $i = j$ assumption (7-80) states that the disturbance in any single equation is homoscedastic and non-autocorrelated. The value of the constant variance can, of course, be different in different equations. When $i \neq j$ the assumption gives a nonzero correlation between contemporaneous disturbances in the ith and jth equations but zero correlations between all lagged disturbances. Substituting (7-80) in $\mathbf{\Sigma}$ gives

$$\mathbf{\Sigma} = \begin{bmatrix} \sigma_{11} & \sigma_{12} & \cdots & \sigma_{1m} \\ \sigma_{21} & \sigma_{22} & \cdots & \sigma_{2m} \\ \vdots & \vdots & & \vdots \\ \sigma_{m1} & \sigma_{m2} & \cdots & \sigma_{mm} \end{bmatrix} \otimes \mathbf{I}$$

$$= \mathbf{\Sigma}_c \otimes \mathbf{I} \tag{7-81}$$

where $\mathbf{I}$ is a unit matrix of order $n \times n$.[1]

Applying Aitken's generalized least-squares to (7-79) then gives the estimator

$$\mathbf{b} = (\mathbf{X}'\mathbf{\Sigma}^{-1}\mathbf{X})^{-1}\mathbf{X}'\mathbf{\Sigma}^{-1}\mathbf{y} \tag{7-82}$$

as a best linear unbiased estimator, where

$$\mathbf{\Sigma}^{-1} = \mathbf{\Sigma}_c^{-1} \otimes \mathbf{I}$$

$$= \begin{bmatrix} \sigma^{11}\mathbf{I} & \cdots & \sigma^{1m}\mathbf{I} \\ \vdots & & \vdots \\ \sigma^{m1}\mathbf{I} & \cdots & \sigma^{mm}\mathbf{I} \end{bmatrix} \tag{7-83}$$

Substituting (7-83) in (7-82)

$$\mathbf{b} = \begin{bmatrix} \sigma^{11}\mathbf{X}_1'\mathbf{X}_1 & \sigma^{12}\mathbf{X}_1'\mathbf{X}_2 & \cdots & \sigma^{1m}\mathbf{X}_1'\mathbf{X}_m \\ \vdots & \vdots & & \vdots \\ \sigma^{m1}\mathbf{X}_m'\mathbf{X}_1 & \sigma^{m2}\mathbf{X}_m'\mathbf{X}_2 & \cdots & \sigma^{mm}\mathbf{X}_m'\mathbf{X}_m \end{bmatrix}^{-1} \begin{bmatrix} \sum_{j=1}^{m} \sigma^{1j}\mathbf{X}_1'\mathbf{y}_j \\ \vdots \\ \sum_{j=1}^{m} \sigma^{mj}\mathbf{X}_m'\mathbf{y}_j \end{bmatrix} \tag{7-84}$$

[1] The symbol $\otimes$ denotes Kronecker multiplication of matrices. See Chap. 4, p. 92.

with variance–covariance matrix

$$\operatorname{var}(\mathbf{b}) = (\mathbf{X}'\boldsymbol{\Sigma}^{-1}\mathbf{X})^{-1} = \begin{bmatrix} \sigma^{11}\mathbf{X}_1'\mathbf{X}_1 & \cdots & \sigma^{1m}\mathbf{X}_1'\mathbf{X}_m \\ \vdots & & \vdots \\ \sigma^{m1}\mathbf{X}_m'\mathbf{X}_1 & \cdots & \sigma^{mm}\mathbf{X}_m'\mathbf{X}_m \end{bmatrix}^{-1} \tag{7-85}$$

If $\sigma_{ij} = 0$ for $i \neq j$, that is the disturbances in the different equations have zero covariances, then (7-84) collapses to the ordinary least-squares estimators for

$$\mathbf{b} = \begin{bmatrix} \sigma^{11}\mathbf{X}_1'\mathbf{X}_1 & \mathbf{0} & \cdots & \mathbf{0} \\ \mathbf{0} & \sigma^{22}\mathbf{X}_2'\mathbf{X}_2 & \cdots & \mathbf{0} \\ \vdots & \vdots & & \vdots \\ \mathbf{0} & \mathbf{0} & \cdots & \sigma^{mm}\mathbf{X}_m'\mathbf{X}_m \end{bmatrix}^{-1} \begin{bmatrix} \sigma^{11}\mathbf{X}_1'\mathbf{y}_1 \\ \sigma^{22}\mathbf{X}_2'\mathbf{y}_2 \\ \vdots \\ \sigma^{mm}\mathbf{X}_m'\mathbf{y}_m \end{bmatrix}$$

$$= \begin{bmatrix} (\mathbf{X}_1'\mathbf{X}_1)^{-1}\mathbf{X}_1'\mathbf{y}_1 \\ (\mathbf{X}_2'\mathbf{X}_2)^{-1}\mathbf{X}_2'\mathbf{y}_2 \\ \vdots \\ (\mathbf{X}_m'\mathbf{X}_m)^{-1}\mathbf{X}_m'\mathbf{y}_m \end{bmatrix}$$

Similarly, if the $\mathbf{X}$ matrix is the same for each equation, $\mathbf{X}_1 = \mathbf{X}_2 = \cdots = \mathbf{X}_m$, even if the disturbances are correlated, (7-84) again reduces to ordinary least-squares estimators.[1]

The basic operational difficulty with (7-82) is that $\boldsymbol{\Sigma}$ is unknown. Zellner proposes that ordinary least-squares be applied to each equation and the computed residuals used to estimate the elements of $\boldsymbol{\Sigma}_c$. The vector of ordinary least-squares residuals for the ith equation is

$$(\mathbf{y}_i - \mathbf{X}_i\hat{\boldsymbol{\beta}}_i)$$

where

$$\hat{\boldsymbol{\beta}}_i = (\mathbf{X}_i'\mathbf{X}_i)^{-1}\mathbf{X}_i'\mathbf{y}_i$$

Thus σ_{ii} is estimated by

$$s_{ii} = (\mathbf{y}_i - \mathbf{X}_i\hat{\boldsymbol{\beta}}_i)'(\mathbf{y}_i - \mathbf{X}_i\hat{\boldsymbol{\beta}}_i)/(n - k_i)$$

and σ_{ij} is estimated by

$$s_{ij} = (\mathbf{y}_i - \mathbf{X}_i\hat{\boldsymbol{\beta}}_i)'(\mathbf{y}_j - \mathbf{X}_j\hat{\boldsymbol{\beta}}_j)/(n - k_i)^{1/2}(n - k_j)^{1/2}$$

These estimates are substituted in $\boldsymbol{\Sigma}_c$ and the inverse obtained, thus giving an estimated $\boldsymbol{\Sigma}^{-1}$ for use in formulae (7-82) and (7-85).

[1] See Exercise (7-4).

The gain in efficiency yielded by the Zellner estimator over the ordinary least-squares estimator increases directly with the correlation between the disturbances from the different equations and inversely with the correlation between the different sets of explanatory variables. Even if the true correlation between equation disturbances is zero the sample least-squares residuals may yield non-negligible covariances and one might mistakenly compute the generalized least-squares estimates. The result will be estimates with somewhat greater standard errors than those of the ordinary least-squares coefficients. This will even be true for very small disturbance correlations but as these correlations increase the efficiency of the generalized over the ordinary estimates rises substantially.[1]

EXERCISES

7-1. Show that (7-63) follows directly from (7-59).

7-2. Derive the standard errors of the estimators b_2 and b_3 of (7-71).

7-3. Estimate the coefficients of $Y = \beta_1 + \beta_2 X_2 + \beta_3 X_3 + u$ together with standard errors and R^2 from the data of Table 7-3. Compare with the results for Table 7-2 already obtained in Chap. 5.

7-4. Prove that (7-84) yields ordinary least-squares estimators when $\mathbf{X}_1 = \mathbf{X}_2 = \cdots = \mathbf{X}_m$. Derive the variance-covariance matrix.

7-5. If $\mathbf{u}$ in $\mathbf{y} = \mathbf{X}\boldsymbol{\beta} + \mathbf{u}$ has a multivariate normal distribution $N(\mathbf{0}, \sigma^2\boldsymbol{\Omega})$ show that the maximum likelihood estimator $\mathbf{b}$ of $\boldsymbol{\beta}$ is found by choosing $\mathbf{b}$ to minimize $(\mathbf{y} - \mathbf{Xb})'\boldsymbol{\Omega}^{-1}(\mathbf{y} - \mathbf{Xb})$, and show that this gives $\mathbf{b} = (\mathbf{X}'\boldsymbol{\Omega}^{-1}\mathbf{X})^{-1}\mathbf{X}'\boldsymbol{\Omega}^{-1}\mathbf{y}$.

7-6. From the Family Expenditure Survey information is available for the following variables in respect of the standard regions (of the U.K.) in the two-year period 1964–1965:

1. Average weekly food expenditure per person in shillings.
2. Average weekly income per person in shillings.
3. Average number of persons per household.

These data were used to estimate by the method of least-squares the parameters A, b, and c in an equation of the form

$$y = Ax_1^b x_2^c$$

where y, x_1, and x_2 correspond to the variables described in (1), (2) and (3) above. The results obtained and the standard errors were

$$\log_{10} A = 0.980 \pm 0.394$$

$$b = 0.338 \pm 0.115$$

$$c = 0.296 \pm 0.370$$

with $R^2 = 0.76$ and $\bar{R}^2 = 0.66$.

(a) Explain what the two estimates of correlation, R^2 and $\bar{R}^2$, measure and why they are different.

(b) Interpret the parameters b and c. Does the numerical value of c throw any light on the existence of economics of scale in food consumption?

[1] For a comprehensive set of Monte Carlo results on the sample properties of the Zellner estimator see J. Kmenta and R. F. Gilbert, "Small Sample Properties of Alternative Estimators of Seemingly Unrelated Regressions," *J. Am. Statist. Assoc.*, vol. 63, pp. 1180–1200, 1968.

(c) If you knew that the parameter corresponding to b had been estimated as 0.28 ± 0.05 from a large budget study conducted in 1964–1965 using substantially the same definitions but not analyzed regionally, could you use this knowledge to improve the results set out above?
(Cambridge Economics Tripos, 1969)

7-7. In cross-sectional studies all the variables are frequently deflated, e.g., by a measure of "size," before a regression is carried out. Why? Under what condition is this a sensible procedure? How would you expect the multiple correlation coefficient to be affected in a "typical" economic application? Comment. (Oxford Diploma, 1965)

7-8. Consider the regression model

$$\mathbf{y} = \beta \mathbf{x} + \mathbf{u}$$

where $\mathbf{y}$, $\mathbf{x}$ are $T \times 1$ vectors of observations of the dependent and independent variables respectively, and where $\mathbf{u}$ is a vector of errors such that $E(\mathbf{u}) = \mathbf{0}$ and $E(\mathbf{uu}') = \mathbf{V}$. Show that the efficiency of the least-squares estimator b of β is

$$\frac{(\mathbf{x}'\mathbf{x})^2}{\mathbf{x}'\mathbf{V}\mathbf{x}\mathbf{x}'\mathbf{V}^{-1}\mathbf{x}}$$

Regarding $\mathbf{V}$ as an arbitrary but fixed positive-definite matrix, under what conditions on $\mathbf{x}$ is b

(a) efficient,
(b) very inefficient?

(L.S.E. 1967)

7-9. If $\mathbf{G}^*$ is the pooled Houthakker matrix and it is of rank r and if $\mathbf{F}$ is any $r \times n$ submatrix of $\mathbf{G}^*$ of full row rank, then noting that any other such submatrix may be written $\mathbf{F}^* = \mathbf{AF}$, where $\mathbf{A}$ is an $r \times r$ non-singular matrix, prove that whichever submatrix of full rank we choose we still obtain the same estimator $\mathbf{b}$.

8
Autocorrelation

8-1 NATURE OF AUTOCORRELATION

One of the crucial assumptions of the linear model of Chap. 5 is that of zero covariance for the disturbance terms implied in the assumption

$$E(\mathbf{uu}') = \sigma^2\mathbf{I}$$

in which the off-diagonal terms give

$$E(u_t u_{t+s}) = 0 \quad \text{for all } t \text{ and for all } s \neq 0$$

For a model with normally distributed disturbances this implies that all such disturbances are pairwise independent. For cross-section data this means we are assuming that the disturbance value that is "drawn" for any one unit is uninfluenced by the values drawn for other units, and in time-series data it means *serial* independence for the disturbance terms.

There are, however, circumstances in which the assumption of a serially independent disturbance term may not be very plausible. For example, one may make an incorrect specification of the *form* of the relationship between the variables. Suppose we specify a linear relation between Y and X when the true relation is, say, a quadratic. Even though the disturbance term in the true relation may be non-autocorrelated, the quasi-disturbance term associated with the linear relation will contain a term in X^2. If there is any serial correlation in the X values, then we will have serial correlation in the composite disturbance term. This example is a special case of the problem of omitted variables. In general, we include only certain important variables in the specified relation, and the disturbance term must then represent the influence of omitted variables. Serial correlation in individual omitted variables need not necessarily imply a serially correlated disturbance term, for individual components may cancel one another out. However, if the serial correlation in the omitted variables is pervasive and if the omitted variables tend to move in phase, then there is a real possibility of an autocorrelated disturbance term. A disturbance term may also contain a component due to measurement error in the "explained" variable. This too may be a source of serial correlation in the composite disturbance.

To illustrate the problem we shall consider a simple two-variable relation. Let us postulate

$$Y_t = \alpha + \beta X_t + u_t \tag{8-1}$$

where we assume that the disturbance u_t follows a first-order autoregressive scheme

$$u_t = \rho u_{t-1} + \varepsilon_t \tag{8-2}$$

where $|\rho| < 1$ and ε_t satisfies the assumptions

$$\left.\begin{aligned} E(\varepsilon_t) &= 0 \\ E(\varepsilon_t \varepsilon_{t+s}) &= \sigma_\varepsilon^2 \qquad s = 0 \\ &= 0 \qquad\; s \neq 0 \end{aligned}\right\} \text{ for all } t \tag{8-3}$$

We then have

$$\begin{aligned} u_t &= \rho u_{t-1} + \varepsilon_t \\ &= \rho(\rho u_{t-2} + \varepsilon_{t-1}) + \varepsilon_t \\ &= \cdots \\ &= \varepsilon_t + \rho\varepsilon_{t-1} + \rho^2\varepsilon_{t-2} + \cdots \end{aligned}$$

that is

$$u_t = \sum_{r=0}^{\infty} \rho^r \varepsilon_{t-r} \tag{8-4}$$

Therefore

$$E(u_t) = 0$$

since

$$E(\varepsilon_t) = 0 \quad \text{for all } t$$

Furthermore,

$$E(u_t^2) = E(\varepsilon_t^2) + \rho^2 E(\varepsilon_{t-1}^2) + \rho^4 E(\varepsilon_{t-2}^2) + \cdots$$

since the ε are serially independent, and so

$$E(u_t^2) = (1 + \rho^2 + \rho^4 + \cdots)\sigma_\varepsilon^2$$

Thus

$$\sigma_u^2 = \frac{\sigma_\varepsilon^2}{1 - \rho^2} \quad \text{for all } t \tag{8-5}$$

$$\begin{aligned} E(u_t u_{t-1}) &= E[(\varepsilon_t + \rho\varepsilon_{t-1} + \rho^2\varepsilon_{t-2} + \cdots) \\ &\qquad \times (\varepsilon_{t-1} + \rho\varepsilon_{t-2} + \rho^2\varepsilon_{t-3} + \cdots)] \\ &= E\{[\varepsilon_t + \rho(\varepsilon_{t-1} + \rho\varepsilon_{t-2} + \cdots)](\varepsilon_{t-1} + \rho\varepsilon_{t-2} + \cdots)\} \\ &= \rho E[(\varepsilon_{t-1} + \rho\varepsilon_{t-2} + \cdots)^2] \\ &= \rho\sigma_u^2 \end{aligned}$$

Similarly,

$$E(u_t u_{t-2}) = \rho^2\sigma_u^2$$

and in general,

$$E(u_t u_{t-s}) = \rho^s \sigma_u^2 \tag{8-6}$$

so that relation (8-1) does not satisfy the assumption of a serially independent disturbance term. Scheme (8-2) is the simplest possible type of autoregressive scheme; more complicated types will of course still fail to satisfy the assumption of serial independence.

Relation (8-6) may be rewritten to give

$$\frac{E(u_t u_{t-s})}{\sigma_u^2} = \rho^s$$

The left-hand side of this expression defines the sth autocorrelation coefficient of the u series. The autocorrelation coefficient of zero order for any series is simply unity, and for a *random* series all coefficients of higher order will be zero. Collecting these terms together we may write assumption (8-2) as

$$E(\mathbf{uu}') = \mathbf{V} = \sigma_u^2 \begin{bmatrix} 1 & \rho & \rho^2 & \cdots & \rho^{n-1} \\ \rho & 1 & \rho & \cdots & \rho^{n-2} \\ \vdots & \vdots & \vdots & & \vdots \\ \rho^{n-1} & \rho^{n-2} & \rho^{n-3} & \cdots & 1 \end{bmatrix} \tag{8-7}$$

so that just as heteroscedastic disturbances in Chap. 7 implied one form of breakdown of the standard assumption, $E(\mathbf{uu}') = \sigma^2\mathbf{I}$, so do autocorrelated disturbances imply another form of breakdown for this assumption.

8-2 CONSEQUENCES OF AUTOCORRELATED DISTURBANCES

If the ordinary least-squares formulae of Chap. 5 are applied to a model in which the disturbances are autocorrelated there are three main consequences.

First, we shall obtain unbiased estimates of $\boldsymbol{\beta}$, but the sampling variances of these estimates may be unduly large compared with those achievable by a slightly different method of estimation. Second, if we apply the usual least-squares formulae for the sampling variances of the regression coefficients, we are likely to obtain a serious underestimate of these variances. In any case these formulae are no longer valid, nor are the precise forms of the t and F tests derived for the linear model in Chap. 5. Third, we shall obtain inefficient predictions, that is, predictions with needlessly large sampling variances.

To prove these assertions recall that

$$\begin{aligned}\hat{\boldsymbol{\beta}} &= (\mathbf{X}'\mathbf{X})^{-1}\mathbf{X}'\mathbf{y} \\ &= \boldsymbol{\beta} + (\mathbf{X}'\mathbf{X})^{-1}\mathbf{X}'\mathbf{u}\end{aligned}$$

Thus

$$E(\hat{\boldsymbol{\beta}}) = \boldsymbol{\beta} \quad \text{since } E(\mathbf{u}) = \mathbf{0}$$

Next, the sampling variance–covariance matrix for $\hat{\boldsymbol{\beta}}$ in the orthodox case is

$$\sigma_u^2(\mathbf{X}'\mathbf{X})^{-1} \tag{8-8}$$

but in this case

$$\begin{aligned}\text{var}(\hat{\boldsymbol{\beta}}) &= E\{(\hat{\boldsymbol{\beta}} - \boldsymbol{\beta})(\hat{\boldsymbol{\beta}} - \boldsymbol{\beta})'\} \\ &= E\{(\mathbf{X}'\mathbf{X})^{-1}\mathbf{X}'\mathbf{uu}'\mathbf{X}(\mathbf{X}'\mathbf{X})^{-1}\} \\ &= (\mathbf{X}'\mathbf{X})^{-1}\mathbf{X}'\mathbf{VX}(\mathbf{X}'\mathbf{X})^{-1}\end{aligned} \tag{8-9}$$

To illustrate the error involved in using (8-8) rather than (8-9) consider the very simple model

$$y_t = \beta x_t + u_t$$

$$u_t = \rho u_{t-1} + \varepsilon_t$$

where ε_t obeys assumptions (8-3).

For this model (8-9) gives

$$\operatorname{var}(\hat{\beta}) = \left(\frac{1}{\sum_{i=1}^{n} x_i^2}\right) \sigma_u^2 [x_1 \cdots x_n] \times \begin{bmatrix} 1 & \rho & \rho^2 & \cdots & \rho^{n-1} \\ \rho & 1 & \rho & \cdots & \rho^{n-2} \\ \vdots & \vdots & \vdots & & \vdots \\ \rho^{n-1} & \rho^{n-2} & \rho^{n-3} & \cdots & 1 \end{bmatrix} \begin{bmatrix} x_1 \\ \vdots \\ x_n \end{bmatrix} \left(\frac{1}{\sum_{i=1}^{n} x_i^2}\right)$$

$$= \frac{\sigma_u^2}{\sum_{i=1}^{n} x_i^2} \times \left(1 + 2\rho \frac{\sum_{i=1}^{n-1} x_i x_{i+1}}{\sum_{i=1}^{n} x_i^2} + 2\rho^2 \frac{\sum_{i=1}^{n-2} x_i x_{i+2}}{\sum_{i=1}^{n} x_i^2} + \cdots + 2\rho^{n-1} \frac{x_i x_n}{\sum_{i=1}^{n} x_i^2}\right) \qquad (8\text{-}10)$$

The ordinary least-squares formula (8-8) for this simple model gives $\sigma_u^2 / \sum_{i=1}^{n} x_i^2$ and is seen to ignore the term in parentheses in (8-10). If ρ is positive and if x is also positively autocorrelated the expression in parentheses is almost certainly greater than unity so that the ordinary least-squares formula will underestimate the true sampling variance of $\hat{\beta}$. As an illustration suppose x is also subject to a first-order autoregressive scheme with the same parameter ρ as u. Then for large n the expression in parentheses is approximately equal to

$$(2 + 2\rho^2 + 2\rho^4 + \cdots - 1) = \frac{1 + \rho^2}{1 - \rho^2}$$

since the terms involving x inside the parentheses are estimates of the autocorrelation coefficients of x. If $\rho = 0.5$, $(1 + \rho^2)/(1 - \rho^2) = 5/3$ so that this factor alone would cause the usual formula to underestimate the true variance by about 40 per cent. If $\rho = 0.8$, $(1 + \rho^2)/(1 - \rho^2) = 4.5$ so that the true variance is more than four times that given by the ordinary least-squares formula. Notice, however, that if x is approximately random then even if u is autocorrelated the bias is not likely to be serious.

The situation, however, is likely to be even worse than that pictured above for the other element in the computation of standard errors is the estimation of σ_u^2 and the ordinary least-squares residuals are likely to underestimate σ_u^2 when the u's are autocorrelated. As we saw in (5-19) the sum of squared residuals from the ordinary least-squares regression is

$$\mathbf{e'e} = \mathbf{u'u} - \mathbf{u'X(X'X)^{-1}X'u}$$

Thus

$$E(\mathbf{e'e}) = E(\mathbf{u'u}) - E\{\mathbf{u'X(X'X)^{-1}X'u}\} \tag{8-11}$$

Now

$$E(\mathbf{u'u}) = n\sigma_u^2$$

$$E\{\mathbf{u'X(X'X)^{-1}X'u}\} = E \operatorname{tr} \{\mathbf{u'X(X'X)^{-1}X'u}\} \quad \text{since this expression is a scalar}$$

$$= E \operatorname{tr} \{\mathbf{X(X'X)^{-1}X'uu'}\}$$

$$= \operatorname{tr} \{\mathbf{X(X'X)^{-1}X'V}\}$$

As an illustration if we again postulate

$$y_t = \beta x_t + u_t$$

and

$$u_t = \rho u_{t-1} + \varepsilon_t$$

then (8-11) becomes

$$E(\mathbf{e'e}) = \sigma_u^2 \left\{ n - \left(1 + 2\rho \frac{\sum_{i=1}^{n-1} x_i x_{i+1}}{\sum_{i=1}^{n} x_i^2} + 2\rho^2 \frac{\sum_{i=1}^{n-2} x_i x_{i+2}}{\sum_{i=1}^{n} x_i^2} + \cdots + 2\rho^{n-1} \frac{x_1 x_n}{\sum_{i=1}^{n} x_i^2} \right) \right\}$$

If $\rho = 0$ then $E(\mathbf{e'e}) = (n - 1)\sigma_u^2$ so that $\mathbf{e'e}/(n - 1)$ provides an unbiased estimator of σ_u^2, as least-squares theory suggests. If x is approximately random, even if $\rho \neq 0$, there is probably little serious danger of bias. However, if u and x are both positively autocorrelated then the least-squares formula $\mathbf{e'e}/(n - 1)$ is likely to underestimate σ_u^2. If we make the same simplifying assumption as above that u and x has the same first-order autoregressive scheme

$$E(\mathbf{e}'\mathbf{e}) \simeq \sigma_u^2\left[n - \frac{1+\rho^2}{1-\rho^2}\right]$$

If $\rho = 0.5$ and $n = 20$

$$E\left(\frac{\mathbf{e}'\mathbf{e}}{n-1}\right) \simeq \frac{18.3}{19}\sigma_u^2 \quad \text{an underestimate of 4 per cent}$$

while if $\rho = 0.8$ and $n = 20$

$$E\left(\frac{\mathbf{e}'\mathbf{e}}{n-1}\right) \simeq \frac{15.4}{19}\sigma_u^2 \quad \text{an underestimate of about 19 per cent}$$

Both factors thus work in the same direction, so that in the case of a model with autocorrelated disturbances the simple least-squares formulae will give unbiased estimators of the coefficients but the sampling variances are likely to be seriously understated. Notice that even if some upward correction could be made to the estimated sampling variances the significance levels of the conventional t and F tests would in any case no longer be correct since the serial dependence of the u's means that $\mathbf{e}'\mathbf{e}/\sigma^2$ is no longer distributed as χ^2 nor is it now independent of $(\hat{\boldsymbol{\beta}} - \boldsymbol{\beta})$. It is probable, however, that the underestimation of var $(\hat{\boldsymbol{\beta}})$ is the more serious error.

Since $E(\mathbf{uu}') = \mathbf{V}$ it is clear from the discussion in Chap. 7 that the generalized least-squares estimator is best linear unbiased, if $\mathbf{V}$ is known. Simple least-squares will then give inefficient estimates and predictions, but we will return to this point in sections 8-5 and 8-6.

8-3 CONVENTIONAL TESTS FOR AUTOCORRELATION

Autocorrelated disturbances pose such a serious problem for the use of simple least squares that it is extremely important to be able to test for their presence. For large samples we have a choice of tests that may be applied to the computed residuals from the least-squares regression. These residuals are

$$\begin{aligned}\mathbf{e} &= \mathbf{y} - \mathbf{X}\hat{\boldsymbol{\beta}} \\ &= \mathbf{u} + \mathbf{X}(\boldsymbol{\beta} - \hat{\boldsymbol{\beta}})\end{aligned}$$

Since[1]

$$\operatorname{plim} \hat{\boldsymbol{\beta}} = \boldsymbol{\beta}$$

$$\operatorname{plim} \mathbf{e} = \mathbf{u}$$

[1] See Chap. 9 for the definition and meaning of plim.

So for large samples we may treat the e's as if they actually were observations on the u's and apply various tests for randomness, which, strictly speaking, are only applicable when we have sample observations on the actual series whose randomness is under test. These include

(a) nonparametric tests[1]

and

(b) tests based on theoretical distributions.

The most useful of the theoretical tests is the von Neumann ratio,

$$\frac{\delta^2}{s^2} = \frac{\sum_{t=2}^{n} (e_t - e_{t-1})^2/(n-1)}{\sum_{t=1}^{n} (e_t - \bar{e})^2/n} \tag{8-12}$$

the ratio of the mean square successive difference to the variance.[2] In an ordinary least-squares application $\bar{e}$ is, of course, zero. For large n, δ^2/s^2 may be taken as approximately normally distributed with

$$E\left(\frac{\delta^2}{s^2}\right) = \frac{2n}{n-1}$$

and

$$\operatorname{var}\left(\frac{\delta^2}{s^2}\right) = \frac{4n^2(n-2)}{(n+1)(n-1)^3}$$

A large sample test for positive autocorrelation may then be made by contrasting the empirical value obtained for the von Neumann ratio with a pre-selected critical region from the normal distribution with the appropriate mean and variance, but it is important to emphasize that even the formulae for the mean and variance are only true if the e values are independently distributed and this, in fact, is not true of least squares residuals, even when the true disturbance terms are independently distributed.

It is much more vital, however, for the econometrician to have small-sample tests. To this end Durbin and Watson investigated the sampling

[1] For accounts of various nonparametric tests see D. A. S. Fraser, *Nonparametric Methods in Statistics*, Wiley, New York, 1957; or S. Siegel, *Nonparametric Statistics for the Behavioral Sciences*, McGraw-Hill, New York, 1956.

[2] J. von Neumann, "Distribution of the Ratio of the Mean Square Successive Difference to the Variance," *Ann. Math. Statist.*, vol. 12, pp. 367–395 1941; and B. I. Hart, "Tabulation of the Probabilities of the Ratio of The Mean Square Difference to the Variance and Significance Levels for the Ratio of the Mean Square Difference to the Variance," *Ann. Math. Statist.*, vol. 13, pp. 207–214, 1942.

distribution of the statistic which has become known as the Durbin–Watson "d" statistic,[1] namely,

$$d = \frac{\sum_{t=2}^{n} (e_t - e_{t-1})^2}{\sum_{t=1}^{n} e_t^2} \tag{8-13}$$

which is, of course, related to the von Neumann ratio by

$$d = \left(\frac{\delta^2}{s^2}\right)\left(\frac{n-1}{n}\right)$$

The e values are both positive and negative with mean zero. It is intuitively clear that for a positively autocorrelated series the first differences will tend to be small in absolute value compared with the absolute values of e, while for a negatively autocorrelated series they will often be larger than the e values so that d will tend to be small for positively autocorrelated series, large for negatively autocorrelated series and somewhere in between for random series. For random u

$$E(d) = \frac{\text{tr}\,\mathbf{A} - \text{tr}\,\{\mathbf{X}'\mathbf{A}\mathbf{X}(\mathbf{X}'\mathbf{X})^{-1}\}}{n-k} \tag{8-14}$$

where $\mathbf{A}$ is the symmetric $n \times n$ matrix

$$\mathbf{A} = \begin{bmatrix} 1 & -1 & 0 & 0 & \cdots & 0 & 0 & 0 \\ -1 & 2 & -1 & 0 & \cdots & 0 & 0 & 0 \\ \vdots & & & & & & & \vdots \\ 0 & 0 & 0 & 0 & \cdots & -1 & 2 & -1 \\ 0 & 0 & 0 & 0 & \cdots & 0 & -1 & 1 \end{bmatrix} \tag{8-15}$$

so that $\text{tr}\,(\mathbf{A}) = 2(n-1)$. $E(d)$ thus depends on the X values in the sample, but illustrative calculations by Durbin and Watson show that it ranges around 2. If the X's are orthogonal

$$\text{tr}\,\{\mathbf{X}'\mathbf{A}\mathbf{X}(\mathbf{X}'\mathbf{X})^{-1}\} = \frac{\Sigma(\Delta X_1)^2}{\Sigma X_1^2} + \cdots + \frac{\Sigma(\Delta X_k)^2}{\Sigma X_k^2}$$

where $\Sigma(\Delta X_i)^2$ indicates the sum of the squares of the first differences of X_i. If the first differences were small in absolute value in relation to X values

[1] J. Durbin and G. S. Watson, "Testing for Serial Correlation in Least-squares Regression," *Biometrika*, vol. 37, pp. 409–428, 1950, and vol. 38, pp. 159–178, 1951.

we might ignore this term and $E(d)$ is approximately

$$\frac{2(n-1)}{n-k} = 2 + \frac{2(k-1)}{n-k}$$

The problem with determining the sampling distribution of d is that it depends on the **X** values so it was only possible for Durbin and Watson to establish upper (d_U) and lower (d_L) limits for the significance levels of d. These are to test the hypothesis of zero autocorrelation against the alternative hypothesis of positive first-order autocorrelation.

If $d < d_L$ reject the hypothesis of non-autocorrelated u in favor of the hypothesis of positive autocorrelation.

If $d > d_U$ do not reject the null hypothesis.

If $d_L < d < d_U$ the test is inconclusive.

If, in the case of sample values of d in excess of 2, we wish to test against the alternative hypothesis of negative first-order autocorrelation, compute $(4 - d)$ and refer this value to d_L and d_U as if one were testing for positive autocorrelation. Appendix A-5 gives the tabulated values of d_L and d_U for the 5 per cent and 1 per cent levels of significance.

It is important to emphasize that this test was derived for nonstochastic **X** and thus is not applicable, for example, when lagged Y values appear among the explanatory variables, but we will take up that problem in Chap. 10.

The inconclusive range for the Durbin–Watson test has been something of a drawback in its use. Theil and Nagar have attempted a solution at the expense of making more specific assumptions about the X variables.[1] On the assumption that the first and second differences of the explanatory variables are small in absolute value compared with the range of these variables, they derive unique (though, of course, approximate) significance limits for d. Variables with fairly small cyclical components and a strong time trend would satisfy the Theil–Nagar assumptions, but data expressed in first difference form almost certainly would not. The tabulated critical values in the Theil–Nagar article are on average closer to the d_U than to the d_L values in the Durbin–Watson table. A rather similar result is reached by Malinvaud who conjectures that if the X variables are approximately linear combinations of a constant and of sinusoidal sequences with long periods then the critical value of d is near d_U so that we should reject the hypothesis of random u if $d < d_U$.[2] An accurate and conclusive test has recently been proposed by Henshaw but it is complicated and computationally burdensome.[3]

[1] H. Theil and A. L. Nagar, "Testing the Independence of Regression Disturbances," *J. Am. Statist. Assoc.*, vol. 56, pp. 793–806, 1961.

[2] E. Malinvaud, *Statistical Methods of Econometrics*, North-Holland, Amsterdam, 1966, p. 425.

[3] R. C. Henshaw, Jr., "Testing Single-equation Least-squares Regression Models for Autocorrelated Disturbances," *Econometrica*, vol. 34, pp. 646–660, 1966.

Durbin has recently tackled the inclusive case again and now proposes a procedure for the case when d lies in the inconclusive region.[1] The statistic d may be expressed as

$$d = \mathbf{e}'\mathbf{A}\mathbf{e}'/\mathbf{e}'\mathbf{e}$$

where $\mathbf{A}$ is the symmetric matrix of the order n already defined in (8-15). The n characteristic roots of $\mathbf{A}$ are

$$\lambda_j = 2\left(1 - \cos\frac{\pi j}{n}\right) \qquad j = 0, 1, \ldots, n-1$$

and the corresponding characteristic vectors are

$$l_j = \begin{bmatrix} \cos\frac{j\pi}{2n} \\ \cos\frac{3j\pi}{2n} \\ \vdots \\ \cos\frac{(2n-1)j\pi}{2n} \end{bmatrix} \qquad j = 0, 1, \ldots, n-1$$

When $j = 0$, $\lambda_j = 0$ and $\mathbf{l}_j$ is a column of units. Ignore $\lambda_j = 0$ and take the k' smallest characteristic roots where k' is the number of explanatory variables in the model (i.e., $k' = k - 1$). Assemble the corresponding k' characteristic vectors in a matrix

$$\mathbf{L} = [\mathbf{l}_1 \ \mathbf{l}_2 \ \ldots \ \mathbf{l}_{k'}]$$

Let $\mathbf{X}$ denote the $n \times k'$ matrix of the explanatory variables expressed as deviations from the sample means. Then compute the least-squares regression

$$\mathbf{y} = a\mathbf{1} + \mathbf{X}\mathbf{b}_1 + \mathbf{L}\mathbf{b}_2$$

where $\mathbf{1}$ denotes an $n \times 1$ vector of units. Compute lower triangular matrices $\mathbf{P}_1$ and $\mathbf{P}_2$ such that

$$\mathbf{P}_1\mathbf{P}_1' = (\mathbf{X}_L'\mathbf{X}_L)^{-1} \quad \text{and} \quad \mathbf{P}_2\mathbf{P}_2' = (\mathbf{L}_X'\mathbf{L}_X)^{-1}$$

where

$$\mathbf{X}_L = \mathbf{X} - \mathbf{L}(\mathbf{L}'\mathbf{L})^{-1}\mathbf{L}'\mathbf{X}$$

and

$$\mathbf{L}_X = \mathbf{L} - \mathbf{X}(\mathbf{X}'\mathbf{X})^{-1}\mathbf{X}'\mathbf{L}$$

[1] J. Durbin, "An Alternative to the Bounds Test for Testing for Serial Correlation in Least-squares Regression," *Econometrica*, vol. 38, pp. 422–429, 1970.

Finally compute

$$\mathbf{c} = \mathbf{P}_1\mathbf{P}_2^{-1}\mathbf{b}_2$$

the vector

$$\mathbf{z} = \mathbf{y} - a\mathbf{1} - \mathbf{X}\mathbf{b}_1 - \mathbf{L}\mathbf{b}_2 + \mathbf{X}_L\mathbf{c}$$

and

$$d' = \sum_{t=2}^{n} (z_t - z_{t-1})^2 \bigg/ \sum_{t=1}^{n} z_t^2 \tag{8-16}$$

The d' defined by (8-16) has the same distribution as d_U and a test of serial independence may therefore be carried out by comparing the observed value of d' with the significance points of d_U tabulated in Appendix A-5.

8-4 THE THEIL BLUS PROCEDURE[1]

Instead of attempting to develop further tests on the least-squares residuals Theil proposes a different estimator of the disturbance vector. This estimator has simpler properties than the vector of least-squares residuals and hence is more amenable to direct tests of autocorrelation. One of the sources of difficulty with the least-squares residuals is that even when the elements of **u** are independent the elements of **e** are not. As we have already seen in Chap. 5

$$\mathbf{e} = \mathbf{M}\mathbf{u}$$

where

$$\mathbf{M} = \mathbf{I} - \mathbf{X}(\mathbf{X}'\mathbf{X})^{-1}\mathbf{X}'$$

is a symmetric, idempotent matrix of order n. Thus

$$E(\mathbf{e}\mathbf{e}') = \sigma_u^2\mathbf{M}$$

so that the estimated disturbances are intercorrelated. The purpose of Theil's 1965 paper is to develop an estimator of **u** which will be best linear unbiased (BLU) and have scalar (S) covariance matrix of the form $\sigma^2\mathbf{I}$, hence the name BLUS estimator. Best here refers to minimizing the expected sums of squares of the estimation errors. The usefulness of the scalar covariance matrix is that the significance levels of the von Neumann ratio, for

[1] The articles on which this section is based are: H. Theil, "The Analysis of Disturbances in Regression Analysis," *J. Am. Statist. Assoc.*, vol. 60, pp. 1067–1079, 1965; J. Koerts, "Some Further Notes on Disturbance Estimates in Regression Analysis," *J. Am. Statist. Assoc.*, vol. 62, pp. 169–183, 1962; H. Theil, "A Simplification of the BLUS Procedure for Analyzing Regression Disturbances," *J. Am. Statist. Assoc.*, vol. 63, pp. 242–251, 1968; J. Koerts and A. P. J. Abrahamse, "On the Power of the BLUS Procedure," *J. Am. Statist. Assoc.*, vol 63, pp. 1227–1236, 1968.

example, would be directly applicable to the ratio calculated from these estimated disturbances.

Let us denote the BLUS residuals by $\hat{\mathbf{e}}$, keeping $\mathbf{e}$ as before for the vector of ordinary least-squares residuals. Let

$$\hat{\mathbf{e}} = \mathbf{By} \tag{8-17}$$

where $\mathbf{B}$ is an $n \times n$ matrix of constants. The estimation error is then

$$\hat{\mathbf{e}} - \mathbf{u} = \mathbf{BX}\boldsymbol{\beta} + \mathbf{Bu} - \mathbf{u}$$

Thus

$$E(\hat{\mathbf{e}} - \mathbf{u}) = \mathbf{BX}\boldsymbol{\beta}$$

since $E(\mathbf{u}) = \mathbf{0}$. The estimation error will then have zero expectation if and only if

$$\mathbf{BX} = \mathbf{0} \tag{8-18}$$

The $\mathbf{X}$ matrix, by assumption, consists of k linearly independent columns. Thus Eq. (8-18) imposes k independent linear restrictions on the columns of $\mathbf{B}$ so that $\mathbf{B}$ has a rank of at most $(n - k)$. The variance–covariance matrix for $\hat{\mathbf{e}}$, given that (8-18) is satisfied, is

$$E(\hat{\mathbf{e}}\hat{\mathbf{e}}') = \sigma_u^2\mathbf{BB}'$$

since, by assumption, $E(\mathbf{uu}') = \sigma_u^2\mathbf{I}$. The requirement that $\hat{\mathbf{e}}$ should have a scalar dispersion matrix gives the condition

$$\mathbf{BB}' = \mathbf{I} \tag{8-19}$$

However, (8-19) cannot be satisfied since by (8-18) the rank of $\mathbf{BB}'$ cannot exceed $(n - k)$. Thus at best we can achieve a matrix on the right-hand side with $(n - k)$ units on the principal diagonal and the remaining k elements zero. This is equivalent to saying that the BLUS vector $\hat{\mathbf{e}}$ cannot estimate n disturbances but only $(n - k)$ disturbances. There is thus an element of choice as to which subset of k disturbances are not estimated. Let us, for the moment, suppose that it is the first k disturbances so we can partition $\mathbf{B}$ into the first k and the remaining $(n - k)$ rows.

$$\mathbf{B} = \begin{bmatrix} \mathbf{0} \\ \mathbf{C} \end{bmatrix} \tag{8-20}$$

where $\mathbf{0}$ is of order $k \times n$ and $\mathbf{C}$ of order $(n - k) \times n$. Conditions (8-18) and (8-19) now give

$$\mathbf{CX} = \mathbf{0} \quad \text{and} \quad \mathbf{CC}' = \mathbf{I}_{n-k} \tag{8-21}$$

Now

$$\mathbf{MC}' = [\mathbf{I} - \mathbf{X}(\mathbf{X}'\mathbf{X})^{-1}\mathbf{X}']\mathbf{C}'$$
$$= \mathbf{C}' \qquad (8\text{-}22)$$

since $\mathbf{X}'\mathbf{C}' = \mathbf{0}$. Since $\mathbf{M}$ is an indempotent matrix of rank $(n - k)$ it has $(n - k)$ unit latent roots and k zero roots. Equation (8-22) thus indicates that $\mathbf{C}'$ consists of $(n - k)$ latent vectors of $\mathbf{M}$ corresponding to the unit roots. But $\mathbf{C}'$ is not unique since first of all we have a choice of which k disturbances are not to be estimated: as can be seen from (8-20) this corresponds to deciding which rows of $\mathbf{X}$ are to be labeled 1 to k and different choices give different $\mathbf{M}$ matrices. Secondly, for any given choice of subset the latent vectors corresponding to the unit roots are not unique since the unit root has multiplicity $(n - k)$.

So far we have imposed the conditions that the estimator should be linear unbiased and have a scalar dispersion matrix. In the 1965 article Theil resolves the second cause of nonuniqueness mentioned in the previous paragraph by minimizing the expected sum of squares of estimation errors. This amounts to selecting one particular matrix $\mathbf{C}'$ out of the class of all matrices whose columns are characteristic vectors of $\mathbf{M}$ corresponding to the unit roots and are pairwise orthogonal with unit length. The solution may be presented as follows. Partition $\mathbf{C}$ by the first k and the remaining $(n - k)$ columns

$$\mathbf{C} = [\mathbf{C}_0 \quad \mathbf{C}_1] \qquad (8\text{-}23)$$

and partition $\mathbf{X}$ by the first k and the remaining $(n - k)$ rows

$$\mathbf{X} = \begin{bmatrix} \mathbf{X}_0 \\ \mathbf{X}_1 \end{bmatrix}$$

and form the matrix

$$\mathbf{M}_{11} = \mathbf{I} - \mathbf{X}_1(\mathbf{X}'\mathbf{X})^{-1}\mathbf{X}_1' \qquad (8\text{-}24)$$

Then the BLUS estimator of the last $(n - k)$ disturbances is

$$\hat{\mathbf{e}}_1 = \mathbf{Cy} \qquad (8\text{-}25)$$

where

$$\mathbf{C}_1 = \mathbf{PD}^{1/2}\mathbf{P}' \qquad (8\text{-}26)$$

and

$$\mathbf{C}_0 = -\mathbf{C}_1(\mathbf{X}_1\mathbf{X}_0^{-1}) \qquad (8\text{-}27)$$

In (8-26) $\mathbf{D}^{1/2}$ is the diagonal matrix whose diagonal elements are the positive square roots of the latent roots of $\mathbf{M}_{11}$ and the columns of $\mathbf{P}$ are the latent vectors of $\mathbf{M}_{11}$. Since $\mathbf{M}_{11}$ is of order $(n - k)$ this approach requires the computation of $(n - k)$ latent roots and vectors, their substitution in (8-26) to obtain $\mathbf{C}_1$, from which $\mathbf{C}_0$ may be obtained through (8-27) and finally $\hat{\mathbf{e}}_1$ from (8-25).

In his 1968 article Theil has derived an alternative method of computing $\hat{\mathbf{e}}_1$ which involves the computation of only k latent vectors rather than $n - k$. If we partition the vector of ordinary least-squares residuals by the first k and the remaining $(n - k)$ rows

$$\mathbf{e} = \begin{bmatrix} \mathbf{e}_0 \\ \mathbf{e}_1 \end{bmatrix}$$

the basic result is

$$\hat{\mathbf{e}}_1 = \mathbf{e}_1 - \mathbf{X}_1\mathbf{X}_0^{-1}\left[\sum_{i=1}^{k} \frac{d_i}{1 + d_i}\mathbf{q}_i\mathbf{q}_i'\right]\mathbf{e}_0 \tag{8-28}$$

where d_i^2 and $\mathbf{q}_i$ $(i = 1, \ldots, k)$ indicate the latent roots and vectors of the matrix $\mathbf{X}_0(\mathbf{X}'\mathbf{X})^{-1}\mathbf{X}_0'$ and d_i the positive square root of d_i^2. In general, all k roots will be less than unity but, if not, the summation over i in (8-28) should be restricted to those which are less than unity.

Finally the problem remains of which subset of k disturbances is not to be estimated, or equivalently which observations are to be deleted. For testing against positive autocorrelation Theil recommends that we delete the first m and the last $k - m$ observations, where m is a non-negative integer $\leq k$. This gives a choice of $k + 1$ different sets of k observations that might be deleted. For each set we must partition $\mathbf{X}$ in such a way that the deleted observations constitute $\mathbf{X}_0$ and the remaining observations $\mathbf{X}_1$. In the 1968 article Theil recommends that the choice between these $k + 1$ sets should be made as follows. For each set compute $\mathbf{X}_0(\mathbf{X}'\mathbf{X})^{-1}\mathbf{X}_0'$ and the roots $d_1^2, \ldots, d_k^2$ of this matrix. If one or more of the roots is zero, proceed no further with this set since its $\mathbf{X}_0$ matrix is singular. For the remaining sets compute the sum of the positive square roots $d_1 + \cdots + d_k$ and select the set for which this sum takes the largest value. This gives the set which minimizes the expected sum of the estimation errors. The corresponding vectors $\mathbf{q}_i$ for this set are obtained as the latent vectors of $\mathbf{X}_0(\mathbf{X}'\mathbf{X})^{-1}\mathbf{X}_0'$ corresponding to the roots $d_i^2 < 1$.

The BLUS procedure clearly involves a substantial amount of calculation just to obtain a valid test of autocorrelation. The choice between BLUS and Durbin-Watson must depend on the balance of computational cost and the relative power of the two procedures. Koerts and Abrahamse have run some simulation experiments which give valuable information on the relative powers of the two procedures. They postulate a first-order scheme for the disturbances, namely,

$$u_t = \rho u_{t-1} + \varepsilon_t$$

and simulate for values of 0.2, 0.5, and 0.8 for ρ. Their $\mathbf{X}$ matrices come from demand studies and consist of a unit vector plus time series on incomes and relative prices. Table 8-1 gives a selection of their results corresponding to the use of a five per cent level of significance.

Table 8-1[1] Powers of BLUS and Durbin–Watson (in percentage terms)

Study	n	ρ	*BLUS*		*Durbin–Watson*		
			first three u's not estimated	*last three u's not estimated*	*power*	*no inference*	$d < d_U$
Textiles	15	0.2	10	10	0	14	14
		0.5	22	24	2	32	34
		0.8	36	41	10	43	53
Spirits	28	0.2	17	19	8	17	25
		0.5	62	64	37	34	71
		0.8	89	92	80	12	92
Spirits	63	0.2	39	not	24	16	40
		0.5	97	computed	94	3	97
		0.8	100		100	0	100

[1] Koerts and Abrahamse, *op. cit.*, 1968, Tables 1, 2 and 3.

For the textile example the power of BLUS is not very impressive, owing to the small sample size: it is, however, considerably in excess of the power of the Durbin–Watson test. Notice, however, that if the Durbin–Watson procedure were amended to lead to the rejection of the null hypothesis when $d < d_U$ its power, as shown in the last column, which we have added to the Koerts–Abrahamse tables, would exceed that of BLUS. The same relative position still holds in the spirits examples, but the powers of both procedures increase with the sample size. Amending the Durbin–Watson test to reject the null hypothesis if $d < d_U$ is only a rough and ready procedure, which is not to be recommended in general since the exact significance level of the test will almost certainly differ from the nominal 5 per cent or 1 per cent being used. However, since the consequences of incorrectly accepting the null hypothesis in this case are so much more serious than those of incorrectly rejecting it, one might have a preference for rejecting the null hypothesis in cases of doubt and proceeding to use one of the estimation techniques described in the next section.

8-5 ESTIMATION

We are considering the model

$$\mathbf{y} = \mathbf{X}\boldsymbol{\beta} + \mathbf{u} \tag{8-29}$$

with

$$E(\mathbf{u}) = \mathbf{0} \quad \text{and} \quad E(\mathbf{uu}') = \mathbf{V}$$

If the disturbance follows a first-order scheme $u_t = \rho u_{t-1} + \varepsilon_t$ as specified in (8-2) and (8-3) then as we have seen in (8-7)

$$\mathbf{V} = \sigma_u^2 \begin{bmatrix} 1 & \rho & \rho^2 & \cdots & \rho^{n-1} \\ \rho & 1 & \rho & \cdots & \rho^{n-2} \\ \vdots & \vdots & \vdots & & \vdots \\ \rho^{n-1} & \rho^{n-2} & \rho^{n-3} & \cdots & 1 \end{bmatrix} = \sigma_u^2 \boldsymbol{\Omega}$$

Since the dispersion matrix for **u** is not scalar, ordinary least-squares is inefficient, and best linear unbiased estimates of $\boldsymbol{\beta}$ are provided by generalized least-squares. If, for example, it is known that the disturbance follows a first-order scheme and if the value of the parameter ρ is known then generalised least-squares may be applied directly and the estimator is

$$\mathbf{b} = (\mathbf{X}'\boldsymbol{\Omega}^{-1}\mathbf{X})^{-1}\mathbf{X}'\boldsymbol{\Omega}^{-1}\mathbf{y} \tag{8-30}$$

The estimated dispersion matrix for **b** is

$$\text{var}(\mathbf{b}) = s^2(\mathbf{X}'\boldsymbol{\Omega}^{-1}\mathbf{X})^{-1}$$

where

$$s^2 = \mathbf{e}'\boldsymbol{\Omega}^{-1}\mathbf{e}/(n-k) \quad \text{and} \quad \mathbf{e} = \mathbf{y} - \mathbf{Xb} \tag{8-31}$$

and

$$\boldsymbol{\Omega}^{-1} = \frac{1}{1-\rho^2} \begin{bmatrix} 1 & -\rho & 0 & \cdots & 0 & 0 & 0 \\ -\rho & 1+\rho^2 & -\rho & \cdots & 0 & 0 & 0 \\ 0 & -\rho & 1+\rho^2 & \cdots & 0 & 0 & 0 \\ \vdots & & & & & & \vdots \\ 0 & 0 & 0 & \cdots & -\rho & 1+\rho^2 & -\rho \\ 0 & 0 & 0 & \cdots & 0 & -\rho & 1 \end{bmatrix} \tag{8-32}$$

In the case of a first-order scheme for the disturbances the above estimates may alternatively be obtained by a simple two-stage procedure, namely,

1. transform the original observations by appropriate use of the known parameter ρ, and,
2. apply ordinary least-squares to the transformed data.

We are thus seeking a transformation matrix **T** such that the relation

$$\mathbf{Ty} = \mathbf{TX}\boldsymbol{\beta} + \mathbf{Tu} \tag{8-33}$$

will have a scalar dispersion matrix, that is,

$$E(\mathbf{Tuu'T'}) = \sigma^2\mathbf{I} \tag{8-34}$$

Consider the $n \times n$ matrix[1] $\mathbf{T}_1$

$$\mathbf{T}_1 = \begin{bmatrix} \sqrt{1-\rho^2} & 0 & 0 & \cdots & 0 & 0 & 0 \\ -\rho & 1 & 0 & \cdots & 0 & 0 & 0 \\ 0 & -\rho & 1 & \cdots & 0 & 0 & 0 \\ \vdots & & & & & & \vdots \\ 0 & 0 & 0 & \cdots & -\rho & 1 & 0 \\ 0 & 0 & 0 & \cdots & 0 & -\rho & 1 \end{bmatrix} \tag{8-35}$$

It may easily be verified by multiplying out that

$$E(\mathbf{T}_1\mathbf{uu'T}_1') = \sigma_\varepsilon^2\mathbf{I}_n$$

so that simple least-squares may be applied to the transformed data $\mathbf{T}_1\mathbf{y}$, $\mathbf{T}_1\mathbf{X}$ which are

$$\mathbf{T}_1\mathbf{y} = \begin{bmatrix} \sqrt{1-\rho^2}\,Y_1 \\ Y_2 - \rho Y_1 \\ Y_3 - \rho Y_2 \\ \vdots \\ Y_n - \rho Y_{n-1} \end{bmatrix}$$

[1] See K. R. Kadiyala, "A Transformation Used to Circumvent the Problem of Autocorrelation," *Econometrica*, vol. 36, pp. 93–96, 1968.

and

$$
\mathbf{T}_1\mathbf{X} = \begin{bmatrix} \sqrt{1-\rho^2} & \sqrt{1-\rho^2}X_{2,1} & \cdots & \sqrt{1-\rho^2}X_{k,1} \\ 1-\rho & X_{2,2}-\rho X_{2,1} & \cdots & X_{k,2}-\rho X_{k,1} \\ \vdots & \vdots & & \vdots \\ 1-\rho & X_{2,n}-\rho X_{2,n-1} & \cdots & X_{k,n}-\rho X_{k,n-1} \end{bmatrix}
$$

In more common use is the $(n - 1) \times n$ matrix $\mathbf{T}_2$

$$
\mathbf{T}_2 = \begin{bmatrix} -\rho & 1 & 0 & \cdots & 0 & 0 & 0 \\ 0 & -\rho & 1 & \cdots & 0 & 0 & 0 \\ \vdots & \vdots & \vdots & & \vdots & \vdots & \vdots \\ 0 & 0 & 0 & \cdots & -\rho & 1 & 0 \\ 0 & 0 & 0 & \cdots & 0 & -\rho & 1 \end{bmatrix} \tag{8-36}
$$

which is merely $\mathbf{T}_1$ with the first row deleted, so that we are now using $(n - 1)$ transformed observations rather than n, where each transformed observation is the original observation minus ρ times the previous observation. It can easily be shown that the application of simple least-squares to $\mathbf{T}_1\mathbf{y}$, $\mathbf{T}_1\mathbf{X}$ will give the estimator (8-30) exactly, while the application to $\mathbf{T}_2\mathbf{y}$, $\mathbf{T}_2\mathbf{X}$ will generally be a close approximation.

In general, of course, neither the order of the autocorrelation structure nor the value(s) of the parameter(s) is known and so the generalized least-squares estimates cannot be computed directly. They may, however, be approximated by various methods. We will illustrate these methods with reference to the simple model

$$
Y_t = \alpha + \beta X_t + u_t \qquad t = 1, \ldots, n \tag{8-37}
$$

$$
u_t = \rho u_{t-1} + \varepsilon_t \qquad |\rho| < 1 \tag{8-38}
$$

$$
E(\varepsilon_t) = 0
$$

$$
\begin{aligned} E(\varepsilon_t \varepsilon_{t+s}) &= \sigma_\varepsilon^2 \quad \text{for all } t \text{ and } s = 0 \\ &= 0 \quad \text{for all } t \text{ and } s \neq 0 \end{aligned}
$$

As we have already seen, the transformed relation

$$
Y_t - \rho Y_{t-1} = \alpha(1 - \rho) + \beta(X_t - \rho X_{t-1}) + \varepsilon_t \tag{8-39}
$$

has a scalar dispersion matrix. Denoting estimates of α, β, and ρ by a, b, and r the sum of squared residuals from (8-39) is given by

$$\sum_{t=1}^{n} e_t^2 = \sum_{t=1}^{n} [(Y_t - rY_{t-1}) - a(1 - r) - b(X_t - rX_{t-1})]^2 \tag{8-40}$$

where the summation can run from 1 to n if we are given X_0, Y_0, but otherwise must be restricted to the range 2 to n. The direct minimization of (8-40) with respect to a, b, and r leads to nonlinear equations, so that analytic expressions for a, b, and r cannot be obtained.

One method of approximating the values of a, b, and r which minimizes the sum of squares in (8-40) is the Cochrane–Orcutt iterative process.[1] Starting with an arbitrary value for r, say r_1, minimize the sum of squares with respect to the parameters a and b, obtaining values a_1 and b_1. Then keeping a and b fixed at a_1, b_1, minimize the sum of squares with respect to r, obtaining a new value r_2, and keeping this fixed in turn minimize once again with respect to a and b, obtaining new values a_2 and b_2. Continue in this way until successive estimates differ by arbitrarily small amounts. Such iterative processes raise two questions, namely,

(a) convergence, and,
(b) local minima versus global minimum, or the existence of multiple solutions.

Sargan has shown that for this type of problem this iterative process will always converge to a stationary value of the sum of squares in (8-40).[2] The essential reason is that at each stage one is minimizing a quadratic function. The sequence of values of the quadratic function is therefore a bounded decreasing function which necessarily converges to a limit. There is the possibility of the existence of several local minima, in which case the process would converge to one of them, depending on the starting point. The latter point might be investigated by minimizing (8-40) with respect to a and b for each of a set of values of r covering the range from -1 to $+1$. If a sufficiently fine grid of r values is chosen, inspection of the residual sum of squares will show whether there is any indication of multiple minima. In a large number of studies conducted by Sargan and his students they found no case of the occurrence of multiple minima.[3] Sargan also selected the r value giving the minimum sum of squares as the starting point for the iteration. An alternative approach that is often used is to control the iteration by use of the Durbin–

[1] D. Cochrane and G. H. Orcutt, "Application of Least-squares Regressions to Relationships Containing Auto-correlated Error Terms," *J. Am. Statist. Assoc.*, vol. 44, pp. 32–61, 1949.

[2] J. D. Sargan, "Wages and Prices in the United Kingdom: A Study in Econometric Methododology," pp. 25–63 in P. E. Hart, *et. al.*, *Econometric Analysis for National Economic Planning*, Butterworth, London, 1964.

[3] J. D. Sargan, *op. cit.*, p. 30.

Watson test and to start by setting $r_1 = 0$ so that the sum of squares we are minimizing is

$$\sum_{t=1}^{n} (Y_t - a - bX_t)^2$$

that is, a_1 and b_1 are the simple least-squares coefficients of (8-37). Test the hypothesis of zero autocorrelation of u by applying the Durbin–Watson test to the least-squares residuals. If the hypothesis is rejected proceed to the next stage of the iteration which is minimizing the sum of squares with respect to r for given a_1, b_1. Thus we are choosing r_2 to minimize

$$\sum_{t=1}^{n} [(Y_t - a_1 - b_1X_t) - r(Y_{t-1} - a_1 - b_1X_{t-1})]^2$$

that is, r_2 is given by regressing the simple least-squares residual on itself lagged one period. From r_2 obtain a_2 and b_2 by running a least-squares regression on the transformed variables $(Y_t - r_2Y_{t-1})$, $(X_t - r_2X_{t-1})$ and test the residuals from this for autocorrelation. Stop the iterations when the hypothesis of zero autocorrelation is accepted. Tests of significance should be made from the final least-squares regression computed, as the usual formulae will provide consistent estimates of the error variances.[1]

A simple two-stage procedure has been suggested by Durbin, which also gives estimates that will have asymptotically the same mean vector and dispersion matrix as the least-squares estimates obtained by the direct minimization of Σe^2 in (8-40).[2] Combining (8-37) and (8-38) gives

$$Y_t = \alpha(1 - \rho) + \rho Y_{t-1} + \beta X_t - \beta\rho X_{t-1} + \varepsilon_t$$

where the disturbance ε has a scalar dispersion matrix. Least-squares will give consistent estimates of the parameters of this relation, so the first step in Durbin's procedure is to apply simple least-squares to this relation, letting r denote the estimated coefficient of Y_{t-1}. In the second step r is used to compute the transformed variables $(Y_t - rY_{t-1})$ and $(X_t - rX_{t-1})$ and simple least-squares is applied to these transformed variables. The coefficient of $(X_t - rX_{t-1})$ is the estimate of β and the intercept term divided by $(1 - r)$ is the estimate of α.

Durbin's method extends quite simply to more than one explanatory variable and to higher order autoregressive schemes. For example, suppose the model is

$$Y_t = \beta_1 X_{1t} + \cdots + \beta_k X_{kt} + u_t \tag{8-41}$$

$$u_t = \rho_1 u_{t-1} + \rho_2 u_{t-2} + \varepsilon_t \tag{8-42}$$

[1] For the definition of consistent estimates see Chap. 9.

[2] J. Durbin, "Estimation of Parameters in Time-series Regression Models," *J. Royal Statist. Soc.*, Series B, vol. 22, pp. 139–153, 1960.

Combining these two relations gives

$$Y_t = \rho_1 Y_{t-1} + \rho_2 Y_{t-2} + \beta_1 X_{1t} + \cdots + \beta_k X_{kt} - \rho_1 \beta_1 X_{1,t-1}$$
$$- \cdots - \rho_1 \beta_{k,t-1} - \rho_2 \beta_1 X_{1,t-2} - \cdots - \rho_2 \beta_k X_{k,t-2} + \varepsilon_t \quad (8\text{-}43)$$

Let r_1 and r_2 denote the coefficients of Y_{t-1} and Y_{t-2} when a simple least-squares regression is fitted to (8-43). Use these coefficients to compute the transformed data

$$(Y_t - r_1 Y_{t-1} - r_2 Y_{t-2}), \quad (X_{it} - r_1 X_{i,t-1} - r_2 X_{i,t-2})$$
$$i = 1, \ldots k \qquad t = 3, \ldots n$$

and apply simple least-squares to the transformed data to obtain estimates of the β's.

These various iterative or two-step methods are asymptotically more efficient than ordinary least-squares. Two important questions are

(a) Does this gain in efficiency actually show up in small samples, and
(b) Is there any variation in the small-sample efficiency of the various two-step estimators?

A valuable Monte Carlo study by Griliches and Rao sheds light on both questions.[1] They postulate the model

$$y_t = \beta x_t + u_t$$
$$x_t = \lambda x_{t-1} + v_t$$
$$u_t = \rho u_{t-1} + w_t$$

and consider the following five estimators

(a) OLS.

(b) CO—two-step Cochrane–Orcutt, that is, the computation of $\hat{\rho}$ from the OLS residuals and the estimation of β by applying OLS to the transformed data $y_t - \hat{\rho} y_{t-1}$, $x_t - \hat{\rho} x_{t-1}$. As we have already seen this is GLS estimation using the $\mathbf{T}_2$ matrix of (8-36) with $\hat{\rho}$ in place of ρ.

(c) PW—Prais–Winsten estimator, which is GLS estimation using the $\mathbf{T}_1$ matrix of (8-35) again replacing ρ by the $\hat{\rho}$ estimated from the OLS residuals.[2]

(d) Durbin—the Durbin two-step estimator described above.

(e) Nonlinear—the application of least-squares to

$$y_t = \rho y_{t-1} + \beta x_t - \beta \rho x_{t-1} + w_t$$

[1] Z. Griliches and P. Rao, "Small-sample Properties of Several Two-stage Regression Methods in the Context of Autocorrelated Errors," *J. Am. Statist. Assoc.*, vol. 64, pp. 253–272, 1969.

[2] Griliches and Rao trace this method to an unpublished Cowles Foundation Discussion Paper of 1954, thus ante-dating Kadiyala's article in *Econometrica*, 1968.

with the imposition of the nonlinear constraint

$$\widehat{\beta\rho} = \hat{\beta} \cdot \hat{\rho}$$

This method is iterative and computationally much more expensive than the other four. The first main conclusion of the study is that OLS is less efficient than the other estimators for the samples of size 20 used in the study. This is especially true when $|\rho| > 0.3$; for low values of ρ there may be a little loss in efficiency in using the more complicated methods compared with OLS. The second main conclusion is that the Durbin method of estimating ρ is probably better than the others and that a two-stage estimator using the Durbin $\hat{\rho}$ in the $\mathbf{T}_1$ matrix is likely to do best over a wider range of parameters than any of the other estimators examined. This is a combination of estimators (c) and (d) above, namely the first step of (d) and the second step of (c) or, in other words, the Durbin estimator with the first observation retained. Finally it appears that the nonlinear method shows no improvement over the simpler two-stage procedures.

8-6 PREDICTION

The theoretical framework for handling prediction problems has already been developed in 7-2. Suppose we have sample data for periods 1 to n from the model $\mathbf{y} = \mathbf{X}\boldsymbol{\beta} + \mathbf{u}$ with $E(\mathbf{u}) = \mathbf{0}$ and $E(\mathbf{uu}') = \mathbf{V}$. Suppose further that we are given the row vector $\mathbf{x}_{n+1}$ of values of the explanatory variables in period $n+1$ and we wish to estimate Y_{n+1}. Formula (7-23) gives the best linear unbiased predictor

$$\hat{Y}_{n+1} = \mathbf{x}_{n+1}\mathbf{b} + \mathbf{w}'\mathbf{V}^{-1}\mathbf{e}$$

where $\mathbf{b}$ is the generalized least-squares estimator

$$\mathbf{e} = \mathbf{y} - \mathbf{X}\mathbf{b}$$

and

$$\mathbf{w} = \begin{bmatrix} E(u_1 u_{n+1}) \\ E(u_2 u_{n+1}) \\ \vdots \\ E(u_n u_{n+1}) \end{bmatrix}$$

If the disturbance follows a first-order scheme, then from (8-6) we can see

$$\mathbf{w} = \rho\sigma_u^2 \begin{bmatrix} \rho^{n-1} \\ \rho^{n-2} \\ \vdots \\ 1 \end{bmatrix}$$

so that from (8-7) $\mathbf{w}$ is ρ times the last column of $\mathbf{V}$. Now $\mathbf{V}\mathbf{V}^{-1} = \mathbf{I}$, so $\mathbf{w}'\mathbf{V}^{-1}$ gives ρ times the last row of $\mathbf{I}$, hence

$$\mathbf{w}'\mathbf{V}^{-1}\mathbf{e} = \rho e_n$$

and the predictor is

$$\hat{Y}_{n+1} = \mathbf{x}_{n+1}\mathbf{b} + \rho e_n \tag{8-44}$$

Formula (7-23) was developed under the assumption that the elements of $\mathbf{V}$ (that is, the value of ρ) were known. When this is not the case formulae like (8-44) should still be used for prediction purposes with $\mathbf{b}$ and ρ replaced by estimates from the final iteration.

EXERCISES

8-1. Derive (8-32).

8-2. Show that the application of simple least-squares to $\mathbf{T}_1\mathbf{y}$, $\mathbf{T}_1\mathbf{X}$ where $\mathbf{T}_1$ is defined by (8-35) gives the estimator defined in (8-30). What is the difference between the estimator and that given by the application of simple least-squares to $\mathbf{T}_2\mathbf{y}$, $\mathbf{T}_2\mathbf{X}$ where $\mathbf{T}_2$ is defined by (8-36)?

8-3. Sketch the stages in a Cochrane–Orcutt iteration for the model described by (8-41)–(8-42) setting out explicitly the regression being fitted at each stage.

8-4. Work through R. W. Park's "Efficient Estimation of a System of Regression Equations when Disturbances are both Serially and Contemporaneously Correlated," *J. Am. Statist. Assoc.*, vol. 62, pp. 500–509, 1967, which extends the Zellner estimator, described in Chap. 7, section 6, to deal with autocorrelated error terms.

9
Stochastic Regressors, Instrumental Variables, and Errors in Variables

In considering the model

$$\mathbf{y} = \mathbf{X}\boldsymbol{\beta} + \mathbf{u}$$

with

$$E(\mathbf{u}) = \mathbf{0} \quad \text{and} \quad E(\mathbf{u}\mathbf{u}') = \sigma^2\mathbf{I}$$

we have in general been making the assumption that the X's are a set of fixed numbers. However, in Chaps. 2 and 5 we have seen that replacing that assumption by the less restrictive one that the X variables are stochastic leaves most of the main results about significance tests, confidence intervals, and so forth still valid, *provided* that the X variables have a distribution function which does not involve the parameters $\boldsymbol{\beta}$ and σ^2 and that the X's are distributed independently of the u's. So far our results have also pertained to finite sample sizes. In many of the problems to be considered in the rest of the book, however, exact finite sample distributions cannot be obtained and we have to fall back on asymptotic results.

9-1 DEFINITIONS

Let $b^{(n)}$ be an estimate of the scalar parameter β, where the superscript n denotes the number of sample observations from which $b^{(n)}$ has been computed. In general $b^{(n)}$ is a random variable, which has a density function, $f(b^{(n)})$ with mean $E(b^{(n)})$ and variance $E\{[b^{(n)} - E(b^{(n)})]^2\}$. As the sample size n varies we have a sequence of estimates denoted by

$$\{b^{(n)}\} = b^{(1)}, \ldots, b^{(n)}, \ldots$$

a sequence of density functions

$$\{f(b^{(n)})\} = f(b^{(1)}), \ldots, f(b^{(n)}), \ldots$$

a sequence of expectations

$$\{E(b^{(n)})\} = E(b^{(1)}), \ldots, E(b^{(n)}), \ldots$$

and a sequence of variances

$$\{E[b^{(n)} - E(b^{(n)})]^2\} = E[b^{(1)} - E(b^{(1)})]^2, \ldots, E[b^{(n)} - E(b^{(n)})]^2, \ldots$$

Asymptotic theory is concerned with establishing the behavior of these sequences as n becomes very large. If, as the sample size tends to infinity, the sequence $\{f(b^{(n)})\}$ tends towards some given function, that function is said to be the *limiting* or asymptotic *distribution* of $b^{(n)}$. More formally $f(b^{(n)})$ tends to a limiting distribution $g(b)$ if, for any given ε, there is an n_0 such that

$$|f(b^{(n)}) - g(b)| < \varepsilon$$

for all $n > n_0$ and for all b. Likewise if the sequence $\{E(b^{(n)})\}$ tends towards some constant, that constant is the *asymptotic expectation* of b. Using the symbol $\mathscr{E}$ for asymptotic expectation and reserving E for the finite expectation, we write

$$\mathscr{E}(b) = \lim_{n \to \infty} E(b) \tag{9-1}$$

where we have omitted the superscript n, as this need not cause any ambiguity.[1]

It would seem natural to define the asymptotic variance of $b^{(n)}$ as the limiting value of the sequence of variances and write

$$\mathscr{E}[b^{(n)} - E(b^{(n)})]^2 = \lim_{n \to \infty} E[b^{(n)} - E(b^{(n)})]^2 \tag{9-2}$$

but this runs into trouble as in many cases the limit on the right-hand side of (9-2) is zero. In such cases the sampling distribution of $b^{(n)}$ has collapsed

[1] The reader should be warned that this is an unconventional use of $\mathscr{E}$. In the statistical literature $\mathscr{E}$ and E are used interchangeably to denote finite expectations.

around a single point and the distribution is said to be degenerate. For example, if $\bar{x}$ denotes the mean of a random sample of n values from a population with mean μ and finite variance σ^2, elementary sampling theory shows that

$$E(\bar{x}) = \mu \quad \text{and} \quad E[(\bar{x} - \mu)^2] = \sigma^2/n$$

and we also know that $f(\bar{x})$ tends to normality as the sample size increases. But clearly

$$\lim_{n \to \infty} E(\bar{x} - \mu)^2 = 0$$

and $f(\bar{x})$ collapses around the point μ. However, if we consider the quantity $\sqrt{n}(\bar{x} - \mu)$, then it is easily seen that this quantity has zero mean and variance σ^2, that is

$$E[\sqrt{n}(\bar{x} - \mu)] = 0 \quad \text{and} \quad E\{[\sqrt{n}(\bar{x} - \mu)]^2\} = \sigma^2 \tag{9-3}$$

Taking limits of the expressions in (9-3) gives

$$\mathscr{E}(\sqrt{n}(\bar{x} - \mu)] = 0 \quad \text{and} \lim_{n \to \infty} E\{[\sqrt{n}(\bar{x} - \mu)]^2\} = \sigma^2 \tag{9-4}$$

and since $f(\bar{x})$ tends to normality it then follows that $\sqrt{n}(\bar{x} - \mu)$ has an asymptotic normal distribution with zero mean and variance σ^2. By this device we are able to make useful comparisons of two or more estimators, each of which may have degenerate distributions. For instance the distribution of the sample median, m, also collapses around μ as n tends to infinity, but if x is normally distributed $\sqrt{n}(m - \mu)$ has an asymptotic normal distribution with mean zero and variance $\pi\sigma^2/2$, that is,

$$\lim_{n \to \infty} E\{[\sqrt{n}(m - \mu)]^2\} = \pi\sigma^2/2 \tag{9-5}$$

Since $\pi/2$ exceeds unity the mean is a more efficient estimator of μ than is the median. Thus a meaningful and useful *large-sample* comparison of $\bar{x}$ and m can be obtained not from their degenerate limiting distributions but from the limiting distributions of $\sqrt{n} \cdot \bar{x}$ and $\sqrt{n} \cdot m$. These have variances

$$\sigma^2 \quad \text{and} \quad \pi\sigma^2/2$$

The *asymptotic variances* of $\bar{x}$ and m are then defined to be

$$\frac{\sigma^2}{n} \quad \text{and} \quad \frac{\pi\sigma^2}{2n}$$

Reverting to our original notation, the asymptotic variance of $b^{(n)}$ is defined to be

$$\text{asy var}\,(b^{(n)}) = n^{-1} \lim E\{\sqrt{n}[b^{(n)} - E(b^{(n)})]\}^2 \tag{9-6}$$

provided the limit on the right-hand side of (9-6) exists. Using the $\mathscr{E}$ symbol an equivalent definition is

$$\text{asy var}\,(b^{(n)}) = n^{-1}\mathscr{E}\{\sqrt{n}[b^{(n)} - E(b^{(n)})]\}^2 \tag{9-7}$$

As we shall see later one important practical use of formula (9-6) or (9-7) occurs in cases where the exact variance for any given sample size, n, cannot be derived but it is possible to derive the asymptotic variance. Sample estimates may then be substituted for the expressions occurring in the asymptotic formula and the result taken as an approximation to the finite sampling variance. The approximation will of course be better the larger the sample size.

The asymptotic expectation and variance of b are two important pieces of information about the behavior of the estimator as the sample size increases. But they are summary statistics for the distribution and it is also very important to know what the chances are that an estimate based on a single sample (which is all that we usually have) will lie within some specified distance of the true parameter value. The problem is illustrated in Fig. 9-1. A indicates the distribution of $b^{(n)}$ for some given sample size n, and B the distribution for a larger sample size, while β indicates the true value of the parameter being estimated. The figure shows b to be a biased estimator of β but the bias decreases as the sample size increases. The variance of the sampling distribution also decreases as the sample size increases. If we specify a range of $\pm\varepsilon$ around β then, in general, a greater proportion of the B distribution than the A distribution will lie within the perpendiculars erected at $\beta \pm \varepsilon$. Clearly if these two conditions on the mean and variance of $f(b)$ hold we can secure more and more of the density within the limits $\beta \pm \varepsilon$ by increasing n sufficiently. More formally for arbitrarily small positive numbers ε and η there will be a sample size n_0 such that

$$\Pr\{|b^{(n)} - \beta| < \varepsilon\} > 1 - \eta \quad \text{for all } n > n_0 \tag{9-8}$$

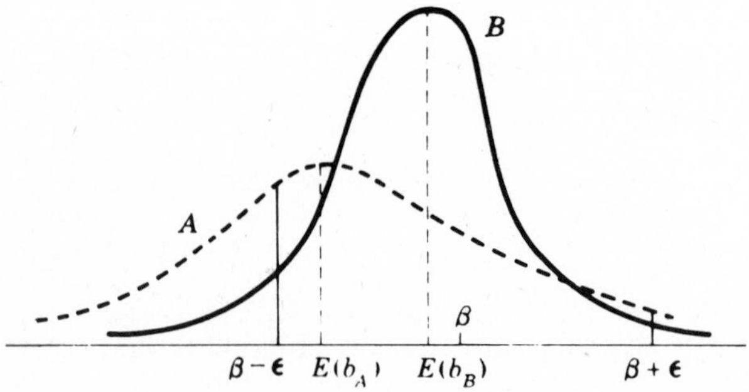

Fig. 9-1.

or alternatively

$$\lim_{n \to \infty} \Pr \{|b^{(n)} - \beta| < \varepsilon\} = 1 \tag{9-9}$$

If this condition holds we say that $b^{(n)}$ is a *consistent* estimator of β, that $b^{(n)}$ converges in probability to β, or that the *probability limit* of the sequence $\{b^{(n)}\}$ is β, and this is often abbreviated to

$$\text{plim}\, b^{(n)} = \beta \tag{9-10}$$

It is important to emphasize that consistency is a large sample property and implies nothing about the small sample properties of the estimator. Having found a consistent estimator any number of other consistent estimators may be constructed from it. For example, as Kendall and Stuart have suggested,

$$\frac{n - c_1}{n - c_2} b^{(n)}$$

is also consistent, for fixed c_1 and c_2.[1]

The above discussion of consistent estimators has suggested that a *sufficient* condition for a consistent estimator is that the bias and the variance should both tend to zero as the sample size increases. This may be shown formally as follows. Let $b^{(n)}$ be an estimator of β with expectation

$$E(b^{(n)}) = \beta + k^{(n)} \tag{9-11}$$

and variance

$$\text{var}\, b^{(n)} = v^{(n)} \tag{9-12}$$

and suppose that

$$\lim_{n \to \infty} k^{(n)} = \lim_{n \to \infty} v^{(n)} = 0 \tag{9-13}$$

Then by Tchebycheff's inequality[2]

$$\Pr \{|b^{(n)} - (\beta + k^{(n)})| < \varepsilon\} \geq 1 - \frac{v^{(n)}}{\varepsilon^2} \tag{9-14}$$

Taking the limits of (9-14) and using (9-13) gives

$$\text{plim}\, b^{(n)} = \beta$$

[1] M. G. Kendall and A. Stuart, *The Advanced Theory of Statistics*, vol. 2, Griffin, London, 1961, p. 4.

[2] Tchebycheff's inequality states that for a random variable x with finite mean μ and variance σ^2, and for given $\lambda (> 0)$

$$\Pr \{|x - \mu| < \lambda\sigma\} \geq 1 - \frac{1}{\lambda^2}$$

Thus an estimator which is asymptotically unbiased and whose variance tends to zero is a consistent estimator, and for such an estimator the probability limit equals the asymptotic expectation and both equal the true value of the parameter being estimated, that is,

$$\text{plim}\, b^{(n)} = \mathscr{E}(b^{(n)}) = \beta \tag{9-15}$$

It is possible, however, to find estimators which are consistent but not asymptotically unbiased. Consider, for instance, the estimator $b^{(n)}$ which has the sampling distribution[1]

$$b^{(n)} = \beta \text{ with probability } 1 - \frac{1}{n}$$

$$b^{(n)} = n^k \text{ with probability } \frac{1}{n}$$

where k is some constant. The finite expectation is

$$E(b^{(n)}) = \beta - n^{-1}\beta + n^{k-1}$$

and the asymptotic expectation is

$$\mathscr{E}(b^{(n)}) = \beta + \lim_{n\to\infty} n^{k-1}$$

We then have

$$\begin{aligned} \mathscr{E}(b^{(n)}) &= \beta && \text{if } k < 1 \\ &= \beta + 1 && \text{if } k = 1 \\ &= \infty && \text{if } k > 1 \end{aligned}$$

Further

$$\text{var}\,(b^{(n)}) = n^{-1}(1 - n^{-1})(n^{2k} - 2n^k\beta + \beta^2)$$

Clearly

$$\text{var}\,(b^{(n)}) \to 0 \quad \text{if } k < \tfrac{1}{2}$$

However, $b^{(n)}$ is clearly a consistent estimator for we can write

$$\Pr\{|b^{(n)} - \beta| < \varepsilon\} = 1 - \frac{1}{n}$$

for arbitrarily small ε and this probability tends to unity as n tends to infinity, so by the definitions (9-8) and (9-9) $b^{(n)}$ is a consistent estimator of β. For cases where $k > 1$ the probability limit of this estimator is thus *not* equal

[1] See W. P. Sewell, "Least Squares, Conditional Predictions, and Estimator Properties," *Econometrica*, vol. 37, pp. 39–43, 1969.

to its asymptotic expectation. This may seem a somewhat pathological case but as Sewell has shown a similar result can hold for certain simultaneous equation estimators. The reason for laboring this point is that it is often much easier to evaluate probability limits than it is to evaluate asymptotic expectations and a great simplification is achieved if the latter can be replaced by the former. As we have seen this is not necessarily always true and one must proceed with caution. To summarize, one may say that $\text{plim}\, b = \mathscr{E}(b)$ in the following cases;

(a) if b is unbiased in finite samples and is also consistent, for then

$\mathscr{E}(b) = E(b) = \beta = \text{plim}\, b$, or more generally,

(b) if $\mathscr{E}(b)$ and $\text{plim}\, b$ exist and $\lim_{n\to\infty} \text{var}\,(b) = 0$, by Tchebycheff's theorem.

One of the great conveniences of operating with probability limits is described in the following result. If $\text{plim}\, b = \beta$ and if $f(b)$ denotes some continuous function of b then $\text{plim}\, f(b) = f(\beta)$, that is, the probability limit of some function of b is simply the value of that function with β substituted for b. Particular examples are

$$\text{plim}\,(b^2) = (\text{plim}\, b)^2$$

$$\text{plim}\,(b^{-1}) = (\text{plim}\, b)^{-1}$$

The definitions of asymptotic expectations, asymptotic variances, and probability limits have been given so far in terms of a single parameter. They all extend quite simply to sets of parameters. Thus

$$\mathscr{E}(\mathbf{b}) = \lim_{n\to\infty} E(b) = \begin{bmatrix} \lim_{n\to\infty} E(b_1) \\ \lim_{n\to\infty} E(b_2) \\ \cdot \\ \cdot \\ \cdot \\ \lim_{n\to\infty} E(b_k) \end{bmatrix} \tag{9-16}$$

defines the asymptotic expectation of a vector $\mathbf{b}$ of estimates of k parameters. Similarly if the asymptotic expectation $\mathscr{E}(b)$ exists the asymptotic variance–covariance matrix is defined as

$$\text{asy var}\,(\mathbf{b}) = n^{-1} \lim_{n\to\infty} E[\sqrt{n}(\mathbf{b} - E(\mathbf{b}))][\sqrt{n}(\mathbf{b} - E(\mathbf{b}))]' \tag{9-17}$$

If each of the elements of $\mathbf{b}$ is a consistent estimator of the corresponding element of $\boldsymbol{\beta}$ we write

$$\text{plim}\, \mathbf{b} = \boldsymbol{\beta}$$

Operations with probability limits in the case of vectors and matrices are just as simple as in the case of scalar quantities. Thus if **A** and **B** are matrices

$$\text{plim}\,(\mathbf{AB}) = (\text{plim}\,\mathbf{A})(\text{plim}\,\mathbf{B})$$

and

$$\text{plim}\,(\mathbf{A}^{-1}) = (\text{plim}\,\mathbf{A})^{-1}$$

9-2 STOCHASTIC REGRESSORS

Using these concepts we can now examine the asymptotic properties of least-squares estimators in the general linear model with stochastic regressors. Let us postulate the relationship

$$\mathbf{y} = \mathbf{X}\boldsymbol{\beta} + \mathbf{u}$$

where $\mathbf{y}$ is $n \times 1$, $\mathbf{X}$ is $n \times k$, etc. The X variables are stochastic but distributed independently of the variable u, so that each row of $\mathbf{X}$ is independent of each and every element of $\mathbf{u}$. The usual assumptions about the u variable now appear as

$$E(\mathbf{u}|\mathbf{X}) = E(\mathbf{u}) = \mathbf{0} \tag{9-18a}$$

$$E(\mathbf{y}|\mathbf{X}) = \mathbf{X}\boldsymbol{\beta} + E(\mathbf{u}|\mathbf{X}) = \mathbf{X}\boldsymbol{\beta} \tag{9-18b}$$

$$E(\mathbf{uu}'|\mathbf{X}) = \sigma_u^2\mathbf{I} \tag{9-18c}$$

In addition we assume

$$\text{plim}\left(\frac{1}{n}\mathbf{u}'\mathbf{u}\right) = \sigma_u^2 \tag{9-19a}$$

$$\text{plim}\left(\frac{1}{n}\mathbf{X}'\mathbf{X}\right) = \boldsymbol{\Sigma}_{XX} \tag{9-19b}$$

$$\text{plim}\left(\frac{1}{n}\mathbf{X}'\mathbf{u}\right) = \mathbf{0} \tag{9-19c}$$

Assumption (9-19b) postulates the existence of probability limits for the second-order moments of the X variables, as given by the constants appearing in the $\boldsymbol{\Sigma}_{XX}$ matrix. Assumption (9-19c) postulates zero probability limits for the covariances between the u variable and each of the X variables.

The OLS estimator $\mathbf{b}$ of $\boldsymbol{\beta}$ is

$$\mathbf{b} = \boldsymbol{\beta} + (\mathbf{X}'\mathbf{X})^{-1}\mathbf{X}'\mathbf{u}$$

Thus

$$\text{plim}\,\mathbf{b} = \boldsymbol{\beta} + \text{plim}\left(\frac{1}{n}\mathbf{X}'\mathbf{X}\right)^{-1} \cdot \text{plim}\left(\frac{1}{n}\mathbf{X}'\mathbf{u}\right)$$
$$= \boldsymbol{\beta} + \boldsymbol{\Sigma}_{XX}^{-1}\mathbf{0}$$
$$= \boldsymbol{\beta}$$

so that the OLS estimators are consistent. To derive the asymptotic variance–covariance matrix for **b**, substitute in (9-17). Thus

$$\text{asy var}\,(\mathbf{b}) = n^{-1} \lim_{n\to\infty} E[\sqrt{n}(\mathbf{b} - \boldsymbol{\beta})][\sqrt{n}(\mathbf{b} - \boldsymbol{\beta})]'$$

since we already know $\mathscr{E}(\mathbf{b}) = E(\mathbf{b}) = \boldsymbol{\beta}$. Now[1]

$$E(\mathbf{b} - \boldsymbol{\beta})(\mathbf{b} - \boldsymbol{\beta})' = E[(\mathbf{X}'\mathbf{X})^{-1}\mathbf{X}'\mathbf{u}\mathbf{u}'\,\mathbf{X}(\mathbf{X}'\mathbf{X})^{-1}]$$
$$= E[E(\mathbf{X}'\mathbf{X})^{-1}\mathbf{X}'\mathbf{u}\mathbf{u}'\,\mathbf{X}(\mathbf{X}'\mathbf{X})^{-1}|\mathbf{X}]$$
$$= E[\sigma_u^2(\mathbf{X}'\mathbf{X})^{-1}]$$
$$= \sigma_u^2 E(\mathbf{X}'\mathbf{X})^{-1} \tag{9-20}$$

Thus

$$\text{asy var}\,(\mathbf{b}) = n^{-1}.\lim_{n\to\infty}\,[n\sigma_u^2 E(\mathbf{X}'\mathbf{X})^{-1}]$$
$$= n^{-1}\sigma_u^2\mathscr{E}\left(\frac{1}{n}\mathbf{X}'\mathbf{X}\right)^{-1} \tag{9-21}$$

By assumption (9-19b) plim $\{(1/n)(\mathbf{X}'\mathbf{X})\}$ exists and is equal to the matrix $\boldsymbol{\Sigma}_{XX}$. Hence plim $\{(1/n)(\mathbf{X}'\mathbf{X})\}^{-1}$ exists and is equal to $\boldsymbol{\Sigma}_{XX}^{-1}$. Since in general the population second-order moments of the X variables can be consistently estimated by the corresponding sample moments we can pass from asymptotic expectations to probability limits and rewrite (9-21) as

$$\text{asy var}\,(\mathbf{b}) = n^{-1}\,\sigma_u^2\boldsymbol{\Sigma}_{XX}^{-1} \tag{9-22}$$

The elements entering into (9-22) are unknown. The error variance matrix that is computed for the OLS estimators from the usual formula in Chap. 5 is

$$s^2(\mathbf{X}'\mathbf{X})^{-1} = n^{-1}s^2\left(\frac{1}{n}\mathbf{X}'\mathbf{X}\right)^{-1} \tag{9-23}$$

where

$$s^2 = \mathbf{e}'\mathbf{e}/(n - k)$$

[1] For the step in the second line of this development see Chap. 2, pp. 30 and 31.

It is easily shown that $\text{plim}\, s^2 = \sigma^2$ and since

$$\text{plim}\left(\frac{1}{n}\mathbf{X}'\mathbf{X}\right)^{-1} = \mathbf{\Sigma}_{XX}^{-1}$$

we see that the usual OLS formulae provide consistent estimators of the asymptotic error variances and covariances in the case of stochastic regressors.

Returning to the definition (9-17)

$$\text{asy var}\,(\mathbf{b}) = n^{-1} \lim_{n\to\infty} E[\sqrt{n}(\mathbf{b} - \boldsymbol{\beta})][\sqrt{n}(\mathbf{b} - \boldsymbol{\beta})]'$$

we see that the asymptotic variance of $\mathbf{b}$ is n^{-1} times the *asymptotic expectation* of the sequence $[\sqrt{n}(\mathbf{b} - \boldsymbol{\beta})][\sqrt{n}(\mathbf{b} - \boldsymbol{\beta})]'$. If the probability limit of this sequence exists and if there are no problems in passing from asymptotic expectations to probability limits an alternative definition of the asymptotic variance matrix is

$$\text{asy var}\,(\mathbf{b}) = n^{-1}\, \text{plim}\, [\sqrt{n}(\mathbf{b} - \boldsymbol{\beta})][\sqrt{n}(\mathbf{b} - \boldsymbol{\beta})]' \tag{9-24}$$

It will be helpful for future developments if we re-derive this asymptotic variance matrix by the alternative formula (9-24). Now

$$\text{asy var}\,(\mathbf{b}) = n^{-1}\, \text{plim}\, [n(\mathbf{X}'\mathbf{X})^{-1}\mathbf{X}'\mathbf{u}\mathbf{u}'\mathbf{X}(\mathbf{X}'\mathbf{X})^{-1}]$$

provided the probability limit exists.

$$\begin{aligned}
&\text{plim}\, [n(\mathbf{X}'\mathbf{X})^{-1}\mathbf{X}'\mathbf{u}\mathbf{u}'\mathbf{X}(\mathbf{X}'\mathbf{X})^{-1}] \\
&= \text{plim}\left[\left(\frac{1}{n}\mathbf{X}'\mathbf{X}\right)^{-1}\left(\frac{1}{n}\mathbf{X}'\mathbf{u}\mathbf{u}'\mathbf{X}\right)\left(\frac{1}{n}\mathbf{X}'\mathbf{X}\right)^{-1}\right] \\
&= \text{plim}\left(\frac{1}{n}\mathbf{X}'\mathbf{X}\right)^{-1} \cdot \text{plim}\left(\frac{1}{n}\mathbf{X}'\mathbf{u}\mathbf{u}'\mathbf{X}\right) \cdot \text{plim}\left(\frac{1}{n}\mathbf{X}'\mathbf{X}\right)^{-1}
\end{aligned}$$

Considering the middle term further, $\mathbf{X}'\mathbf{u}$ is a $k \times 1$ vector whose ith term is $\sum_{t=1}^{n} X_{it}u_t$. Thus the i, jth element in the $k \times k$ matrix $\{(1/n)(\mathbf{X}'\mathbf{u}\mathbf{u}'\mathbf{X})\}$ is

$$\frac{1}{n}\left(\sum_{t=1}^{n} X_{it}u_t\right)\left(\sum_{t=1}^{n} X_{jt}u_t\right)$$

and we require the probability limits of elements such as this. For $i = j$

$$\frac{1}{n}\left(\sum_t X_{it}u_t\right)^2 = \frac{1}{n}\sum_t X_{it}^2u_t^2 + \frac{2}{n}\sum_{t<s}\sum_s X_{it}X_{is}u_tu_s \tag{9-25}$$

Taking expected values

$$E\left[\frac{1}{n}\left(\sum_{t=1}^{n} X_{it}u_t\right)^2\right] = \sigma_u^2 E\left(\frac{1}{n}\sum_{t=1}^{n} X_{it}^2\right) \tag{9-26}$$

for $Eu_t^2 = \sigma_u^2$ for all t and the expectations of the cross-product terms all vanish as the X's and u's are independent and $E(u_t u_s) = 0$ for $t \neq s$. We may rewrite (9-26) in terms of asymptotic expectations and then pass directly to probability limits, which exist by assumption (9-19b). Thus

$$\operatorname{plim}\frac{1}{n}(\Sigma X_{it}u_t)^2 = \sigma_u^2 \operatorname{plim}\left(\frac{1}{n}\Sigma X_{it}^2\right) \qquad i = 1, \ldots, k \tag{9-27}$$

Similarly for $i \neq j$

$$E\left[\frac{1}{n}\left(\sum_{t=1}^{n} X_{it}u_t\right)\left(\sum_{t=1}^{n} X_{jt}u_t\right)\right] = \sigma_u^2 E\left(\frac{1}{n}\sum_{t=1}^{n} X_{it}X_{jt}\right)$$

and so

$$\operatorname{plim}\frac{1}{n}\left(\sum_{t=1}^{n} X_{it}u_t\right)\left(\sum_{t=1}^{n} X_{jt}u_t\right) = \sigma_u^2 \operatorname{plim}\left(\frac{1}{n}\sum_{t=1}^{n} X_{it}X_{jt}\right)$$

$$i \neq j;\, i, j = 1, \ldots, k \tag{9-28}$$

Collecting results (9-27), (9-28), and using (9-19b) gives

$$\operatorname{plim}\left(\frac{1}{n}\mathbf{X}'\mathbf{u}\mathbf{u}'\mathbf{X}\right) = \sigma_u^2 \mathbf{\Sigma}_{XX}$$

and so

$$\begin{aligned}\text{asy var}\,(\mathbf{b}) &= n^{-1}\mathbf{\Sigma}_{XX}^{-1}\sigma_u^2\mathbf{\Sigma}_{XX}\mathbf{\Sigma}_{XX}^{-1} \\ &= n^{-1}\sigma_u^2\mathbf{\Sigma}_{XX}^{-1}\end{aligned}$$

as in (9-22) above.

In some important applications the X variables may not be fully independent of the u variable, as we have been assuming so far in this section. For instance, one of the explanatory variables may be a lagged value of the Y variable, and as we shall see in Chap. 10 this causes a finite sample bias in least-squares estimators. We must now examine what happens to the asymptotic properties of these estimators. Consider the relation

$$Y_t = \beta_1 + \beta_2 X_t + \beta_3 Y_{t-1} + u_t \qquad t = 1, \ldots, n \tag{9-29}$$

where $E(\mathbf{uu}') = \sigma^2\mathbf{I}$. Since u_{t-1} influences Y_{t-1} and since Y_{t-1} in turn influences Y_t we may expect some correlation between u_{t-1} and Y_t, even though the u's are serially independent: the correlation will be small if X plays a major role in determining the variation in Y but we cannot assume its existence away. However, in the absence of serial correlation among the u's we have no reason to expect u_t to be correlated with Y_{t-1}. As we have seen above the consistency of the least-squares estimator in the general model depends on the double assumption that plim $\{(1/n)(\mathbf{X}'\mathbf{X})\}$ is some matrix of finite constants and that plim $\{(1/n)(\mathbf{X}'\mathbf{u})\} = \mathbf{0}$. For (9-29) the latter matrix is

$$\text{plim}\left(\frac{1}{n}\mathbf{X}'\mathbf{u}\right) = \begin{bmatrix} \text{plim}\,\frac{1}{n}\sum_{t=1}^{n} u_t \\ \text{plim}\,\frac{1}{n}\sum_{t=1}^{n} X_t u_t \\ \text{plim}\,\frac{1}{n}\sum_{t=1}^{n} Y_{t-1} u_t \end{bmatrix}$$

From the discussion above we can assert plim $\{(1/n)(\Sigma Y_{t-1}u_t)\} = 0$ and since the other two terms give no trouble we can still assert plim $\{(1/n)(\mathbf{X}'\mathbf{u})\} = 0$ for a relation containing lagged values of the dependent variable, so that least-squares estimators may be expected to be consistent.

In deriving the asymptotic variance matrix for this case the only difficulty centres around the term plim $\{(1/n)(\mathbf{X}'\mathbf{uu}'\mathbf{X})\}$. If, say, $X_{it} = Y_{t-1}$ some cross-product terms occurring in (9-25) are of the form $Y_{t-1}Y_{s-1}u_t u_s$ where $t < s$. Now

$$E(Y_{t-1}Y_{s-1}u_t u_s) = E(Y_{t-1}Y_{s-1}u_t)E(u_s) = 0$$

since u_s is independent of all previous values of u and Y and since $E(u_s) = 0$ for all s. Thus formulae (9-26) and (9-28) still apply even though some of the X's may be lagged values of Y, and the asymptotic properties of the estimator are unchanged.

9-3 INSTRUMENTAL VARIABLES

If one or more of the X variables is in the limit correlated with u, then

$$\text{plim}\left(\frac{1}{n}\mathbf{X}'\mathbf{u}\right) \neq \mathbf{0}$$

and we see immediately that least-squares estimates will be inconsistent. It is important to notice that only one nonzero element in the vector, plim $\{1/n(\mathbf{X}'\mathbf{u})\}$, can render all the elements in $\mathbf{b}$ inconsistent. We have

$$\text{plim}\,\mathbf{b} = \boldsymbol{\beta} + \text{plim}\left(\frac{1}{n}\mathbf{X}'\mathbf{X}\right)^{-1}\cdot\text{plim}\left(\frac{1}{n}\mathbf{X}'\mathbf{u}\right)$$

If, for instance, plim $\{(1/n)(\mathbf{X}'u)\}$ has a constant c in the ith position and zeros everywhere else and if $\{s^{1i}s^{2i}\cdots s^{ni}\}$ denotes the ith column of plim $\{(1/n)(\mathbf{X}'\mathbf{X})\}^{-1}$

$$\text{plim } \mathbf{b} = \boldsymbol{\beta} + c \begin{bmatrix} s^{1i} \\ s^{2i} \\ \vdots \\ s^{ni} \end{bmatrix}$$

and all elements of **b** are affected, except in the special case of orthogonal X variables when all but one of the s^{ji} would be zero.

Correlation between explanatory variables and the disturbance term is thus extremely serious for ordinary least-squares estimators. It may occur for a number of reasons, which we shall examine later in this chapter and also in Chap. 13. For the moment we turn to an alternative method of estimation which has wide applicability, namely the method of instrumental variables. Consider the model

$$\mathbf{y} = \mathbf{X}\boldsymbol{\beta} + \mathbf{u} \tag{9-30}$$

with

$$\text{plim}\left(\frac{1}{n}\mathbf{X}'\mathbf{u}\right) \neq \mathbf{0} \tag{9-31}$$

Suppose that an $n \times k$ matrix **Z** exists with the following properties.

$$\text{plim}\left(\frac{1}{n}\mathbf{Z}'\mathbf{u}\right) = 0 \tag{9-32}$$

$$\text{plim}\left(\frac{1}{n}\mathbf{Z}'\mathbf{X}\right) = \boldsymbol{\Sigma}_{ZX} \quad \text{exists and is nonsingular} \tag{9-33}$$

$$\text{plim}\left(\frac{1}{n}\mathbf{Z}'\mathbf{Z}\right) = \boldsymbol{\Sigma}_{ZZ} \text{ exists} \tag{9-34}$$

Thus the Z variables are postulated to be uncorrelated in the limit with the disturbance u and to have nonzero cross-products with the X variables. If some of the X variables are likely to be uncorrelated with u they can be used to form some of the columns of **Z** and extraneous variables found only for the remaining columns.

Consider now the instrumental variable estimator of $\boldsymbol{\beta}$ defined by

$$\mathbf{b} = (\mathbf{Z}'\mathbf{X})^{-1}\mathbf{Z}'\mathbf{y} \tag{9-35}$$

A rationale for the estimator may be obtained by premultiplying Eq. (9-30) by $(1/n)(\mathbf{Z}')$ to give

$$\frac{1}{n}\mathbf{Z}'\mathbf{y} = \frac{1}{n}\mathbf{Z}'\mathbf{X}\boldsymbol{\beta} + \frac{1}{n}\mathbf{Z}'\mathbf{u} \tag{9-36}$$

The probability limit of the last term on the right-hand side of (9-36) is zero which suggests setting this term to zero and replacing the unknown $\boldsymbol{\beta}$ by an estimator $\mathbf{b}$ to give $\mathbf{b} = (\mathbf{Z}'\mathbf{X})^{-1}\mathbf{Z}'\mathbf{y}$ as in (9-35). The asymptotic properties of the estimator are easily established. First of all it is consistent, for substituting (9-30) in (9-35) gives

$$\mathbf{b} = \boldsymbol{\beta} + (\mathbf{Z}'\mathbf{X})^{-1}\mathbf{Z}'\mathbf{u}$$

so

$$\begin{aligned}\text{plim } \mathbf{b} &= \boldsymbol{\beta} + \text{plim}\left(\frac{1}{n}\mathbf{Z}'\mathbf{X}\right)^{-1} \cdot \text{plim}\left(\frac{1}{n}\mathbf{Z}'\mathbf{u}\right) \\ &= \boldsymbol{\beta} + \boldsymbol{\Sigma}_{ZX}^{-1} \cdot \mathbf{0} \\ &= \boldsymbol{\beta}\end{aligned}$$

To obtain the asymptotic variance–covariance matrix we have

$$\begin{aligned}\text{asy var}(\mathbf{b}) &= n^{-1}\,\text{plim}\,[n(\mathbf{b}-\boldsymbol{\beta})(\mathbf{b}-\boldsymbol{\beta})'] \\ &= n^{-1}\,\text{plim}\,[n(\mathbf{Z}'\mathbf{X})^{-1}\mathbf{Z}'\mathbf{u}\mathbf{u}'\mathbf{Z}(\mathbf{X}'\mathbf{Z})^{-1}] \\ &= n^{-1}\,\text{plim}\left(\frac{1}{n}\mathbf{Z}'\mathbf{X}\right)^{-1} \cdot \text{plim}\left(\frac{1}{n}\mathbf{Z}'\mathbf{u}\mathbf{u}'\mathbf{Z}\right) \cdot \text{plim}\left(\frac{1}{n}\mathbf{X}'\mathbf{Z}\right)^{-1}\end{aligned}$$

By repeating the argument through Eqs. (9-25) to (9-28) with Z's replacing X's we have

$$\text{plim}\left(\frac{1}{n}\mathbf{Z}'\mathbf{u}\mathbf{u}'\mathbf{Z}\right) = \sigma_u^2\boldsymbol{\Sigma}_{ZZ}$$

and so

$$\text{asy var}(\mathbf{b}) = n^{-1}\sigma_u^2\boldsymbol{\Sigma}_{ZX}^{-1}\boldsymbol{\Sigma}_{ZZ}\boldsymbol{\Sigma}_{ZX}^{-1'} \tag{9-37}$$

In practice (9-37) would be estimated by

$$s^2(\mathbf{Z}'\mathbf{X})^{-1}(\mathbf{Z}'\mathbf{Z})(\mathbf{X}'\mathbf{Z})^{-1} \tag{9-38}$$

where

$$s^2 = (\mathbf{y} - \mathbf{X}\mathbf{b})'(\mathbf{y} - \mathbf{X}\mathbf{b})/(n-k) \tag{9-39}$$

The real difficulty in practice of course is actually finding variables to play the role of instruments. The true disturbance is unobservable and so it is difficult to be confident that the instruments really are uncorrelated in the limit with the disturbances. On the other hand the instruments should be fairly highly correlated with the X's otherwise the sampling variances of the instrumental variable estimator may be unduly large. For example, in the case of a single explanatory variable the instrumental variable estimator of the slope is

$$b = \frac{\Sigma zy}{\Sigma zx}$$

the small letters denoting deviations from the means. Formula (9-38) gives the sampling variance of this estimator as

$$s^2 \Sigma z^2 / (\Sigma zx)^2$$

If Z were uncorrelated with X the sampling variance would be infinitely large. With only a small correlation between Z and X we may be paying a very high price for consistency. The dilemma may be stated succinctly: X is correlated with u, and we must find a new variable Z which ideally should be fairly strongly correlated with X but uncorrelated with u. However, as we shall see in subsequent sections the technique can often be applied successfully.

9-4 ERRORS IN VARIABLES

So far we have implicitly assumed that the X variables have been measured without error and the only form of error admitted to the relation has been in the disturbance term u. The latter has generally been thought of as representing the influence of various explanatory variables that have not actually been included in the relation. It could of course also have a component representing measurement error in the dependent variable Y and the previous results would still be valid. We now have to ask the question of what happens if the X variables are subject to measurement error. We assume that the $\boldsymbol{\beta}$ vector represents the coefficients of the correctly measured X variables. What will happen if we apply our least-squares techniques to the actual measurements available of the X and Y variables? The answer is that OLS estimates will not only be biased but will also be inconsistent. This may be shown as follows.

Let the observed data matrix be

$$\mathbf{X} = \tilde{\mathbf{X}} + \mathbf{V} \tag{9-40}$$

where $\tilde{\mathbf{X}}$ denotes the $(n \times k)$ matrix of true values and $\mathbf{V}$ a matrix of measurement errors. The presumed model is now

$$\mathbf{y} = \tilde{\mathbf{X}}\boldsymbol{\beta} + \mathbf{u}$$

which may be written as

$$\mathbf{y} = \mathbf{X}\boldsymbol{\beta} + (\mathbf{u} - \mathbf{V}\boldsymbol{\beta}) \tag{9-41}$$

The least-squares estimator from (9-41) is

$$\hat{\boldsymbol{\beta}} = \boldsymbol{\beta} + (\mathbf{X}'\mathbf{X})^{-1}\mathbf{X}'(\mathbf{u} - \mathbf{V}\boldsymbol{\beta})$$

Thus consistency depends on

$$\text{plim}\left[\frac{1}{n}\mathbf{X}'(\mathbf{u} - \mathbf{V}\boldsymbol{\beta})\right]$$

vanishing. We see that

$$\text{plim}\left[\frac{1}{n}\mathbf{X}'(\mathbf{u} - \mathbf{V}\boldsymbol{\beta})\right] = \text{plim}\left(\frac{1}{n}\mathbf{X}'\mathbf{u}\right) - \text{plim}\left(\frac{1}{n}\mathbf{X}'\mathbf{V}\right)\boldsymbol{\beta}$$

It is often plausible to assume that the disturbance u is uncorrelated in the limit with both the true values and the measurement errors of the explanatory variables. Thus we may assert

$$\text{plim}\left(\frac{1}{n}\mathbf{X}'\mathbf{u}\right) = \mathbf{0}$$

But

$$\text{plim}\left(\frac{1}{n}\mathbf{X}'\mathbf{V}\right) = \text{plim}\left(\frac{1}{n}\tilde{\mathbf{X}}'\mathbf{V}\right) + \text{plim}\left(\frac{1}{n}\mathbf{V}'\mathbf{V}\right)$$

Even if measurement errors in the X's are uncorrelated with the true values so that the first term on the right-hand side of this expression vanishes the second term is the variance–covariance matrix of the measurement errors and on our present assumptions does not vanish. Thus OLS estimators are inconsistent, and the asymptotic bias is given by

$$\text{plim}\,\hat{\boldsymbol{\beta}} - \boldsymbol{\beta} = -\text{plim}\left(\frac{1}{n}\mathbf{X}'\mathbf{X}\right)^{-1} \cdot \text{plim}\left(\frac{1}{n}\mathbf{V}'\mathbf{V}\right)\boldsymbol{\beta} \tag{9-42}$$

For example, if we are estimating a simple two-variable relation between observed values Y and X where the true slope is β, (9-42) gives the asymptotic bias of the OLS estimator as

$$\text{plim}\,\hat{\beta} - \beta = -\frac{\sigma_v^2\beta}{\sigma_{\tilde{x}}^2 + \sigma_v^2}$$

or alternatively

$$\text{plim}\,\hat{\beta} = \frac{\beta}{1 + \sigma_v^2/\sigma_{\tilde{x}}^2} \tag{9-43}$$

where σ_v^2 denotes the variance of the measurement error in X, $\sigma_{\tilde{x}}^2$ the variance of the true X values and we are assuming the measurement errors and true values to be uncorrelated. Equation (9-43) shows that the true slope will be underestimated. For instance, if σ_v^2 is say 10 per cent of $\sigma_{\tilde{x}}^2$ we are likely to underestimate β by about 10 per cent no matter how large a sample size is available.

Measurement error in the X variables thus poses a serious estimation problem and alternative estimators are required. There are two main types of estimator described in the literature; one type is based on instrumental variables of various kinds and the other on maximum likelihood methods buttressed with fairly strong assumptions about the covariance matrix of the measurement errors. Before describing these estimators it is worth emphasizing the possibility that in certain circumstances economic agents may react to the measured values rather than the true values of economic variables. Firms may base investment decisions on some extrapolation of national income trends and in so doing will use the latest national income statistics complete with such errors as they contain. The firms' researchers have even less chance than the government statisticians of knowing the "true" national income figures, and the firms' decisions will have to be based on the published data. If decision makers respond to measured data then measurement error is irrelevant and our previous least-squares techniques will be valid.

We have seen in the previous section that under suitable conditions instrumental variables may yield consistent estimators. From (9-41) it is clear that if a matrix $\mathbf{Z}$ of instrumental variables can be found which is uncorrelated in the limit both with the disturbance term $\mathbf{u}$ and the measurement errors $\mathbf{V}$ then

$$\mathbf{b} = (\mathbf{Z}'\mathbf{X})^{-1}\mathbf{Z}'\mathbf{y} \tag{9-44}$$

will be a consistent estimator of $\boldsymbol{\beta}$, with asymptotic covariance matrix

$$\text{asy var}\,(\mathbf{b}) = \sigma_u^2(\mathbf{Z}'\mathbf{X})^{-1}\mathbf{Z}'\mathbf{Z}(\mathbf{X}'\mathbf{Z})^{-1} \tag{9-45}$$

To illustrate some of the instrumental variables that have been suggested let us consider first of all the two-variable model

$$Y_i = \alpha + \beta\tilde{X}_i + u_i \tag{9-46}$$

$$i = 1, \ldots, n$$

$$X_i = \tilde{X}_i + v_i \tag{9-47}$$

where $\tilde{X}_i$ indicates the true value of the ith observation on the explanatory variable and v_i is the measurement error in X_i. Any measurement error in Y has been merged with the disturbance into the single term u. To simplify the exposition still further, rewrite (9-46) as

$$Y_i = \alpha + \beta X_i + (u_i - \beta v_i)$$

$$Y_i = (\alpha + \beta\bar{X}) + \beta x_i + (u_i - \beta v_i) \tag{9-48}$$

where $x_i = (X_i - \overline{X})$ as usual. Suppose there is an even number of sample observations and we define a **Z** matrix as

$$\mathbf{Z}' = \begin{bmatrix} 1 & 1 & 1 & \cdots & 1 \\ -1 & -1 & 1 & \cdots & -1 \end{bmatrix}$$

where the elements in the second row of $\mathbf{Z}'$ are plus or minus one according as the corresponding value of X is above or below the median X value. The **X** matrix for use in the regression corresponding to (9-48) is

$$\mathbf{X}' = \begin{bmatrix} 1 & 1 & 1 & 1 & \cdots & 1 \\ x_1 & x_2 & x_3 & x_4 & \cdots & x_n \end{bmatrix}$$

The instrumental variable estimator defined by (9-44) is then

$$\mathbf{b} = \begin{bmatrix} n & 0 \\ 0 & \frac{n}{2}(\bar{x}_2 - \bar{x}_1) \end{bmatrix}^{-1} \begin{bmatrix} n\overline{Y} \\ \frac{n}{2}(\overline{Y}_2 - \overline{Y}_1) \end{bmatrix}$$

where $\bar{x}_2$ and $\bar{x}_1$ denote the mean values of the deviations for those values of X above and below the median and $\overline{Y}_2$ and $\overline{Y}_1$ are the means of the corresponding Y values. Thus

$$\mathbf{b} = \begin{bmatrix} \overline{Y} \\ \left(\dfrac{\overline{Y}_2 - \overline{Y}_1}{\bar{x}_2 - \bar{x}_1}\right) \end{bmatrix}$$

The estimated slope is

$$\hat{\beta} = \frac{\overline{Y}_2 - \overline{Y}_1}{\bar{x}_2 - \bar{x}_1} = \frac{\overline{Y}_2 - \overline{Y}_1}{\overline{X}_2 - \overline{X}_1} \tag{9-49}$$

and from (9-48) it is seen that $\overline{Y}$ is the estimator of $\alpha + \beta\overline{X}$ and so

$$\hat{\alpha} = \overline{Y} - \hat{\beta}\overline{X} \tag{9-50}$$

Equations (9-49) and (9-50) define the estimator first proposed by Wald.[1] If n is odd one should omit the central observation before beginning the computations. Under fairly general conditions the Wald estimator is consistent but likely to have a large sampling variance. Bartlett has shown that the efficiency may be increased by dividing the ranked X values into three equal-sized groups, the first containing the smallest X values and the

[1] A. Wald, "The Fitting of Straight Lines if Both Variables are Subject to Error," *Ann. Math. Statist.*, vol. 11, pp. 284–300, 1940.

third containing the greatest X values.[1] Omitting the central $n/3$ observations the slope is estimated by

$$\hat{\beta} = \frac{\bar{Y}_3 - \bar{Y}_1}{\bar{X}_3 - \bar{X}_1} \tag{9-51}$$

where the $\bar{X}_i$, $\bar{Y}_i$ indicate the means of the observations in the two extreme groups. The intercept would again be estimated as in (9-50). Theil and Van Yzeren have investigated how the efficiency of the Bartlett estimator varies according to the distributions of the X values.[2] In particular if X has a Beta distribution the two extreme groups should each contain 30 per cent for optimal efficiency. A division of the sample into three equal-sized groups should suffice for practical applications since we are not likely to have precise knowledge of the distributions of the X values. Durbin has suggested what is likely to be the most efficient estimator of this type.[3] The X's should be ranked in order and an instrumental variable defined as the rank order (that is, with values $1, 2, 3, \ldots, n$). Durbin has shown that for large samples the efficiency of this estimator, relative to that of least-squares is approximately 96 per cent and for a sample size of twenty is likely to be about 86 per cent.

Durbin's model did not have an intercept term. To apply his method to estimate the intercept and slope in model (9-48) one would use formula (9-44) with[4]

$$\mathbf{Z}' = \begin{bmatrix} 1 & 1 & 1 & \cdots & 1 \\ 1 & 2 & 3 & \cdots & n \end{bmatrix}$$

and

$$\mathbf{X}' = \begin{bmatrix} 1 & 1 & 1 & \cdots & 1 \\ x_1 & x_2 & x_3 & \cdots & x_n \end{bmatrix}$$

where we assume the x deviations to have been ranked by size. This is equivalent to estimating the slope from

$$\hat{\beta} = \frac{\sum_{i=1}^{n} iy_i}{\sum_{i=1}^{n} ix_i} \tag{9-52}$$

[1] M. S. Bartlett, "Fitting a Straight Line when Both Variables are subject to Error," *Biometrics*, vol. 5, pp. 207–212, 1949. It is easily seen that this is equivalent to making the second row in Z' consist of equal numbers of zeros and plus and minus ones.

[2] H. Theil and J. van Yzeren, "On the Efficiency of Wald's Method of Fitting Straight Lines." *Rev. Intern. Statist. Inst.*, vol. 24, pp. 17–26, 1956.

[3] J. Durbin, "Errors in Variables," *Rev. Intern. Statist. Inst.*, vol. 22, 23–32, 1954.

[4] This Z' matrix does not satisfy assumption (9-34), but it will do if the second row is replaced by $\frac{1}{n}, \frac{2}{n}, \cdots, 1$ and the same estimates as in (9-52) and (9-53) will result.

and the intercept from

$$\hat{\alpha} = \bar{Y} - \hat{\beta}\bar{X} \tag{9-53}$$

Formula (9-45) may be used to provide an estimate of the sampling variances of instrumental variable estimators.

The extension of these instrumental estimators to relations containing more than one explanatory variable depends crucially upon obtaining a suitable **Z** matrix for insertion in formula (9-44). One obvious and plausible method would be to use Durbin's suggestion on each explanatory variable, that is, to have a column of **Z** correspond to the rank order of each explanatory variable, the X variable being expressed in deviation form as usual. Extensions of the grouping method of Wald and Bartlett to the case of two or more explanatory variables is rather cumbersome and tedious.[1] They are also likely to be less efficient than a Durbin type estimator.

Turning now to maximum likelihood methods let us consider again the two-variable model of (9-46) and (9-47) namely

$$Y = \alpha + \beta\tilde{X} + u$$

$$X = \tilde{X} + v$$

The simplest possible set of assumptions to make is that $\tilde{X}$, u, and v have independent normal distributions with means $E(\tilde{X}) = \mu$, $E(u) = 0$, and $E(v) = 0$ and variances denoted by σ^2, σ_u^2, and σ_v^2. Then the X, Y variables have bivariate normal distributions with parameters.

$$\begin{aligned} E(X) &= \mu \\ E(Y) &= \alpha + \beta\mu \\ \sigma_x^2 &= E[(X - \mu)^2] = \sigma^2 + \sigma_v^2 \\ \sigma_y^2 &= E[(Y - \alpha - \beta\mu)^2] = \beta^2\sigma^2 + \sigma_u^2 \\ \sigma_{xy} &= E[(X - \mu)(Y - \alpha - \beta\mu)] = \beta\sigma^2 \end{aligned} \tag{9-54}$$

The corresponding sample statistics will be maximum likelihood estimates of these parameters. However, the difficulty is that only five sample statistics are available for the left-hand side of (9-54) and the right-hand side contains six unknown parameters, namely, α, β, μ, σ^2, σ_u^2, and σ_v^2. In the language of Chap. 12 the model is not identified and the only parameter that can be estimated is μ, given by $\hat{\mu} = \bar{X}$.

The classical solution to this problem is to assume that one further piece of information is given, typically that the *ratio* of the variances of u

[1] For details see J. W. Hooper and H. Theil, "The Extension of Wald's Method of Fitting Straight Lines to Multiple Regression," *Rev. Intern. Statist. Inst.*, vol. 26, pp. 37–47, 1958, and the references given there.

and v is a known constant. This does not seem a useful solution in the context of econometrics since the u variable in general contains two components, the measurement error in Y and the stochastic disturbance term. While it may be possible to hazard an estimate of the ratio of the variances of two measurement errors it would seem impossible to know *a priori* what the variance of the disturbance term is likely to be. In fact one of the prime purposes of econometric analysis is to estimate the fit of a relation. The classical approach to this problem stemmed from the assumption of an exact relation between the true values of Y and X so that u represented solely measurement error in Y. The only possible escape in an econometric problem is then to assume a knowledge of the variance of the measurement error in the explanatory variable. In many cases this is not impossible. It is becoming increasingly common for national income statistics to be published with some indication of the likely range of the errors. Suppose, for example, that an observed X variable has an average value of 100 and we are told that the maximum error in any value is very unlikely to exceed 10 per cent. We might then set $3\sigma_v = 10$ and $\sigma_v^2 = 11$.

Let us examine then the derivation of estimators from (9-54) on the assumption that σ_v^2 is known. Replacing the left-hand symbols by sample values.

$$\bar{X} = \hat{\mu}$$

$$\bar{Y} = \hat{\alpha} + \hat{\beta}\hat{\mu}$$

$$m_{xx} = \hat{\sigma}^2 + \sigma_v^2$$

$$m_{yy} = \hat{\beta}^2\hat{\sigma}^2 + \hat{\sigma}_u^2$$

$$m_{xy} = \hat{\beta}\hat{\sigma}^2$$

giving the estimators

$$\hat{\beta} = \frac{m_{xy}}{\hat{\sigma}^2} = \frac{m_{xy}}{m_{xx} - \sigma_v^2} \tag{9-55}$$

$$\hat{\alpha} = \bar{Y} - \hat{\beta}\bar{X} \tag{9-56}$$

and

$$\hat{\sigma}_u^2 = m_{yy} - \hat{\beta}m_{xy} \tag{9-57}$$

where

$$m_{xx} = \frac{1}{n}\Sigma(X_i - \bar{X})^2 \text{ etc.}$$

The estimators (9-55) to (9-57) will be consistent and it is easily seen that for the special case of no measurement errors in $X(\sigma_v^2 = 0)$ they reduce to the OLS estimators of Chap. 2.

It may not seem plausible in some contexts to assume that the X values come from a single normal distribution with mean μ. If, for example, the $\tilde{X}$ values displayed a cyclical movement about a time trend we would need to modify the simple assumption. One might then postulate each $\tilde{X}_i$ to be normal with

$$E(\tilde{X}_i) = \mu_i \qquad i = 1, \ldots, n \tag{9-58}$$

with a constant variance σ^2. One can proceed to find maximum likelihood estimators for this more complicated model. The difficulty is that n additional parameters have been introduced $(\mu_1, \mu_2, \ldots, \mu_n)$. The resultant estimator is complicated; $\hat{\beta}$ is obtained as the solution of a cubic equation.[1]

An alternative procedure is to regard the $\tilde{X}_1, \tilde{X}_2, \ldots, \tilde{X}_n$ values as fixed in repeating sampling and study the properties of estimators conditional on the set of $\tilde{X}$ values that generated the sample data. From (9-46) and (9-47) we then have

$$m_{xx} = m_{\tilde{x}\tilde{x}} + m_{vv} + 2m_{\tilde{x}v}$$

$$m_{xy} = \beta m_{\tilde{x}\tilde{x}} + \beta m_{\tilde{x}v} + m_{\tilde{x}u} + m_{uv}$$

where the m's indicate sample variances and covariances between the variables indicated by the subscripts. Assuming σ_v^2 known as before and taking expected values of both equations gives

$$\begin{aligned} E(m_{xx} - \sigma_v^2) &= m_{\tilde{x}\tilde{x}} \\ E(m_{xy}) &= \beta m_{\tilde{x}\tilde{x}} \end{aligned} \tag{9-59}$$

The estimator of $\hat{\beta}$ obtained in (9-55) may be expressed as

$$(m_{xx} - \sigma_v^2)\hat{\beta} - m_{xy} = 0 \tag{9-60}$$

If we replace $\hat{\beta}$ in (9-60) by β and take expectations we have

$$E[(m_{xx} - \sigma_v^2)\beta - m_{xy}] = 0 \qquad \text{from (9-59)}$$

Equation (9-60) thus defines an unbiased linear estimating equation.[2] The estimator $\hat{\beta}$ of (9-55) thus turns out to have desirable properties under more general assumptions than those from which it was originally derived.

[1] See J. Johnston, *Econometric Methods,* first edition, 157–159.

[2] See J. Durbin, "Estimation of Parameters in Time-series Regression Model," *J. Royal Statist. Soc.:* Series B, vol. 22, pp. 139–153, 1960, for the definition and discussion of unbiased linear estimating equations.

To study the extension of this method to the case of two explanatory variables, consider the model

$$Y = \alpha + \beta_1 \tilde{X}_1 + \beta_2 \tilde{X}_2 + u \tag{9-61}$$

$$X_1 = \tilde{X}_1 + v_1 \tag{9-62}$$

$$X_2 = \tilde{X}_2 + v_2 \tag{9-63}$$

Suppose that the true values $\tilde{X}_1$, $\tilde{X}_2$ have a bivariate normal distribution with means μ_1, μ_2, variances σ_1^2, σ_2^2, and covariance σ_{12}. Suppose also that u, v_1, and v_2 are independent of $\tilde{X}_1$, $\tilde{X}_2$ and have independent normal distributions with zero means and variances denoted by σ_u^2, $\sigma_{v_1}^2$, $\sigma_{v_2}^2$. The observed variables Y_1, X_1, and X_2 then have a multivariate normal distribution with parameters,

$$\begin{aligned}
E(Y) &= \alpha + \beta_1\mu_1 + \beta_2\mu_2 \\
E(X_1) &= \mu_1 \\
E(X_2) &= \mu_2 \\
\sigma_y^2 &= \beta_1^2\sigma_1^2 + \beta_2^2\sigma_2^2 + 2\beta_1\beta_2\sigma_{12} + \sigma_u^2 \\
\sigma_{x_1}^2 &= \sigma_1^2 + \sigma_{v_1}^2 \\
\sigma_{x_2}^2 &= \sigma_2^2 + \sigma_{v_2}^2 \\
\sigma_{yx_1} &= \beta_1\sigma_1^2 + \beta_2\sigma_{12} \\
\sigma_{yx_2} &= \beta_1\sigma_{12} + \beta_2\sigma_2^2 \\
\sigma_{x_1x_2} &= \sigma_{12}
\end{aligned} \tag{9-64}$$

This gives nine equations in eleven unknown parameters. If $\sigma_{v_1}^2$ and $\sigma_{v_2}^2$ are assumed to be known the remaining parameters might be estimated as follows

$$\begin{aligned}
\hat{\sigma}_{12} &= m_{x_1x_2} \\
\hat{\sigma}_1^2 &= m_{x_1x_2} - \sigma_{v_1}^2 \\
\hat{\sigma}_2^2 &= m_{x_2x_2} - \sigma_{v_2}^2
\end{aligned}$$

and, using these, $\hat{\beta}_1$ and $\hat{\beta}_2$ are obtained from

$$\begin{bmatrix} m_{x_1x_1} - \sigma_{v_1}^2 & m_{x_1x_2} \\ m_{x_1x_2} & m_{x_2x_2} - \sigma_{v_2}^2 \end{bmatrix} \begin{bmatrix} \hat{\beta}_1 \\ \hat{\beta}_2 \end{bmatrix} = \begin{bmatrix} m_{yx_1} \\ m_{yx_2} \end{bmatrix} \tag{9-65}$$

$$\hat{\alpha} = \bar{Y} - \hat{\beta}_1\bar{X}_1 - \hat{\beta}_2\bar{X}_2 \tag{9-66}$$

and

$$\hat{\sigma}_u^2 = m_{yy} - [\hat{\beta}_1 \quad \hat{\beta}_2]\begin{bmatrix} m_{x_1x_1} - \sigma_{v_1}^2 & m_{x_1x_2} \\ m_{x_1x_2} & m_{x_2x_2} - \sigma_{v_2}^2 \end{bmatrix}\begin{bmatrix} \hat{\beta}_1 \\ \hat{\beta}_2 \end{bmatrix} \tag{9-67}$$

The extension of these estimators to more than two explanatory variables is straightforward.

Finally we may notice that for some types of prediction problems OLS may still be a useful technique. Suppose that Y denotes measured consumption expenditure and X denotes measured income and that the assumed relation is that measured consumption depends on the true income of the previous period, that is,

$$Y_t = \alpha + \beta\tilde{X}_{t-1} + u_t \tag{9-68}$$

For period n, say, we have measured income X_n, but we do not know the true income $\tilde{X}_n$, and our problem is to predict Y_{n+1}, given X_n. The expected value of Y_{n+1}, given X_n is

$$\begin{aligned} E(Y_{n+1}|X_n) &= E(\alpha + \beta\tilde{X}_n + u_{n+1}|X_n) \\ &= \alpha + \beta E(\tilde{X}_n|X_n) \end{aligned}$$

Thus we require to evaluate $E(\tilde{X}_n|X_n)$.

If we assume as before that $X = \tilde{X} + v$ and that $\tilde{X}$ and v have independent normal distributions with $E(\tilde{X}) = \mu$, $E(v) = 0$ and variances denoted by σ^2 and σ_v^2, then

$$E(\tilde{X}_n|X_n) = \frac{\sigma_v^2\mu + \sigma^2 X_n}{\sigma_v^2 + \sigma^2}$$

thus

$$E(Y_{n+1}|X_n) = \alpha + \beta\frac{(\sigma_v^2\mu + \sigma^2 X_n)}{(\sigma_v^2 + \sigma^2)} \tag{9-69}$$

Our problem is to obtain a consistent predictor of $E(Y_{n+1}|X_n)$. If α and β are replaced by the consistent estimators $\hat{\alpha}$ and $\hat{\beta}$ given in (9-55) and (9-56) above then the form of (9-69) shows that a consistent predictor would be given by

$$\hat{\alpha} + \hat{\beta}\left(\frac{\sigma_v^2\bar{X} + \hat{\sigma}^2 X_n}{\sigma_v^2 + \hat{\sigma}^2}\right) \tag{9-70}$$

where $\hat{\sigma}^2 = m_{xx} - \sigma_v^2$, for $\hat{\sigma}^2$ and $\bar{X}$ are consistent estimators of σ^2 and μ.

Alternatively consider the least-squares predictor

$$\hat{Y}_{n+1} = \bar{Y} + b(X_n - \bar{X}) \tag{9.71}$$

[1] See Exercise 9-4.

where b is the slope of the least-squares regression of Y on X. We have seen in (9-43) that

$$\text{plim } b = \frac{\beta}{1 + \sigma_v^2/\sigma^2}$$

Thus

$$\begin{aligned}\text{plim } \hat{Y}_{n+1} &= \text{plim } \bar{Y} + \text{plim } b\,(X_n - \text{plim } \bar{X}) \\ &= \alpha + \beta\mu + \frac{\beta}{1 + \sigma_v^2/\sigma^2}(X_n - \mu) \\ &= \alpha + \beta\left(\frac{\sigma_v^2\mu + \sigma^2 X_n}{\sigma_v^2 + \sigma^2}\right) \\ &= E(Y_{n+1}|X_n)\end{aligned}$$

Thus for prediction purposes a simple least-squares regression and the use of (9-71) would be adequate even though one would not use OLS to estimate the structural parameters.

EXERCISES

9-1. Show that in the stochastic regression model $\mathbf{y} = \mathbf{X}\boldsymbol{\beta} + \mathbf{u}$ with assumptions (9-18) and (9-19), $\mathbf{e}'\mathbf{e}/(n - k)$ is a consistent estimator of σ_u^2.

9-2. In the relation $\mathbf{y} = \mathbf{X}\boldsymbol{\beta} + \mathbf{u}$, $\boldsymbol{\beta}$ is estimated by the instrumental variable estimator $\mathbf{b} = (\mathbf{Z}'\mathbf{X})^{-1}\mathbf{Z}'\mathbf{y}$. Show that the instruments $\mathbf{Z}$ are uncorrelated with the estimated residuals $\hat{\mathbf{u}} = \mathbf{y} - \mathbf{X}\mathbf{b}$.

9-3. Prove that Eqs. (9-52) and (9-53) do result from the application of the Durbin method to relation (9-48).

9-4. Let x and y have independent normal distributions with means μ_x, μ_y and standard deviations σ_x, and σ_y and define $z = x + y$. Derive the conditional distribution of x given z, $f(x|z)$, and hence show that

$$E(x|z) = \frac{\sigma_y^2\mu_x - \sigma_x^2\mu_y + \sigma_x^2 z}{\sigma_x^2 + \sigma_y^2}$$

9-5. Extend formulae (9-65), (9-66), and (9-67) to the general case of k explanatory variables.

10
Lagged Variables

We are using the term "lagged variables" to cover both the inclusion of lagged values of the explanatory variables (the X's) and also lagged values of the dependent variable (Y). In each case we will outline possible reasons for particular specifications and then discuss the estimation problems that arise.

10-1 LAGGED EXPLANATORY VARIABLES

Realistic formulations of economic relations often require the insertion of lagged values of the explanatory variables on the right-hand side. For example in studying investment expenditure by a firm we must recognize that time is required for the collection and analysis of statistical and other information about markets, time is required for reaching a decision on the basis of the information, further time may be used up in a queuing process if an order for capital equipment cannot be put into production right away, and finally time is required for the production, delivery, and installation of the equipment. If the sum of these lags amounted to a constant number, θ, of time periods then we might simply postulate that investment expenditure responded to sales data with a lag θ,

$$Y_t = f(X_{t-\theta})$$

or, say

$$Y_t = \alpha + \beta X_{t-\theta} + u_t \tag{10-1}$$

Relation (10-1) is especially simple since it assumes that the effect of $X_{t-\theta}$ appears only within period t and is fully completed within that period. It is often more realistic to assume that the effect of a variable is *distributed* over several time periods. A capital appropriation in a given quarter, for instance, may result in capital expenditure in several subsequent quarters. Suppose, for example, that a causal force X_t produces a component $\beta_0 X_t$ in Y_t, a component $\beta_1 X_t$ in Y_{t+1}, and so forth up to $\beta_s X_t$ in Y_{t+s}, then if this system of reactions is constant over time the value of Y in any period may be expressed as a linear function of the current and the s previous values of X, namely,

$$Y_t = \beta_0 X_t + \beta_1 X_{t-1} + \cdots + \beta_s X_{t-s} + u_t \tag{10-2}$$

Under the usual assumption about the distribution of u and the independence of X and u there are in principle no new estimation problems in this model. Least-squares will give best linear unbiased estimates, if the model has been specified correctly. Several difficulties, however, are likely to arise in practice. First of all one cannot really expect any precise and firm indication from theory of the length of lag to be incorporated; rather one hopes to determine the lag from the data by fitting a fairly long lag and then examining the significance of the coefficients of various lagged values of X. But this in turn raises two main statistical difficulties; one is that long lags may leave very few degrees of freedom for the estimation process and the other is that typically the various lagged values of X will be highly intercorrelated leading to very imprecise estimates of the lagged coefficients and great difficulty in making useful inferences about them.

These difficulties have lead to the *a priori* imposition of various assumptions about the form of the weights $\beta_0, \ldots, \beta_s$ in an attempt to produce a more amenable estimation problem involving fewer than $s + 1$ parameters. The most extreme assumption specifies not just the form of the weights but the actual numerical values. For example, from a given set of observations on X one might construct new variables,

$$X_t^{(1)} = \tfrac{1}{3}X_t + \tfrac{1}{2}X_{t-1} + \tfrac{1}{6}X_{t-2}$$

$$X_t^{(2)} = \tfrac{3}{8}X_t + \tfrac{1}{4}X_{t-1} + \tfrac{1}{4}X_{t-2} + \tfrac{1}{8}X_{t-3}$$

$$X_t^{(3)} = \tfrac{1}{2}X_{t-1} + \tfrac{1}{2}X_{t-2} \text{ etc.}$$

and use each in turn as a single explanatory variable, finally choosing the $X^{(i)}$ which gives the best explanation of the Y variable in the sample period.[1] In a study of capital investment De Leeuw found evidence in favor of the weights following an "inverted V" distribution, that is, for a total lag of s periods the first half of the weights are taken as proportional to the rising series $1, 2, 3, \ldots s/2$ (for even values of s) and the last half proportional to the declining series $s/2, s/2 - 1, \ldots, 3, 2, 1$.[2]

A more flexible approach to the problem has recently been suggested by Almon.[3] Return again to (10-2),

$$Y_t = \beta_0 X_t + \beta_1 X_{t-1} + \cdots + \beta_s X_{t-s} + u_t$$

where we postulate a lagged effect up to s periods. To apply the Almon scheme we do have to specify a value for s, but, as will be seen we can specify a number of different values and later make a choice between them. Consider a set of β's as shown in Fig. (10-1a). We rule out the direct approach of attempting to estimate all $(s + 1)$ β's and assume instead that the β's can be approximated by some function $\beta_z \simeq f(z)$ as in Fig. (10-1b). The function $f(z)$ is unknown,

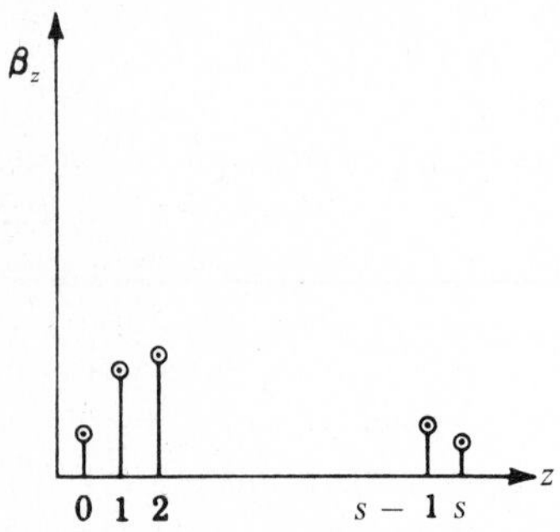

Fig. 10-1a.

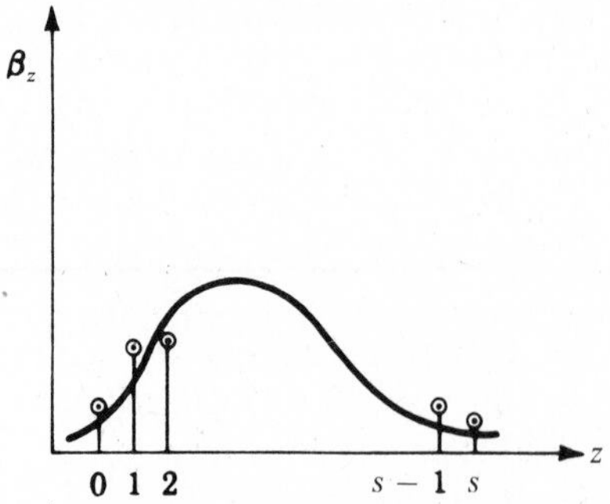

Fig. 10-1b.

in the absence of any *a priori* assumptions about its form. Almon's method, however, is based on Weierstrass's theorem which states that a function continuous in a closed interval can be approximated over the whole interval by a *polynomial* of suitable degree which differs from the function by less than any given positive quantity at every point of the interval.[4] Thus we may

[1] For an illustration of this approach see P. J. Lund and K. Holden, "An Econometric Study of Private Sector Gross Fixed Capital Formation in the United Kingdom, 1923–1938," *Oxford Economic papers*, vol. 20, pp. 56–73, 1968.

[2] F. de Leeuw, "The Demand for Capital Goods by Manufacturers, A Study of Quarterly Time Series," *Econometrica*, vol. 30, pp. 407–423, 1962.

[3] S. Almon, "The Distributed Lag between Capital Appropriations and Expenditures," *Econometrica*, vol. 30, pp. 178–196, 1965.

[4] B. R. Morton, *Numerical Approximation*, Routledge and Kegan Paul, London, 1964, p. 4.

represent $f(z)$ approximately by a polynomial in z, that is,

$$f(z) \simeq a_0 + a_1 z + a_2 z^2 + \cdots + a_r z^r \tag{10-3}$$

Weierstrass's theorem gives no indication of the degree of polynomial required for a given level of accuracy. For our purposes we hope that a polynomial of fairly low degree, say $r = 3$ or 4, will give good results. So far then there are two approximations involved; first of all β_z is approximated by $f(z)$ and $f(z)$ in turn by a polynomial in z. If we ignore the approximations and take say, $r = 3$ and $s = 7$ we have the following scheme for the β's

$$\begin{aligned} \beta_0 &= f(0) = a_0 \\ \beta_1 &= f(1) = a_0 + a_1 + a_2 + a_3 \\ \beta_2 &= f(2) = a_0 + 2a_1 + 4a_2 + 8a_3 \\ \beta_3 &= f(3) = a_0 + 3a_1 + 9a_2 + 27a_3 \\ &\vdots \\ \beta_7 &= f(7) = a_0 + 7a_1 + 49a_2 + 343a_3 \end{aligned} \tag{10-4}$$

which expresses the eight unknown β's in terms of four unknown a's. Substituting (10-4) in (10-2) gives

$$\begin{aligned} Y_t = {} & a_0(X_t + X_{t-1} + X_{t-2} + \cdots + X_{t-7}) \\ & + a_1(X_{t-1} + 2X_{t-2} + 3X_{t-3} + \cdots + 7X_{t-7}) \\ & + a_2(X_{t-1} + 4X_{t-2} + 9X_{t-3} + \cdots + 49X_{t-7}) \\ & + a_3(X_{t-1} + 8X_{t-2} + 27X_{t-3} + \cdots + 343X_{t-7}) + u_t \end{aligned} \tag{10-5}$$

In principle the a's in (10-5) can be estimated by regressing Y on the four variables defined in the parentheses on the right-hand side, and the estimates of the β coefficients then obtained by substitution in (10-4). The quality of the estimates of the a's will depend on the variances and correlations between the four explanatory variables in (10-5). Denoting the matrix of explanatory variables in (10-5) by $\mathbf{W}$, the dispersion matrix for $\hat{\mathbf{a}}$, the vector of estimates of the a's is

$$\operatorname{var}(\hat{\mathbf{a}}) = \sigma_u^2(\mathbf{W}'\mathbf{W})^{-1} \tag{10-6}$$

The sampling variances of the $\hat{\beta}$ coefficients obtained by substituting for the $\hat{a}$ values in (10-4) are then given by

$$\operatorname{var}(\hat{\beta}_i) = \sigma_u^2 \mathbf{k}_i(\mathbf{W}'\mathbf{W})^{-1}\mathbf{k}_i' \qquad i = 0, 1, \ldots, s \tag{10-7}$$

where $\mathbf{k}_i$ denotes the coefficients in the row of (10-4) corresponding to β_i. For example, for β_3,

$$\mathbf{k}_3 = [1 \quad 3 \quad 9 \quad 27]$$

These are an especially simple case of the Almon estimates. Her general approach is to return to the polynomial in (10-3) and to use the result that if we know $(r + 1)$ ordinates, $f(z_0)$, $f(z_1), \ldots, f(z_r)$ of the polynomial and the corresponding abscissae $z_0, z_1, \ldots, z_r$, the value $f(z)$ at any point can be expressed in terms of these known quantities by the Lagrange interpolation formula.[1]

$$\begin{aligned} f(z) = & \frac{(z - z_1)(z - z_2)\ldots(z - z_r)}{(z_0 - z_1)(z_0 - z_2)\ldots(z_0 - z_r)} f(z_0) \\ & + \frac{(z - z_0)(z - z_2)\ldots(z - z_r)}{(z_1 - z_0)(z_1 - z_2)\ldots(z_1 - z_r)} f(z_1) \\ & + \cdots\cdots\cdots\cdots\cdots\cdots \\ & + \frac{(z - z_0)(z - z_1)\ldots(z - z_{r-1})}{(z_r - z_0)(z_r - z_1)\ldots(z_r - z_{r-1})} f(z_r) \end{aligned} \tag{10-8}$$

If we knew $z_0, z_1, \ldots, z_r$ and $f(z_0), f(z_1), \ldots, f(z_r)$, (10-8) could be used to evaluate $f(0), f(1), \ldots, f(s)$ and so (10-2) could be written as

$$Y_t = f(0)X_t + f(1)X_{t-1} + \cdots + f(s)X_{t-s} + u_t \tag{10-9}$$

However, the ordinates $f(z_0), \ldots, f(z_r)$ are unknown so the procedure is to pick an arbitrary set of values $z_0, z_1, \ldots, z_r$ and then to estimate $f(z_0), \ldots,$ $f(z_r)$ from the data and finally to estimate the weights by substitution in (10–8). To illustrate the approach let us again set $r = 3$ and $s = 7$. Denote the Lagrangian coefficients in (10–8) by $c_{zi} (i = 0, \ldots, r)$ so that for a third-degree polynomial we can write (10–8) as

$$f(z) = c_{z0}f(z_0) + c_{z1}f(z_1) + c_{z2}f(z_2) + c_{z3}f(z_3)$$

Substitution in (10-9) for $s = 7$ then gives

$$\begin{aligned} Y_t = & [c_{00}f(z_0) + c_{01}f(z_1) + c_{02}f(z_2) + c_{03}f(z_3)]X_t \\ & + [c_{10}f(z_0) + c_{11}f(z_1) + c_{12}f(z_2) + c_{13}f(z_3)]X_{t-1} \\ & \vdots \\ & + [c_{70}f(z_0) + c_{71}f(z_1) + c_{72}f(z_2) + c_{73}f(z_3)]X_{t-7} + u_t \end{aligned}$$

or, re-arranging

$$\begin{aligned} Y_t = & f(z_0)[c_{00}X_t + c_{10}X_{t-1} + \cdots + c_{70}X_{t-7}] \\ & + f(z_1)[c_{01}X_t + c_{11}X_{t-1} + \cdots + c_{71}X_{t-7}] \\ & + f(z_2)[c_{02}X_t + c_{12}X_{t-1} + \cdots + c_{72}X_{t-7}] \\ & + f(z_3)[c_{03}X_t + c_{13}X_{t-1} + \cdots + c_{73}X_{t-7}] + u_t \end{aligned} \tag{10-10}$$

[1] cf. B. R. Morton, *op. cit.*, p. 38.

For $r = 3$ and $s = 7$ the practical steps involved are:

1. Select four $(r + 1)$ arbitrary values z_0, z_1, z_2, z_3.
2. For $z = 0, 1, 2, \ldots, 7$ compute the 32 Lagrangian coefficients c_{zi} $(z = 0, 1, \ldots, 7; i = 0, 1, 2, 3)$ defined in (10-8).
3. Apply these c_{zi} coefficients to the X variable to compute the values of the four explanatory variables in (10-10).
4. Apply ordinary least-squares to (10-10) to obtain estimates of $f(z_0)$, $f(z_1)$, $f(z_2)$, $f(z_3)$.
5. Combine the estimates from (4) with the c_{zi} coefficients to compute the estimated lag coefficients $\hat{\hat{\beta}}_0 = f(0), \hat{\hat{\beta}}_1 = f(1), \ldots, \hat{\hat{\beta}}_7 = f(7)$ from (10-8).

If $\mathbf{V}$ denotes the matrix of explanatory variables in (10-10) the sampling variances of the lag coefficients, $\hat{\hat{\beta}}_z$, are given by

$$\text{var}\,(\hat{\hat{\beta}}_z) = \sigma_u^2 \mathbf{c}_z (\mathbf{V}'\mathbf{V})^{-1} \mathbf{c}_z' \qquad z = 0, 1, \ldots, s \tag{10-11}$$

where

$$\mathbf{c}_z = [c_{z0} \quad c_{z1} \quad c_{z2} \quad c_{z3}]$$

denotes the row vector of Lagrangian coefficients in (10-8) for any z. These estimators are in general much more complicated and computationally burdensome than those outlined in (10-4) and (10-5). It will be seen that the latter correspond to setting $z_0 = 0$, $z_1 = 1$, $z_2 = 2$ and $z_3 = 3$ in the first step of the Almon procedure. These simpler estimates have two additional strong advantages. First of all in the general Almon scheme the degree of the approximating polynomial (the value of r) has to be specified *a priori* and thus one has to fit several different approximations to any set of data and attempt a judgment as to which is best. However, as (10-5) shows, the simple approach yields a direct test of the degree of the approximating polynomial. In that example a third-degree polynomial was specified and a_3 denotes the coefficient of the third-degree term, and it is clear that a test of significance for a_3 can be based directly on the regression specified in (10-5). Secondly, in the general case changing the degree of the polynomial involves recomputing all the Lagrangian coefficients in (10-8) and the corresponding explanatory variables in (10-10), but again, as (10-5) shows, changing the degree in the simple case merely involves adding extra explanatory variables to (10-5) leaving the previous variables unchanged.

The above exposition has been in terms of a single explanatory variable X with a total lag of length s, but the method can easily be extended to allow for explanatory variables X_2, X_3 with lags s_2, s_3 etc. The flexibility of schemes of type (10-2) has recently been further extended.[1] The basic assumption in

[1] P. A. Tinsley, "An Application of Variable Weight Distributed Lags," *J. Am. Statist. Assoc.*, vol. 62, pp. 1277–1289, 1967; and see also S. Almon, "Lags Between Investment Decisions and their Causes," *Rev. Economics and Statistics*, vol. 50, pp. 193–206, 1968.

(10-2) is that the effect of say X_{t-i} on Y_t depends only on the length of time from period $(t - i)$ to period t. Likewise X_t is presumed to have an effect $\beta_i X_t$ on Y_{t+i} and so forth. In some cases, however, it may be more realistic to suppose that the size of the effect depends, not only on the lapse of time and the specific X value, but also on the value of some other variable, W. Thus we might postulate

$$\beta_i = \alpha_i + \gamma_i W_{t-i} \qquad i = 0, 1, \dots, s \tag{10-12}$$

Substituting (10-12) in (10-2) then gives

$$Y_t = \alpha_0 X_t + \alpha_1 X_{t-1} + \cdots + \alpha_s X_{t-s} + \gamma_0(W_t X_t) + \gamma_1(W_{t-1}X_{t-1}) + \cdots + \gamma_s(W_{t-s}X_{t-s}) + u_t$$

This is now a relation in the lagged values of two explanatory variables X and WX, and a twofold application of the Almon scheme could yield estimates of the α and γ coefficients.

The Almon scheme assumes that a polynomial of fairly low degree can represent the lag coefficients. A stronger assumption which assumes an explicit form for the lag coefficients is the basis of the Koyck scheme.[1] Let us rewrite (10-2), without terminating the lag at a finite number of periods, as

$$Y_t = \beta_0 X_t + \beta_1 X_{t-1} + \beta_2 X_{t-2} + \cdots + u_t \tag{10-13}$$

Let us also assume that the β's are all of the same sign and have a finite sum so that we can rewrite (10-13) as

$$Y_t = \beta(w_0 + w_1 D + w_2 D^2 + \cdots)X_t + u_t \tag{10-14}$$

where the weights w_i are all non-negative and sum to unity. D is the delay operator such that $DX_t = X_{t-1}, D^2 X_t = X_{t-2}$ etc.[2] Koyck proposed a declining geometric sequence for the w's, namely,

$$w_i = (1 - \lambda)\lambda^i \qquad 0 < \lambda < 1 \tag{10-15}$$

Thus we have

$$w_0 + w_1 D + w_2 D^2 + \cdots = (1 - \lambda)[1 + \lambda D + \lambda^2 D^2 + \cdots] = \frac{1 - \lambda}{1 - \lambda D}$$

and (10-14) may be re-written as

$$Y_t = \frac{\beta(1 - \lambda)}{1 - \lambda D} X_t + u_t \tag{10-16}$$

[1] L. M. Koyck, *Distributed Lags and Investment Analysis*, North-Holland Publishing Company, Amsterdam, 1954.

[2] See R. G. D. Allen, *Mathematical Economics*, Macmillan, London, 1956, Appendix A, and Z. Griliches, "Distributed Lags: A Survey," *Econometrica*, vol. 35, pp. 16–49, 1967.

which gives

$$Y_t = \beta(1 - \lambda)X_t + \lambda Y_{t-1} + (u_t - \lambda u_{t-1}) \tag{10-17}$$

The Koyck assumption thus achieves a tremendous simplification of (10-13) in that instead of having to estimate a string of β coefficients one merely has to estimate the two parameters β and λ from a relation giving Y_t as a function of X_t and Y_{t-1}. From the estimated λ and the weight formula in (10-15) the weights can be estimated. On the assumptions made the w's could be regarded formally as the probabilities of a discrete variable taking on the values 0, 1, 2, etc. The mean of the λ distribution is $\lambda/(1 - \lambda)$ and so we say that for the geometric distribution

$$\text{Mean Lag} = \frac{\lambda}{1 - \lambda}$$

The lagged Y value in (10-17) will usually ensure a fairly good fit for the relation. One must be cautious in interpreting a good fit to mean that the lag distribution is necessarily of the Koyck type, for the Koyck assumption gives the first X value the greatest weight and all subsequent values successively smaller weights, and this may not necessarily be very realistic. Where this seems implausible it is possible to let the first few weights be free and impose the Koyck pattern after a certain lag. For example, we might write

$$\begin{aligned} Y_t &= \beta_0 X_t + \beta_1 X_{t-1} + \beta_2 X_{t-2} + \lambda\beta_2 X_{t-3} + \lambda^2 \beta_2 X_{t-4} + \cdots + u_t \\ &= \beta_0 X_t + \beta_1 X_{t-1} + \frac{\beta_2}{1 - \lambda D} X_{t-2} + u_t \end{aligned} \tag{10-18}$$

where the first two β coefficients are free and starting with β_2 they are assumed to decline geometrically. Equation (10-18) may be rewritten as

$$\begin{aligned} Y_t = \beta_0 X_t &+ (\beta_1 - \lambda\beta_0)X_{t-1} + (\beta_2 - \lambda\beta_1)X_{t-2} + \lambda Y_{t-1} \\ &+ (u_t - \lambda u_{t-1}) \end{aligned} \tag{10-19}$$

If we have two explanatory variables, say X and Z, the Koyck lag distribution may be applied to both. The simplest assumption is that both distributions have the same parameter λ. Following (10-16) we may then write the relation as

$$Y_t = \frac{\beta(1 - \lambda)}{1 - \lambda D} X_t + \frac{\gamma(1 - \lambda)}{1 - \lambda D} Z_t + u_t$$

which gives

$$Y_t = \beta(1 - \lambda)X_t + \gamma(1 - \lambda)Z_t + \lambda Y_{t-1} + (u_t - \lambda u_{t-1})$$

as the equation to be estimated. If the λ parameter is different for each variable, the basic relationship may be written

$$Y_t = \frac{\beta(1-\lambda_1)}{1-\lambda_1 D}X_t + \frac{\gamma(1-\lambda_2)}{1-\lambda_2 D}Z_t + u_t$$

which gives

$$\begin{aligned} Y_t = {} & \beta(1-\lambda_1)X_t - \beta\lambda_2(1-\lambda_1)X_{t-1} + \gamma(1-\lambda_2)Z_t \\ & - \gamma\lambda_1(1-\lambda_2)Z_{t-1} + (\lambda_1+\lambda_2)Y_{t-1} - \lambda_1\lambda_2 Y_{t-2} \\ & + [u_t - (\lambda_1+\lambda_2)u_{t-1} + \lambda_1\lambda_2 u_{t-2}] \end{aligned}$$

We thus see that the application of the Koyck assumption results in the appearance of Y_{t-1}, and possibly Y_{t-2} on the right-hand side of the equation. This raises difficult estimation problems which we will postpone till later in the chapter.

10-2 LAGGED DEPENDENT VARIABLES

We have seen that the application of a Koyck scheme to lagged X values produces a final equation such as (10-17) with one or more lagged values of the *dependent* variable on the right-hand side. A number of other models, however, can lead to a similar final equation. The two best-known such models are the *partial adjustment* and the *adaptive expectations* models.

The reasons for partial adjustment typically include ignorance, inertia, and the costs of change. Let Y_t^*, given by

$$Y_t^* = \alpha + \beta X_t \tag{10-20}$$

indicate the optimal Y value associated with X_t. For instance if X_t represents a consumer's disposable income Y_t^* might represent the corresponding optimal rate of expenditure. However, if the income change that has produced X_t has been a large upward (or downward) one, the consumer may not have the requisite knowledge of his utility surface to adjust immediately to the new situation, or he may have contractual obligations from his old income level that constrain his immediate behavior to some degree. We thus postulate a reaction or adjustment function

$$Y_t - Y_{t-1} = \gamma(Y_t^* - Y_{t-1}) + u_t \qquad 0 < \gamma \leq 1. \tag{10-21}$$

which asserts that in the current period he will probably move only part of the way from his starting position (Y_{t-1}) to the optimal position (Y_t^*). The closer γ is to unity the greater is the adjustment made in the current period. Alternatively X_t might represent sales and Y_t^* the corresponding optimal long-run production rate. Griliches has shown how simple cost considerations might produce an adjustment function like (10-21).[1] Suppose that the relevant costs consist of (a) the costs of being out of equilibrium and (b) the costs of change. If both types are quadratic we could write

$$C_t = a(Y_t - Y_t^*)^2 + b(Y_t - Y_{t-1})^2$$

The problem is to choose Y_t, given Y_{t-1} and Y_t^*, to minimize C. Thus

$$\frac{\partial C_t}{\partial Y_t} = 2a(Y_t - Y_t^*) + 2b(Y_t - Y_{t-1}) = 0$$

giving

$$Y_t - Y_{t-1} = \frac{a}{a+b}(Y_t^* - Y_{t-1})$$

which is of the form (10-21) since a and b are both positive. Only in the case of zero adjustment cost ($b = 0$) would the γ parameter of (10-21) be unity and adjustment complete within the current period.

Combining (10-20) and (10-21) gives

$$Y_t = \alpha\gamma + \beta\gamma X_t + (1 - \gamma)Y_{t-1} + u_t \tag{10-22}$$

where the interesting thing to notice is the similarity to the final equation (10-17) of the Koyck scheme. The only differences are that (10-22) has a simpler disturbance term than (10-17) and also possesses an intercept term.

An obvious difficulty with the partial adjustment model is that it is sometimes rather implausible to assume that the optimal value of Y depends on the *current* and only on the current value of X. If X is subject to change from period to period it might not be sensible to base important decisions solely on the current value. This point of view is expressed in an *expectations* model which postulates that Y is set in relation to the "expected" level of X, namely X^*, that is,

$$Y_t = \alpha + \beta X_t^* + u_t \tag{10-23}$$

where X_t^* denotes the expectation formed at time period t and u_t is a disturbance term to indicate that it may be difficult to control the Y value precisely. Equation (10-23) is non-operational as it stands since X^* is an unobservable variable. It must therefore be supplemented with some assumption about how expectations are formed. A common assumption is that of *adaptive expectations*, expressed by

$$X_t^* - X_{t-1}^* = \delta(X_t - X_{t-1}^*) \qquad 0 < \delta \leq 1 \tag{10-24}$$

so that expectations are updated each period by a fraction of the discrepancy between the current observed value of the variable and the previous expected

[1] Z. Griliches, "Distributed Lags: A Survey," *Econometrica*, vol. 35, pp. 16–49, 1967.

value. The problem now is to combine (10-23) and (10-24) into an operational equation that will contain only observable variables. To do this rewrite (10-24) as

$$X_t^* - \lambda X_{t-1}^* = \delta X_t \tag{10-25}$$

where

$$\lambda = 1 - \delta \tag{10-26}$$

Using the delay operator D we can write (10-25) as

$$(1 - \lambda D)X_t^* = \delta X_t$$

or

$$X_t^* = \frac{\delta}{1 - \lambda D} X_t$$

Substituting this in (10-23) gives

$$Y_t = \alpha + \frac{\beta\delta}{1 - \lambda D} X_t + u_t$$

or, multiplying through by $(1 - \lambda D)$ and re-arranging,

$$Y_t = \alpha(1 - \lambda) + \beta(1 - \lambda)X_t + \lambda Y_{t-1} + (u_t - \lambda u_{t-1}) \tag{10-27}$$

Equation (10-27) is the final equation of a simple adaptive expectations model. We see on comparing it with (10-22) that it contains exactly the same variables as the final equation of the partial adjustment model. The only discrepancy between the two is that on the assumption we have made about disturbance terms (10-27) would have a differently behaved disturbance term than (10-22). Equation (10-27) is, apart from the intercept term, identical with the final equation of the Koyck scheme. The reason for the equivalence of the final equations of all three schemes is that the partial adjustment and the adaptive expectations models each involve declining geometric weights. Assumption (10-21) may be rewritten as

$$Y_t = \gamma[1 + (1 - \gamma)D + (1 - \gamma)^2 D^2 + \cdots]Y_t^*$$

and (10-25) as

$$X_t^* = \delta[1 + (1 - \delta)D + (1 - \delta)^2 D^2 + \cdots]X_t$$

Further variations on both adjustment and expectations models can be made by changing the time lags. For instance, it might be more appropriate to write (10-24) as

$$X_t^* - X_{t-1}^* = \delta(X_{t-1} - X_{t-1}^*)$$

In each case the final equations of the models would still be identical and now of the form

$$Y_t = f(X_{t-1}, Y_{t-1})$$

with X_{t-1} replacing X_t in the earlier formulation.

The adaptive expectations model can in turn be criticized for the assumption that the Y variable is adjusted immediately to the X^* variable, subject only to the discrepancy caused by a stochastic disturbance term. A more general model is achieved by combining the two assumptions of partial adjustment and adaptive expectations. Thus we now postulate

$$Y_t^* = \alpha + \beta X_t^* \tag{10-28}$$

$$Y_t - Y_{t-1} = \gamma(Y_t^* - Y_{t-1}) + u_t \qquad 0 < \gamma \le 1 \tag{10-29}$$

$$X_t^* - X_{t-1}^* = \delta(X_t - X_{t-1}^*) \qquad 0 < \delta \le 1 \tag{10-30}$$

We can rewrite (10-29) as

$$Y_t = \gamma Y_t^* + (1 - \gamma)Y_{t-1} + u_t$$

and (10-30) as

$$X_t^* = \frac{\delta}{1 - \lambda D} X_t \quad \text{where } \lambda = 1 - \delta$$

Substitution then yields

$$Y_t = \gamma\left[\alpha + \frac{\beta\delta}{1 - \lambda D} X_t\right] + (1 - \gamma)Y_{t-1} + u_t$$

or

$$\begin{aligned} Y_t = \alpha\gamma\delta + \beta\gamma\delta X_t + [(1 - \delta) + (1 - \gamma)]Y_{t-1} \\ - (1 - \delta)(1 - \gamma)Y_{t-2} + (u_t - (1 - \delta)u_{t-1}) \end{aligned} \tag{10-31}$$

Compared with the previous final equations (10-22) and (10-27) we now have an additional term in Y_{t-2} on the right-hand side, but the parameters γ and δ enter (10-31) symmetrically so that it is impossible to obtain estimates of their separate values from the regression coefficients. One can, however, estimate $\gamma + \delta$, $\gamma\delta$, and hence α and β.

10-3 ESTIMATION METHODS

So far we have dealt, in Section 10-1, with the estimation of a lagged relationship where it is only lagged values of one or more X variables which appear on the right-hand side. The three basic approaches are to fit the relation directly if the collinearity problem is not too serious, or to specify numerically a number of arbitrary weight patterns, or else to use the Almon polynomial approximation. The assumption of the Koyck weight pattern or the use of adjustment or expectations models produce a lagged value of Y on the right-hand side and raise new estimation problems, to which we now turn.

We will postulate the simplest possible relation, namely,

$$Y_t = \beta_0 + \beta_1 Y_{t-1} + \beta_2 X_t + v_t \tag{10-32}$$

The methods described below can easily be extended to deal with additional explanatory variables and additional lagged values of Y. Estimation problems and procedures now depend on the assumptions made about the disturbance term v, and we distinguish the following possibilities.

Assumption I: v's are NID $(0, \sigma_v^2)$

Assumption II: $v_t = u_t - \lambda u_{t-1} \qquad 0 < \lambda < 1$

(a) u's are NID $(0, \sigma_u^2)$

(b) $u_t = \rho u_{t-1} + \varepsilon_t \qquad |\rho| < 1$, ε's NID $(0, \sigma_\varepsilon^2)$

Assumption III: $v_t = \rho v_{t-1} + \varepsilon_t \qquad |\rho| < 1$, ε's NID $(0, \sigma_\varepsilon^2)$

Assumption I states that the v's are normally and independently distributed with zero mean and a constant variance. This is the simplest possible assumption and means that the only complication in (10-32) is the presence of the lagged dependent variable, Y_{t-1}, on the right-hand side. Assumption II derives from the Koyck scheme or the adaptive expectations model which gives v_t explicitly as $(u_t - \lambda u_{t-1})$, where u_t is the disturbance in the original equation for Y. Assumption II(a) allows the u's to be independent while II(b) lets them follow a first-order Markov scheme. Assumption III allows the v's to follow the simplest possible non-random scheme without tying the derivation of (10-32) explicitly to the assumption of a Koyck model or an adaptive expectations model.

Assumption 1 Suppose we have a given initial value, Y_0, of the dependent variable. Then the conditional distribution of $Y_1, Y_2, \ldots, Y_n$ for given Y_0 and given $\mathbf{X}$ matrix is

$$p(Y_1, Y_2, \ldots, Y_n | Y_0, \mathbf{X}) = p(v_1, v_2, \ldots, v_n) \left| \frac{\partial(v_1, v_2, \ldots, v_n)}{\partial(Y_1, Y_2, \ldots, Y_n)} \right|$$

where

$$\left| \frac{\partial(v_1, v_2, \ldots, v_n)}{\partial(Y_1, Y_2, \ldots, Y_n)} \right|$$

denotes the absolute value of the determinant

$$\begin{vmatrix} \frac{\partial v_1}{\partial Y_1} & \frac{\partial v_1}{\partial Y_2} & \cdots & \frac{\partial v_1}{\partial Y_n} \\ \frac{\partial v_2}{\partial Y_1} & \frac{\partial v_2}{\partial Y_2} & \cdots & \frac{\partial v_2}{\partial Y_n} \\ \vdots & & & \vdots \\ \frac{\partial v_n}{\partial Y_1} & \frac{\partial v_n}{\partial Y_2} & \cdots & \frac{\partial v_n}{\partial Y_n} \end{vmatrix} = \begin{vmatrix} 1 & 0 & 0 & \cdots & 0 \\ -\beta_1 & 1 & 0 & \cdots & 0 \\ 0 & -\beta_1 & 1 & \cdots & 0 \\ \vdots & & & & \vdots \\ 0 & 0 & 0 & \cdots & 1 \end{vmatrix} = 1$$

On the assumptions made about the v's

$$p(Y_1, Y_2, \ldots, Y_n | Y_0, \mathbf{X}) \propto \exp\left\{-\frac{1}{2\sigma_v^2}\sum_{t=1}^{n}(Y_t - \beta_0 - \beta_1 Y_{t-1} - \beta_2 X_t)^2\right\}$$

Thus maximum-likelihood estimators of the β's are identical with the ordinary least-squares estimators obtained by minimizing

$$\sum_{t=1}^{n}(Y_t - \beta_0 - \beta_1 Y_{t-1} - \beta_2 X_t)^2$$

So least-squares applied to (10-32) will, under these assumptions, yield consistent and asymptotically efficient estimators. It is important to emphasize that we are assuming serially uncorrelated disturbances so that the only complication is the presence of lagged Y values among the explanatory variables. This, however, means that the disturbance term is no longer uncorrelated with all the explanatory variables for (10-32) implies

$$E(v_t Y_t) \neq 0$$

and so

$$E(v_t Y_{t+s}) \neq 0$$

for $s \geq 0$ and all t.

As a consequence least-squares will produce biased estimates in small samples. This result has been proved for some fairly simple cases. Consider

$$Y_t = \beta Y_{t-1} + v_t$$

where $|\beta| < 1$ and v is serially uncorrelated. The least-squares estimator for this model is

$$\hat{\beta} = \sum_{t=2}^{n} Y_t Y_{t-1} \Big/ \sum_{t=2}^{n} Y_{t-1}^2$$

Ignoring terms in n^{-2} and above the bias in $\hat{\beta}$ is[1]

$$E(\hat{\beta}) - \beta \simeq -2\beta/n \tag{10-33}$$

Another possible estimator of β is the sample first-order, autocorrelation coefficient of the Y's, namely,

$$r_1 = \frac{\dfrac{1}{n-1}\sum_{t=2}^{n} Y_t Y_{t-1} - \dfrac{1}{(n-1)^2}\left(\sum_{t=2}^{n} Y_t\right)\left(\sum_{t=2}^{n} Y_{t-1}\right)}{\dfrac{1}{n}\sum_{t=1}^{n} Y_t^2 - \dfrac{1}{n^2}\left(\sum_{t=1}^{n} Y_t\right)^2} \tag{10-34}$$

This is approximately the least-squares estimator of β if $Y_t = \beta Y_{t-1} + v_t$ were fitted with an intercept term. Again to order n^{-1} the bias in this estimator is[2]

$$E(r_1) - \beta \simeq -\frac{1}{n}(1 + 3\beta) \tag{10-35}$$

so that both estimators tend to underestimate β, the amount of the bias being greater for r_1 than for $\hat{\beta}$.

Copas has provided some interesting Monte Carlo evidence on estimators of β in $Y_t = \beta Y_{t-1} + v_t$.[3] Among the estimators considered are:

(a) r_1 as defined in (10-34) above

(b) r_1 bias corrected, namely,

$$b = \frac{nr_1 + 1}{n - 3}.$$

This has been obtained by noting from (10-35) above that

$$b = r_1 + \frac{1}{n}(1 + 3b)$$

will be an approximately unbiased estimator of β.

(c) the OLS estimator, $\hat{\beta}$, defined above.

In Model I Copas generated 100 series of 10 terms for each β at intervals of 0.1 in the range -0.9 to 0.9, and in Model II 100 series of 20 terms for $\beta = -0.8(0.2)\ 0.8$. Each estimate was computed for each series and for a given value of β figures were thus obtained for the mean square error of each estimator. These were in turn averaged over all the values of β. Table 10-1 presents some of the results.

[1] J. S. White, "Asymptotic Expansions for the Mean and Variance of the Serial Correlation Coefficient," *Biometrika*, vol. 48, pp. 85–94, 1961.

[2] F. H. C. Marriott and J. A. Pope, "Bias in the Estimation of Autocorrelations," *Biometrika*, vol. 41, pp. 390–402, 1954.

[3] J. B. Copas, "Monte Carlo Results for Estimation in a Stable Markov Time Series," *J. Royal Statist. Soc.*, Series A, vol. 129, pp. 110–116, 1966.

Table 10-1[1] **Mean squared errors for three estimators in $Y_t = \beta Y_{t-1} + v_t$**

Estimator	*Model I*	*Model II*
r_1	0.1279	0.0515
b	0.1660	0.0585
$\hat{\beta}$	0.0882	0.0412

[1] Copas *op. cit.* pp. 114 and 115.

The bias-corrected estimator is worse than r_1, the improvement in bias being more than offset by the increase in variance, while the simple least-squares estimator has the smallest mean squared error of the three. Thus if the disturbance term is random, least-squares still seems the best estimating technique, but it will now give biased estimates in finite samples.

One is never on firm ground in specifying the existence and properties of disturbance terms. In formulating the above models we have not inserted disturbance terms in relations defining expectational variables, which are expressed in terms of an infinite series of explanatory variables, and only inserted them in relations defining observed variables. The partial adjustment model, so formulated, has a random disturbance term in the final equation (10-22), but the adaptive expectations and the more general model have a more complicated disturbance term. While there may well be cases where lagged Y's and serially uncorrelated disturbances may be valid assumptions we must now extend the analysis to cover the case of lagged Y's and serially correlated disturbances.

Assumptions II and III The first point to be made here is that the combination of lagged Y values and serially correlated disturbances means that the OLS estimators will now not even be consistent. Autocorrelated disturbances without lagged Y values do not produce biased estimators, even in small samples; lagged Y values with random disturbances will give OLS estimators which are consistent, though biased in finite samples; the combination of the two problems, however, throws OLS off-beam and gives inconsistent estimators. The second important and related point is that the conventional Durbin–Watson test is biased towards the value for a random disturbance in these same circumstances. Both these points may be illustrated from the following simple model.

Consider the model

$$Y_t = \beta Y_{t-1} + v_t \tag{10-36}$$

$$v_t = \rho v_{t-1} + \varepsilon_t \tag{10-37}$$

with $|\beta| < 1$, $|\rho| < 1$ and the ε's serially uncorrelated. Suppose we estimate β by the OLS estimator

$$\hat{\beta} = \sum_{t=2}^{n} Y_t Y_{t-1} \Big/ \sum_{t=2}^{n} Y_{t-1}^2 \tag{10-38}$$

Our problem is to determine the asymptotic bias of $\hat{\beta}$ and d. Combining (10-36) and (10-37) gives

$$Y_t = (\beta + \rho)Y_{t-1} - \beta\rho Y_{t-2} + \varepsilon_t \tag{10-39}$$

Multiplying by Y_{t-1} and summing gives

$$\Sigma Y_t Y_{t-1} = (\beta + \rho)\Sigma Y_{t-1}^2 - \beta\rho \Sigma Y_{t-1} Y_{t-2} + \Sigma \varepsilon_t Y_{t-1}$$

Thus

$$\hat{\beta} = (\beta + \rho) - \beta\rho \frac{\Sigma Y_{t-1} Y_{t-2}}{\Sigma Y_{t-1}^2} + \frac{\Sigma \varepsilon_t Y_{t-1}}{\Sigma Y_{t-1}^2}$$

Taking probability limits

$$\text{plim } \hat{\beta} = (\beta + \rho) - \beta\rho \text{ plim } \hat{\beta}$$

so that

$$\text{plim } \hat{\beta} = \frac{\beta + \rho}{1 + \beta\rho} \tag{10-40}$$

or

$$\text{plim } \hat{\beta} - \beta = \frac{\rho(1 - \beta^2)}{1 + \beta\rho} \tag{10-41}$$

The asymptotic bias is consequently positive or negative according as ρ is positive or negative. An interesting point to notice here is that lagged values alone produce a negative small sample bias in OLS estimators but the combination of lagged Y values and a positively autocorrelated disturbance term gives a positive bias and one which persists at all sample sizes. Table 10-2 shows some values of the asymptotic bias in $\hat{\beta}$ for various values of

Table 10-2[1] **Values of $\rho(1 - \beta^2)/(1 + \beta\rho)$**

β	0.2	0.2	0.2	0.5	0.5	0.5	0.8	0.8	0.8
ρ	0.1	0.5	0.8	0.1	0.5	0.8	0.1	0.5	0.8
Asym. Bias.	0.09	0.44	0.66	0.07	0.30	0.43	0.03	0.13	0.18

[1] Taken from Z. Griliches, "A Note on the Serial Correlation Bias in Estimates of Distributed Lags," *Econometrica*, vol. 29, pp. 65–73, 1961.

β and ρ. The bias can be alarmingly large especially for combinations of low values of β and large values of ρ. As ρ tends to unity the asymptotic bias tends to the value $(1 - \beta)$.

These results show the danger of applying OLS to (10-36) on the assumption that the disturbance is serially uncorrelated. Despite explicit warnings in the original paper that the Durbin–Watson test is not applicable to an equation containing lagged Y values among the explanatory variables it has often been applied, for want of anything better, to such cases. It is likely, however, to give misleading information. Using $\hat{\beta}$ the estimated residuals are

$$\hat{v}_t = Y_t - \hat{\beta} Y_{t-1} \qquad t = 2, \ldots, n.$$

The first-order autocorrelation coefficient of the $\hat{v}$'s may be taken as an estimator of ρ and it is

$$r_1 = \frac{\Sigma \hat{v}_t \hat{v}_{t-1}}{\Sigma \hat{v}_{t-1}^2}$$

It is easy to show that[1]

$$\operatorname{plim} r_1 = \frac{\beta\rho(\beta + \rho)}{1 + \beta\rho} \tag{10-42}$$

so that

$$\operatorname{plim} r_1 - \rho = \frac{-\rho(1 - \beta^2)}{1 + \beta\rho}$$

The asymptotic bias in r_1 is exactly the negative of the asymptotic bias in $\hat{\beta}$ so that

$$\operatorname{plim} \hat{\beta} + \operatorname{plim} r_1 = \beta + \rho$$

Turning now to the Durbin–Watson statistic

$$d = \frac{\Sigma(\hat{v}_t - \hat{v}_{t-1})^2}{\Sigma \hat{v}_t^2}$$

$$= \frac{1}{\Sigma \hat{v}_t^2} \left(\Sigma \hat{v}_t^2 + \Sigma \hat{v}_{t-1}^2 - 2\Sigma \hat{v}_t \hat{v}_{t-1} \right)$$

[1] See E. Malinvaud, *Statistical Methods of Econometrics*, North-Holland, Amsterdam, 1966, pp. 460–461.

Thus[1]

$$\operatorname{plim} d = 2\left(1 - \operatorname{plim}\frac{\Sigma\hat{v}_t\hat{v}_{t-1}}{\Sigma\hat{v}_t^2}\right)$$

that is

$$\operatorname{plim} d = 2\left[1 - \frac{\beta\rho(\beta+\rho)}{1+\beta\rho}\right] \quad \text{using (10-42)}$$

If we knew the true disturbance values then the true value of the Durbin–Watson statistic would be

$$d^* = \frac{\Sigma(v_t - v_{t-1})^2}{\Sigma v_t^2}$$

In very large samples we then have

$$d^* = 2(1-\rho).$$

Thus

$$\operatorname{plim} d - d^* = 2\left[\rho - \frac{\beta\rho(\beta+\rho)}{1+\beta\rho}\right]$$

that is

$$\operatorname{plim} d - d^* = \frac{2\rho(1-\beta^2)}{1+\beta\rho} \tag{10-43}$$

[1] Notice that when we are taking probability limits we need not worry about the fact that some terms involve summation over $(n-1)$ terms and others over n terms. For example, the first term in the above expression for d is

$$\frac{\sum_{t=2}^{n}\hat{v}_t^2}{\sum_{t=1}^{n}\hat{v}_t^2} = \left(\frac{n-1}{n}\right)\frac{\frac{1}{n-1}\sum_{t=2}^{n}\hat{v}_t^2}{\frac{1}{n}\sum_{t=1}^{n}\hat{v}_t^2}$$

Thus

$$\operatorname{plim}\left(\frac{\sum_{t=2}^{n}\hat{v}_t^2}{\sum_{t=1}^{n}\hat{v}_t^2}\right) = \operatorname{plim}\left(1-\frac{1}{n}\right)\frac{\operatorname{plim}\frac{1}{n-1}\sum_{t=2}^{n}\hat{v}_t^2}{\operatorname{plim}\frac{1}{n}\sum_{t=1}^{n}\hat{v}_t^2}$$

$$= 1.\ \frac{\operatorname{var}(\hat{v})}{\operatorname{var}(\hat{v})}$$

$$= 1.$$

so that the asymptotic bias for d is twice the asymptotic bias in $\hat{\beta}$. Table 10-3 shows plim d for various values of β for a model in which $\rho = 0.5$ so that $d^* = 1.0$. In all these cases plim d exceeds d^* and for some values of β it approaches very close to 2.00.

Table 10-3[1] Values of plim d, when $\rho = 0.5$ and $d^* = 1.0$

β	0.9	0.7	0.5	0.3	−0.5	−0.7	−0.9
plim d	1.13	1.38	1.60	1.79	2.00	1.78	1.35

[1] Taken from M. Nerlove and K. F. Wallis, "Use of the Durbin–Watson Statistic in Inappropriate Situations," *Econometrica*, vol. 34, pp. 235–238, 1966, where a much more extensive table is given.

The above development of asymptotic biases in $\hat{\beta}$, r_1 and d is excessively alarmist for the model used has only Y_{t-1} as an explanatory variable. Malinvaud has shown that the presence of exogenous (X) variables tends to reduce the absolute values of the asymptotic biases, though they will remain significant in most cases.[2] Extensive evidence on the power of the Durbin–Watson test in inappropriate situations is provided incidentally in an article by Taylor and Wilson.[3] Their experiments covered the following models

$$Y_t = \alpha Y_{t-1} + \beta X_t + v_t: \qquad v_t = \rho v_{t-1} + \varepsilon_t$$
Experiments 1–3

$$Y_t = \alpha Y_{t-1} + \beta X_t + \gamma X_{t-1} + v_t: \qquad v_t = \rho v_{t-1} + \varepsilon_t$$
Experiments 4–15

$$Y_t = \alpha Y_{t-1} + \beta X_t + \gamma X_{t-1} + v_t: \qquad v_t = \rho_1 v_{t-1} + \rho_2 v_{t-2} + \varepsilon_t$$
Experiments 16–18

and the relevant results are shown in Table 10-4. The authors followed the procedure of rejecting the null hypothesis whenever d was less than d_L or when it lay in the indeterminate range. Thus the column N.H.A. in Table 10-4 indicates the number of times the null hypothesis was accepted ($d > d_U$). The authors' own conclusion was—"the test on the OLS residuals was quite powerful. Considering only experiments with $\rho \geq 0.6$ in absolute value, the Durbin–Watson test detected the presence of autocorrelation in from 80 to 100 per cent of the samples from most experiments."[4] From the table

[2] Malinvaud, *op. cit.*, pp. 462–465.

[3] L. D. Taylor and T. A. Wilson, "Three-Pass Least-squares: A Method for Estimating Models with a Lagged Dependent Variable," *Rev. Economics and Statistics*, vol. 46, pp. 329–346, 1964.

[4] Taylor and Wilson, *op. cit.*, p. 337.

one sees that the power of the test is directly related to sample size (cf. Experiments 4, 5, and 6) and that it is directly related to the absolute value of the autocorrelation parameter (cf. Experiments 9 and 10). The power of the test also declines as R^2 declines. The test also works well for stable second-order schemes (Experiments 16 and 17) but badly for explosive first- and second-order schemes (Experiments 19 and 18).

Table 10-4[1] Power of the Durbin–Watson test applied to OLS Residuals

Experiment	*True ρ*	*No. of observations per sample*	*No. of samples*	*N.H.A.*
1	0.7	50	25	0
2	0.7	50	25	2
3	0.8	50	25	0
4	0.7	50	100	11
5	0.7	30	25	5
6	0.7	20	23	6
7	0.7	50	25	0
8	0.7	50	25	11
9	0.4	50	25	14
10	0.1	50	25	21
11	−0.9	50	25	0
12	0.8	50	25	0
13	−0.2	50	25	14
14	0	50	25	18
15	0.7	50	25	14
16	$0.6u_{t-1} - 0.1u_{t-2}$	50	25	4
17	$0.8u_{t-1} - 0.4u_{t-2}$	50	25	0
18	$1.3u_{t-1} - 0.3u_{t-1}$	50	50	28
19	1.0	50	25	11

[1] Part of Table 22 in Taylor and Wilson, *op. cit.*

A *large sample* test for serial correlation when lagged dependent variables are present has recently been developed by Durbin.[2] A great advantage of the test is that the statistics required for its computation are generated routinely in OLS applications. Let e_t $(t = 1, \ldots, n)$ denote the OLS residuals from the fitted regression. Define

$$r = \frac{\sum_{t=2}^{n} e_t e_{t-1}}{\sum_{t=1}^{n-1} e_t^2} \tag{10-44}$$

[2] J. Durbin, "Testing for Serial Correlation in Least-Squares Regression when Some of the Regressors are Lagged Dependent Variables," *Econometrica*, vol. 38, pp. 410–421, 1970.

This is the estimated first-order autocorrelation coefficient of the residuals. It need not be computed afresh since it is given approximately by

$$r \simeq 1 - \tfrac{1}{2}d \tag{10-45}$$

where

$$d = \sum_{t=2}^{n} (e_t - e_{t-1})^2 \bigg/ \sum_{t=1}^{n} e_t^2$$

is the conventional Durbin–Watson statistic. From r compute

$$h = r\sqrt{\frac{n}{1 - n\hat{V}(b_1)}} \tag{10-46}$$

where $\hat{V}(b_1)$ is the estimate of the sampling variance of b_1, the coefficient of Y_{t-1}, in the simple least-squares regression. The statistic h is then tested as a standard normal deviate; thus if $h > 1.645$ one would reject the hypothesis of zero autocorrelation at the 5 per cent level. The correction to r which leads to this test merely involves the estimated variance of b_1. This is perfectly general; it does not matter how many X variables or other lagged values of Y such as Y_{t-2}, Y_{t-3} etc. appear in the relation, it is only the sampling variance of the coefficient of Y_{t-1} that is required. This is only a large-sample test (say $n > 30$) and nothing is known about its small-sample properties. From (10-46) it is seen that the test breaks down if $n\hat{V}(b_1) \geq 1$. Durbin shows that an asymptotically equivalent test is obtained by regressing e_t on e_{t-1} and the set of explanatory variables (that is, X's and lagged Y's) in the original relation and testing the significance of the coefficient of e_{t-1} by ordinary least-squares procedures.

Assumption II(a) $v_t = u_t - \lambda u_{t-1}$, $0 < \lambda < 1$ and u's are NID$(0, \sigma_u^2)$. This is the form of v that comes from the final equation (10-27) of the adaptive expectations model or from the transformed Koyck relation (10-17). On this assumption about the u's it then follows that

$$\begin{aligned} E(v_t) &= 0 \text{ for all } t \\ E(v_t^2) &= \sigma_u^2(1 + \lambda^2) \text{ for all } t \\ E(v_t v_{t+s}) &= -\lambda\sigma_u^2 \text{ for } s = \pm 1, \text{ for all } t \\ &= 0 \text{ for } |s| \geq 2, \text{ and for all } t. \end{aligned}$$

Thus

$$\mathbf{V} = E(\mathbf{vv}') = \sigma_u^2 \begin{bmatrix} 1 + \lambda^2 & -\lambda & 0 & \cdots & 0 \\ -\lambda & 1 + \lambda^2 & -\lambda & \cdots & 0 \\ \vdots & & & & \vdots \\ 0 & 0 & 0 & \cdots & 1 + \lambda^2 \end{bmatrix} \tag{10-47}$$

If λ were known then $\mathbf{V}$ is known and the GLS estimator $(\mathbf{X}'\mathbf{V}^{-1}\mathbf{X})^{-1}\mathbf{X}'\mathbf{V}^{-1}\mathbf{y}$ could be formed where the data matrix $\mathbf{X}$ is given by[1]

$$\mathbf{X} = \begin{bmatrix} 1 & Y_0 & X_1 \\ 1 & Y_1 & X_2 \\ 1 & Y_2 & X_3 \\ \vdots & \vdots & \vdots \\ 1 & Y_{n-1} & X_n \end{bmatrix}$$

In fact, if we refer to Eqs. (10-17) and (10-27) we see that β_1, the coefficient of Y_{t-1}, is equal to λ, so if λ really were known the model simplifies to

$$(Y_t - \lambda Y_{t-1}) = \beta_0 + \beta_2 X_t + v_t \tag{10-48}$$

and the data matrix for the GLS estimator is now simply a two-column matrix, comprising a first column of units and a second column of the observations on X, while the $\mathbf{y}$ vector contains the values of the transformed variable $Y_t - \lambda Y_{t-1}$. If λ is unknown we can resort to search procedures.[2] Substituting for v_t in (10-48) gives

$$Y_t = \beta_0 + \lambda Y_{t-1} + \beta_2 X_t + u_t - \lambda u_{t-1} \tag{10-49}$$

Define

$$w_t = Y_t - u_t$$

Therefore

$$w_t - \lambda w_{t-1} = Y_t - \lambda Y_{t-1} - (u_t - \lambda u_{t-1}) = \beta_0 + \beta_2 X_t$$

or

$$w_t = \lambda w_{t-1} + \beta_0 + \beta_2 X_t$$

By continuous substitution for w on the right-hand side of this equation we have

$$w_t = \lambda^t w_0 + \beta_0(1 + \lambda + \lambda^2 + \cdots + \lambda^{t-1}) + \beta_2(X_t + \lambda X_{t-1} + \lambda^2 X_{t-2} + \cdots + \lambda^{t-1} X_1) \tag{10-50}$$

In (10-50) $w_0 = Y_0 - u_0$ can be taken as some constant starting value and (10-50) rewritten as

$$Y_t = \lambda^t w_0 + \beta_0(1 + \lambda + \lambda^2 + \cdots + \lambda^{t-1}) + \beta_2(X_t + \lambda X_{t-1} + \lambda^2 X_{t-2} + \cdots + \lambda^{t-1} X_1) + u_t \tag{10-51}$$

[1] If Y_0 is not known we have to drop the first row in $\mathbf{X}$.

[2] See A. Zellner and M. S. Geisel, "Analysis of Distributed Lag Models with Applications to Consumption Function Estimation." Paper presented to European Meeting of the Econometric Society, 1968.

So that, *if λ were known*, Y has been expressed as a linear function of the unknown parameters w_0, β_0, and β_2 with a random disturbance u. OLS estimators derived from (10-51) would then have the usual optimal properties and the data matrix would be

$$\mathbf{X} = \begin{bmatrix} \lambda & 1 & X_1 \\ \lambda^2 & 1 + \lambda & X_2 + \lambda X_1 \\ \lambda^3 & 1 + \lambda + \lambda^2 & X_3 + \lambda X_2 + \lambda^2 X_1 \\ \vdots & \vdots & \vdots \\ \lambda^n & 1 + \lambda + \lambda^2 + \cdots + \lambda^{n-1} & X_n + \lambda X_{n-1} + \lambda^2 X_{n-2} \\ & & + \cdots + \lambda^{n-1} X_1 \end{bmatrix} \tag{10-52}$$

But, of course, λ is unknown, so $\mathbf{X}$ is unknown.

The Zellner–Geisel suggestion is to select λ values in the range $0 < \lambda < 1$, compute the $\mathbf{X}$ matrix for each value and then fit (10-51) by OLS. The λ value and the associated estimates of β_0 and β_2 are chosen which yield the minimum sum of squares. Greater accuracy may be achieved by specifying a finer grid of λ values around the value selected at the end of the first stage and concentrating a second search procedure in this smaller range. It would also appear that an alternative search procedure would be to use each specified value of λ in turn to compute the $\mathbf{V}$ matrix of (10-47), thence to compute the GLS estimator and then to choose the λ giving the minimum value for the weighted sum of squares $\hat{\mathbf{v}}'\mathbf{V}^{-1}\hat{\mathbf{v}}$.

Assumption II(b)

$$v_t = u_t - \lambda u_{t-1}, \qquad 0 < \lambda < 1,$$

$$u_t = \rho u_{t-1} + \varepsilon_t \quad \text{with } |\rho| < 1 \text{ and the } \varepsilon\text{'s NID } (0, \sigma_\varepsilon^2)$$

Zellner and Geisel have also suggested a search procedure for this model. As before let

$$w_t = Y_t - u_t$$

so that

$$w_t - \rho w_{t-1} = Y_t - \rho Y_{t-1} - (u_t - \rho u_{t-1})$$

which we may rewrite as

$$w_t(\rho) = Y_t(\rho) - u_t(\rho)$$

where

$$w_t(\rho) = w_t - \rho w_{t-1} \text{ etc.}$$

From the relation

$$Y_t = \beta_0 + \lambda Y_{t-1} + \beta_2 X_t + v_t$$

we have

$$Y_t(\rho) = \beta_0(1 - \rho) + \lambda Y_{t-1}(\rho) + \beta_2 X_t(\rho) + u_t(\rho) - \lambda u_{t-1}(\rho)$$

that is,

$$w_t(\rho) = \beta_0(1 - \rho) + \lambda w_{t-1}(\rho) + \beta_2 X_t(\rho)$$

As in the development of Assumption II(a) we can, by a process of successive substitution in this last equation, obtain

$$\begin{aligned} w_t(\rho) = \lambda^t w_0(\rho) &+ \beta_0(1 - \rho)[1 + \lambda + \lambda^2 + \cdots + \lambda^{t-1}] + \beta_2[X_t(\rho) \\ &+ \lambda X_{t-1}(\rho) + \cdots + \lambda^{t-1} X_1(\rho)] \end{aligned}$$

or

$$\begin{aligned} Y_t(\rho) = \lambda^t w_0(\rho) &+ \beta_0(1 - \rho)[1 + \lambda + \lambda^2 + \cdots + \lambda^{t-1}] + \beta_2[X_t(\rho) \\ &+ \lambda X_{t-1}(\rho) + \cdots + \lambda^{t-1} X_1(\rho)] + \varepsilon_t \end{aligned} \tag{10-53}$$

If λ and ρ were known (10-53) would represent $Y_t(\rho)$ as a linear function of the three unknown parameters, $w_0(\rho)$, $\beta_0(1 - \rho)$, and β_2. The data matrix for OLS regression would be

$$\mathbf{X}(\rho) = \begin{bmatrix} \lambda & 1 & X_1(\rho) \\ \lambda^2 & 1+\lambda & X_2(\rho)+\lambda X_1(\rho) \\ \lambda^3 & 1+\lambda+\lambda^2 & X_3(\rho)+\lambda X_2(\rho)+\lambda^2 X_1(\rho) \\ \vdots & \vdots & \vdots \\ \lambda^n & 1+\lambda+\lambda^2+\cdots+\lambda^{n-1} & X_n(\rho)+\lambda X_{n-1}(\rho)+\cdots+\lambda^{n-1} X_1(\rho) \end{bmatrix}$$

Since λ and ρ are unknown, the Zellner-Geisel suggestion is to select a grid of λ, ρ values. For each pair of λ, ρ values on the grid compute $Y_t(\rho)$, $(t = 1, \ldots, n)$, and the data matrix $\mathbf{X}(\rho)$, fit (10-53) by OLS and compute the residual sum of squares. Finally select the pair giving the smallest sum of squares. The search procedures under Assumptions II(a) and II(b) are computationally burdensome and one would only embark on them if one felt very convinced about the specification of the disturbance term.

Assumption III Assumption III specifies the model

$$Y_t = \beta_0 + \beta_1 Y_{t-1} + \beta_2 X_t + v_t$$

where

$$v_t = \rho v_{t-1} + \varepsilon_t \quad \text{with } |\rho| < 1 \text{ and the } \varepsilon\text{'s NID } (0, \sigma_\varepsilon^2).$$

One no longer ties the derivation of the model to a Koyck scheme or to an adaptive expectations model but wishes to have a more general model which allows for a lagged dependent variable and an autocorrelated disturbance term.

If ρ were known, then $\mathbf{\Omega}$ in

$$E(\mathbf{vv}') = \sigma_v^2\mathbf{\Omega} = \sigma_v^2 \begin{bmatrix} 1 & \rho & \rho^2 & \cdots & \rho^{n-1} \\ \rho & 1 & \rho & \cdots & \rho^{n-2} \\ \vdots & \vdots & \vdots & & \vdots \\ \rho^{n-1} & \rho^{n-2} & \rho^{n-3} & \cdots & 1 \end{bmatrix}$$

is known and the straightforward procedure is to compute the GLS estimator

$$\mathbf{b} = (\mathbf{X}'\mathbf{\Omega}^{-1}\mathbf{X})^{-1}\mathbf{X}'\mathbf{\Omega}^{-1}\mathbf{y}$$

where the data matrix $\mathbf{X}$ has already been specified on page 314 above. As we have already seen this is approximately equivalent to applying OLS to the transformed data in

$$(Y_t - \rho Y_{t-1}) = \beta_0(1 - \rho) + \beta_1(Y_{t-1} - \rho Y_{t-2}) + \beta_2(X_t - \rho X_{t-1}) + \varepsilon_t$$

which will give consistent and asymptotically efficient estimators, but because of the lagged dependent variable there will be a finite sample bias.

If ρ is unknown then one may use a search routine for some specified set of ρ values in the range -1 to 1, on the same lines as that described under Assumption II. An alternative is an iterative procedure. Rewrite this last equation in the form

$$Y_t = \beta_0(1 - \rho) + (\beta_1 + \rho)Y_{t-1} - \beta_1\rho Y_{t-2} + \beta_2 X_t - \beta_2\rho X_{t-1} + \varepsilon_t \tag{10-54}$$

The attempt to estimate all four parameters β_0, β_1, β_2, and ρ by direct minimization of the sum of squares in (10-54) leads to nonlinear estimating equations. However, if we divide the parameters into two sets, namely $\beta_0, \beta_1, \beta_2$ on the one hand and ρ on the other and derive a *conditional* minimum of the sum of squares in (10-54) with respect to the parameters of each set in turn we obtain simple linear estimating equations. For example if we choose some initial value $\hat{\rho}$ for ρ and minimize the sum of squares in (10-54) conditional on ρ we are in fact minimizing the sum of squared errors in

$$(Y_t - \hat{\rho} Y_{t-1}) = \beta_0(1 - \hat{\rho}) + \beta_1(Y_{t-1} - \hat{\rho} Y_{t-2}) + \beta_2(X_t - \hat{\rho} X_{t-1}) + \text{Error} \tag{10-55}$$

This is done by applying OLS to (10-55) obtaining estimates $\hat{\beta}_0$, $\hat{\beta}_1$, and $\hat{\beta}_2$. Substituting these back in (10-54) and choosing $\hat{\hat{\rho}}$ to minimize the sum of squares in (10-54) conditionally on $\hat{\beta}_0$, $\hat{\beta}_1$, and $\hat{\beta}_2$ is equivalent to minimizing the sum of squared errors in

$$(Y_t - \hat{\beta}_0 - \hat{\beta}_1 Y_{t-1} - \hat{\beta}_2 X_t) = \rho(Y_{t-1} - \hat{\beta}_0 - \hat{\beta}_1 Y_{t-2} - \hat{\beta}_2 X_{t-1}) + \text{Error} \tag{10-56}$$

that is, to applying OLS to

$$\hat{v}_t = \rho \hat{v}_{t-1} + \text{Error}$$

which yields an estimate $\hat{\hat{\rho}}$

Given $\hat{\rho}$ one can then obtain estimates $\hat{\hat{\beta}}_0, \hat{\hat{\beta}}_1$, and $\hat{\hat{\beta}}_2$ and proceed in this way until the estimates achieve a specified degree of convergence. Some econometricians combine the search and iterative procedures, using the search procedure on a fairly wide grid of ρ values and taking the error minimizing $\hat{\rho}$ as the starting point for an iteration.

Iteration and search procedures are computationally expensive and a number of shorter two-step or three-step procedures have been suggested. A two-step procedure sometimes used is the following. Equation (10-54) is suitable for the application of OLS since it has a random, homoscedastic disturbance. Difficulties only arise because the coefficients of (10-54) imply nonlinear restrictions on the parameters that we are estimating. The suggestion is to fit (10-54) by OLS without any restrictions on the coefficients and then to estimate ρ by

$$\hat{\rho} = -\frac{\text{coefficient of } X_{t-1}}{\text{coefficient of } X_t}$$

In the second step this value of $\hat{\rho}$ is used to compute the transformed variables $(Y_t - \hat{\rho} Y_{t-1})$ and $(X_t - \hat{\rho} X_{t-1})$. OLS is then applied to (10-55) to produce estimates of the β coefficients.

A second procedure is the use of instrumental variables.[1] One of the difficulties with this model is that Y_{t-1} is correlated with v_t. By assumption, however, the X variable is uncorrelated, in the probability limit, with v. Thus the suggestion is made to regress Y on lagged values of X by OLS to obtain the predicted value

$$\hat{Y}_t = a_0 + a_1 X_{t-1} + a_2 X_{t-2} + \cdots + e_t$$

The number of lagged X values to include can be decided in relation to the number of sample observations and incremental explanatory power. If X is highly autocorrelated little may be gained by having more than two or three lagged terms. The above relation is lagged one period to yield $\hat{Y}_{t-1}$, which is substituted for Y_{t-1} on the right-hand side of (10-32) and OLS applied to that

[1] A simplified version of this approach was suggested in N. Liviatan, "Consistent Estimation of Distributed Lags," *Intern. Econ. Rev.*, vol. 4, pp. 44–52, 1963.

equation to estimate the β's. This will yield consistent estimates of the β's since both explanatory variables are uncorrelated in the limit with the disturbance, but the estimates will not be efficient since the adjustment has only corrected one of the difficulties with (10-32) and has not dealt with the autocorrelation of the disturbance terms.

Finally we may note a slightly more complicated estimation method, recently proposed by Wallis.[1] The method consists of three steps:

1. Estimate the coefficients of the regression

$$Y_t = \beta_0 + \beta_1 Y_{t-1} + \beta_2 X_t + v_t$$

using X_{t-1} as an instrumental variable for Y_{t-1}. That is, compute

$$\hat{\boldsymbol{\beta}} = (\mathbf{Z}'\mathbf{X})^{-1}\mathbf{Z}'\mathbf{y}$$

$$\text{where } \mathbf{Z} = \begin{bmatrix} 1 & X_0 & X_1 \\ 1 & X_1 & X_2 \\ \vdots & \vdots & \vdots \\ 1 & X_{n-1} & X_n \end{bmatrix} \quad \text{and } \mathbf{X} = \begin{bmatrix} 1 & Y_0 & X_1 \\ 1 & Y_1 & X_2 \\ \vdots & \vdots & \vdots \\ 1 & Y_{n-1} & X_n \end{bmatrix}$$

2. From the regression residuals

$$\hat{\mathbf{v}} = \mathbf{y} - \mathbf{X}\hat{\boldsymbol{\beta}}$$

calculate the first-order serial correlation coefficient, making a correction for bias[2]

$$r = \frac{\sum_{t=2}^{n} \hat{v}_t \hat{v}_{t-1}/(n-1)}{\sum_{t=1}^{n} \hat{v}_t^2/n} + \frac{3}{n}$$

3. Using this estimate of ρ obtain the matrix

$$\hat{\boldsymbol{\Omega}} = \begin{bmatrix} 1 & r & r^2 & \cdots & r^{n-1} \\ r & 1 & r & \cdots & r^{n-2} \\ \vdots & & & & \vdots \\ r^{n-1} & r^{n-2} & r^{n-3} & \cdots & 1 \end{bmatrix}$$

and thence compute the GLS estimator

$$\mathbf{b} = (\mathbf{X}'\hat{\boldsymbol{\Omega}}^{-1}\mathbf{X})^{-1}\mathbf{X}'\hat{\boldsymbol{\Omega}}^{-1}\mathbf{y}$$

[1] K. F. Wallis, "Lagged Dependent Variables and Serially Correlated Errors: A Reappraisal of Three-Pass Least-Squares," *Rev. Economics and Statistics*, vol. 49, pp. 555–567, 1967.

[2] In general the correction for bias is k/n where k is the number of parameters in the equation.

The rationale of this method is that steps (1) and (2) produce a consistent estimate of ρ so that the GLS estimates computed in step (3) will be consistent though not fully efficient, since ρ is unknown. Sampling experiments reported by Wallis show that his estimator is, as expected, much better than applying OLS to Eq. (10-32) in terms of substantially smaller biases and lower mean square errors. It is also superior to the method of Three-Pass Least-Squares proposed by Taylor and Wilson.[1] The latter method is not consistent in general, for its consistency requires X to be random. Even for random X the Wallis estimator appears to be more efficient than Three-Pass Least-Squares. Wallis' stage (1) produces an instrumental variable estimate $\hat{\beta}$: this is an example of the type of estimator described on page 279 above and its performance may be compared with that of the GLS estimator at stage (3). Wallis' results suggest that the instrumental variable estimator is inferior to the GLS estimator on the mean square error criterion, as one would expect since the latter estimator attempts to deal with the autocorrelation problem. Some additional evidence of a rather poor performance by an instrumental variable estimator is given by Sargent.[2] Finally one may note that the two-step estimator described on page 318 above will probably have fairly large sampling errors if X is highly autocorrelated, for the numerator and denominator of $\hat{\rho}$ would probably have large variances. The practical choice would appear to lie between the Wallis estimator and some iterative search procedure depending on the importance of the problem and the computational facilities available.

EXERCISES

10-1. For $i = 0, 1, 2, \ldots$ and $w_i = (1 - \lambda)\lambda^i$, $0 < \lambda < 1$, show that $E(i) = \lambda/(1 - \lambda)$. $\lambda/(1 - \lambda)$.

10-2. Sketch the application of the Almon method to the case of two explanatory variables with different lengths of lags.

10-3. The Liviatan estimators of α and λ in the equation $y_t = \alpha x_t + \lambda y_{t-1} + v_t$ are given by

$$\Sigma y_t x_t = \hat{\alpha}\Sigma x_t^2 + \hat{\lambda}\Sigma y_{t-1} x_t$$

$$\Sigma y_t x_{t-1} = \hat{\alpha}\Sigma x_t x_{t-1} + \hat{\lambda}\Sigma y_{t-1} x_{t-1}$$

Are these the same as the estimators yielded by the two-step process (a) regress y_{t-1} on x_{t-1} to obtain $\hat{y}_{t-1}$; (b) regress y_t on x_t and $\hat{y}_{t-1}$ to estimate α and λ?

10-4. Show how the estimation methods of Section 10-3 might be extended to deal with relations involving several lagged Y values and several X variables.

[1] L. D. Taylor and T. A. Wilson, "Three-Pass Least-Squares: A Method for Estimating Models with a Lagged Dependent Variable," *Rev. Economics and Statistics*, vol. 46, pp. 329–346, 1964.

[2] T. J. Sargent, "Some Evidence on the Small Sample Properties of Distributed Lag Estimators in the Presence of Autocorrelated Disturbances," *Rev. Economics and Statistics*, vol. 50, pp. 87–95, 1968.

10-5. In the equation

$$y_t = \alpha y_{t-1} + \beta x_t + u_t \qquad |\alpha| < 1$$

the x_t are drawn at random from a fixed population with a finite variance while the u's are generated by the stationary process $u_t = \rho u_t + v_t$, where the v_t are independently distributed with mean 0 and finite variance. Show that the least-squares estimate of β is consistent. Find the asymptotic bias of the estimate of α. What happens when $\beta = 0$? When $|\beta| \to \infty$? Comment.

(Oxford Diploma, 1966)

10-6. Discuss the criteria for choosing instrumental variables. Describe suitable methods of estimating the model

$$y_t = \alpha y_{t-1} + \beta x_{1t} + \beta_2 x_{2t} + u_t$$

(a) where $u_t = \rho u_{t-1} + \varepsilon_t$

$E(\varepsilon_t) = 0$, var $(\varepsilon_t) = \sigma^2$, $E(\varepsilon_t \varepsilon_s) = 0 \qquad t \neq s.$

(b) where u_t is generated by an unspecified autocorrelated process.

10-7. In the regression model

$$y_t = \beta x_t + u_t, \qquad (t = 1, 2, \ldots, T)$$

the x_t are fixed and it is known that

$$u_t = \varepsilon_t + \delta\varepsilon_{t-1}, \qquad (-1 < \delta < 1)$$

where

$$E(\varepsilon_t) = 0 \text{ and } E(\varepsilon_t \varepsilon_{t-r}) = \begin{cases} \sigma^2 \text{ when } r = 0 \\ 0 \text{ when } r \neq 0 \end{cases}$$

(a) Show that the least-squares estimator of β is unbiased and derive an expression for its sampling variance.

(b) Assuming that the value of δ is known, give expressions for the generalized least-squares estimator of β and its sampling variance.

(c) If the model is changed to

$$y_t = \beta y_{t-1} + u_t, (-1 < \beta < 1)$$

where the u_t are as before, show that a consistent estimator of β can be obtained by using y_{t-2} as an instrument for y_{t-1}.

(L.S.E. 1967)

11
Other Multivariate Methods

11-1 PRINCIPAL COMPONENTS

Suppose we have a matrix **X** of n observations on k variables

$$\mathbf{X} = \begin{bmatrix} x_{11} & \cdots & x_{k1} \\ \vdots & & \vdots \\ x_{1n} & \cdots & x_{kn} \end{bmatrix}$$

where the observations have been expressed as deviations from the sample means, for we are concerned with studying the variation in the data.

The nature of principal components may be approached in a number of ways. One is to ask how many dimensions or how much independence there really is in the set of k variables. More explicitly we consider the transformation of the X's to a new set of variables which will be pairwise uncorrelated and of which the first will have the maximum possible variance, the second the maximum possible variance among those uncorrelated with the first, and so forth. Let

$$z_{1t} = a_{11}x_{1t} + a_{21}x_{2t} + \cdots + a_{k1}x_{kt} \qquad t = 1, \ldots, n$$

denote the first new variable. In matrix form

$$\mathbf{z}_1 = \mathbf{X}\mathbf{a}_1 \tag{11-1}$$

where $\mathbf{z}_1$ is an n-element vector and $\mathbf{a}_1$ a k-element vector. The sum of squares of $\mathbf{z}_1$ is

$$\mathbf{z}_1'\mathbf{z}_1 = \mathbf{a}_1'\mathbf{X}'\mathbf{X}\mathbf{a}_1 \tag{11-2}$$

We wish to choose $\mathbf{a}_1$ to maximize $\mathbf{z}_1'\mathbf{z}_1$, but clearly some constraint must be imposed on $\mathbf{a}_1$, otherwise $\mathbf{z}_1'\mathbf{z}_1$ could be made infinitely large, so let us normalize by setting

$$\mathbf{a}_1'\mathbf{a}_1 = 1 \tag{11-3}$$

The problem now is to maximize (11-2) subject to (11-3). Define

$$\varphi = \mathbf{a}_1'\mathbf{X}'\mathbf{X}\mathbf{a}_1 - \lambda_1(\mathbf{a}_1'\mathbf{a}_1 - 1)$$

where λ_1 is a Lagrange multiplier. Thus

$$\frac{\partial\varphi}{\partial\mathbf{a}_1} = 2\mathbf{X}'\mathbf{X}\mathbf{a}_1 - 2\lambda_1\mathbf{a}_1$$

Setting

$$\frac{\partial\varphi}{\partial\mathbf{a}_1} = \mathbf{0} \quad \text{gives}$$

$$(\mathbf{X}'\mathbf{X})\mathbf{a}_1 = \lambda_1\mathbf{a}_1 \tag{11-4}$$

Thus $\mathbf{a}_1$ is a latent vector of $\mathbf{X}'\mathbf{X}$ corresponding to the root λ_1. From (11-2) and (11-4) we see that

$$\mathbf{z}_1'\mathbf{z}_1 = \lambda_1\mathbf{a}_1'\mathbf{a}_1 = \lambda_1$$

and so we must choose λ_1 as the largest latent root of $\mathbf{X}'\mathbf{X}$. The $\mathbf{X}'\mathbf{X}$ matrix, in the absence of perfect collinearity, will be positive definite and thus have positive latent roots. The first principal component of $\mathbf{X}$ is then $\mathbf{z}_1$.

Now define $\mathbf{z}_2 = \mathbf{X}\mathbf{a}_2$. We wish to choose $\mathbf{a}_2$ to maximize $\mathbf{a}_2'\mathbf{X}'\mathbf{X}\mathbf{a}_2$ subject to $\mathbf{a}_2'\mathbf{a}_2 = 1$ and $\mathbf{a}_1'\mathbf{a}_2 = 0$. The reason for the second condition is that $\mathbf{z}_2$ is to be uncorrelated with $\mathbf{z}_1$. The covariation between them is given by

$$\begin{aligned}\mathbf{a}_1'\mathbf{X}'\mathbf{X}\mathbf{a}_2 &= \lambda_1\mathbf{a}_1'\mathbf{a}_2 \\ &= 0 \text{ if and only if } \mathbf{a}_1'\mathbf{a}_2 = 0\end{aligned}$$

Define

$$\varphi = \mathbf{a}_2'\mathbf{X}'\mathbf{X}\mathbf{a}_2 - \lambda_2(\mathbf{a}_2'\mathbf{a}_2 - 1) - \mu(\mathbf{a}_1'\mathbf{a}_2)$$

where λ_2 and μ are Lagrange multipliers.

$$\frac{\partial \varphi}{\partial \mathbf{a}_2} = 2\mathbf{X}'\mathbf{X}\mathbf{a}_2 - 2\lambda_2\mathbf{a}_2 - \mu\mathbf{a}_1 = \mathbf{0}$$

Premultiply by $\mathbf{a}_1'$

$$2\mathbf{a}_1'\mathbf{X}'\mathbf{X}\mathbf{a}_2 - \mu = \mathbf{0}$$

But from

$$(\mathbf{X}'\mathbf{X})\mathbf{a}_1 = \lambda_1\mathbf{a}_1$$

$$\mathbf{a}_2'(\mathbf{X}'\mathbf{X})\mathbf{a}_1 = \lambda_1\mathbf{a}_2'\mathbf{a}_1 = 0$$

Thus

$$\mu = 0$$

and we have

$$(\mathbf{X}'\mathbf{X})\mathbf{a}_2 = \lambda_2\mathbf{a}_2 \qquad (11\text{-}5)$$

and λ_2 should obviously be chosen as the second largest latent root of $\mathbf{X}'\mathbf{X}$.

We can proceed in this way for each of the k roots of $\mathbf{X}'\mathbf{X}$, and assemble the resultant vectors in the orthogonal matrix

$$\mathbf{A} = [\mathbf{a}_1 \quad \mathbf{a}_2 \quad \cdots \quad \mathbf{a}_k] \qquad (11\text{-}6)$$

The k principal components of $\mathbf{X}$ are then given by the $n \times k$ matrix $\mathbf{Z}$,

$$\mathbf{Z} = \mathbf{X}\mathbf{A} \qquad (11\text{-}7)$$

Moreover,

$$\mathbf{Z}'\mathbf{Z} = \mathbf{A}'\mathbf{X}'\mathbf{X}\mathbf{A} = \Lambda = \begin{bmatrix} \lambda_1 & 0 & \cdots & 0 \\ 0 & \lambda_2 & \cdots & 0 \\ \vdots & \vdots & & \vdots \\ 0 & 0 & \cdots & \lambda_k \end{bmatrix} \qquad (11\text{-}8)$$

showing that the principal components are indeed pairwise uncorrelated and that their variances are given by

$$\mathbf{z}_i'\mathbf{z}_i = \lambda_i \qquad i = 1, \ldots, k \qquad (11\text{-}9)$$

If the rank of $\mathbf{X}$ were $r < k$, $(k - r)$ latent roots would be zero and the variation in the X's could be completely expressed in terms of r independent variables. Even if $\mathbf{X}$ has full column rank, some of the λ's may be fairly close to zero so that a small number of principal components account for a substantial proportion of the variance of the X's. The total variation in the

X's is given by

$$\sum_t x_{1t}^2 + \sum_t x_{2t}^2 + \cdots + \sum_t x_{kt}^2 = \text{tr}\,(\mathbf{X}'\mathbf{X})$$

but

$$\begin{aligned} \text{tr}\,(\mathbf{A}'\mathbf{X}'\mathbf{X}\mathbf{A}) &= \text{tr}\,(\mathbf{X}'\mathbf{X}\mathbf{A}\mathbf{A}') \\ &= \text{tr}\,(\mathbf{X}'\mathbf{X}) \qquad \text{since } \mathbf{A}\mathbf{A}' = \mathbf{I} \end{aligned}$$

and so from (11-8)

$$\sum_{i=1}^{k} \sum_{t=1}^{n} x_{it}^2 = \text{tr}\,(\mathbf{X}'\mathbf{X}) = \sum_{i=1}^{k} \lambda_i = \mathbf{z}_1'\mathbf{z}_1 + \cdots + \mathbf{z}_k'\mathbf{z}_k$$

Thus

$$\frac{\lambda_1}{\Sigma\lambda}, \frac{\lambda_2}{\Sigma\lambda}, \ldots, \frac{\lambda_k}{\Sigma\lambda}$$

represent the proportionate contributions of each principal component to the total variation of the X's, and since the components are orthogonal these contributions sum to unity.

It is sometimes difficult to attach a concrete meaning to specific principal components. Occasionally a suggestion may be found in the correlations of a component with various X's. To find the correlation between, say, the first principal component and the X variables we proceed as follows. The vector $\mathbf{X}'\mathbf{z}_1$ gives the cross-products between z_1 and each X variable. But

$$\mathbf{X}'\mathbf{z}_1 = \mathbf{X}'\mathbf{X}\mathbf{a}_1 = \lambda_1 \mathbf{a}_1$$

Thus the correlation between X_i and z_1 is

$$\begin{aligned} r_{i1} &= \frac{\lambda_1 a_{i1}}{\sqrt{\lambda_1}\sqrt{\sum_{t=1}^{n} x_{it}^2}} \\ &= \frac{a_{i1}\sqrt{\lambda_1}}{\sqrt{\sum_{t=1}^{n} x_{it}^2}} \qquad i = 1, \ldots, k \end{aligned} \tag{11-10}$$

where a_{i1} is the ith element in the vector $\mathbf{a}_1$. In general the correlation between X_i and z_j is

$$r_{ij} = \frac{a_{ij}\sqrt{\lambda_j}}{\sqrt{\sum_t x_{it}^2}} \qquad i, j = 1, \ldots, k \tag{11-11}$$

These correlation coefficients may also be used to show how the variations in *each* X variable may be decomposed into the contribution due to each component. From

$$\mathbf{Z} = \mathbf{XA}$$

we have

$$\mathbf{Z}' = \mathbf{A}'\mathbf{X}'$$

and

$$\mathbf{X}' = \mathbf{AZ}' \quad \text{since } \mathbf{A} \text{ is orthogonal.}$$

So

$$\begin{aligned} \mathbf{X}'\mathbf{X} &= \mathbf{AZ}'\mathbf{ZA}' \\ &= \mathbf{A\Lambda A}' \text{ from (11-8)} \end{aligned}$$

and

$$\sum_{t=1}^{n} x_{it}^2 = \sum_{j=1}^{k} a_{ij}^2 \lambda_j \qquad i = 1, \ldots, k \tag{11-12}$$

Dividing through both sides of (11-12) by $\sum_t x_{it}^2$ gives

$$1 = \frac{a_{i1}^2 \lambda_1}{\sum_t x_{it}^2} + \frac{a_{i2}^2 \lambda_2}{\sum_t x_{it}^2} + \cdots + \frac{a_{ik}^2 \lambda_k}{\sum_t x_{it}^2} \tag{11-13}$$

where the terms on the right-hand side are the squares of the correlation coefficients defined in (11-11). Thus the proportions of the variation in X_i associated with the various principal components are given by

$$r_{i1}^2, r_{i2}^2, \ldots, r_{ik}^2$$

and since the components are uncorrelated these proportions sum to unity, as is shown by (11-13).

A note of warning should be inserted here. The development so far has proceeded on the implicit assumption that the X variables are all measured in the same units. If not, it is difficult to attach a meaning to concepts such as the total variation of the X's and the partitioning of that total variation into the contribution due to each component. It is still, of course, possible to compute the latent roots and vectors of $\mathbf{X}'\mathbf{X}$ even if the dimensions of the variables are not all the same and the correlations in (11-11) and the partitioning in (11-13) would still be meaningful even though the partitioning of the *total* variation in the X's would not. As an alternative, analyses are sometimes carried out after all the X variables have been *standardized*, that is each deviation from the sample mean is divided by $\sqrt{n}$ times the sample standard deviation of that variable. $\mathbf{X}'\mathbf{X}$ is now the matrix of zero-order correlation coefficients of the X variables. The analysis can proceed from $\mathbf{X'X}$ as before. Now $\operatorname{tr}(\mathbf{X'X}) = k$ and from the development following (11-8)

$$\lambda_1 + \lambda_2 + \cdots + \lambda_k = k.$$

The latent roots and vectors will in general be different from those yielded by unstandardized variables. We leave it as an exercise for the reader to establish whether the correlation coefficients in (11-11) are affected by the standardization of the X variables.

Empirically, then, one may compute the principal components for a given $\mathbf{X}$ matrix and see how much of the variation of the X's is accounted for by various components. Frequently the intercorrelation of economic and social data means that a small number of components will account for a large proportion of the total variation and it is desirable to have a test for judging the number of components to retain for further analysis. Suppose that we have computed the roots $\lambda_1, \lambda_2, \ldots, \lambda_k$ and that the first r roots $\lambda_1, \lambda_2, \ldots, \lambda_r$ $(r < k)$ seem both sufficiently large and sufficiently different to be retained. The question then is whether the remaining $(k - r)$ roots and their associated vectors and components are sufficiently alike for one to conclude that the true values are equal. A very approximate test is based on

$$\rho = (\lambda_{r+1}\lambda_{r+2}\cdots\lambda_k)^{-1}\left(\frac{\lambda_{r+1} + \lambda_{r+2} + \cdots + \lambda_k}{k - r}\right)^{k-r} \tag{11-14}$$

The proposed test is to consider $n \log_e \rho$ to follow a χ^2 distribution with $\frac{1}{2}(k - r - 1)(k - r + 2)$ degrees of freedom, if the null hypothesis of equality of the remaining latent roots is true.[1] One hopes in practical applications that the number, r, of significantly different components to be retained is substantially less than the number of variables, k, from which the components have been computed.

A somewhat similar result is achieved by Factor Analysis in which the X variables are specified *ab initio* to be linear combinations of a small number of independent standard normal variables (factors) plus an independent normal error term. From the principal component analysis we have

$$\mathbf{Z} = \mathbf{XA} \quad \text{and hence}$$

$$\mathbf{X} = \mathbf{ZA}' \tag{11-15}$$

Equations (11-15) express the X's as exact linear combinations of the components with coefficients given by the elements of $\mathbf{A}$. If however, we retain less than k principal components the equations in (11-15) would have to be replaced by

$$\mathbf{X} = \mathbf{Z}^*\mathbf{A}^{*\prime} + \mathbf{U} \tag{11-16}$$

[1] See M. G. Kendall and A. Stuart, *The Advanced Theory of Statistics*, vol. 3, Griffin, London, 1966, pp. 292–293, for details and qualifications.

where $\mathbf{Z}^*$ and $\mathbf{A}^*$ denote the submatrices of $\mathbf{Z}$ and $\mathbf{A}$ giving the retained components and the corresponding latent vectors and $\mathbf{U}$ is a matrix of errors. Principal components is obviously a possible estimation method in factor analysis, but slight modifications are required to the $\mathbf{A}^*$ coefficients to conform to the imposed assumption that the factors should have unit variance. Without additional restrictions $\mathbf{z}_i'\mathbf{z}_i = \lambda_i$, as we have seen in (11-8). When the $\mathbf{A}^*$ coefficients have been adjusted they are referred to as factor loadings. However, several other estimation methods are used in factor analysis and we do not propose to discuss them here.[1] An interesting application of factor analysis is given by Adelman and Morris, who find 66 per cent of the variance of GNP per capita in 74 underdeveloped countries associated with just four factors which have in turn been based on a complex of more than 20 social and political variables.[2]

Table 11-1 shows another example in which a small number of components effectively accounts for the variation in a set of data. The basic data are 11 series of average quarterly interest rates in the United Kingdom from the first quarter of 1963 to the first quarter of 1969. They include various national and local government rates as well as commercial rates such as those on Building Society deposits. The series were standardized and the second row of the table gives the values of $\lambda_i/\Sigma\lambda$ for the first four principal components. The first principal component which turned out to be effectively a simple arithmetic average of the standardized series, accounts for over 83 per cent of the total variance and the first three components for almost 97 per cent. The last seven components account for less than 2 per cent of the total variation.

Table 11-1[1] Contribution of principal components to the total variation of 11 interest rates

Component	1	2	3	4
Contribution	0.8368	0.0831	0.0482	0.0156
Cumulative Contribution	0.8368	0.9199	0.9681	0.9837

[1] I am indebted to Mr. L. D. D. Price and Mr. P. Burman of the Bank of England for these results.

[1] See J. T. Scott, Jr, "Factor Analysis and Regression," *Econometrica*, vol. 34, pp. 552–562, 1966, Kendall and Stuart, *op. cit.* pp. 306–311, and H. H. Hyman, *Modern Factor Analysis*, The University of Chicago Press, Chicago, 1960.

[2] I. Adelman and C. T. Morris, "Factor Analysis of the Inter-relationship between Social and Political Variables and Per Capita Gross National Product," *Quart. J. Economics*, Vol. 79, pp. 555–578, 1965.

An important but as yet unresolved question concerns the use of principal components in conventional econometric regression problems. There appear to be at least two possibilities that are worth distinguishing. In both we are still assuming that some Y variable is to be explained in terms of a set of X variables. In the first problem, however, the number of variables that might possibly be included in the **X** matrix on theoretical or other grounds is so large and possibly so intercorrelated that conventional estimation procedures would be dubious for lack of degrees of freedom aggravated by multicollinearity. An obvious approach is then to apply principal component analysis *to the X variables* to see if a small number of components might account for a sufficiently large proportion of the total variation of the X's and then to use these components as explanatory variables in a conventional regression with Y as the dependent variable. Further discussion of this use will be given in the treatment of two-stage least-squares in Chap. 13. A possible variant on this approach is to retain a small number of specific important X variables in the final regression along with principal components determined from the other X variables.[1] This seems valid and useful, as far as it goes, and if some economic or social significance can be attached to specific components so much the better. The second suggested use is more doubtful and requires more examination than it has yet received.[2] It concerns the case where multicollinearity rather than an excessive number of the X variables is the problem. As is well known, least-squares estimation of the coefficients of the X variables becomes very imprecise. Kendall's suggestion is to compute the principal components of the X variables, discard those with low latent roots, regress Y on the retained principal components and transform back from the regression coefficients on the principal components to obtain estimates of the coefficients of the X variables. Suppose, for example, that there are five X variables and we retain just two principal components.

$$z_1 = a_{11}x_1 + a_{21}x_2 + \cdots + a_{51}x_5$$

$$z_2 = a_{12}x_1 + a_{22}x_2 + \cdots + a_{52}x_5$$

The regression of Y on z_1, z_2 is then

$$\begin{aligned} Y &= b_1z_1 + b_2z_2 + e \\ &= b_1(a_{11}x_1 + \cdots + a_{51}x_5) + b_2(a_{12}x_1 + \cdots + a_{52}x_5) + e \\ &= (b_1a_{11} + b_2a_{12})x_1 + \cdots + (b_1a_{51} + b_2a_{52})x_5 + e \qquad (11\text{-}17) \end{aligned}$$

If one retained all five principal components the coefficients of the x's in (11-17) would be identical with those given by a direct regression of Y on the

[1] For an illustration see G. B. Pidot Jr., "A Principal Components Analysis of the Determinants of Local Government Fiscal Patterns," *Rev. Economics and Statistics*, vol. 51, pp. 176–188, 1969.
[2] See M. G. Kendall, *A Course in Multivariate Analysis*, Griffin, London, 1957, pp. 70–74.

x's. How should we decide on the number of components to retain? Purely subjective decision on the size of the latent roots, as in Kendall's illustrative example, is hardly satisfactory. Should one use the test based on (11-14) or use a conventional analysis of variance test on the regression? The procedure would give a nonsense result in the case of perfectly collinear X variables. For example, suppose $x_2 = 2x_1$ and let

$$\mathbf{X'X} = \begin{bmatrix} 1 & 2 \\ 2 & 4 \end{bmatrix}$$

The latent roots are $\lambda_1 = 5, \lambda_2 = 0$. For $\lambda_1 = 5$,

$$\mathbf{a}_1' = \begin{bmatrix} \frac{1}{\sqrt{5}} & \frac{2}{\sqrt{5}} \end{bmatrix}$$

and for $\lambda_2 = 0$,

$$\mathbf{a}_2' = \begin{bmatrix} \frac{2}{\sqrt{5}} & -\frac{1}{\sqrt{5}} \end{bmatrix}$$

The second principal component does not exist for

$$z_2 = \frac{2}{\sqrt{5}}x_1 - \frac{1}{\sqrt{5}}x_2 = 0, \qquad \text{since } x_2 = 2x_1$$

However, the first component does exist, for

$$z_1 = \frac{1}{\sqrt{5}}x_1 + \frac{2}{\sqrt{5}}x_2 = \sqrt{5}x_1$$

and so the coefficient of z_1 in the regression with Y as the dependent variable can be computed as

$$b_1 = \frac{\Sigma z_1 y}{\Sigma z_1^2} = \frac{\Sigma z_1 y}{\lambda_1} = \frac{1}{\sqrt{5}}\Sigma x_1 y$$

Substituting in (11-17) gives

$$\begin{aligned} Y &= b_1 z_1 + e \\ &= \left(\frac{b_1}{\sqrt{5}}\right)x_1 + 2\left(\frac{b_1}{\sqrt{5}}\right)x_2 + e \end{aligned}$$

and apparently the relative influence of x_1 and x_2 has been determined in a perfectly collinear case where such a determination is impossible. The coefficients on x_1 and x_2 from the principal component regression are seen to reflect simply the fact that $x_2 = 2x_1$ and are unrelated to the true but unknown parameters. Nevertheless the question remains whether or not the approach might work reasonably well in a less than perfectly collinear case.[1]

11-2 CANONICAL CORRELATIONS

In component analysis one is finding uncorrelated linear combinations of a set of variables with the maximum possible variances. In canonical correlation analysis, one postulates first of all the existence of *two* sets of variables. Let

$$\mathbf{Y} = [\mathbf{y}_1 \quad \mathbf{y}_2 \quad \cdots \quad \mathbf{y}_p] \qquad \mathbf{X} = [\mathbf{x}_1 \quad \mathbf{x}_2 \quad \cdots \quad \mathbf{x}_q] \qquad p \leq q$$

be $(n \times p)$ and $(n \times q)$ matrices of data on two sets of variables and we assume all the data to be expressed as deviations from sample means. The set of Y variables is presumed to depend in some way on the set of X variables and the object of the analysis is to find those linear combinations of Y and X which have maximum correlation subject to certain conditions. Let

$$\mathbf{u} = \mathbf{Ya} \quad \text{and } \mathbf{v} = \mathbf{Xb} \tag{11-18}$$

where $\mathbf{u}$ and $\mathbf{v}$ are $(n \times 1)$ vectors and $\mathbf{a}$ and $\mathbf{b}$ $(p \times 1)$ and $(q \times 1)$ respectively. The correlation between u and v is

$$r = \frac{\mathbf{a}'\mathbf{Y}'\mathbf{Xb}}{\sqrt{\mathbf{a}'\mathbf{Y}'\mathbf{Ya} \cdot \mathbf{b}'\mathbf{X}'\mathbf{Xb}}}$$

We need only consider positive values of r, for if we had $\mathbf{a}$, $\mathbf{b}$ vectors such that r was negative, replacing $\mathbf{a}$ by $(-\mathbf{a})$ produces a positive correlation of the same absolute value. The problem now is to maximize r subject to the normalizing conditions

$$\mathbf{a}'\mathbf{Y}'\mathbf{Ya} = 1 = \mathbf{b}'\mathbf{X}'\mathbf{Xb}$$

Define

$$\varphi = \mathbf{a}'\mathbf{Y}'\mathbf{Xb} - \tfrac{1}{2}\lambda(\mathbf{a}'\mathbf{Y}'\mathbf{Ya} - 1) - \tfrac{1}{2}\mu(\mathbf{b}'\mathbf{X}'\mathbf{Xb} - 1)$$

where λ and μ are Lagrange multipliers.

$$\frac{\partial\varphi}{\partial\mathbf{a}} = \mathbf{Y}'\mathbf{Xb} - \lambda\mathbf{Y}'\mathbf{Ya}$$

$$\frac{\partial\varphi}{\partial\mathbf{b}} = \mathbf{X}'\mathbf{Ya} - \mu\mathbf{X}'\mathbf{Xb}$$

[1] For a recent contribution which shows that the principal component approach can be an improvement over OLS in certain circumstances see B. T. McCallum, "Artificial Orthogonalization in Regression Analysis", *Rev. Economics and Statistics*, vol. 52, pp. 110–113, 1970. The basic point is that the principal component estimators will be biased but will have smaller variances than the unbiased OLS estimators. Thus, under certain conditions, the principal components estimators may have smaller mean square errors than OLS estimators.

Thus r is stationary for

$$\mathbf{Y'Xb} - \lambda\mathbf{Y'Ya} = \mathbf{0} \tag{11-19}$$

$$\mathbf{X'Ya} - \mu\mathbf{X'Xb} = \mathbf{0} \tag{11-20}$$

Premultiply the first equation by $\mathbf{a}'$ and the second by $\mathbf{b}'$ giving

$$\lambda = \mu = \mathbf{a'Y'Xb} = r$$

Thus equations (11-19) and (11-20) may be written

$$\begin{bmatrix} -\lambda\mathbf{Y'Y} & \mathbf{Y'X} \\ \mathbf{X'Y} & -\lambda\mathbf{X'X} \end{bmatrix} \begin{bmatrix} \mathbf{a} \\ \mathbf{b} \end{bmatrix} = \mathbf{0} \tag{11-21}$$

For a nonzero solution the determinant must vanish, that is

$$\begin{vmatrix} -\lambda\mathbf{Y'Y} & \mathbf{Y'X} \\ \mathbf{X'Y} & -\lambda\mathbf{X'X} \end{vmatrix} = 0$$

If we multiply each of the first p rows of the determinant by $(-\lambda)$ the new determinant will be $(-\lambda)^p$ times the old. So to correct for this we must multiply outside the determinant by $(-\lambda)^{-p}$. If in addition we divide through the last q columns by $(-\lambda)$ and multiply outside by $(-\lambda)^q$ the determinant may be expressed as

$$(-\lambda)^{q-p} \begin{vmatrix} \lambda^2\mathbf{Y'Y} & \mathbf{Y'X} \\ \mathbf{X'Y} & \mathbf{X'X} \end{vmatrix} = (-\lambda)^{q-p}|\mathbf{X'X}| \cdot |\lambda^2\mathbf{Y'Y} - \mathbf{Y'X}(\mathbf{X'X})^{-1}\mathbf{X'Y}|$$

Since $|\mathbf{X'X}| \neq 0$ we have

$$(-\lambda)^{q-p}|\lambda^2\mathbf{Y'Y} - \mathbf{Y'X}(\mathbf{X'X})^{-1}\mathbf{X'Y}| = 0 \tag{11-22}$$

This equation is of order $p + q$ in λ with $(q - p)$ of the roots zero and the other $2p$ roots coming in pairs from the solution of

$$|\lambda^2\mathbf{Y'Y} - \mathbf{Y'X}(\mathbf{X'X})^{-1}\mathbf{X'Y}| = 0 \tag{11-23}$$

For each λ_i^2 $(i = 1, \ldots, p)$ which is a solution of (11-23) we have $\pm\lambda_i$. Since each λ is equal to the correlation coefficient between the corresponding u and v we need consider only the positive roots $\lambda_1, \lambda_2, \ldots, \lambda_p$, or $r_1, r_2, \ldots, r_p$. The substitution of each positive root in turn in (11-21) yields a pair of vectors $\mathbf{a}_i, \mathbf{b}_i$ $(i = 1, \ldots, p)$ which in turn give a set of p, u-vectors $\mathbf{u}_1, \mathbf{u}_2, \ldots, \mathbf{u}_p$ and a set of p, v-vectors $\mathbf{v}_1, \mathbf{v}_2, \ldots, \mathbf{v}_p$. These u, v vectors satisfy the following conditions.

$$\mathbf{u}_i'\mathbf{u}_i = 1 \qquad i = 1, \ldots, p \tag{11-24}$$

$$\mathbf{v}_i'\mathbf{v}_i = 1 \qquad i = 1, \ldots, p \tag{11-25}$$

$$\mathbf{u}_i'\mathbf{v}_i = r_i \qquad i = 1, \ldots, p \tag{11-26}$$

These r_i are the canonical correlation coefficients, r_1 being the greatest possible correlation between linear combinations of Y and X variables, r_2 being the next greatest correlation and so forth. The u, v vectors also satisfy certain additional conditions; the u vectors are pairwise uncorrelated, similarly the v vectors are pairwise uncorrelated, and noncorresponding u and v vectors are uncorrelated, that is

$$\mathbf{u}_i'\mathbf{u}_j = 0 \qquad i \neq j \tag{11-27}$$

$$\mathbf{v}_i'\mathbf{v}_j = 0 \qquad i \neq j \tag{11-28}$$

and

$$\mathbf{u}_i'\mathbf{v}_j = 0 \qquad i \neq j \tag{11-29}$$

To prove these last three results write out Eqs. (11-21) for $\lambda_i = r_i$ as

$$-r_i\mathbf{Y}'\mathbf{Y}\mathbf{a}_i + \mathbf{Y}'\mathbf{X}\mathbf{b}_i = \mathbf{0}$$

$$\mathbf{X}'\mathbf{Y}\mathbf{a}_i - r_i\mathbf{X}'\mathbf{X}\mathbf{b}_i = \mathbf{0}$$

Premultiplying the first equation by $\mathbf{a}_j'$, the second by $\mathbf{b}_j'$ and using (11-18) gives

$$\begin{aligned} -r_i\mathbf{u}_j'\mathbf{u}_i + \mathbf{u}_j'\mathbf{v}_i &= 0 \\ \mathbf{v}_j'\mathbf{u}_i - r_i\mathbf{v}_j'\mathbf{v}_i &= 0 \end{aligned} \tag{11-30}$$

Likewise, writing out (11-21) for $\lambda_j = r_j$, premultiplying the first by $\mathbf{a}_i'$ and the second by $\mathbf{b}_i'$ gives

$$\begin{aligned} -r_j\mathbf{u}_i'\mathbf{u}_j + \mathbf{u}_i'\mathbf{v}_j &= 0 \\ \mathbf{v}_i'\mathbf{u}_j - r_j\mathbf{v}_i'\mathbf{v}_j &= 0 \end{aligned} \tag{11-31}$$

Equations (11-30) and (11-31) may be re-arranged as

$$\begin{bmatrix} 1 & -r_i & 0 & 0 \\ 0 & 0 & 1 & -r_i \\ 0 & -r_j & 1 & 0 \\ 1 & 0 & 0 & -r_j \end{bmatrix} \begin{bmatrix} \mathbf{u}_j'\mathbf{v}_i \\ \mathbf{u}_j'\mathbf{u}_i \\ \mathbf{v}_j'\mathbf{u}_i \\ \mathbf{v}_j'\mathbf{v}_i \end{bmatrix} = \begin{bmatrix} 0 \\ 0 \\ 0 \\ 0 \end{bmatrix}$$

Provided $r_i \neq r_j$ the matrix of coefficients has full rank and the solution is the zero vector, which proves the results on the covariances.

It is even more difficult to attach economic significance to the linear combinations arising in canonical correlation analysis than it is to principal components. It would appear to be a useful tool in areas where the investigator has little if any theoretical or *a priori* knowledge about the relations between the Y's and the X's. As we shall see in Chaps. 12 and 13 economic situations are indeed characterized by the dependence of a set of Y variables on a set of X variables but strong *a priori* specifications of the structure of the dependence have led to the development of various specific methods of estimating that structure. Probably for that reason interesting and important economic applications of canonical correlations are not readily found in the literature, and our sketch of the technique has been very rudimentary. More detailed accounts are available in Anderson and Kendall and Stuart.[1]

11-3 DISCRIMINANT ANALYSIS[2]

Let us assume that two or more populations exist and that we have a sample set of observations from each. The problem in discriminant analysis is to construct a rule from these sample observations which will enable us to assign a new observation to one of the populations. Many of the standard applications of the technique are found in the biological sciences, but it is also potentially fruitful in the social sciences. For example, Adelman and Morris have applied the technique in an attempt to identify underdeveloped countries with good development potential.[3] In their analysis 73 underdeveloped countries were classified into three groups according to their past economic performance and a linear discriminant function estimated from a number of social, political, and economic variables. Once such a function has been estimated the values of these variables for a new country can be fed into the discriminant function and the country assigned to one of the three groups for development potential.

To illustrate the underlying theory we will deal first of all with the case of two mutually exclusive populations. Let us introduce the following symbols.

Two populations: P_1 and P_2

Vector of measurements: $\mathbf{x}' = [x_1 \quad x_2 \quad \cdots \quad x_k]$

Density functions: $f_1(\mathbf{x})$ and $f_2(\mathbf{x})$

A priori probabilities: p_1 and p_2, where $p_1 + p_2 = 1$

Classification rule: $\mathbf{x}$ space divided into two regions R_1 and R_2. If $\mathbf{x}$ falls in R_1, individual (observation) is allocated to P_1.
If $\mathbf{x}$ falls in R_2, individual (observation) is allocated to P_2.

[1] T. W. Anderson, *An Introduction to Multivariate Statistical Analysis*, Wiley, New York, 1958, Chap. 12, and M. G. Kendall and A. Stuart, *The Advanced Theory of Statistics*, Griffin, London, 1966, vol. 3, Chap. 43.

[2] This section again contains only a brief outline. For more extensive coverage and greater detail the reader should consult, T. W. Anderson, *op. cit.*, Chap. 6 and M. G. Kendall and A. Stuart, *op. cit.*, Chap. 44.

[3] I. Adelman and C. T. Morris, "Performance Criteria for Evaluating Economic Development Potential—An Operational Approach," *Quart. J. Economics*, 82, pp. 268–280, 1968.

Costs of misclassification: $c(2|1)$ denotes the cost of classifying an observation from P_1 in P_2 and $c(1|2)$ the cost of classifying an observation from P_2 in P_1.
Correct classifications are costless.

The two populations are multivariate; an individual drawing from either population consists of measurements on k variables. The *a priori* probabilities refer to the probability that a new observation comes from P_1 or P_2. In many practical problems the *a priori* probabilities and/or the costs of misclassification may be unknown, and we have to see how our procedures should be modified in such cases. Let us find, for the above problem, a classifications rule which will *minimize the expected costs of misclassification.* The probability that an individual from P_1 is wrongly classified is obviously

$$\int_{R_2} f_1(\mathbf{x})\, d\mathbf{x}$$

and likewise the probability that an individual from P_2 is wrongly classified is

$$\int_{R_1} f_2(\mathbf{x})\, d\mathbf{x}$$

Thus the expected costs of misclassification are given by

$$c(2|1)p_1 \int_{R_2} f_1(\mathbf{x})\, d\mathbf{x} + c(1|2)p_2 \int_{R_1} f_2(\mathbf{x})\, d\mathbf{x}$$

$$= \int_{R_2} [c(2|1)p_1 f_1(\mathbf{x}) - c(1|2)p_2 f_2(\mathbf{x})]\, d\mathbf{x} + c(1|2)p_2 \int f_2(\mathbf{x})\, d\mathbf{x} \tag{11-32}$$

for

$$\int_{R_1} f_2(\mathbf{x})\, d\mathbf{x} = 1 - \int_{R_2} f_2(\mathbf{x})\, d\mathbf{x} = \int f_2(\mathbf{x})\, d\mathbf{x} - \int_{R_2} f_2(\mathbf{x})\, d\mathbf{x}$$

The last term on the right-hand side of (11-32) is a positive constant, and so the expression as a whole is minimized if R_2 is defined as the set of $\mathbf{x}$'s for which

$$[c(2|1)p_1 f_1(\mathbf{x}) - c(1|2)p_2 f_2(\mathbf{x})] < 0$$

giving R_1 as the set of x's for which this quantity is positive. Should a particular $\mathbf{x}$ make this quantity zero it may be consigned at random to either population. The classification rule is thus

$$\begin{aligned} R_1 &: \frac{f_1(\mathbf{x})}{f_2(\mathbf{x})} > \frac{c(1|2)p_2}{c(2|1)p_1} \\ R_2 &: \frac{f_1(\mathbf{x})}{f_2(\mathbf{x})} < \frac{c(1|2)p_2}{c(2|1)p_1} \end{aligned} \tag{11-33}$$

The practical significance of (11-33) as it stands is not very great for its application requires that we know the numerical values of the *a priori* probabilities and the costs as well as the form of the density functions and the numerical values of the parameters in those functions. Given such data the right-hand side of (11-33) is some constant and we classify into P_1 or P_2 as the ratio of the likelihoods for the individual under consideration exceeds or falls short of that constant.

A less demanding requirement is that the form of the density function should be known but not the values of the parameters. An alternative expression for (11-33) can then be derived which points the way to practical implementation from sample data. Let us assume that $f_1(\mathbf{x})$ and $f_2(\mathbf{x})$ are each multivariate normal with different mean vectors $\boldsymbol{\mu}_1$ and $\boldsymbol{\mu}_2$ but with the same covariance matrix $\boldsymbol{\Sigma}$. The ratio of the densities is then

$$\frac{f_1(\mathbf{x})}{f_2(\mathbf{x})} = \frac{\exp\left[-\frac{1}{2}(\mathbf{x}-\boldsymbol{\mu}_1)'\boldsymbol{\Sigma}^{-1}(\mathbf{x}-\boldsymbol{\mu}_1)\right]}{\exp\left[-\frac{1}{2}(\mathbf{x}-\boldsymbol{\mu}_2)'\boldsymbol{\Sigma}^{-1}(\mathbf{x}-\boldsymbol{\mu}_2)\right]} \tag{11-34}$$

which may easily be simplified to

$$\frac{f_1(\mathbf{x})}{f_2(\mathbf{x})} = \exp\left[\mathbf{x}'\boldsymbol{\Sigma}^{-1}(\boldsymbol{\mu}_1-\boldsymbol{\mu}_2) - \tfrac{1}{2}(\boldsymbol{\mu}_1+\boldsymbol{\mu}_2)'\boldsymbol{\Sigma}^{-1}(\boldsymbol{\mu}_1-\boldsymbol{\mu}_2)\right] \tag{11-35}$$

and if we define

$$\boldsymbol{\delta} = \boldsymbol{\Sigma}^{-1}(\boldsymbol{\mu}_1-\boldsymbol{\mu}_2) \tag{11-36}$$

and let c^* denote the constant on the right-hand side of (11-33) the classification rule can now be written

$$\begin{aligned} R_1 &: \mathbf{x}'\boldsymbol{\delta} - \tfrac{1}{2}(\boldsymbol{\mu}_1+\boldsymbol{\mu}_2)'\boldsymbol{\delta} > \log_e c^* \\ R_2 &: \mathbf{x}'\boldsymbol{\delta} - \tfrac{1}{2}(\boldsymbol{\mu}_1+\boldsymbol{\mu}_2)'\boldsymbol{\delta} < \log_e c^* \end{aligned} \tag{11-37}$$

$\mathbf{x}'\boldsymbol{\delta}$ is referred to as a discriminant function.

If the *a priori* probabilities were equal and if the costs of misclassification were also equal we have the special case where $c^* = 1$ and $\log c^* = 0$, giving the classification rule

$$\begin{aligned} R_1 &: \mathbf{x}'\boldsymbol{\delta} > \tfrac{1}{2}(\boldsymbol{\mu}_1 + \boldsymbol{\mu}_2)'\boldsymbol{\delta} \\ R_2 &: \mathbf{x}'\boldsymbol{\delta} < \tfrac{1}{2}(\boldsymbol{\mu}_1 + \boldsymbol{\mu}_2)'\boldsymbol{\delta} \end{aligned} \tag{11-38}$$

so that we would classify the individual in P_1 if the actual value of the discriminant function exceeded the value obtained by substituting the simple average of the mean vectors in the discriminant function and in P_2 if it were less than that value.

Rules (11-37) and (11-38), however, still involve the population parameters, which in general are unknown. Suppose now that we have a set of n_1 sample observations that we know have come from P_1 and another set of n_2 sample observations that we know to have come from P_2. Let $\bar{\mathbf{x}}_1$ and $\bar{\mathbf{x}}_2$ denote the vectors of sample means computed from each set of data. These are maximum likelihood estimates of $\boldsymbol{\mu}_1$ and $\boldsymbol{\mu}_2$. Compute the deviations from the sample means for each set of data so that

$\mathbf{X}_1$ is an $(n_1 \times k)$ matrix of deviations from $\bar{\mathbf{x}}_1$

and

$\mathbf{X}_2$ is an $(n_2 \times k)$ matrix of deviations from $\bar{\mathbf{x}}_2$

Then

$$\mathbf{S} = \frac{1}{n_1 + n_2 - 2}[\mathbf{X}_1'\mathbf{X}_1 + \mathbf{X}_2'\mathbf{X}_2] \tag{11-39}$$

based on the pooled sums of squares from the two samples is a maximum likelihood estimate of the common variance matrix $\boldsymbol{\Sigma}$. The elements of the discriminant function $\mathbf{d}$, may then be estimated by

$$\mathbf{d} = \mathbf{S}^{-1}(\bar{\mathbf{x}}_1 - \bar{\mathbf{x}}_2) \tag{11-40}$$

If the scalar z is defined as $z = \mathbf{x}'\mathbf{d}$ for any vector of observations $\mathbf{x}$ it will have a mean value $\bar{z}_1$ taken over the sample observations from P_1 and a mean value $\bar{z}_2$ taken over the sample observations from P_2. It can be shown that (11-40) gives the vector $\mathbf{d}$ which maximizes the ratio

$$\frac{(\bar{z}_1 - \bar{z}_2)^2}{\sum_{i=1}^{2}\sum_{j=1}^{n_i}(z_{ij} - \bar{z}_i)^2}$$

which provides an intuitive justification for the discriminant function for we would like to have a vector $\mathbf{d}$ which would differentiate the two populations as much as possible by making the squared difference between $\bar{z}_1$ and

$\bar{z}_2$ as great as possible. On the other hand increasing this difference may well increase the variance of z within each sample and so we find $\mathbf{d}$ to maximize the variance between samples relative to the pooled variance within samples.

Armed now with the estimates $\bar{\mathbf{x}}_1, \bar{\mathbf{x}}_2$, $\mathbf{S}$, and $\mathbf{d}$ from the sample data a practical discrimination procedure is to replace $\boldsymbol{\mu}_1$ $\boldsymbol{\mu}_2$ and $\boldsymbol{\delta}$ in rules such as (11-37) and (11-38) with the corresponding estimated values. The larger the samples from which our estimates have been drawn the greater is the probability that the practical procedures will approximate to the optimal properties of theoretical procedures such as (11-37).

Now we must turn to the case where *a priori* probabilities are not available or are not relevant. It is no longer possible to define a scalar expected cost associated with a given procedure or rule. Rather one now has a vector of expected costs; in the present case, a vector of two elements, namely,

Expected cost from classifying incorrectly into

$$P_1 = c(1|2)\int_{R_1} f_2(\mathbf{x})\,d\mathbf{x}$$

Expected cost from classifying incorrectly into

$$P_2 = c(2|1)\int_{R_2} f_1(\mathbf{x})\,d\mathbf{x}$$

A minimax procedure (that is, minimizing the maximum expected cost) would then suggest finding R_1, R_2 to make these expected costs equal. If the costs $c(1|2)$ and $c(2|1)$ were equal the minimax procedure simply reduces to making the probabilities of misclassification equal, that is

$$\int_{R_1} f_2(\mathbf{x})\,d\mathbf{x} = \int_{R_2} f_1(\mathbf{x})\,d\mathbf{x} \tag{11-41}$$

If we define

$$\zeta = \mathbf{x}'\boldsymbol{\delta} - \tfrac{1}{2}(\boldsymbol{\mu}_1 + \boldsymbol{\mu}_2)'\boldsymbol{\delta} \quad \text{where} \quad \boldsymbol{\delta} = \boldsymbol{\Sigma}^{-1}(\boldsymbol{\mu}_1 - \boldsymbol{\mu}_2) \tag{11-42}$$

then ζ is a normally distributed variable with mean $E_1(\zeta)$ if the $\mathbf{x}$ vector comes from P_1 and mean $E_2(\zeta)$ if the $\mathbf{x}$ vector comes from P_2. The variance of ζ is the same for each distribution since it depends in each case on $\boldsymbol{\Sigma}$. The parameters are easily found to be

$$\begin{aligned} E_1(\zeta) &= \tfrac{1}{2}(\boldsymbol{\mu}_1 - \boldsymbol{\mu}_2)'\boldsymbol{\delta} \\ E_2(\zeta) &= -\tfrac{1}{2}(\boldsymbol{\mu}_1 - \boldsymbol{\mu}_2)'\boldsymbol{\delta} \\ \operatorname{var}_1(\zeta) &= \operatorname{var}_2(\zeta) = (\boldsymbol{\mu}_1 - \boldsymbol{\mu}_2)'\boldsymbol{\delta} \end{aligned} \tag{11-43}$$

and we will use $f_1(\zeta)$ and $f_2(\zeta)$ to denote the densities of ζ when the $\mathbf{x}$ vector comes from P_1 and P_2 respectively. A classification procedure amounts to finding some constant ζ_0 and assigning an observation to P_1 if the corresponding $\zeta > \zeta_0$, and vice versa. Thus the probabilities of misclassification can be stated in terms of the ζ distributions as

$$\int_{\zeta_0}^{\infty} f_2(\zeta)\, d\zeta \quad \text{and} \quad \int_{-\infty}^{\zeta_0} f_1(\zeta)\, d\zeta$$

From (11-43) the $f_i(\zeta)$ are normal distributions with equal variance and means equidistant about zero. Thus the probabilities of misclassification will be equalized if ζ_0 is set at zero. This gives the classification rule (11-38) again, which stated in terms of estimated quantities, is

$$\begin{aligned} R_1 &: \mathbf{x}'\mathbf{d} > \tfrac{1}{2}(\bar{\mathbf{x}}_1 + \bar{\mathbf{x}}_2)'\mathbf{d} \\ R_2 &: \mathbf{x}'\mathbf{d} < \tfrac{1}{2}(\bar{\mathbf{x}}_1 + \bar{\mathbf{x}}_2)'\mathbf{d} \end{aligned} \tag{11-44}$$

where

$$\mathbf{d} = \mathbf{S}^{-1}(\bar{\mathbf{x}}_1 - \bar{\mathbf{x}}_2)$$

$\mathbf{S}$ being defined in (11-39). Clearly in rules like (11-44) the vector $\mathbf{d}$ may be multiplied by any constant without affecting the results of the classification and it usually simplifies the application of the rule to transform $\mathbf{d}$ to make one element unity.

Extensions to more than two populations may be made. To illustrate the method for the case of three populations suppose we have samples of n_1 observations from P_1, n_2 observations from P_2, and n_3 observations from P_3. The mean vectors $\bar{\mathbf{x}}_1, \bar{\mathbf{x}}_2$, and $\bar{\mathbf{x}}_3$ may be estimated. If $\mathbf{X}_1, \mathbf{X}_2$, and $\mathbf{X}_3$ denote matrices of deviations from the sample means the assumed common covariance matrix $\mathbf{\Sigma}$ may be estimated as

$$\mathbf{S} = \frac{1}{(n_1 + n_2 + n_3 - 3)}[\mathbf{X}_1'\mathbf{X}_1 + \mathbf{X}_2'\mathbf{X}_2 + \mathbf{X}_3'\mathbf{X}_3]$$

For a new observation $\mathbf{x}$ one then computes

$$u_{12}(\mathbf{x}) = [\mathbf{x} - \tfrac{1}{2}(\bar{\mathbf{x}}_1 + \bar{\mathbf{x}}_2)]'\mathbf{S}^{-1}(\bar{\mathbf{x}}_1 - \bar{\mathbf{x}}_2)$$

$$u_{13}(\mathbf{x}) = [\mathbf{x} - \tfrac{1}{2}(\bar{\mathbf{x}}_1 + \bar{\mathbf{x}}_3)]'\mathbf{S}^{-1}(\bar{\mathbf{x}}_1 - \bar{\mathbf{x}}_3)$$

$$u_{23}(\mathbf{x}) = [\mathbf{x} - \tfrac{1}{2}(\bar{\mathbf{x}}_2 + \bar{\mathbf{x}}_3)]'\mathbf{S}^{-1}(\bar{\mathbf{x}}_2 - \bar{\mathbf{x}}_3)$$

The other three discriminant functions are

$$u_{21}(\mathbf{x}) = -u_{12}(\mathbf{x}), \qquad u_{31}(\mathbf{x}) = -u_{13}(\mathbf{x}) \quad \text{and} \quad u_{32}(\mathbf{x}) = -u_{23}(\mathbf{x})$$

If all costs and *a priori* probabilities are equal the approximate cost minimizing set of regions are given by[1]

$$R_1 = u_{12}(\mathbf{x}) \geq 0, \qquad u_{13}(\mathbf{x}) \geq 0$$

$$R_2 = u_{21}(\mathbf{x}) \geq 0, \qquad u_{23}(\mathbf{x}) \geq 0$$

$$R_3 = u_{31}(\mathbf{x}) \geq 0, \qquad u_{32}(\mathbf{x}) \geq 0$$

PROBLEMS

11-1. If λ_1 is the largest latent root of $\mathbf{M}$, a_1 is the corresponding vector, and if $\mathbf{M}_2 = \mathbf{M} - \lambda_1 \mathbf{a}_1 \mathbf{a}_1'$, show that λ_2 (the second largest root of $\mathbf{M}$) is the largest root of $\mathbf{M}_2$. Can you find the matrix $\mathbf{M}_3$ such that λ_3 (the third largest root of $\mathbf{M}$) is its largest root and so forth?

11-2. Determine whether the correlations between X variables and principal components, given in (11-11), are affected by the standardization of the X variables.

11-3. Derive (11-35) from (11-34).

11-4. Prove the statement following Eq. (11-40).

11-5. Prove Eqs. (11-43).

[1] See T. W. Anderson, *op. cit.*, for derivation and for procedures under other possible assumptions.

12
Simultaneous-equation Methods: Identification

12-1 SIMULTANEOUS-EQUATION SYSTEMS

So far our interest has centered upon estimation and prediction problems for a single equation. Now we must extend the analysis in two respects. First, our interest may still center upon a single equation, but we now take explicit account of the system of relations in which our equation is embedded and ask to what extent the simultaneous nature of economic relations invalidates the single-equation procedures described in earlier chapters. Second, we must recognize that in many instances the problem may be to estimate all the parameters in a model and to make predictions from the complete model. Should we then apply our previous single-equation techniques to each relation in the model seriatim? Are there alternative techniques whether for single equations or complete systems? These are the questions to which we now turn, but to obtain a simple introduction to the major topics, let us postulate a very simple two-equation model.

Consider an income-determination model consisting of a consumption function and an income identity, namely,

$$C_t = \alpha + \beta Y_t + u_t \tag{12-1}$$

$$Y_t = C_t + Z_t \tag{12-2}$$

where

C = consumption expenditure
Y = income
Z = nonconsumption expenditure
u = a stochastic disturbance term
t = time period

In this two-equation model Z is assumed to be a set of numbers determined outside the model. For example, Z may be determined by public authorities in a manner independently of C and Y. We then classify C and Y as *endogenous* variables, that is, variables whose values are determined by the simultaneous interaction of the relations in the model, and Z as an *exogenous* variable, that is, one whose value is determined outside the model.

Alternatively, if we think that nonconsumption expenditure Z is influenced by, say, recent changes in the level of income and by the rate of interest r, we may extend the model to include a third relation,

$$Z_t = \gamma(Y_{t-1} - Y_{t-2}) + \delta r_t + v_t$$

If r_t is regarded as an exogenous variable, we now have a model with three relations in the three endogenous variables C, Y, and Z. In general, one must specify as many relations in a model as one has endogenous variables. The classification into endogenous and exogenous is a relative one, depending upon the nature and extent of the system being studied and the purpose for which the model is being built.

To simplify the statistical exposition, we regard Z as exogenous and return to the two-equation system (12-1) and (12-2). Let us specify the following properties of the disturbance term u.

$$E(u_t) = 0 \qquad \text{for all } t \tag{12-3a}$$

$$E(u_t u_{t+s}) = \begin{cases} 0 & \text{for } s \neq 0 \text{ and for all } t \\ \sigma^2 & \text{for } s = 0 \text{ and for all } t \end{cases} \tag{12-3b}$$

Z and u are independent, which will be satisfied if either Z is a set of fixed numbers or if Z is a random variable distributed independently of u (12-3c)

If our problem is to obtain "good" estimates of the parameters of the consumption function (12-1), we may consider first of all applying least squares to C and Y in (12-1). Assumptions (12-3a) and (12-3b) have removed the problems of heteroscedasticity and autocorrelation. For the valid application of simple least squares there remains only the question of the independence of u and Y. Substituting (12-1) in (12-2) gives

$$Y_t = \alpha + \beta Y_t + Z_t + u_t$$

that is,

$$Y_t = \frac{\alpha}{1-\beta} + \frac{1}{1-\beta} Z_t + \frac{u_t}{1-\beta}$$

so that Y_t is seen in general to be influenced by u_t.

$$E(Y_t) = \frac{\alpha}{1-\beta} + \frac{1}{1-\beta} Z_t$$

and

$$E\{u_t[Y_t - E(Y_t)]\} = \frac{1}{1-\beta} E(u_t^2) \neq 0$$

The disturbance term and the explanatory variable in the consumption equation are thus correlated, and as in the error-in-variables case in Chap. 9, the direct application of least squares to (12-1) will not yield unbiased estimates of α and β. This is a bias for a finite sample size, but direct-least-squares estimators are also inconsistent; that is, a bias persists even for infinitely large samples.

Defining second-order moments

$$m_{CY} = \frac{1}{n} \sum_{t=1}^{n} (C_t - \bar{C})(Y_t - \bar{Y}), \text{ etc.}$$

the least-squares estimators of α and β in (12-1) were seen in Chap. 2 to be

$$\hat{\beta} = \frac{m_{CY}}{m_{YY}} \quad \text{and} \quad \hat{\alpha} = \frac{m_{YY}\bar{C} - m_{CY}\bar{Y}}{m_{YY}}$$

Solving the pair of equations (12-1) and (12-2) for the endogenous variables gives

$$C_t = \frac{\beta}{1-\beta} Z_t + \frac{\alpha}{1-\beta} + \frac{u_t}{1-\beta} \tag{12-4}$$

$$Y_t = \frac{1}{1-\beta} Z_t + \frac{\alpha}{1-\beta} + \frac{u_t}{1-\beta} \tag{12-5}$$

Averaging these equations over the sample observations then yields the following deviations:

$$C_t - \bar{C} = \frac{\beta}{1-\beta}(Z_t - \bar{Z}) + \frac{1}{1-\beta}(u_t - \bar{u})$$

$$Y_t - \bar{Y} = \frac{1}{1-\beta}(Z_t - \bar{Z}) + \frac{1}{1-\beta}(u_t - \bar{u})$$

so that

$$m_{CY} = \frac{\beta}{(1-\beta)^2}m_{ZZ} + \frac{1+\beta}{(1-\beta)^2}m_{Zu} + \frac{1}{(1-\beta)^2}m_{uu}$$

$$m_{YY} = \frac{1}{(1-\beta)^2}m_{ZZ} + \frac{2}{(1-\beta)^2}m_{Zu} + \frac{1}{(1-\beta)^2}m_{uu}$$

which gives

$$\hat{\beta} = \frac{\beta m_{ZZ} + (1+\beta)m_{Zu} + m_{uu}}{m_{ZZ} + 2m_{Zu} + m_{uu}}$$

By assumption as $n \to \infty$, $m_{Zu} \to 0$, $m_{uu} \to \sigma^2$, and we can let m_{ZZ} tend to some constant $\bar{m}_{ZZ}$. Thus

$$\begin{aligned}\text{plim } \hat{\beta} &= \frac{\beta \bar{m}_{ZZ} + \sigma^2}{\bar{m}_{ZZ} + \sigma^2} \\ &= \beta + \frac{(1-\beta)\sigma^2/\bar{m}_{ZZ}}{1 + \sigma^2/\bar{m}_{ZZ}}\end{aligned}$$

So long as $\beta < 1$, the second term on the right-hand side of this expression is positive. Thus

$$\text{plim } \hat{\beta} > \beta \qquad \beta < 1$$

that is, the least-squares estimate of the slope is biased *upward*, and this bias cannot be eliminated by increasing the sample size.

Since the trouble is due to correlation between u and Y in (12-1), it is natural to look for alternative estimation methods which avoid this difficulty. One such method is based on the relations (12-4) and (12-5). These two equations are an alternative way of expressing the model embodied in (12-1) and (12-2), and are known as the *reduced form* of the model. The basic characteristic of the reduced form is that the original system has been solved to express the current values of the endogenous variables as functions of all the other variables in the system, so that each equation of the reduced form contains only one current endogenous variable.

By the assumptions made in (12-3), least squares may be applied directly to estimate the coefficients of the reduced-form equations (12-4) and (12-5). Thus

$$\frac{m_{CZ}}{m_{ZZ}} = \text{best linear unbiased estimator of} \frac{\beta}{1-\beta} \tag{12-6}$$

$$\frac{m_{YZ}}{m_{ZZ}} = \text{best linear unbiased estimator of} \frac{1}{1-\beta} \tag{12-7}$$

$$\frac{m_{ZZ}\bar{C} - m_{CZ}\bar{Z}}{m_{ZZ}} = \text{best linear unbiased estimator of} \frac{\alpha}{1-\beta} \tag{12-8}$$

$$\frac{m_{ZZ}\bar{Y} - m_{YZ}\bar{Z}}{m_{ZZ}} = \text{best linear unbiased estimator of} \frac{\alpha}{1-\beta} \tag{12-9}$$

Either (12-6) or (12-7) will yield an estimator of β, (β^*), and, given that, (12-8) or (12-9) will yield an estimator of α, (α^*). From (12-6)

$$\beta^* = \frac{m_{CZ}}{m_{ZZ} + m_{CZ}}$$

But since

$$Y = C + Z$$

$$y = c + z$$

where the lowercase letters indicate deviations from means, and so

$$m_{YZ} = m_{CZ} + m_{ZZ}$$

Thus

$$\beta^* = \frac{m_{CZ}}{m_{YZ}} \tag{12-10}$$

Likewise, from (12-7),

$$\beta^* = \frac{m_{YZ} - m_{ZZ}}{m_{YZ}} = \frac{m_{CZ}}{m_{YZ}}$$

so that the two equations yield identical estimators of β. Likewise, (12-8) and (12-9) yield estimators of α, namely,

$$\alpha^* = \frac{m_{ZZ}\bar{C} - m_{CZ}\bar{Z}}{m_{YZ}} \tag{12-11}$$

The estimators (12-10) and (12-11), though formed from unbiased estimators of the reduced-form parameters, will not themselves be unbiased estimators of the *structural* parameters α and β.[1] They will, however, be consistent estimators. For example, it can easily be shown from (12-4) and (12-5) that β^*, as defined in (12-10), gives

$$\beta^* = \frac{m_{CZ}}{m_{YZ}} = \frac{\beta m_{ZZ} + m_{Zu}}{m_{ZZ} + m_{Zu}} \tag{12-12}$$

Since $m_{Zu} \to 0$ as $n \to \infty$,

$$\text{plim } \beta^* = \beta \tag{12-13}$$

To establish the bias for a finite sample size we should have to evaluate

$$E(\beta^*) = E\left(\frac{\beta + m_{Zu}/m_{ZZ}}{1 + m_{Zu}/m_{ZZ}}\right)$$

Let us take Z as a set of constants so that m_{ZZ} is constant. Because of the assumptions about u, $E(m_{Zu}) = 0$, for any given sample size, but this result is not sufficient to make β^* an unbiased estimator. For example, let us assume that the u values are such as to produce the values of m_{Zu}/m_{ZZ}, with the associated probabilities shown in Table 12-1. These satisfy the condition $E(m_{Zu}) = 0$. Assuming the true value of β to be 0.5 and calculating the estimates β^* from (12-12), we see that $E(\beta^*)$ is 0.4870, which displays a downward bias.

Table 12-1

$\frac{m_{Zu}}{m_{ZZ}}$	*Probability*	β^*
−0.2	0.25	3/8 = 0.3750
−0.1	0.25	4/9 = 0.4444
0.1	0.25	6/11 = 0.5454
0.2	0.25	7/12 = 0.5833
		$E(\beta^*) = 0.4870$

The method employed in the above approach is that of *indirect least squares*; that is simple least squares is applied to find estimates of the parameters of the reduced form, and from these, in turn, estimates of the structural parameters are obtained. As we shall see below, this method can be applied only in certain special circumstances.

[1] Structural parameters refer to the parameters of the original model (or system) as exemplified by (12-1) and (12-2).

Two-stage least squares The fundamental difficulty in this model, as we have seen, is the correlation between the disturbance term u and the explanatory variable Y in the consumption relation (12-1). Indirect least squares provides one method of estimation which is sometimes feasible. Two-stage least squares provides a method of more general applicability. A fuller description of the approach will be given in Chap. 13. The objective here is to provide a simple introduction to the basic idea. This idea is to "purge" the explanatory variable Y of the stochastic component associated with the disturbance term u. This may be attempted by taking the least-squares regression of Y on the exogenous variable in the system, namely, Z, and then replacing Y in the original relation by its estimated value in terms of Z and applying least-squares to this reformulated relation. The first least-squares step is thus to compute

$$Y = \hat{\pi}_1 + \hat{\pi}_2 Z + e \tag{12-14}$$

where

$$\hat{\pi}_2 = \frac{m_{YZ}}{m_{ZZ}} \tag{12-15}$$

and

$$\hat{\pi}_1 = \bar{Y} - \hat{\pi}_2 \bar{Z}$$

The estimated Y values are given by

$$\hat{Y} = \hat{\pi}_1 + \hat{\pi}_2 Z \tag{12-16}$$

In the second step we now substitute these $\hat{Y}$ values in (12-1) to give

$$C = \alpha + \beta(\hat{Y}) + (u + \beta e) \tag{12-17}$$

In this reformulation of (12-1), $\hat{Y}$ is an exact function of Z, which is uncorrelated with u; it is also a property of the least-squares approach that in (12-14) e is uncorrelated with Z; thus $\hat{Y}$ is uncorrelated with the composite disturbance in (12-17). The second step is now completed by applying least squares directly to (12-17) to obtain estimates of α and β. Thus, for example,

$$\hat{\beta} = \frac{m_{C\hat{Y}}}{m_{\hat{Y}\hat{Y}}}$$

From (12-14) $\hat{y} = \hat{\pi}_2 z$, where the lowercase letters, as usual, indicate deviations from arithmetic means. Hence

$$m_{C\hat{Y}} = \hat{\pi}_2 m_{CZ}$$

and

$$m_{\hat{Y}\hat{Y}} = \hat{\pi}_2^2 m_{ZZ}$$

therefore

$$\hat{\beta} = \frac{m_{CZ}}{\hat{\pi}_2 m_{ZZ}}$$

$$= \frac{m_{CZ}}{m_{YZ}} \quad \text{using (12-15)}$$

which is seen to be identical with the indirect-least-squares estimate in (12-10). It then follows directly that the least-squares estimate of α in (12-17) is identical with the indirect-least-squares estimate in (12-11).

Least-variance ratio A third approach to the estimation of the parameters of the consumption relation (12-1) may be obtained by means of the least-variance-ratio principle. The specification of the model implies as in (12-1) that consumption is directly determined by income and that non-consumption expenditure Z does not enter the consumption relation *in addition* to income Y. Thus if we compare

$$C = \alpha + \beta Y + u \tag{12-18a}$$

$$C = \alpha + \beta Y + \gamma Z + u \tag{12-18b}$$

the force of the specification is that $\gamma = 0$. In any finite sample, however, the inclusion of Z as an explanatory variable in addition to Y will, in general, yield a nonzero coefficient for Z and a smaller residual variance for the second of the above relations compared with the first. The least-variance ratio principle asserts that the estimators of the parameters α and β should be chosen to minimize the ratio of the residual variance of (12-18a) to that of (12-18b).

Define

$$C^* = C - (\alpha^* + \beta^* Y) \tag{12-19}$$

where α^* and β^* denote least-variance-ratio estimators. Taking means over the sample observations gives

$$c^* = c - \beta^* y \tag{12-20}$$

The residual sum of squares from (12-18a) is then Σc^{*2}. Using the definition of C^*, relation (12-18*b*) may be regarded as a relation between C^* and Z. Since Z is an exogenous variable, least squares is appropriate for this relation and the residual sum of squares from (12-18b) is then

$$\Sigma(c^* - \hat{\gamma}z)^2$$

where $\hat{\gamma}$ is the least-squares estimator

$$\hat{\gamma} = \frac{\Sigma c^* z}{\Sigma z^2}$$

Hence

$$\Sigma(c^* - \hat{\gamma}z)^2 = \Sigma c^{*2} - \frac{(\Sigma c^* z)^2}{\Sigma z^2}$$

The variance ratio to be minimized is then

$$l = \frac{\Sigma c^{*2}}{\Sigma c^{*2} - (\Sigma c^* z)^2/\Sigma z^2} \tag{12-21}$$

It is clear that in this case the minimum possible value for this ratio is unity and that it will be achieved only when $\Sigma c^* z = 0$. Substitution from (12-20) gives the condition

$$\Sigma(c - \beta^* y)z = 0$$

that is,

$$\beta^* = \frac{m_{CZ}}{m_{YZ}}$$

so that in this simple example all three principles of estimation, namely, indirect least squares, two-stage least squares, and least-variance ratio, yield identical estimators. As we shall see later, this result is due to a rather special feature of this simple model, but the model has introduced some of the basic ideas needed for handling simultaneous-equation problems.

Relations (12-1) and (12-2) are the structural relations of the model, the first being a behavioristic relation embodying a hypothesis about the determination of consumption expenditures and the second being a definitional identity. The model contains two structural relations and two endogenous variables. The structural relations plus the assumptions about stochastic disturbance terms in (12-3a) to (12-3c) complete the specification of the model. A set of numerical values for the unknown parameters α, β, and σ^2 gives a specific *structure* within the model. Relations (12-4) and (12-5) constitute the reduced form of the model, showing the current values of the endogenous variables as explicit functions of all other variables in the model. The disturbances in the reduced form are seen to be linear functions of the disturbances in the original structural relations. Three estimation principles have been introduced, apart from simple least squares applied to single structural relations. For the example used here, they are seen to give identical results, but this will not in general be true. We have not yet explicitly touched on problems of *identification* apart from the brief discussion in the indirect-least-squares case of the transformation of estimates of the reduced-form coefficients into estimates of the structural parameters. A discussion of the identification problem will show that in cases of underidentification it is impossible to obtain estimates of some or all parameters, in cases of exact identification all three estimating methods give identical results, while in cases of overidentification indirect least squares is impossible but two-stage least squares and least-variance ratio will yield determinate estimates, which will not, however, be identical. We now proceed to a fuller treatment of simultaneous-equation problems by setting up a general linear model and reverting once again to matrix notation.

Let us assume a linear model containing G structural relations. The ith relation at time t may be written

$$\beta_{i1}y_{1t} + \beta_{i2}y_{2t} + \cdots + \beta_{iG}y_{Gt} + \gamma_{i1}x_{1t} + \cdots + \gamma_{iK}x_{Kt} = u_{it} \qquad t = 1, \ldots, n \tag{12-22}$$

where the y_{it} denote endogenous variables at time t and every x_{it} is either an exogenous variable or a lagged value of an endogenous variable. These latter two groups are combined to give the class of *predetermined* variables. The model may then be regarded as a theory explaining the determination of the jointly dependent variables $y_{it}(i = 1, \ldots, G; t = 1, \ldots, n)$ in terms of the predetermined variables $x_{it}(i = 1, \ldots, K; t = 1, \ldots, n)$ and the disturbances $u_{it}(i = 1, \ldots, G; t = 1, \ldots, n)$. The theory will in general specify that some of the β, γ coefficients in (12-22) are zero. If it did not, statistical estimation would be impossible since all relations in the model would look alike statistically and one could not distinguish between them. We are also using lowercase letters now to denote the actual variables, and not to indicate deviations from arithmetic means. A constant term in each relation may be allowed for by setting one of the x variables at unity.

The model may then be written in matrix form as

$$\mathbf{B}\mathbf{y}_t + \mathbf{\Gamma}\mathbf{x}_t = \mathbf{u}_t \tag{12-23}$$

where $\mathbf{B}$ is a $G \times G$ matrix of coefficients of current endogenous variables, $\mathbf{\Gamma}$ is a $G \times K$ matrix of coefficients of predetermined variables, and $\mathbf{y}_t$, $\mathbf{x}_t$, and $\mathbf{u}_t$ are column vectors of G, K, and G elements, respectively.

$$\mathbf{y}_t = \begin{bmatrix} y_{1t} \\ y_{2t} \\ \vdots \\ y_{Gt} \end{bmatrix} \qquad \mathbf{x}_t = \begin{bmatrix} x_{1t} \\ x_{2t} \\ \vdots \\ x_{Kt} \end{bmatrix} \qquad \mathbf{u}_t = \begin{bmatrix} u_{1t} \\ u_{2t} \\ \vdots \\ u_{Gt} \end{bmatrix}$$

If we assume that the $\mathbf{B}$ matrix is nonsingular, the reduced form of the model may be written

$$\mathbf{y}_t = \mathbf{\Pi}\mathbf{x}_t + \mathbf{v}_t \tag{12-24}$$

where $\mathbf{\Pi}$ is a $G \times K$ matrix of reduced-form coefficients and $\mathbf{v}_t$ is a column vector of G reduced-form disturbances

$$\mathbf{\Pi} = -\mathbf{B}^{-1}\mathbf{\Gamma} \qquad \mathbf{v}_t = \mathbf{B}^{-1}\mathbf{u}_t \tag{12-25}$$

Equations (12-24) and (12-25) show explicitly that each endogenous variable $y_{1t}, \ldots, y_{Gt}$ in $\mathbf{y}_t$ may, in general, be influenced by each and every disturbance $u_{1t}, \ldots, u_{Gt}$. For instance, from (12-24) we may write

$$y_{2t} = \boldsymbol{\pi}_2\mathbf{x}_t + v_{2t}$$

where $\boldsymbol{\pi}_2$ is the second row of Π and where, from (12-25)

$$v_{2t} = f_2(u_{1t}, \ldots, u_{Gt})$$

the f_2 function being determined by the elements in the second row of $\mathbf{B}^{-1}$. Thus if y_{2t} appears as an explanatory variable on the right-hand side of the first equation in the system it is almost certainly correlated with the disturbance u_{1t} of that equation: the same will hold of any other current endogenous variable. This correlation between explanatory variables and the disturbance means that OLS estimates are inconsistent. Reverting for a moment to the single-equation notation of Chap. 5 the OLS estimator for $\mathbf{y} = \mathbf{X}\boldsymbol{\beta} + \mathbf{u}$ may be expressed as

$$\begin{aligned}\hat{\boldsymbol{\beta}} &= \boldsymbol{\beta} + (\mathbf{X}'\mathbf{X})^{-1}\mathbf{X}'\mathbf{u} \\ &= \boldsymbol{\beta} + \left(\frac{1}{n}\mathbf{X}'\mathbf{X}\right)^{-1}\left(\frac{1}{n}\mathbf{X}'\mathbf{u}\right)\end{aligned}$$

Thus

$$\operatorname{plim}(\hat{\boldsymbol{\beta}}) = \boldsymbol{\beta} + \operatorname{plim}\left(\frac{1}{n}\mathbf{X}'\mathbf{X}\right)^{-1} \cdot \operatorname{plim}\left(\frac{1}{n}\mathbf{X}'\mathbf{u}\right)$$

Non-zero correlations between the disturbance and explanatory variables mean that

$$\operatorname{plim}\left(\frac{1}{n}\mathbf{X}'\mathbf{u}\right) \neq \mathbf{0}$$

We may assume that

$$\operatorname{plim}\left(\frac{1}{n}\mathbf{X}'\mathbf{X}\right)^{-1} = \mathbf{\Sigma}_{xx}^{-1}$$

where $\mathbf{\Sigma}_{xx}$ is the matrix of probability limits of the second-order moments about zero of the X variables. Thus

$$\operatorname{plim}(\hat{\boldsymbol{\beta}}) \neq \boldsymbol{\beta}$$

and the inconsistency of OLS in this case is established. Our earlier example of the income determination model is an illustration of this general result. Before turning to a detailed discussion of estimators for simultaneous-equation systems we must tackle the prior problem of identification.

12-2 THE IDENTIFICATION PROBLEM

The first step in an econometric investigation is the specification of what is hoped is a realistic model for the system under study. We have seen that such models, if linear, may be expressed in the general form

$$\mathbf{B}\mathbf{y}_t + \mathbf{\Gamma}\mathbf{x}_t = \mathbf{u}_t \quad t = 1, \ldots, n$$

The specification will rely heavily on received economic theory and on any special knowledge or insight that the investigator may have of the system. This *a priori* knowledge will determine the nature of the **B** and **Γ** matrices: for example, the knowledge (or assumption) that certain variables do not play any direct role in a specific equation will imply that certain elements in the rows of **B** and **Γ** corresponding to that equation will be zero. One may also have *a priori* knowledge which places restrictions on combinations of elements in the **B** and **Γ** matrices, say, that the sum of certain elasticities is zero. In addition one has *stochastic* assumptions about the disturbances. The classification of the variables in the model implies that all exogenous variables in $\mathbf{x}_t$ will be uncorrelated in the limit with the elements of $\mathbf{u}_t$. The additional assumption is usually made that any lagged endogenous variables in $\mathbf{x}_t$ are also uncorrelated in the limit with the elements of $\mathbf{u}_t$. This implies zero autocorrelation for the disturbances, for previous disturbances certainly influence previous values of endogenous variables and if autocorrelation exists then previous disturbances also influence current disturbances and so current disturbances and some predetermined variables will be correlated. *A priori* knowledge thus results in a specific configuration for **B** and **Γ** and a specific set of assumptions about the distribution of the disturbances.

When the elements of **B** and **Γ** and the parameters of the probability distribution of the u's take on specific numerical values, then we have a *structure* within the model. If the specification of the model is correct the presumption is that some specific structure has generated the observations under study: and the major objective of econometric work is to estimate the values of these structural parameters. Given the stochastic nature of the u's a natural approach is to write down the likelihood function for the sample observations and to derive estimates of the structural parameters by maximizing the likelihood function. From (12-23) we can write

$$p(\mathbf{y}_t|\mathbf{x}_t) = p(\mathbf{u}_t|\mathbf{x}_t)\left|\frac{\partial \mathbf{u}_t}{\partial \mathbf{y}_t}\right|$$

and since $\mathbf{u}_t$ is independent of $\mathbf{x}_t$

$$p(\mathbf{y}_t|\mathbf{x}_t) = p(\mathbf{u}_t)\left|\frac{\partial \mathbf{u}_t}{\partial \mathbf{y}_t}\right| \tag{12-26}$$

where $|\partial \mathbf{u}_t/\partial \mathbf{y}_t|$ indicates the absolute value of the determinant formed from the matrix of partial derivatives[1]

$$\begin{bmatrix} \frac{\partial u_{1t}}{\partial y_{1t}} & \frac{\partial u_{1t}}{\partial y_{2t}} & \cdots & \frac{\partial u_{1t}}{\partial y_{Gt}} \\ \frac{\partial u_{2t}}{\partial y_{1t}} & \frac{\partial u_{2t}}{\partial y_{2t}} & \cdots & \frac{\partial u_{2t}}{\partial y_{Gt}} \\ \vdots & \vdots & & \vdots \\ \frac{\partial u_{Gt}}{\partial y_{1t}} & \frac{\partial u_{Gt}}{\partial y_{2t}} & \cdots & \frac{\partial u_{Gt}}{\partial y_{Gt}} \end{bmatrix} \tag{12-27}$$

It can be seen from inspection of relations such as (12-22) that the matrix of partial derivatives defined by (12-27) is merely the coefficient matrix **B**. Hence (12-26) may be written

$$p(\mathbf{y}_t|\mathbf{x}_t) = |\det \mathbf{B}|p(\mathbf{u}_t) \tag{12-28}$$

where we use det **B** to indicate the determinant of **B** as we need the || symbol to indicate the absolute value of the determinant.

Assuming serial independence for the disturbances

$$p(\mathbf{u}_t\mathbf{u}_{t+s}) = p(\mathbf{u}_t)\ p(\mathbf{u}_{t+s}) \text{ for all } t \text{ and for } s = \pm 1, \pm 2, \ldots$$

the likelihood of the sample values of the endogenous variables conditional on the values of the exogenous variables is given by[2]

$$L = |\det \mathbf{B}|^n p(\mathbf{u}_1)\, p(\mathbf{u}_2) \cdots p(\mathbf{u}_n) \tag{12-29}$$

Since $\mathbf{u}_t = \mathbf{B}\mathbf{y}_t + \mathbf{\Gamma}\mathbf{x}_t$, L is a function of the elements of **B** and **Γ** and one might try to maximize L with respect to those elements.

Suppose, however, that we multiply through the system (12-23) by a $G \times G$ nonsingular matrix **F**. This would involve replacing each equation of the original structure by a linear combination of the equations in that structure. The new structure may be written

$$(\mathbf{FB})\mathbf{y}_t + (\mathbf{F\Gamma})\mathbf{x}_t = \mathbf{w}_t \tag{12-30}$$

where

$$\mathbf{w}_t = \mathbf{F}\mathbf{u}_t$$

[1] See appendix (i) to this chapter on page 374.
[2] See appendix (ii) to this chapter on page 375.

so that

$$p(\mathbf{w}_t) = p(\mathbf{u}_t)\left|\frac{\partial \mathbf{u}_t}{\partial \mathbf{w}_t}\right|$$

$$= |\det \mathbf{F}^{-1}|p(\mathbf{u}_t) \tag{12-31}$$

Hence the conditional likelihood for the endogenous variables determined from the new structure is

$$L = |\det \mathbf{FB}|^n p(\mathbf{w}_1)p(\mathbf{w}_2)\cdots p(\mathbf{w}_n)$$

$$= |\det \mathbf{F}|^n|\det \mathbf{B}|^n|\det \mathbf{F}^{-1}|^n p(\mathbf{u}_1)p(\mathbf{u}_2)\cdots p(\mathbf{u}_n)$$

$$= |\det \mathbf{B}|^n p(\mathbf{u}_1)p(\mathbf{u}_2)\cdots p(\mathbf{u}_n) \tag{12-32}$$

which is identical with the likelihood (12-29) determined from the original structure, and we say that the two structures (12-23) and (12-30) are *observationally equivalent.*

A special case of (12-30) occurs when we set

$$\mathbf{F} = \mathbf{B}^{-1}$$

so that the transformed structure becomes

$$\mathbf{y}_t + \mathbf{B}^{-1}\mathbf{\Gamma}\mathbf{x}_t = \mathbf{B}^{-1}\mathbf{u}_t$$

which is the reduced form of the original structure, already defined in (12-24) and (12-25). Now if, in general, we solve the structure (12-30) for its reduced form, we obtain

$$(\mathbf{FB})^{-1}(\mathbf{FB})\mathbf{y}_t + (\mathbf{FB})^{-1}\mathbf{F\Gamma}\mathbf{x}_t = (\mathbf{FB})^{-1}\mathbf{F}\mathbf{u}_t$$

that is,

$$\mathbf{y}_t + \mathbf{B}^{-1}\mathbf{\Gamma}\mathbf{x}_t = \mathbf{B}^{-1}\mathbf{u}_t$$

which is the reduced form of the original structure (12-23). Thus, if we postulate a set of structural relations $\mathbf{By}_t + \mathbf{\Gamma x}_t = \mathbf{u}_t$ with reduced form $\mathbf{y}_t + \mathbf{B}^{-1}\mathbf{\Gamma x}_t = \mathbf{B}^{-1}\mathbf{u}_t$, then all structures obtained by premultiplying the original structure by an arbitrary nonsingular matrix of order G will have this same reduced form, and, moreover, all these structures and the reduced forms will be observationally equivalent, in the sense of yielding an identical likelihood function for the endogenous variables.

If there were no *a priori* restrictions on the $\mathbf{B}$ and $\mathbf{\Gamma}$ matrices the situation would indeed be hopeless. All equations of the model would look alike statistically in that each is a linear combination of all G endogenous and all K predetermined variables: an infinite set of structures could have generated any set of sample observations and no equation in the model would be identifiable. *A priori* restrictions of $\mathbf{B}$ and $\mathbf{\Gamma}$, however, imply restrictions on the elements of $\mathbf{F}$, for the coefficient matrices $\mathbf{FB}$ and $\mathbf{F\Gamma}$ of the transformed structure must obey the same restrictions if the transformed structure is to belong to the model that has been specified. As we shall see the crucial question is whether these restrictions on $\mathbf{F}$ suffice to identify one or more equations in the model.

If the likelihood function is written in terms of the reduced form we have

$$L = p(\mathbf{v}_1)p(\mathbf{v}_2)\cdots p(\mathbf{v}_n)$$

Since $\mathbf{v}_t = \mathbf{y}_t - \mathbf{\Pi x}_t$, the parameters of the likelihood function are simply the elements of the matrix of reduced form coefficients, $\mathbf{\Pi}$, and the elements of the variance–covariance matrix of reduced form disturbances. These may be estimated by maximum-likelihood methods but there still remains the problem of whether there is a unique set of structural coefficients corresponding to the reduced form coefficients or whether there exist more than one set of structural coefficients compatible with the reduced form coefficients. This point may be seen in a somewhat different and illuminating fashion.

Transpose (12-23) to give

$$\mathbf{y}_t'\mathbf{B}' + \mathbf{x}_t'\mathbf{\Gamma}' = \mathbf{u}_t'$$

Now define

$$\mathbf{Y} = \begin{bmatrix} \mathbf{y}_1' \\ \mathbf{y}_2' \\ \vdots \\ \mathbf{y}_n' \end{bmatrix} \qquad \mathbf{X} = \begin{bmatrix} \mathbf{x}_1' \\ \mathbf{x}_2' \\ \vdots \\ \mathbf{x}_n' \end{bmatrix} \qquad \mathbf{U} = \begin{bmatrix} \mathbf{u}_1' \\ \mathbf{u}_2' \\ \vdots \\ \mathbf{u}_n' \end{bmatrix}$$

We can write all equations at all n sample periods as

$$\mathbf{YB}' + \mathbf{X\Gamma}' = \mathbf{U} \tag{12-33}$$

The lack of correlation in the limit, between predetermined variables and disturbances is expressed as

$$\text{plim}\left(\frac{1}{n}\mathbf{X}'\mathbf{U}\right) = \mathbf{0} \tag{12-34}$$

that is,

$$\text{plim}\left(\frac{1}{n}\sum_{t=1}^{n} X_{it}u_{jt}\right) = 0 \text{ for all } i = 1, \ldots, K \text{ and } j = 1, \ldots, G$$

This is true by assumption for all exogenous variables and, as we have already seen, will be true for lagged endogenous variables if the disturbances are serially uncorrelated. Premultiplying (12-33) by $(1/n)(\mathbf{X}')$, taking probability limits and using (12-34) gives

$$\text{plim}\left(\frac{1}{n}\mathbf{X}'\mathbf{Y}\right)\mathbf{B}' + \text{plim}\left(\frac{1}{n}\mathbf{X}'\mathbf{X}\right)\mathbf{\Gamma}' = \mathbf{0}$$

Pre-multiply this by plim $[(1/n)(\mathbf{X}'\mathbf{X})]^{-1}$ and post-multiply by $(\mathbf{B}')^{-1}$. Thus

$$\text{plim}\left(\frac{1}{n}\mathbf{X}'\mathbf{X}\right)^{-1} \text{plim}\left(\frac{1}{n}\mathbf{X}'\mathbf{Y}\right) + \text{plim}\left(\frac{1}{n}\mathbf{X}'\mathbf{X}\right)^{-1}$$
$$\times \text{plim}\left(\frac{1}{n}\mathbf{X}'\mathbf{X}\right)\mathbf{\Gamma}'(\mathbf{B}')^{-1} = \mathbf{0}$$

or

$$\begin{aligned} \text{plim}\,(\mathbf{X}'\mathbf{X})^{-1}\mathbf{X}'\mathbf{Y} &= -\mathbf{\Gamma}'(\mathbf{B}')^{-1} \\ &= -\mathbf{\Gamma}'(\mathbf{B}^{-1})' \\ &= \mathbf{\Pi}' \end{aligned} \tag{12-35}$$

If we apply OLS to each equation of the reduced form in turn and collect the results we obtain the matrix of estimated coefficients $(\mathbf{X}'\mathbf{X})^{-1}\mathbf{X}'\mathbf{Y}$, thus (12-35) shows that the reduced form parameters are identifiable and can be consistently estimated by OLS.

The identification problem thus relates to structural parameters and not to reduced form parameters. It may be stated in two alternative but equivalent fashions.

(a) Assuming the elements of $\mathbf{\Pi}$ to be known can one then obtain some or all of the elements of $\mathbf{B}$ and $\mathbf{\Gamma}$ uniquely?

(b) If one considers the transformation matrix $\mathbf{F}$ used to obtain the transformed structure in (12-30) above, do the *a priori* restrictions on $\mathbf{B}$ and $\mathbf{\Gamma}$ imply sufficient restrictions on the elements of $\mathbf{F}$ to make some or all of the coefficients in the original and transformed structures identical (and thus identifiable)?

12-3 RESTRICTIONS ON STRUCTURAL PARAMETERS

We shall outline both approaches to the identification problem and then illustrate them with a number of examples.[1] The connection between structural and reduced form coefficients is

$$\mathbf{\Pi} = -\mathbf{B}^{-1}\mathbf{\Gamma}$$

or

$$\mathbf{B}\mathbf{\Pi} + \mathbf{\Gamma} = \mathbf{0}$$

[1] The most comprehensive treatment of identification problems is given in F. M. Fisher, *The Identification Problem*, McGraw-Hill, New York, 1966, which has greatly influenced the form of this section. To facilitate cross reference to his book I have used Fisher's notation as far as possible.

which may be rewritten as

$$\mathbf{AW} = \mathbf{0} \tag{12-36}$$

where

$$\mathbf{A} = [\mathbf{B} \quad \mathbf{\Gamma}] \quad \text{and} \quad \mathbf{W} = \begin{bmatrix} \mathbf{\Pi} \\ \mathbf{I}_K \end{bmatrix} \tag{12-37}$$

$\mathbf{A}$ is the $G \times (G + K)$ matrix of all structural coefficients in the model and $\mathbf{W}$ is a matrix of order $(G + K) \times K$, which has rank K. The first equation in (12-36) may be written

$$\boldsymbol{\alpha}_1 \mathbf{W} = \mathbf{0} \tag{12-38}$$

where $\boldsymbol{\alpha}_1$ is the first row of $\mathbf{A}$. The elements of $\mathbf{W}$ may be assumed known since the elements of $\mathbf{\Pi}$ can always be consistently estimated and $\mathbf{I}_K$ is the unit matrix of order K. Since the rank of $\mathbf{W}$ is K, equation (12-38) constitutes a set of K independent equations in $G + K$ unknowns (the elements of $\boldsymbol{\alpha}_1$) and so $\boldsymbol{\alpha}_1$ cannot be determined from this equation alone. To put the same point another way, the subspace of solutions to $\boldsymbol{\alpha}_1 \mathbf{W} = 0$ has dimension G and the equation is satisfied by any of the G rows of $\mathbf{A}$ or by any linear combination of them.[1] This is again the result obtained above that in the absence of *a priori* restrictions no equations in the model can be identified.

A priori restrictions may be exclusion restrictions, stating that certain elements of $\boldsymbol{\alpha}_1$ are zero because the variables to which they relate do not appear in the first equation. Or they may be linear homogeneous restrictions involving two or more of the elements of $\boldsymbol{\alpha}_1$. These restrictions may be expressed in the form

$$\boldsymbol{\alpha}_1 \boldsymbol{\varphi} = \mathbf{0} \tag{12-39}$$

where $\boldsymbol{\varphi}$ has $G + K$ rows and a column for each restriction. For instance if the restrictions are $\beta_{12} = 0$ and $\beta_{14} = \beta_{15}$

$$\boldsymbol{\varphi} = \begin{bmatrix} 0 & 0 \\ 1 & 0 \\ 0 & 0 \\ 0 & 1 \\ 0 & -1 \\ 0 & 0 \\ \vdots & \vdots \\ 0 & 0 \end{bmatrix}$$

[1] See Chap. 4, pp. 100 to 102.

Putting (12-38) and (12-39) together the elements of $\boldsymbol{\alpha}_1$ must satisfy

$$\boldsymbol{\alpha}_1[\mathbf{W} \quad \boldsymbol{\varphi}] = \mathbf{0} \tag{12-40}$$

Since $\boldsymbol{\alpha}_1$ has $G + K$ elements identification of the first equation requires that the rank of $[\mathbf{W} \quad \boldsymbol{\varphi}]$ should be $G + K - 1$, for then all solutions to (12-40) lie on a single ray through the origin. This suffices to determine the coefficients of the first equation uniquely, for in specifying the general model in (12-22) we attached a β or γ coefficient to each variable in each equation. Normalizing the first equation by setting one coefficient at unity will now give a single point on the solution ray and this determines $\boldsymbol{\alpha}_1$ uniquely.

The condition

$$\rho[\mathbf{W} \quad \boldsymbol{\varphi}] = G + K - 1 \tag{12-41}$$

is not a convenient one to apply in actually examining the identifiability of a model since it requires the construction of the $\boldsymbol{\Pi}$ matrix and we shall give below a simpler equivalent criterion in terms of the matrix $\mathbf{A}$ of structural coefficients. Condition (12-41) however, does yield simple necessary conditions for identification. Since $[\mathbf{W} \quad \boldsymbol{\varphi}]$ has $G + K$ rows and $K + R$ columns where R is the number of restrictions (columns of $\boldsymbol{\varphi}$) a necessary condition for (12-41) to hold is

$$R \geq G - 1$$

that is;

the number of a priori *restrictions should not be less than the number of equations in the model less one.*

When the restrictions are solely exclusion restrictions the necessary condition for the identifiability of a specific equation becomes:

the number of variables excluded from the equation must be at least as great as the number of equations in the model less one.

Finally, an alternative form of this last condition may be derived by letting

g = number of current endogenous variables included in the equation

k = number of predetermined variables included in the equation

The number of excluded variables is then

$$R = (G - g) + (K - k)$$

Thus the necessary condition becomes

$$G - g + K - k \geq G - 1$$

or

$$K - k \geq g - 1$$

that is;

the number of predetermined variables excluded from the equation must be at least as great as the number of endogenous variables included less one.

Turning now to the rank condition for identifiability the basic result is[1]

$$\rho[\mathbf{W} \quad \boldsymbol{\varphi}] = G + K - 1 \qquad \text{if and only if } \rho(\mathbf{A}\boldsymbol{\varphi}) = G - 1$$

From the definitions of $\mathbf{A}$ and $\mathbf{W}$ the matrix $[\mathbf{A}' \quad \mathbf{W}]$ may be written

$$[\mathbf{A}' \quad \mathbf{W}] = \begin{bmatrix} \mathbf{B}' & \boldsymbol{\Pi} \\ \boldsymbol{\Gamma}' & \mathbf{I}_K \end{bmatrix} = \begin{bmatrix} \mathbf{I}_G & \boldsymbol{\Pi} \\ -\boldsymbol{\Pi}' & \mathbf{I}_K \end{bmatrix} \begin{bmatrix} \mathbf{B}' & \mathbf{0} \\ \mathbf{0} & \mathbf{I}_K \end{bmatrix}$$

The second matrix on the extreme right is nonsingular since $\mathbf{B}$ is nonsingular. To see that the other matrix is also nonsingular let $\mathbf{x}$ be a nonnull vector partitioned into the first G and the remaining K components

$$\mathbf{x} = \begin{bmatrix} \mathbf{x}_G \\ \mathbf{x}_K \end{bmatrix}$$

and consider the quadratic form

$$[\mathbf{x}_G' \quad \mathbf{x}_K'] \begin{bmatrix} \mathbf{I} & \boldsymbol{\Pi} \\ -\boldsymbol{\Pi}' & \mathbf{I} \end{bmatrix} \begin{bmatrix} \mathbf{x}_G \\ \mathbf{x}_K \end{bmatrix}$$

$$= \mathbf{x}_G'\mathbf{I}\mathbf{x}_G + \mathbf{x}_G'\boldsymbol{\Pi}\mathbf{x}_K - \mathbf{x}_K'\boldsymbol{\Pi}'\mathbf{x}_G + \mathbf{x}_K'\mathbf{I}\mathbf{x}_K = \mathbf{x}'\mathbf{x} > 0$$

Thus $[\mathbf{A}' \quad \mathbf{W}]$ is a square nonsingular matrix of order $(G + K)$. Each column of $\boldsymbol{\varphi}$ is a vector of $(G + K)$ elements and may thus be expressed as a linear combination of the columns of $[\mathbf{A}' \quad \mathbf{W}]$. Thus

$$\boldsymbol{\varphi} = [\mathbf{A}' \quad \mathbf{W}] \begin{bmatrix} \boldsymbol{\xi} \\ \boldsymbol{\eta} \end{bmatrix} = \mathbf{A}'\boldsymbol{\xi} + \mathbf{W}\boldsymbol{\eta}$$

where $\boldsymbol{\xi}$ is $G \times R$ and $\boldsymbol{\eta}$ is $K \times R$

$$\mathbf{A}\boldsymbol{\varphi} = \mathbf{A}\mathbf{A}'\boldsymbol{\xi} \quad \text{since } \mathbf{A}\mathbf{W} = \mathbf{0}$$

Since $\mathbf{A}$ is $G \times (G + K)$ with rank G, $\mathbf{A}\mathbf{A}'$ is $G \times G$ and of rank G and is thus nonsingular. So

$$\rho(\mathbf{A}\boldsymbol{\varphi}) = \rho(\boldsymbol{\xi})$$

Now $\rho[\mathbf{W} \ \boldsymbol{\varphi}]$ is greater than $\rho(\mathbf{W})$ only by the number of linearly independent columns of $\boldsymbol{\varphi}$ which are linearly independent of the columns of $\mathbf{W}$. Thus

$$\rho[\mathbf{W} \quad \boldsymbol{\varphi}] = \rho(\mathbf{W}) + \rho(\mathbf{A}'\boldsymbol{\xi})$$

[1] I am indebted to R. W. Farebrother of the University of Manchester for this proof.

But

$$(\mathbf{A}'\boldsymbol{\xi}) = [\mathbf{A}' \quad \mathbf{W}]\begin{bmatrix}\boldsymbol{\xi} \\ \mathbf{0}\end{bmatrix}$$

Therefore

$$\rho(\mathbf{A}'\boldsymbol{\xi}) = \rho\begin{bmatrix}\boldsymbol{\xi} \\ \mathbf{0}\end{bmatrix} = \rho(\boldsymbol{\xi}) = \rho(\mathbf{A}\boldsymbol{\varphi})$$

and so

$$\rho[\mathbf{W} \quad \boldsymbol{\varphi}] = K + \rho(\mathbf{A}\boldsymbol{\varphi})$$

from which

$$\rho[\mathbf{W} \quad \boldsymbol{\varphi}] = G + K - 1 \qquad \text{if and only if } \rho(\mathbf{A}\boldsymbol{\varphi}) = G - 1$$

The alternative approach to identification through restrictions on the transformation matrix leads to a simple derivation of the rank condition on the $(\mathbf{A}\boldsymbol{\varphi})$ matrix. Let us write (12-23) as

$$\mathbf{A}\mathbf{z}_t = \mathbf{u}_t \tag{12-42}$$

where, as before,

$$\mathbf{A} = [\mathbf{B} \quad \boldsymbol{\Gamma}] \quad \text{and} \quad \mathbf{z}_t = \begin{bmatrix}\mathbf{y}_t \\ \mathbf{x}_t\end{bmatrix}$$

Applying a $G \times G$ nonsingular transformation matrix $\mathbf{F}$, the transformed structure is

$$\mathbf{F}\mathbf{A}\mathbf{z}_t = \mathbf{F}\mathbf{u}_t \tag{12-43}$$

$\mathbf{F}$ is defined as an admissible transformation matrix if the new structure (12-43) satisfies all the *a priori* conditions imposed on (12-42). As we have already seen the *a priori* restrictions on $\boldsymbol{\alpha}_1$ may be expressed as

$$\boldsymbol{\alpha}_1\boldsymbol{\varphi} = \mathbf{0}$$

which may be written alternatively as

$$\mathbf{e}_1(\mathbf{A}\boldsymbol{\varphi}) = \mathbf{0} \tag{12-44}$$

where $\mathbf{e}_1$ is a row vector with unity in the first position and zeros everywhere else. The first row of coefficients in the transformed structure is given by $\mathbf{f}_1\mathbf{A}$ where $\mathbf{f}_1$ is the first row of $\mathbf{F}$. If this is to obey the same *a priori* restrictions as $\boldsymbol{\alpha}_1$ we must then have

$$\mathbf{f}_1(\mathbf{A}\boldsymbol{\varphi}) = \mathbf{0} \tag{12-45}$$

If the first equation of the model is to be identified the coefficients of the transformed first equation must be identical with those of the original first equation up to a scalar multiplication, that is, $\mathbf{f}_1$ must be a scalar multiple of $\mathbf{e}_1$, which gives the condition that the rank of $(\mathbf{A}\boldsymbol{\varphi})$ must be $G - 1$.

Examples. To illustrate the application of the conditions for identifiability we shall work with the two-equation system

$$\beta_{11}y_{1t} + \beta_{12}y_{2t} + \gamma_{11}x_{1t} + \gamma_{12}x_{2t} = u_{1t}$$

$$\beta_{21}y_{1t} + \beta_{22}y_{2t} + \gamma_{21}x_{1t} + \gamma_{22}x_{2t} = u_{2t}$$

As it stands both equations are unidentifiable since no *a priori* restrictions have yet been imposed. Each example will postulate a different set of restrictions.

Example (i). Suppose the *a priori* restrictions are

$$\gamma_{12} = 0, \qquad \gamma_{21} = 0$$

For the first equation $\boldsymbol{\varphi}$ is then a four-element column vector

$$\boldsymbol{\varphi} = \begin{bmatrix} 0 \\ 0 \\ 0 \\ 1 \end{bmatrix}$$

and

$$\mathbf{A}\boldsymbol{\varphi} = \begin{bmatrix} \gamma_{12} \\ \gamma_{22} \end{bmatrix} = \begin{bmatrix} 0 \\ \gamma_{22} \end{bmatrix}$$

Thus $\rho(\mathbf{A}\boldsymbol{\varphi}) = 1 = G - 1$ and the first equation is identified, provided of course that $\gamma_{22} \neq 0$. If γ_{22} were zero the variable x_2 would not appear in either equation and so the fact that it was absent from the first would be of no help in identifying that equation. In a similar fashion, the restriction on the second equation gives

$$\boldsymbol{\varphi} = \begin{bmatrix} 0 \\ 0 \\ 1 \\ 0 \end{bmatrix}$$

$$\mathbf{A}\boldsymbol{\varphi} = \begin{bmatrix} \gamma_{11} \\ 0 \end{bmatrix}$$

and

$$\rho(\mathbf{A}\boldsymbol{\varphi}) = 1 = G - 1$$

Alternatively the equations

$$\boldsymbol{\alpha}_1[\mathbf{W} \quad \boldsymbol{\varphi}] = \mathbf{0}$$

in the parameters of the first equation give

$$[\beta_{11} \quad \beta_{12} \quad \gamma_{11} \quad \gamma_{12}] \begin{bmatrix} \pi_{11} & \pi_{12} & 0 \\ \pi_{21} & \pi_{22} & 0 \\ 1 & 0 & 0 \\ 0 & 1 & 1 \end{bmatrix} = [0 \quad 0 \quad 0]$$

that is

$$\beta_{11}\pi_{11} + \beta_{12}\pi_{21} + \gamma_{11} = 0$$
$$\beta_{11}\pi_{12} + \beta_{12}\pi_{22} + \gamma_{12} = 0$$
$$\gamma_{12} = 0$$

If we normalize by setting, say, $\beta_{11} = 1$, these give,

$$\beta_{12} = -\pi_{12}/\pi_{22}$$

and

$$\gamma_{11} = \frac{\pi_{12}\pi_{21} - \pi_{11}\pi_{22}}{\pi_{22}}$$

which shows explicitly how the parameters of the first equation may be derived uniquely from those of the reduced form. The parameters of the second equation may be obtained in a similar fashion.

Example (ii). $\gamma_{12} = 0, \gamma_{22} = 0.$

For the first equation

$$\boldsymbol{\varphi} = \begin{bmatrix} 0 \\ 0 \\ 0 \\ 1 \end{bmatrix}$$

and

$$\mathbf{A}\boldsymbol{\varphi} = \begin{bmatrix} 0 \\ 0 \end{bmatrix}$$

which has zero rank. Thus the first equation is not identifiable; nor is the second, for this is the case we alluded to in the previous example where x_2 appears in neither equation.

Example (iii). $\gamma_{11} = 0, \gamma_{12} = 0, \gamma_{22} = 0.$

From the previous example we see that the only effective restriction is the first one. For the first equation

$$\boldsymbol{\varphi} = \begin{bmatrix} 0 \\ 0 \\ 1 \end{bmatrix} \qquad \mathbf{A}\boldsymbol{\varphi} = \begin{bmatrix} 0 \\ \gamma_{21} \end{bmatrix}$$

and

$$\rho(\mathbf{A}\boldsymbol{\varphi}) = 1 = G - 1$$

so the first equation is identified. There are no restrictions on the second equation and no $\boldsymbol{\varphi}$ matrix, so it is not identifiable.

$$\boldsymbol{\alpha}_2[\mathbf{W} \quad \boldsymbol{\varphi}] = \mathbf{0}$$

gives

$$\beta_{21}\pi_{11} + \beta_{22}\pi_{21} + \gamma_{21} = 0$$

Setting $\beta_{22} = 1$ still leaves only one equation in the two unknowns β_{21} and γ_{21}.

Example (iv). $\gamma_{11} = 0$, $\gamma_{12} = 0$.

For the first equation

$$\boldsymbol{\varphi} = \begin{bmatrix} 0 & 0 \\ 0 & 0 \\ 1 & 0 \\ 0 & 1 \end{bmatrix} \qquad \mathbf{A}\boldsymbol{\varphi} = \begin{bmatrix} 0 & 0 \\ \gamma_{21} & \gamma_{22} \end{bmatrix}$$

so $\rho(\mathbf{A}\boldsymbol{\varphi}) = 1$ and the first equation is identified, while the second is not.

$$\boldsymbol{\alpha}_1[\mathbf{W} \quad \boldsymbol{\varphi}] = \mathbf{0}$$

gives

$$\begin{aligned} \beta_{11}\pi_{11} + \beta_{12}\pi_{21} + \gamma_{11} &= 0 \\ \beta_{11}\pi_{12} + \beta_{12}\pi_{22} + \gamma_{12} &= 0 \\ \gamma_{11} &= 0 \\ \gamma_{12} &= 0 \end{aligned}$$

which, on setting $\beta_{11} = 1$, gives

$$\beta_{12} = -\frac{\pi_{11}}{\pi_{21}} = -\frac{\pi_{12}}{\pi_{22}}$$

This does not imply a contradiction for both expressions for β_{12} will yield an identical value. The prior specifications and the normalization rule in this example give the model

$$y_{1t} + \beta_{12}y_{2t} = u_{1t}$$

$$\beta_{21}y_{1t} + y_{2t} + \gamma_{21}x_{1t} + \gamma_{22}x_{2t} = u_{2t}$$

The matrix of reduced form coefficients is

$$\mathbf{\Pi} = \begin{bmatrix} \pi_{11} & \pi_{12} \\ \pi_{21} & \pi_{22} \end{bmatrix} = \frac{1}{\Delta}\begin{bmatrix} \beta_{12}\gamma_{21} & \beta_{12}\gamma_{22} \\ -\gamma_{21} & -\gamma_{22} \end{bmatrix}$$

where $\Delta = 1 - \beta_{12}\beta_{21}$. Although $\mathbf{\Pi}$ is a 2×2 matrix, its rank is only one. This is an example of *overidentification*. Only one prior restriction is needed to identify the first equation, but we have two. The consequence is a restriction on the reduced form coefficients. Notice also that even in the overidentified case $\rho(\mathbf{A}\boldsymbol{\varphi})$ cannot exceed $G - 1$. $\mathbf{A}\boldsymbol{\varphi}$ has G rows but the first row is always zero for homogeneous restrictions so $\rho(\mathbf{A}\boldsymbol{\varphi}) \leq G - 1$ even in cases of overidentification where $\mathbf{A}\boldsymbol{\varphi}$ has G or more columns. If $\mathbf{\Pi}$ is replaced in an actual two equation problem by $\hat{\mathbf{\Pi}}$, the matrix of *estimated* reduced form coefficients, then $\rho(\hat{\mathbf{\Pi}})$ will almost certainly be two and not one, so that estimating β_{12} by $-\hat{\pi}_{11}/\hat{\pi}_{21}$ or by $-\hat{\pi}_{12}/\hat{\pi}_{22}$ would yield two different values. Indirect least-squares is thus not a suitable estimation method for overidentified equations.

Example (*v*). $\gamma_{11} = 0, \gamma_{12} = 0$

$$\beta_{21} + \gamma_{21} = 0 \qquad \gamma_{22} = 0$$

This is example (iii) with the additional specification $\beta_{21} + \gamma_{21} = 0$. In example (iii) the first equation was identifiable and the second not. For the second equation we now have

$$\boldsymbol{\varphi} = \begin{bmatrix} 1 \\ 0 \\ 1 \end{bmatrix} \qquad \mathbf{A}\boldsymbol{\varphi} = \begin{bmatrix} \beta_{11} \\ 0 \end{bmatrix}$$

so $\rho(\mathbf{A}\boldsymbol{\varphi}) = 1$ and the second equation is now identified.

In all the above examples the reader should check for himself that the necessary condition (or *order* condition as it is often called) would correctly indicate the presence or absence of identification. This need not always be the case. For example, if β_{11} in example (v) were zero the rank condition would fail even though there is one restriction on the second equation.

Sometimes restrictions indicated by economic theory occur naturally in non-homogeneous form, an illustration being the specification, say, that the elasticities in a production function sum to unity. Such restrictions, however, have no meaning *until* a normalization rule has been imposed. Thus if we have a restriction

$$\beta_{12} + \gamma_{11} = 1$$

it can be rewritten before normalization as

$$\beta_{12} + \gamma_{11} - \beta_{11} = 0$$

plus the normalization rule, $\beta_{11} = 1$, and in this form the restriction is homogeneous.

12-4 RESTRICTIONS ON VARIANCES AND COVARIANCES

So far the only explicit assumption about the disturbances has been that of serial independence, but we have made no explicit assumptions about contemporaneous correlations between disturbances in different structural equations. Let

$$\mathbf{\Sigma} = E(\mathbf{u}_t \mathbf{u}_t') \tag{12-46}$$

$\mathbf{\Sigma}$ is then a $G \times G$ matrix, the terms on the principal diagonal indicating the variances (assumed constant) of the disturbances in the G structural equations and the off-diagonal terms indicating the covariances between pairs of disturbances. If specific restrictions can be placed on some of these elements they constitute an additional source of identifying power.

Let us examine first of all restrictions on covariances. Consider the model

$$\begin{aligned} y_1 + \gamma_{11}x_1 &= u_1 \\ \beta_{21}y_1 + y_2 + \gamma_{21}x_1 &= u_2 \end{aligned}$$

As is easily seen the first equation of this model is identifiable and the second is not. We shall, however, examine the identifiability of the model again by considering admissible transformation matrices as this approach facilitates the study of restrictions on variances and covariances.

Using

$$\mathbf{F} = \begin{bmatrix} f_{11} & f_{12} \\ f_{21} & f_{22} \end{bmatrix}$$

the transformed first equation becomes

$$(f_{11} + f_{12}\beta_{21})y_1 + f_{12}y_2 + (f_{11}\gamma_{11} + f_{12}\gamma_{21})x_1 = f_{11}u_1 + f_{12}u_2$$

If the coefficients of the transformed equation are to obey the same restrictions as those of the original equation we must have

$$f_{11} + f_{12}\beta_{21} = 1$$
$$f_{12} = 0$$

giving $f_{11} = 1$ and $f_{12} = 0$. The only restriction on the second equation is the normalization condition, which is held in abeyance. Thus admissible transformation matrices are given by

$$\mathbf{F} = \begin{bmatrix} 1 & 0 \\ f_{21} & f_{22} \end{bmatrix}$$

showing that the first equation is identified and the second not.

Suppose we can now postulate

$$\mathbf{\Sigma} = \begin{bmatrix} \sigma_{11} & 0 \\ 0 & \sigma_{22} \end{bmatrix}$$

The vector of disturbances in the transformed structure is $\mathbf{Fu}_t$, and so the variance–covariance matrix for the disturbances of the transformed structure is

$$\begin{aligned} \mathbf{\Psi} &= E(\mathbf{Fu}_t\mathbf{u}_t'\mathbf{F}') \\ &= \mathbf{F\Sigma F}' \end{aligned} \tag{12-47}$$

This must obey the restriction that the covariance between the two transformed disturbances is zero, that is,

$$\mathbf{f}_1\mathbf{\Sigma f}_2' = 0$$

or

$$[1 \quad 0]\begin{bmatrix} \sigma_{11} & 0 \\ 0 & \sigma_{22} \end{bmatrix}\begin{bmatrix} f_{21} \\ f_{22} \end{bmatrix} = 0$$

that is,

$$f_{21}\sigma_{11} = 0$$

which gives

$$f_{21} = 0$$

The value of f_{22} is then settled by the normalization condition that the coefficient of y_2 in the second equation must be unity. The coefficients of the transformed structure are given by

$$\mathbf{FA} = \begin{bmatrix} 1 & 0 \\ f_{21} & f_{22} \end{bmatrix}\begin{bmatrix} 1 & 0 & \gamma_{11} \\ \beta_{21} & 1 & \gamma_{21} \end{bmatrix}$$

giving the coefficient of y_2 in the second equation as f_{22}. Thus $f_{22} = 1$ and admissible transformation matrices are now

$$\mathbf{F} = \begin{bmatrix} 1 & 0 \\ 0 & 1 \end{bmatrix}$$

so that both equations are identified.

It is illuminating to consider the model geometrically in Figure 12-1.

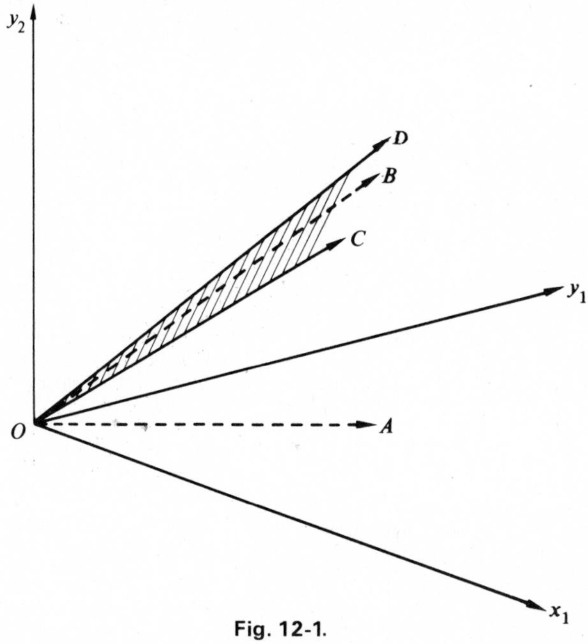

Fig. 12-1.

If there were no distrubances in the first equation, $y_1 + \gamma_{11}x_1 = 0$ would then be represented by the line OA in the Oy_1x_1 plane. If, as well, there were no disturbances in the second equation all observations would lie on the ray OB vertically above OA in three-dimensional space and it would, of course, be impossible to fit a regression plane to the three variables y_1, y_2, x_1. If we now introduce disturbances in the first equation only observations on y_1 and x_1 are scattered about the line OA in the Oy_1x_1 plane, while the y_2 observations will be vertically above these points on the shaded plane OCD which contains the ray OB. It is clear that the second equation will now be identifiable. Suppose we then allow disturbances in the second equation and assume that they are positively correlated with those in the first, that is,

$$u_{2t} = \rho u_{1t} + \varepsilon_t \qquad \rho > 0$$

When an observation on y_1 lies above (below) the line OA in the Oy_1x_1 plane there will be a tendency for the corresponding observation on y_2 to lie above (below) the plane OCD. Thus the observations will be scattered not around the true plane OCD but another plane tilted around the axis OB, the degree of the tilt depending on the value of ρ. If we merely know that ρ is nonzero we do not know the plane about which the observations are scattered and the second equation is unidentifiable. If, however, ρ is known to be zero ($\sigma_{12} = 0$) the observations will be clustered around the true plane and the second equation is identifiable.

As a further illustration consider the model

$$y_1 + \gamma_{11}x_1 = u_1$$

$$\beta_{21}y_1 + y_2 + \gamma_{21}x_1 = u_2$$

$$\beta_{31}y_1 + \beta_{32}y_2 + y_3 + \gamma_{31}x_1 = u_3$$

Without further restrictions only the first equation is identifiable. If, however, we assume

$$\mathbf{\Sigma} = \begin{bmatrix} \sigma_{11} & 0 & 0 \\ 0 & \sigma_{22} & 0 \\ 0 & 0 & \sigma_{33} \end{bmatrix}$$

the second and third equations become identifiable. Consider

$$\mathbf{FA} = \begin{bmatrix} 1 & 0 & 0 \\ f_{21} & f_{22} & f_{23} \\ f_{31} & f_{32} & f_{33} \end{bmatrix} \begin{bmatrix} 1 & 0 & 0 & \gamma_{11} \\ \beta_{21} & 1 & 0 & \gamma_{21} \\ \beta_{31} & \beta_{32} & 1 & \gamma_{31} \end{bmatrix}$$

The normalization condition on y_2 in the second equation and on y_3 in the third give

$$f_{22} + f_{23}\beta_{32} = 1$$

$$f_{33} = 1$$

and the exclusion of y_3 from the second equation gives

$$f_{23} = 0$$

which also implies

$$f_{22} = 1$$

Thus $\mathbf{F}$ is now

$$\mathbf{F} = \begin{bmatrix} 1 & 0 & 0 \\ f_{21} & 1 & 0 \\ f_{31} & f_{32} & 1 \end{bmatrix}$$

We have not yet considered the effect of the zero covariance restrictions, $\sigma_{12} = \sigma_{13} = \sigma_{23} = 0$. These must be satisfied by the transformed structure. Hence

$$\mathbf{f}_1\mathbf{\Sigma}\mathbf{f}'_2 = 0$$

$$\mathbf{f}_1\mathbf{\Sigma}\mathbf{f}'_3 = 0$$

$$\mathbf{f}_2\mathbf{\Sigma}\mathbf{f}'_3 = 0$$

The first of these gives

$$[1 \quad 0 \quad 0]\begin{bmatrix} \sigma_{11} & 0 & 0 \\ 0 & \sigma_{22} & 0 \\ 0 & 0 & \sigma_{33} \end{bmatrix}\begin{bmatrix} f_{21} \\ 1 \\ 0 \end{bmatrix} = f_{21}\sigma_{11} = 0 \text{ so that } f_{21} = 0$$

and in a similar fashion the second and third conditions give $f_{31} = 0$ and $f_{32} = 0$. Thus the only admissible transformation matrix is

$$\mathbf{F} = \begin{bmatrix} 1 & 0 & 0 \\ 0 & 1 & 0 \\ 0 & 0 & 1 \end{bmatrix}$$

and all three equations are identified.

The model above has two special features, namely a triangular **B** matrix and a diagonal **Σ** matrix. The presence of these two features defines a *recursive* system. All the equations of the recursive system are identified and, as we shall see in Chap. 13, simple estimation procedures are available for this model.

Zero covariances can aid identification and not necessarily just in recursive systems. For example, in

$$y_1 + \beta_{12}y_2 = u_1$$

$$\beta_{21}y_1 + y_2 + \gamma_{21}x_1 = u_2$$

the first equation is identified and the second is not. However, the additional specification, $\sigma_{12} = 0$, would serve to identify the second equation as the reader can easily prove for himself. There is no simple necessary and sufficient condition for the zero covariance case as there was for restrictions on the β and γ parameters, so each case must be examined from first principles.

So far we have only considered off-diagonal terms (covariances) being zero. Another possibility is that terms on the principal diagonal of **Σ** may be zero. For example, if $\sigma_{11} = 0$ the variance of the first equation is zero and this equation is exact rather than stochastic. To consider its identifiability we use two conditions. Firstly, any transformed first equation must satisfy the *a priori* restrictions on the first equation, that is,

$$\mathbf{f}_1\mathbf{A}\boldsymbol{\varphi} = \mathbf{0}$$

Secondly, the disturbance of any transformed first equation must be zero, that is,

$$\mathbf{f}_1\boldsymbol{\Sigma}\mathbf{f}_1' = 0$$

Since $\boldsymbol{\Sigma}$ is positive semidefinite this condition is satisfied if and only if

$$\mathbf{f}_1\boldsymbol{\Sigma} = \mathbf{0}$$

Putting these two conditions together gives

$$\mathbf{f}_1[\mathbf{A}\boldsymbol{\varphi} \quad \boldsymbol{\Sigma}] = \mathbf{0} \tag{12-48}$$

If the first equation is to be identified the $\mathbf{f}_1$ vectors satisfying (12-48) must be scalar multiples of one another. Thus the necessary and sufficient condition for the identifiability of the first equation under the additional restriction $\sigma_{11} = 0$ is

$$\rho[\mathbf{A}\boldsymbol{\varphi} \quad \boldsymbol{\Sigma}] = G - 1 \tag{12-49}$$

Notice that if all the other G disturbances are nonzero $\rho(\boldsymbol{\Sigma}) = G - 1$ and the rank condition in (12-49) will be satisfied even if there are no *a priori* restrictions on the β and γ coefficients. We have already noticed an example of this result in the geometrical treatment of the model

$$y_1 + \gamma_{11}x_1 = u_1$$

$$\beta_{21}y_1 + y_2 + \gamma_{21}x_1 = u_2$$

Without restrictions on $\boldsymbol{\Sigma}$ the second equation is not identified. If, however, the second equation becomes

$$\beta_{21}y_1 + y_2 + \gamma_{21}x_1 = 0$$

then

$$\boldsymbol{\Sigma} = \begin{bmatrix} \sigma_{11} & 0 \\ 0 & 0 \end{bmatrix}$$

and for the second equation

$$[\mathbf{A}\boldsymbol{\varphi} \quad \boldsymbol{\Sigma}] = \begin{bmatrix} \sigma_{11} & 0 \\ 0 & 0 \end{bmatrix}$$

with rank $1 = G - 1$, so that the second equation is identified.

A special form of non-stochastic equation which occurs frequently in econometric models is the *identity*, where the disturbance is zero and the coefficients of the variables are known (and usually plus or minus one), for instance

$$\underset{\text{National Income}}{Y} \equiv \underset{\text{Cons. Exp.}}{C} + \underset{\text{Inv. Exp.}}{I} + \underset{\text{Govt. Expenditure on Goods and Services}}{G}$$

or

$$\underset{\text{Disposable Income}}{Y_D} \equiv \underset{\text{Income}}{Y} - \underset{\text{Taxes on Income}}{T}$$

In such cases no problems of identification or estimation arise for the identity itself. In examining the identifiability of any other relation, say the ith relation, in the model we have $\sigma_{ii} \neq 0$ and so the rank condition will not involve $\mathbf{\Sigma}$. In the absence of restrictions on covariances the only source of identification is the restrictions on $\boldsymbol{\alpha}_i$ embodied in

$$\boldsymbol{\alpha}_i \boldsymbol{\varphi} = \mathbf{0}$$

with the requirement that $\rho(\mathbf{A}\boldsymbol{\varphi})$ should be $G - 1$. This rank condition may be examined using the $\mathbf{A}$ matrix that comes from writing out the model in full so that the elements in $\mathbf{A}$ corresponding to identities are simply known numbers and G is the total number of equations in the model as written. Alternatively one or more identities may be substituted in all relevant equations thus reducing by one or more the number of endogenous variables and equations in the model and the rank condition applied to the resultant system. As an illustration consider the simple supply and demand model

$$q^D = \alpha_0 + \alpha_1 p + u_1$$

$$q^S = \beta_0 + \beta_1 p + \beta_2 w + u_2$$

$$q^D \equiv q^S$$

where

q^D = quantity demanded

q^S = quantity supplied

p = price

w = an index of weather conditions

This is a model containing three endogenous variables q^D, q^S, and p, $(G = 3)$ and two exogenous variables w and z (a dummy variable) set at unity to take care of the intercept term in the first two equations. Rearranging the model in more suitable form we have

$$\begin{bmatrix} 1 & 0 & -\alpha_1 & 0 & -\alpha_0 \\ 0 & 1 & -\beta_1 & -\beta_2 & -\beta_0 \\ 1 & -1 & 0 & 0 & 0 \end{bmatrix} \begin{bmatrix} q^D \\ q^S \\ p \\ w \\ z \end{bmatrix} = \begin{bmatrix} u_1 \\ u_2 \\ 0 \end{bmatrix}$$

For the first equation

$$\mathbf{A\varphi} = \begin{bmatrix} 0 & 0 \\ 1 & -\beta_2 \\ -1 & 0 \end{bmatrix}$$

and $\rho(\mathbf{A\varphi}) = 2 = G - 1$ so that the equation is identified. Notice that when we have exclusion restrictions the $\mathbf{A\varphi}$ matrix can be written down directly by taking the columns of the **A** matrix which contain zeros in the row corresponding to the equation under study. For the second equation

$$\mathbf{A\varphi} = \begin{bmatrix} 1 \\ 0 \\ 1 \end{bmatrix}$$

which only has rank unity and so the second equation is not identified.

If we rewrite the model without the identity it becomes a two-equation model in two endogenous variables q and p

$$q = \alpha_0 + \alpha_1 p + u_1$$

$$q = \beta_0 + \beta_1 p + \beta_2 w + u_2$$

where now $G = 2$ and the first equation is again just identified because it has one restriction on its coefficients while the second equation is not identified because there are no restrictions on its coefficients.

The last three sections have dealt only with models which are linear in variables and parameters. Many realistic models, however, may be non-linear in variables and/or *a priori* restrictions. Identification theory for such models is difficult and has only been partially developed. Owing to the unsatisfactory state of the theory it will not be summarized here: interested readers should consult F. M. Fisher.[1]

[1] F. M. Fisher, *op. cit.*, Chap. 5.

EXERCISES

12-1. Examine the indentifiability of the parameters in the model

$$y_{1t} + \beta_{12}y_{2t} = u_{1t}$$
$$\beta_{21}y_{1t} + y_{2t} + \gamma_{21}x_{1t} = u_{2t}$$

when λ the regression coefficient of the u_{2t} on the u_{1t} is assumed to be (a) zero, (b) unity, (c) unknown. (Cambridge Economics Tripos, 1964)

12-2. Obtain the reduced form of the following set of structural equations:

$$y_{1t} = -2y_{2t} + 7x_{1t} + 4x_{2t} + x_{3t} - 8x_{4t} + u_{1t}$$
$$y_{2t} = 2y_{1t} + y_{3t} - x_{1t} + 7x_{3t} - 9x_{5t} + u_{2t}$$
$$y_{3t} = 2y_{1t} - 7x_{2t} + 7x_{3t} + 14x_{4t} + u_{3t}$$

Investigate the identifiability of each equation, both (a) by using only the structural equations and (b) by using the reduced form equations. (L.S.E. 1966)

12-3. $C_t = \alpha_0 + \alpha_1 Y_t + \alpha_2 Y_{t-1} + u_t$ (1)

$I_t = \beta_0 + \beta_1 Y_t + \beta_2 Y_{t-1} + v_t$ (2)

$Y_t \equiv C_t + I_t + G_t$ (3)

Discuss the identification of the above equations if G is the only exogenous variable (apart from the dummy variable for the constant term)

(a) as written
(b) if $\beta_1 + \beta_2 = 0$
(c) as in (a) but over the sample period G is constant
(d) as in (b) but over the sample period G is constant
(e) as in (d) but it is known that u is independent of v.

12-4. Discuss the restrictions, if any, which are implied for the reduced form by each of the following structural equations, assuming nothing is known about the covariance matrix of the disturbance terms.

$$y_{1t} = \gamma_{11}x_{1t} + \gamma_{12}x_{2t} + u_{1t}$$
$$y_{2t} = \beta_{21}y_{1t} + \gamma_{21}x_{2t} + \gamma_{22}x_{2t} + \gamma_{23}x_{3t} + u_{2t}$$
$$y_{3t} = \beta_{31}y_{1t} + \beta_{32}y_{2t} + u_{3t}$$

What additional restrictions, if any, are implied by

(a) $\gamma_{12} = 0$
(b) $\text{cov}(u_1, u_2) = 0$? (L.S.E. 1969)

12-5. The reduced form of a certain model can be written

$$y_{1t} = 5 + 6z_{1t} + 3z_{2t} + 2z_{3t} + v_{1t}$$
$$y_{2t} = 2 + 3z_{1t} + 4z_{2t} + z_{3t} + v_{2t}$$
$$y_{3t} = z_{1t} + z_{3t} + v_{3t}$$

Consider for each equation whether the following restrictions are

(a) inconsistent with the given coefficients or sufficient to
(b) just identify, or
(c) over identify it.

$\beta_{11} = 1, \quad \beta_{12} = 0, \quad \gamma_{11} = 0$

$\beta_{22} = 1, \quad \beta_{21} = 0, \quad \gamma_{22} = 0$

$\beta_{33} = 1, \quad \beta_{32} = 0, \quad \gamma_{31} = -2, \quad \gamma_{33} = 0$

APPENDIX (I) CHANGE OF VARIABLES IN DENSITY FUNCTIONS

This step often gives students difficulty. The basic idea may be simply illustrated for the univariate case. Suppose u is a random variable with density function $p(u)$, and suppose that a new variable y is defined by the function $y = f(u)$. The y variable must then also have a density function. The problem is to determine the density function for y in terms of the density function for u and the relation $y = f(u)$. Suppose the relation between y and u is as shown in the accompanying figure. Whenever u lies in the interval

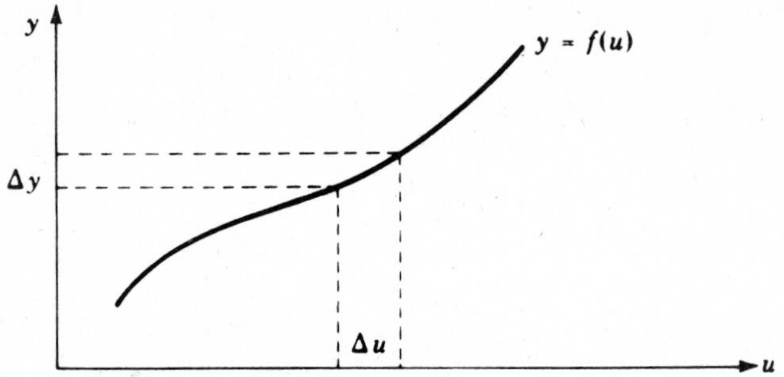

Δu, y will lie in the corresponding interval Δy. Thus

$$\Pr\{y \text{ lies in } \Delta y\} = \Pr\{u \text{ lies in } \Delta u\}$$

or

$$p(y') \cdot \Delta y = p(u') \cdot \Delta u$$

where u' and y' denote appropriate values of u and y in the intervals Δu and Δy, and $p(y)$ indicates the postulated density function for y. Taking limits of this relation as Δu tends to zero gives

$$p(y) = p(u) \cdot \frac{du}{dy} \tag{1}$$

If y were a decreasing function of u the derivative in (1) would be negative thus giving a negative value for the density function, which is impossible. Thus the *absolute* value of the derivative in (1) must be taken and the relation reformulated to read

$$p(y) = p(u)\left|\frac{du}{dy}\right| \tag{2}$$

where $|du/dy|$ indicates the absolute value of the derivative du/dy. If y were not a single-valued function of u relation (2) has to be amended to include a number of terms on the right-hand side since several values of u can now produce a given value of y, but for linear functions this complication does not arise. In the multi-variate case **u** and **y** now indicate vectors of, say, n variables each. A similar relation to (2) still holds, namely,

$$p(\mathbf{y}) = p(\mathbf{u})\left|\frac{\partial \mathbf{u}}{\partial \mathbf{y}}\right| \tag{3}$$

where $|\partial \mathbf{u}/\partial \mathbf{y}|$ indicates the absolute value of the determinant formed from the matrix of partial derivatives

$$\begin{bmatrix} \frac{\partial u_1}{\partial y_1} & \frac{\partial u_1}{\partial y_2} & \cdots & \frac{\partial u_1}{\partial y_n} \\ \frac{\partial u_2}{\partial y_1} & \frac{\partial u_2}{\partial y_2} & \cdots & \frac{\partial u_2}{\partial y_n} \\ \vdots & \vdots & & \vdots \\ \frac{\partial u_n}{\partial y_1} & \frac{\partial u_n}{\partial y_2} & \cdots & \frac{\partial u_n}{\partial y_n} \end{bmatrix}$$

This is the result used in the text.

APPENDIX (II)

Equation (12-29) follows simply when the **x** vectors contain only exogenous variables for then

$$\begin{aligned} p(\mathbf{y}_1\mathbf{y}_2\cdots\mathbf{y}_n|\mathbf{x}_1\mathbf{x}_2\cdots\mathbf{x}_n) &= |\det \mathbf{B}|^n p(\mathbf{u}_1\mathbf{u}_2\cdots\mathbf{u}_n) \\ &= |\det \mathbf{B}|^n p(\mathbf{u}_1)\cdot p(\mathbf{u}_2)\cdots p(\mathbf{u}_n) \end{aligned}$$

For the case where the **x** vectors contain both lagged endogenous variables and exogenous variables let us write the model as

$$\mathbf{B}\mathbf{y}_t + \mathbf{B}_1\mathbf{y}_{t-1} + \mathbf{\Gamma}\mathbf{z}_t = \mathbf{u}_t$$

where for simplicity we have only allowed a one-period lag in the endogenous variables, but this is sufficient to illustrate the general principle. The **z** vectors indicate strictly exogenous variables. We now have

$$\begin{aligned} p(\mathbf{y}_1\mathbf{y}_2\cdots\mathbf{y}_n|\mathbf{z}_1\mathbf{z}_2\cdots\mathbf{z}_n) &= p(\mathbf{y}_1|\mathbf{z}_1)p(\mathbf{y}_2|\mathbf{y}_1\mathbf{z}_1\mathbf{z}_2)p(\mathbf{y}_3|\mathbf{y}_1\mathbf{y}_2\mathbf{z}_1\mathbf{z}_2\mathbf{z}_3)\ldots \\ &= |\det \mathbf{B}|^n p(\mathbf{u}_1)\cdot p(\mathbf{u}_2)\cdots p(\mathbf{u}_n) \end{aligned}$$

as before.

13
Simultaneous-equation Methods: Estimation

Whether we wish to estimate an equation which is one of a set of equations constituting a complete model or whether we wish to estimate every equation in a model we are in a situation where ordinary least-squares (OLS) and the variants of ordinary least-squares that we have considered so far in the context of a single-equation model are, in general, unsatisfactory estimating techniques. If OLS is applied to an equation in a model there will usually be more than one current endogenous variable in the relation and whichever variable one selects as the "dependent" variable the remaining endogenous variable(s) will generally be correlated with the disturbance in the equation so that OLS estimates will be biased and inconsistent. Only in the case of *recursive models* will OLS provide an optimal estimating technique. These are considered in Section 13-1.

In the more general simultaneous-equation model where the special assumptions of the recursive model are not fulfilled a simple method of estimation is still available for exactly identified equations, namely the method of indirect least-squares (ILS). This consists of estimating the parameters of the reduced form by the application of OLS to each reduced form equation separately and then deriving estimates of the structural parameters from the estimated reduced form parameters, using $\mathbf{B\Pi} = -\mathbf{\Gamma}$ and replacing $\mathbf{\Pi}$ by $\hat{\mathbf{\Pi}}$. The elements of $\hat{\mathbf{\Pi}}$ will be best linear unbiased estimators but this property does not hold under transformation and the derived structural estimators are likely to be biased. Both $\hat{\mathbf{\Pi}}$, however, and the ILS estimators will be consistent. For overidentified equations ILS is infeasible and OLS is in general not to be recommended, so we have methods that have been developed specifically for this case. These are described in Sections 13-2 to 13-6.

13-1 RECURSIVE SYSTEMS

From the estimation viewpoint the simplest of all simultaneous-equation systems are recursive systems. As we have already seen in Chap. 12 these are characterized by a triangular $\mathbf{B}$ matrix and a diagonal $\mathbf{\Sigma}$ matrix. Consider again the model

$$\begin{aligned} y_{1t} + \gamma_{11}x_t &= u_{1t} \\ \beta_{21}y_{1t} + y_{2t} + \gamma_{21}x_t &= u_{2t} \\ \beta_{31}y_{1t} + \beta_{32}y_{2t} + y_{3t} + \gamma_{31}x_t &= u_{3t} \end{aligned} \tag{13-1}$$

with the additional specification

$$E(\mathbf{uu}') = \mathbf{\Sigma} = \begin{bmatrix} \sigma_{11} & 0 & 0 \\ 0 & \sigma_{22} & 0 \\ 0 & 0 & \sigma_{33} \end{bmatrix} \tag{13-2}$$

We have already seen that difficulties arise in simultaneous-equation systems because of the correlation between disturbances and endogenous variables and so we must now examine whether the special features of the recursive model remove these difficulties.

Writing the structural equations for all sample periods as in (12-33) gives

$$\mathbf{YB}' + \mathbf{X\Gamma}' = \mathbf{U} \tag{13-3}$$

with reduced form

$$\mathbf{Y} = \mathbf{X\Pi}' + \mathbf{V} \tag{13-4}$$

where

$$\mathbf{V} = \mathbf{U}(\mathbf{B}')^{-1} \tag{13-5}$$

Premultiplying (13-4) by $(1/n)\mathbf{U}'$ and taking probability limits gives

$$\text{plim}\left(\frac{1}{n}\mathbf{U}'\mathbf{Y}\right) = \text{plim}\left(\frac{1}{n}\mathbf{U}'\mathbf{V}\right)$$

since plim $\{(1/n)(\mathbf{U}'\mathbf{X})\} = \mathbf{0}$ by assumption. Using (13-5) then gives

$$\operatorname{plim}\left(\frac{1}{n}\mathbf{U}'\mathbf{Y}\right) = \operatorname{plim}\left(\frac{1}{n}\mathbf{U}'\mathbf{U}\right)(\mathbf{B}')^{-1}$$

$$= \mathbf{\Sigma}(\mathbf{B}')^{-1} \tag{13-6}$$

For a 3×3 recursive system (13-6) becomes

$$\begin{bmatrix} \operatorname{plim}\left(\frac{1}{n}\sum_t u_{1t}y_{1t}\right) & \operatorname{plim}\left(\frac{1}{n}\sum_t u_{1t}y_{2t}\right) & \operatorname{plim}\left(\frac{1}{n}\sum_t u_{1t}y_{3t}\right) \\ \operatorname{plim}\left(\frac{1}{n}\sum_t u_{2t}y_{1t}\right) & \operatorname{plim}\left(\frac{1}{n}\sum_t u_{2t}y_{2t}\right) & \operatorname{plim}\left(\frac{1}{n}\sum_t u_{2t}y_{3t}\right) \\ \operatorname{plim}\left(\frac{1}{n}\sum_t u_{3t}y_{1t}\right) & \operatorname{plim}\left(\frac{1}{n}\sum_t u_{3t}y_{2t}\right) & \operatorname{plim}\left(\frac{1}{n}\sum_t u_{3t}y_{3t}\right) \end{bmatrix}$$

$$= \begin{bmatrix} \sigma_{11} & \sigma_{11}\beta^{21} & \sigma_{11}\beta^{31} \\ 0 & \sigma_{22} & \sigma_{22}\beta^{32} \\ 0 & 0 & \sigma_{33} \end{bmatrix}$$

where

$$(\mathbf{B}')^{-1} = \begin{bmatrix} 1 & \beta^{21} & \beta^{31} \\ 0 & 1 & \beta^{32} \\ 0 & 0 & 1 \end{bmatrix}$$

β^{ij} indicating the cofactor of β_{ij}. Thus we have the crucial results that u_2 is uncorrelated in the limit with y_1 and u_3 is uncorrelated in the limit with y_1 and y_2. This means that the second and third equations of (13-1) may be estimated by a straightforward application of ordinary least-squares, as may of course the first equation, which only contained one endogenous and one prèdetermined variable.

It is also easy to see that if the u's are normally distributed simple least-squares yields maximum-likelihood estimates. Following (12-29) the likelihood function is given by

$$L = |\det \mathbf{B}|^n p(\mathbf{u}_1)p(\mathbf{u}_2)\cdots p(\mathbf{u}_n)$$

on the assumption of serially independent $\mathbf{u}$ vectors. If we assume each $\mathbf{u}_t$ vector to be multivariate normal, $N(\mathbf{0}, \mathbf{\Sigma})$, then the log of the likelihood is

$$L^* = \log L = \text{const} + n \log|\det \mathbf{B}| - \frac{n}{2}\log\det\mathbf{\Sigma} - \frac{1}{2}\sum_{t=1}^{n} \mathbf{u}_t'\mathbf{\Sigma}^{-1}\mathbf{u}_t$$

For recursive systems $\det \mathbf{B} = 1$ and $\boldsymbol{\Sigma}$ and $\boldsymbol{\Sigma}^{-1}$ are diagonal. Finding $\hat{\mathbf{B}}$ and $\hat{\boldsymbol{\Gamma}}$ to maximize L^* is then equivalent to finding the $\hat{\mathbf{B}}$ and $\hat{\boldsymbol{\Gamma}}$ which will minimize

$$\sum_{t=1}^{n} \mathbf{u}_t' \boldsymbol{\Sigma}^{-1} \mathbf{u}_t$$

For our three-equation example this sum of squares is

$$S = \sum_{t=1}^{n} [u_{1t} \quad u_{2t} \quad u_{3t}] \begin{bmatrix} \frac{1}{\sigma_{11}} & 0 & 0 \\ 0 & \frac{1}{\sigma_{22}} & 0 \\ 0 & 0 & \frac{1}{\sigma_{33}} \end{bmatrix} \begin{bmatrix} u_{1t} \\ u_{2t} \\ u_{3t} \end{bmatrix}$$

$$= \sum_{t=1}^{n} \left(\frac{u_{1t}^2}{\sigma_{11}} + \frac{u_{2t}^2}{\sigma_{22}} + \frac{u_{3t}^2}{\sigma_{33}} \right)$$

Thus the partial derivatives of L^* with respect to the coefficients of the first structural equation are simply the partial derivatives of S with respect to those coefficients, which are just the partial derivatives of

$$\sum_{t=1}^{n} \frac{u_{1t}^2}{\sigma_{11}}$$

Setting these partial derivatives to zero gives the OLS normal equations for the first structural equation and similarly for the other two structural equations.

Wold has argued in many publications that economic systems really are recursive. There is much force in his argument when one takes account of institutional realities. It is difficult, for instance, to find examples of markets where equilibrium prices and quantities are *simultaneously* determined. More realistically one must usually specify some sort of adjustment process to be at work. Sellers may set prices, buyers react, stocks may be accumulated or depleted, sellers react to these movements, and so on. A crucial factor, however, is the time period involved. Suppose the unit time period underlying a model is a day and we assume that the price set for day t is adjusted in response to sales in day $t - 1$, while purchases in day t depend on the price ruling in day t. Thus

$$p_t = \alpha_0 + \alpha_1 q_{t-1} + u_t$$

$$q_t = \beta_0 + \beta_1 p_t + v_t$$

This is recursive since p_t and q_t are current endogenous variables and q_{t-1} is predetermined with the causal sequence being

$$q_{t-1} \rightarrow p_t \rightarrow q_t$$

which is a linear chain without any feedback, and we assume the demand and supply disturbances to be independent. Suppose, however, that no daily data but only weekly data are published, where a week consists of, say, five working days. Then available data are in the form

P_t = average price ruling on the 5 days of week t.

Q_t = average daily sales over the 5 days of week t.

It would no longer make economic sense to write the first equation as

$$P_t = \alpha_0 + \alpha_1 Q_{t-1} + U_t$$

where the time subscripts refer to weeks, for the system of daily reactions means that P_t is determined by quantities on 4 days of week t and by the quantity on the last day of week $t - 1$. Measurement on the true explanatory variable is not available but Q_t is clearly a better approximation to it than Q_{t-1} so the first equation, in weekly data, would be approximately

$$P_t = \alpha_0 + \alpha_1 Q_t + U_t$$

which makes it of the same general form as the new second equation

$$Q_t = \beta_0 + \beta_1 P_t + V_t$$

the U_t and V_t representing cumulated disturbances. Without further variables the model would now not even be identified, but even if identifying variables were present it can be seen that, in general, enforced aggregation over time periods can turn a truly recursive model into a fully simultaneous one with all the resultant estimation problems.

13-2 TWO-STAGE LEAST-SQUARES (2SLS) ESTIMATORS

Methods of estimation for simultaneous systems are either single-equation methods, which can be applied to each equation of the system *seriatim*, or complete system methods, which are applied to the system as a whole. Examples of the former are two-stage least-squares (2SLS) and limited-information single-equation (LISE) and of the latter three-stage least-squares (3SLS) and full information maximum likelihood (FIML).

The most important and widely used single-equation method is two-stage least-squares. Let us write the particular equation of the model in which we are interested as

$$\mathbf{y} = \mathbf{Y}_1 \boldsymbol{\beta} + \mathbf{X}_1 \boldsymbol{\gamma} + \mathbf{u} \tag{13-7}$$

where

- $\mathbf{y}$ is the $n \times 1$ vector of observations on the "dependent" variable,
- $\mathbf{Y}_1$ is the $n \times g$ matrix of observations on the other current endogenous variables included in the equation,
- $\boldsymbol{\beta}$ is the $g \times 1$ vector of structural coefficients attached to the variables in $\mathbf{Y}_1$,
- $\mathbf{X}_1$ is the $n \times k$ matrix of observations on the predetermined variables appearing in the equation (including a column of ones if an intercept is required),
- γ is the $k \times 1$ vector of coefficients associated with $\mathbf{X}_1$, and
- $\mathbf{u}$ is the $n \times 1$ vector of disturbances in this equation.

There is an element of arbitrariness in that one of the current endogenous variables has to be singled out as the dependent variable. Conventional practice is to be guided by economic theory; each structural relation specifies the behavioral or technological forces determining some specific variable and it is natural to take that variable as the dependent variable in that structural relation.

We have seen that the trouble about applying OLS to (13-7) is that the variables in $\mathbf{Y}_1$ are correlated with $\mathbf{u}$. The essence of 2SLS is the replacement of $\mathbf{Y}_1$ by a computed matrix $\hat{\mathbf{Y}}_1$, which hopefully is purged of the stochastic element, and then performing an OLS regression of $\mathbf{y}$ on $\hat{\mathbf{Y}}_1$ and $\mathbf{X}_1$.

The matrix $\hat{\mathbf{Y}}_1$ is computed in the first stage by regressing each variable in $\mathbf{Y}_1$ on all the predetermined variables in the complete model and replacing the actual observations on the Y variables by the corresponding regression values. Thus

$$\hat{\mathbf{Y}}_1 = \mathbf{X}(\mathbf{X}'\mathbf{X})^{-1}\mathbf{X}'\mathbf{Y}_1 \tag{13-8}$$

where

$$\mathbf{X} = [\mathbf{X}_1 \quad \mathbf{X}_2]$$

is the $n \times K$ matrix of observations on all the predetermined variables in the complete model, $\mathbf{X}_2$ being the matrix of observations on those predetermined variables which are excluded from the equation under study.

In the second stage $\mathbf{y}$ is regressed on $\hat{\mathbf{Y}}_1$ and $\mathbf{X}_1$. This yields estimating equations

$$\begin{bmatrix} \hat{\mathbf{Y}}_1'\hat{\mathbf{Y}}_1 & \hat{\mathbf{Y}}_1'\mathbf{X}_1 \\ \mathbf{X}_1'\hat{\mathbf{Y}}_1 & \mathbf{X}_1'\mathbf{X}_1 \end{bmatrix} \begin{bmatrix} \mathbf{b} \\ \mathbf{c} \end{bmatrix} = \begin{bmatrix} \hat{\mathbf{Y}}_1'\mathbf{y} \\ \mathbf{X}_1'\mathbf{y} \end{bmatrix} \tag{13-9}$$

where $\begin{bmatrix} \mathbf{b} \\ \mathbf{c} \end{bmatrix}$ denotes the 2SLS estimate of $\begin{bmatrix} \boldsymbol{\beta} \\ \boldsymbol{\gamma} \end{bmatrix}$. For the actual estimation of $\begin{bmatrix} \mathbf{b} \\ \mathbf{c} \end{bmatrix}$ there is no need to compute the regression values in $\hat{\mathbf{Y}}_1$. An alternative form of (13-9) can be derived which involves only the matrices of actual observations. We can rewrite (13-8) in the form

$$\mathbf{Y}_1 = \hat{\mathbf{Y}}_1 + \mathbf{V}_1 \tag{13-10}$$

where $\mathbf{V}_1$ is the $n \times g$ matrix of residuals from the least-squares regressions of $\mathbf{Y}_1$ on $\mathbf{X}$. The usual properties of least-squares residuals give

$$\hat{\mathbf{Y}}_1'\mathbf{V}_1 = \mathbf{0} = \mathbf{X}'\mathbf{V}_1 \tag{13-11}$$

Thus

$$\begin{aligned} \hat{\mathbf{Y}}_1'\hat{\mathbf{Y}}_1 &= \hat{\mathbf{Y}}_1'(\mathbf{Y}_1 - \mathbf{V}_1) \\ &= \hat{\mathbf{Y}}_1'\mathbf{Y}_1 \\ &= \mathbf{Y}_1'\mathbf{X}(\mathbf{X}'\mathbf{X})^{-1}\mathbf{X}'\mathbf{Y}_1 \end{aligned}$$

and

$$\begin{aligned} \hat{\mathbf{Y}}_1'\mathbf{X}_1 &= (\mathbf{Y}_1 - \mathbf{V}_1)'\mathbf{X}_1 \\ &= \mathbf{Y}_1'\mathbf{X}_1 \end{aligned}$$

since

$$\mathbf{X}'\mathbf{V}_1 = \mathbf{0} \quad \text{implies } \mathbf{X}_1'\mathbf{V}_1 = \mathbf{0}$$

Thus the equations for the 2SLS estimates can now be written

$$\begin{bmatrix} \mathbf{Y}_1'\mathbf{X}(\mathbf{X}'\mathbf{X})^{-1}\mathbf{X}'\mathbf{Y}_1 & \mathbf{Y}_1'\mathbf{X}_1 \\ \mathbf{X}_1'\mathbf{Y}_1 & \mathbf{X}_1'\mathbf{X}_1 \end{bmatrix} \begin{bmatrix} \mathbf{b} \\ \mathbf{c} \end{bmatrix} = \begin{bmatrix} \mathbf{Y}_1'\mathbf{X}(\mathbf{X}'\mathbf{X})^{-1}\mathbf{X}'\mathbf{y} \\ \mathbf{X}_1'\mathbf{y} \end{bmatrix} \tag{13-12}$$

An alternative form of the 2SLS equations (13-9) which we shall find useful in further theoretical developments is

$$\begin{bmatrix} \mathbf{Y}_1'\mathbf{Y}_1 - \mathbf{V}_1'\mathbf{V}_1 & \mathbf{Y}_1'\mathbf{X}_1 \\ \mathbf{X}_1'\mathbf{Y}_1 & \mathbf{X}_1'\mathbf{X}_1 \end{bmatrix} \begin{bmatrix} \mathbf{b} \\ \mathbf{c} \end{bmatrix} = \begin{bmatrix} (\mathbf{Y}_1 - \mathbf{V}_1)'\mathbf{y} \\ \mathbf{X}_1'\mathbf{y} \end{bmatrix} \tag{13-13}$$

The equivalence of (13-9) and (13-13) may be proved by the reader as an exercise.

Now we must show that the 2SLS estimators are consistent and we must obtain their asymptotic variance matrix. Using (13-10) the basic relation (13-7) can be rewritten as

$$\mathbf{y} = \hat{\mathbf{Y}}_1\boldsymbol{\beta} + \mathbf{X}_1\boldsymbol{\gamma} + (\mathbf{u} + \mathbf{V}_1\boldsymbol{\beta}) \tag{13-14}$$

or, more compactly, as

$$\mathbf{y} = \mathbf{Z}\boldsymbol{\delta} + (\mathbf{u} + \mathbf{V}_1\boldsymbol{\beta}) \tag{13-15}$$

where

$$\mathbf{Z} = [\hat{\mathbf{Y}}_1 \quad \mathbf{X}_1] \quad \text{and} \quad \boldsymbol{\delta} = \begin{bmatrix} \boldsymbol{\beta} \\ \boldsymbol{\gamma} \end{bmatrix} \tag{13-16}$$

Applying least-squares to (13-15) gives the 2SLS estimator in the form

$$\mathbf{d} = \begin{bmatrix} \mathbf{b} \\ \mathbf{c} \end{bmatrix} = (\mathbf{Z}'\mathbf{Z})^{-1}\mathbf{Z}'\mathbf{y}$$

Thus

$$\mathbf{d} = \boldsymbol{\delta} + (\mathbf{Z}'\mathbf{Z})^{-1}\mathbf{Z}'(\mathbf{u} + \mathbf{V}_1\boldsymbol{\beta})$$

which reduces to

$$\mathbf{d} = \boldsymbol{\delta} + (\mathbf{Z}'\mathbf{Z})^{-1}\mathbf{Z}'\mathbf{u} \tag{13-17}$$

since $\mathbf{Z}'\mathbf{V}_1 = \mathbf{0}$ from (13-11). So

$$\text{plim}\, \mathbf{d} = \boldsymbol{\delta} + \text{plim}\left(\frac{1}{n}\mathbf{Z}'\mathbf{Z}\right)^{-1} \cdot \text{plim}\left(\frac{1}{n}\mathbf{Z}'\mathbf{u}\right)$$

and 2SLS will be consistent if[1]

$$\text{plim}\left(\frac{1}{n}\mathbf{Z}'\mathbf{u}\right) = \begin{bmatrix} \text{plim}\,\frac{1}{n}\hat{\mathbf{Y}}_1'\mathbf{u} \\ \\ \text{plim}\,\frac{1}{n}\mathbf{X}_1'\mathbf{u} \end{bmatrix} = \mathbf{0}$$

There is no difficulty about plim $[(1/n)\mathbf{X}_1'\mathbf{u}]$ since the X variables by assumption are uncorrelated with the disturbance in the limit.

$$\text{plim}\left(\frac{1}{n}\hat{\mathbf{Y}}_1'\mathbf{u}\right) = \text{plim}\left(\frac{1}{n}\hat{\boldsymbol{\Pi}}_1'\mathbf{X}'\mathbf{u}\right)$$

where $\hat{\boldsymbol{\Pi}}_1$ denotes the OLS coefficients in the subset of reduced form regressions $\mathbf{Y}_1 = \mathbf{X}\hat{\boldsymbol{\Pi}}_1 + \mathbf{V}_1$. Thus

$$\begin{aligned} \text{plim}\left(\frac{1}{n}\hat{\mathbf{Y}}_1'\mathbf{u}\right) &= \text{plim}\,\hat{\boldsymbol{\Pi}}_1'\ \text{plim}\left(\frac{1}{n}\mathbf{X}'\mathbf{u}\right) \\ &= \boldsymbol{\Pi}_1' \cdot \mathbf{0} \\ &= \mathbf{0} \end{aligned}$$

[1] We are here assuming that plim$[(1/n)\mathbf{Z}'\mathbf{Z}]$ is finite, that is, that the variables in the system are stable.

for we have already seen in Chap. 12 that OLS yields consistent estimates of reduced form coefficients. Thus 2SLS estimators are consistent.

From (13-17)

$$\mathbf{d} - \boldsymbol{\delta} = (\mathbf{Z}'\mathbf{Z})^{-1}\mathbf{Z}'\mathbf{u}$$

and so, provided the appropriate probability limits exist, the asymptotic variance matrix is

$$\begin{aligned}
\text{asy var}(\mathbf{d}) &= n^{-1}\,\text{plim}\,[n(\mathbf{d} - \boldsymbol{\delta})(\mathbf{d} - \boldsymbol{\delta})'] \\
&= n^{-1}\,\text{plim}\,[n(\mathbf{Z}'\mathbf{Z})^{-1}\mathbf{Z}'\mathbf{u}\mathbf{u}'\mathbf{Z}(\mathbf{Z}'\mathbf{Z})^{-1}] \\
&= n^{-1}\,\text{plim}\left(\frac{1}{n}\mathbf{Z}'\mathbf{Z}\right)^{-1}\cdot\text{plim}\left(\frac{1}{n}\mathbf{Z}'\mathbf{u}\mathbf{u}'\mathbf{Z}\right)\cdot\text{plim}\left(\frac{1}{n}\mathbf{Z}'\mathbf{Z}\right)^{-1} \\
&= n^{-1}\cdot\sigma_u^2\cdot\text{plim}\left(\frac{1}{n}\mathbf{Z}'\mathbf{Z}\right)^{-1} \qquad (13\text{-}18)
\end{aligned}$$

by the arguments of Section 2 of Chap. 9. Formula (13-18) gives the asymptotic variance–covariance matrix of the 2SLS estimators. It would be estimated in practice by

$$s^2(\mathbf{Z}'\mathbf{Z})^{-1} = s^2\begin{bmatrix} \mathbf{Y}_1'\mathbf{X}(\mathbf{X}'\mathbf{X})^{-1}\mathbf{X}'\mathbf{Y}_1 & \mathbf{Y}_1'\mathbf{X}_1 \\ \mathbf{X}_1'\mathbf{Y}_1 & \mathbf{X}_1'\mathbf{X}_1 \end{bmatrix}^{-1} \qquad (13\text{-}19)$$

where

$$s^2 = (\mathbf{y} - \mathbf{Y}_1\mathbf{b} - \mathbf{X}_1\mathbf{c})'(\mathbf{y} - \mathbf{Y}_1\mathbf{b} - \mathbf{X}_1\mathbf{c})/(n - g - k) \qquad (13\text{-}20)$$

13-3 LIMITED-INFORMATION (LEAST-VARIANCE RATIO) ESTIMATORS

Consider again Eq. (13-7), namely,

$$\mathbf{y} = \mathbf{Y}_1\boldsymbol{\beta} + \mathbf{X}_1\boldsymbol{\gamma} + \mathbf{u}$$

which we rewrite as

$$\mathbf{Y}_\Delta\boldsymbol{\beta}_\Delta - \mathbf{X}_1\boldsymbol{\gamma} = \mathbf{u} \qquad (13\text{-}21)$$

where

$$\mathbf{Y}_\Delta = [\mathbf{y} \quad \mathbf{Y}_1] \quad \text{and} \quad \boldsymbol{\beta}_\Delta = \begin{bmatrix} 1 \\ -\boldsymbol{\beta} \end{bmatrix} \qquad (13\text{-}22)$$

If we move to the reduced form of the model and take the $(g + 1)$ equations of the reduced form corresponding to the endogenous variables in $\mathbf{Y}_\Delta$ we can set up the likelihood function for these endogenous variables, under the usual assumptions about the normality and serial independence of the structural disturbances, and hence of the reduced form disturbances. The likelihood function will be in terms of a subset of the elements of $\mathbf{\Pi}$. Let us suppose that the Y variables have been so numbered that $[\mathbf{y} \quad \mathbf{Y}_1]$ constitute the first $(g + 1)$ endogenous variables and likewise $\mathbf{X}_1$ refers to the first k variables in $\mathbf{X}$. If $\mathbf{\Pi}$ is partitioned by the first $(g + 1)$ rows and by the first k and the remaining $(K - k)$ columns, then the likelihood function for the first $(g + 1)$ endogenous variables is in terms of the elements of $[\mathbf{\Pi}_{\Delta 1} \ \mathbf{\Pi}_{\Delta 2}]$ where these matrices are respectively of order $(g + 1)$ by k and $(g + 1)$ by $(K - k)$. The connection between the structural coefficients of (13-21) and those reduced form coefficients is determined as follows. We know

$$\mathbf{B\Pi} = -\mathbf{\Gamma}$$

The first row of each side of this equation may be written

$$[\boldsymbol{\beta}'_\Delta \quad \mathbf{0}_1]\mathbf{\Pi} = [-\boldsymbol{\gamma}' \quad \mathbf{0}_2]$$

where $\mathbf{0}_1$ indicates a row vector of $(G - g - 1)$ zeros and $\mathbf{0}_2$ a row vector of $(K - k)$ zeros. Using the partitioning of $\mathbf{\Pi}$ indicated above then gives

$$\boldsymbol{\beta}'_\Delta \mathbf{\Pi}_{\Delta 1} = -\boldsymbol{\gamma}' \tag{13-23}$$

and

$$\boldsymbol{\beta}'_\Delta \mathbf{\Pi}_{\Delta 2} = \mathbf{0}_2 \tag{13-24}$$

In the overidentified case $(K - k) > g$ so $\mathbf{\Pi}_{\Delta 2}$ has at least $(g + 1)$ columns and (13-24) is then a set of at least $(g + 1)$ homogeneous equations in $(g + 1)$ unknowns. Since $\boldsymbol{\beta}_\Delta$ has one element set at unity we merely need to determine the ratios of the elements of $\boldsymbol{\beta}_\Delta$ and this will be done uniquely if the rank of $\mathbf{\Pi}_{\Delta 2}$ is g. Even in the overidentified case the rank of $\mathbf{\Pi}_{\Delta 2}$ cannot exceed g,[1] and we have had an illustration of this in Example (iv) of Chap. 12. However, the true $\mathbf{\Pi}_{\Delta 2}$ is unknown and when it is replaced in (13-24) by, say, the maximum-likelihood estimate $\hat{\mathbf{\Pi}}_{\Delta 2}$, this matrix in the overidentified case will almost certainly have rank $(g + 1)$ so that we cannot solve for nonzero $\boldsymbol{\beta}_\Delta$, except by arbitrarily dropping one of the equations.

The limited-information maximum-likelihood approach is to maximize the likelihood function for the $(g + 1)$ endogenous variables subject to the restriction that $\rho(\hat{\mathbf{\Pi}}_{\Delta 2}) = g$. This approach was developed by Anderson and Rubin.[2] The application of the method requires one to know, in addition to the specification of the single equation being estimated, merely the predetermined variables appearing in the other equations of the model, as in 2SLS. The mathematical development of the limited-information

[1] See T. C. Koopmans, and W. C. Hood, *Studies in Econometric Methods*, Wiley, New York, 1953, pp. 185–186.

[2] T. W. Anderson and H. Rubin, "Estimation of the Parameters of a Single Equation in a Complete System of Stochastic Equations," *Ann. Math. Statistics*, vol. 20, pp. 46–63, 1949.

method is complicated and lengthy but it may be shown that it reduces in the end to the choice of the elements of $\boldsymbol{\beta}_\Delta$ to minimize[1]

$$l = \frac{\boldsymbol{\beta}'_\Delta \mathbf{W}^*_{\Delta\Delta} \boldsymbol{\beta}_\Delta}{\boldsymbol{\beta}'_\Delta \mathbf{W}_{\Delta\Delta} \boldsymbol{\beta}_\Delta} \tag{13-25}$$

where $\mathbf{W}^*_{\Delta\Delta}$ and $\mathbf{W}_{\Delta\Delta}$ are certain matrices of residuals. The explanation of $\mathbf{W}^*_{\Delta\Delta}$ and $\mathbf{W}_{\Delta\Delta}$ will be given in the development of the least-variance ratio estimators below and will, at the same time, show why the two approaches lead to identical estimators.

Using (13-22) above, define

$$\mathbf{z} = \mathbf{Y}_\Delta \boldsymbol{\beta}_\Delta \tag{13-26}$$

where $\mathbf{z}$ is a vector which is a linear combination of the endogenous variables which appear in the equation, the coefficients of the combination being the unknown β parameters. If $\mathbf{z}$ is regressed on $\mathbf{X}_1$ the residual sum of squares is

$$\begin{aligned} \mathbf{z}'\mathbf{z} - \mathbf{z}'\mathbf{X}_1(\mathbf{X}'_1\mathbf{X}_1)^{-1}\mathbf{X}'_1\mathbf{z} &= \boldsymbol{\beta}'_\Delta \mathbf{Y}'_\Delta \mathbf{Y}_\Delta \boldsymbol{\beta}_\Delta - \boldsymbol{\beta}'_\Delta \mathbf{Y}'_\Delta \mathbf{X}_1(\mathbf{X}'_1\mathbf{X}_1)^{-1}\mathbf{X}'_1\mathbf{Y}_\Delta \boldsymbol{\beta}_\Delta \\ &= \boldsymbol{\beta}'_\Delta \mathbf{W}^*_{\Delta\Delta} \boldsymbol{\beta}_\Delta \end{aligned}$$

where

$$\mathbf{W}^*_{\Delta\Delta} = \mathbf{Y}'_\Delta \mathbf{Y}_\Delta - \mathbf{Y}'_\Delta \mathbf{X}_1(\mathbf{X}'_1\mathbf{X}_1)^{-1}\mathbf{X}'_1\mathbf{Y}_\Delta \tag{13-27}$$

Similarly if $\mathbf{z}$ is regressed on all the predetermined variables $\mathbf{X} = [\mathbf{X}_1 \quad \mathbf{X}_2]$ the residual sum of squares is

$$\boldsymbol{\beta}'_\Delta \mathbf{W}_{\Delta\Delta} \boldsymbol{\beta}_\Delta$$

where

$$\mathbf{W}_{\Delta\Delta} = \mathbf{Y}'_\Delta \mathbf{Y}_\Delta - \mathbf{Y}'_\Delta \mathbf{X}(\mathbf{X}'\mathbf{X})^{-1}\mathbf{X}'\mathbf{Y}_\Delta \tag{13-28}$$

The second residual sum of squares will be no greater than the first since the second regression includes all the explanatory variables in the first regression, $\mathbf{X}_1$, plus the set $\mathbf{X}_2$. However, the specification of the structural equation asserts that $\mathbf{z}$ depends on $\mathbf{X}_1$ and not on $\mathbf{X}_2$. Thus the least variance ratio principle suggests that the estimate of $\boldsymbol{\beta}_\Delta$ should be chosen

[1] *Ibid* and also W. C. Hood and T. C. Koopmans (eds.), *Studies in Econometric Method*, Wiley, New York, 1953, Chap. 6. Hood and Koopmans arrive at (13-25) by a different method from the original approach of Anderson and Rubin, who minimized the likelihood function subject to appropriate constraints by using Lagrange multipliers. Hood and Koopmans start with the likelihood function for the complete model of G equations for all G endogenous variables and then, by a series of stepwise maximizations, eliminate from the likelihood function all parameters other than those of the equation to be estimated. Finally, even γ is eliminated and the concentrated likelihood function expressed in terms of $\boldsymbol{\beta}_\Delta$.

to keep this reduction in the residual sum of squares as small as possible, that is, to minimize the ratio

$$l = \frac{\boldsymbol{\beta}'_\Delta \mathbf{W}^*_{\Delta\Delta} \boldsymbol{\beta}_\Delta}{\boldsymbol{\beta}'_\Delta \mathbf{W}_{\Delta\Delta} \boldsymbol{\beta}_\Delta}$$

Differentiating l with respect to $\boldsymbol{\beta}_\Delta$

$$\frac{\partial l}{\partial \boldsymbol{\beta}_\Delta} = \frac{(\boldsymbol{\beta}'_\Delta \mathbf{W}_{\Delta\Delta} \boldsymbol{\beta}_\Delta)(2\mathbf{W}^*_{\Delta\Delta} \boldsymbol{\beta}_\Delta) - (\boldsymbol{\beta}'_\Delta \mathbf{W}^*_{\Delta\Delta} \boldsymbol{\beta}_\Delta)(2\mathbf{W}_{\Delta\Delta} \boldsymbol{\beta}_\Delta)}{(\boldsymbol{\beta}'_\Delta \mathbf{W}_{\Delta\Delta} \boldsymbol{\beta}_\Delta)^2}$$

$$= \frac{2}{(\boldsymbol{\beta}'_\Delta \mathbf{W}_{\Delta\Delta} \boldsymbol{\beta}_\Delta)} (\mathbf{W}^*_{\Delta\Delta} \boldsymbol{\beta}_\Delta - l \mathbf{W}_{\Delta\Delta} \boldsymbol{\beta}_\Delta)$$

Setting

$$\frac{\partial l}{\partial \boldsymbol{\beta}_\Delta} = \mathbf{0}$$

gives

$$(\mathbf{W}^*_{\Delta\Delta} - l \mathbf{W}_{\Delta\Delta}) \boldsymbol{\beta}_\Delta = \mathbf{0} \tag{13-29}$$

This set of equations will only have a nontrivial solution if the determinantal equation

$$|\mathbf{W}^*_{\Delta\Delta} - l \mathbf{W}_{\Delta\Delta}| = 0 \tag{13-30}$$

is satisfied. This gives a polynomial in l, which must be solved for the smallest root $\hat{l}$. This smallest root is substituted back in (13-29) and the estimator $\hat{\boldsymbol{\beta}}_\Delta$ obtained from

$$(\mathbf{W}^*_{\Delta\Delta} - \hat{l} \mathbf{W}_{\Delta\Delta}) \hat{\boldsymbol{\beta}}_\Delta = \mathbf{0} \tag{13-31}$$

by setting the first element in $\hat{\boldsymbol{\beta}}_\Delta$ equal to unity. We now define

$$\hat{\mathbf{z}} = \mathbf{Y}_\Delta \hat{\boldsymbol{\beta}}_\Delta$$

and obtain the coefficients of the predetermined variables by regressing $\hat{\mathbf{z}}$ on $\mathbf{X}_1$, getting

$$\hat{\boldsymbol{\gamma}} = (\mathbf{X}'_1 \mathbf{X}_1)^{-1} \mathbf{X}'_1 \mathbf{Y}_\Delta \hat{\boldsymbol{\beta}}_\Delta \tag{13-32}$$

Equations (13-31) and (13-32) define the LISE (LVR) estimators of the parameters of (13-7). We shall return to the properties of these estimators later in the chapter.

13-4 *k*-CLASS ESTIMATORS

Referring again to the structural equation (13-7), Theil has defined a family of k-class estimators as[1]

$$\begin{bmatrix} \mathbf{Y}_1'\mathbf{Y}_1 - k\mathbf{V}_1'\mathbf{V}_1 & \mathbf{Y}_1'\mathbf{X}_1 \\ \mathbf{X}_1'\mathbf{Y}_1 & \mathbf{X}_1'\mathbf{X}_1 \end{bmatrix} \begin{bmatrix} \mathbf{b}_k \\ \mathbf{c}_k \end{bmatrix} = \begin{bmatrix} (\mathbf{Y}_1 - k\mathbf{V}_1)'\mathbf{y} \\ \mathbf{X}_1'\mathbf{y} \end{bmatrix} \tag{13-33}$$

where k denotes a number which may be stochastic or nonstochastic. It should not be confused with our other use of k to denote the number of predetermined variables present in the structural equation. The two most important examples of nonstochastic k are zero and unity. When $k = 0$, (13-33) gives the OLS estimators obtained by the direct regression of $\mathbf{y}$ on $[\mathbf{Y}_1 \quad \mathbf{X}_1]$. When $k = 1$, (13-33) gives the 2SLS estimates, as may be seen by a direct comparison with (13-13). If k is stochastic and such that plim $k = 1$ then the solution vector in (13-33) will converge to the 2SLS solution vector and in that case the k-class estimators will be consistent and will have the same asymptotic variance–covariance matrix as the 2SLS estimators. This last result is important because it can be shown that the LISE estimator is a k-class estimator with k replaced by $\hat{l}$, the smallest root of (13-30), and since[2]

$$\text{plim}\,\sqrt{n}(\hat{l} - 1) = 0$$

so that *a fortiori*,

$$\text{plim}\,(\hat{l} - 1) = 0$$

To show that LISE is a k-class estimator with $k = \hat{l}$ we proceed as follows. From the definitions of $\mathbf{W}^*_{\Delta\Delta}$ and $\mathbf{W}_{\Delta\Delta}$ in (13-27) and (13-28) we can write

$$\mathbf{W}^*_{\Delta\Delta} = \mathbf{Y}_\Delta'\mathbf{M}_1\mathbf{Y}_\Delta$$

where

$$\mathbf{M}_1 = \mathbf{I} - \mathbf{X}_1(\mathbf{X}_1'\mathbf{X}_1)^{-1}\mathbf{X}_1'$$

and $\mathbf{M}_1$ is symmetric, idempotent. Also

$$\mathbf{W}_{\Delta\Delta} = \mathbf{Y}_\Delta'\mathbf{M}\mathbf{Y}_\Delta$$

where

$$\mathbf{M} = \mathbf{I} - \mathbf{X}(\mathbf{X}'\mathbf{X})^{-1}\mathbf{X}'$$

[1] H. Theil, *Economic Forecasts and Policy*, 2nd ed., North-Holland Publishing Company, 1961, pp. 231–232, 334–336.

[2] T. W. Anderson and H. Rubin, "The asymptotic properties of estimates of the parameters of a single equation in a complete system of stochastic equations," *Ann. Math. Statistics*, vol. 21, pp. 570–582, 1950.

Using $\mathbf{Y}_\Delta = [\mathbf{y} \quad \mathbf{Y}_1]$

$$\mathbf{W}^*_{\Delta\Delta} = \begin{bmatrix} \mathbf{y}'\mathbf{M}_1\mathbf{y} & \mathbf{y}'\mathbf{M}_1\mathbf{Y}_1 \\ \mathbf{Y}_1'\mathbf{M}_1\mathbf{y} & \mathbf{Y}_1'\mathbf{M}_1\mathbf{Y}_1 \end{bmatrix}$$

and

$$\mathbf{W}_{\Delta\Delta} = \begin{bmatrix} \mathbf{y}'\mathbf{M}\mathbf{y} & \mathbf{y}'\mathbf{M}\mathbf{Y}_1 \\ \mathbf{Y}_1'\mathbf{M}\mathbf{y} & \mathbf{Y}_1'\mathbf{M}\mathbf{Y}_1 \end{bmatrix}$$

This gives a partitioning of $\mathbf{W}^*_{\Delta\Delta}$ and $\mathbf{W}_{\Delta\Delta}$ by the first row and the remaining g rows and by the first column and the remaining g columns. Substituting in (13-31), leaving out the first equation and rewriting $\hat{\boldsymbol{\beta}}_\Delta$ as $\begin{bmatrix} 1 \\ -\hat{\boldsymbol{\beta}} \end{bmatrix}$ gives[1]

$$[\mathbf{Y}_1'\mathbf{M}_1\mathbf{y} - \hat{l}\mathbf{Y}_1'\mathbf{M}\mathbf{y} \quad \mathbf{Y}_1'\mathbf{M}_1\mathbf{Y}_1 - \hat{l}\mathbf{Y}_1'\mathbf{M}\mathbf{Y}_1]\begin{bmatrix} 1 \\ -\hat{\boldsymbol{\beta}} \end{bmatrix} = \mathbf{0}$$

that is,

$$(\mathbf{Y}_1'\mathbf{M}_1\mathbf{Y}_1 - \hat{l}\mathbf{Y}_1'\mathbf{M}\mathbf{Y}_1)\hat{\boldsymbol{\beta}} = (\mathbf{Y}_1'\mathbf{M}_1\mathbf{y} - \hat{l}\mathbf{Y}_1'\mathbf{M}\mathbf{y}) \tag{13-34}$$

Turning now to the k-class estimator defined in (13-33) and rewriting it with $\hat{l}$ substituted for k, gives

$$\begin{aligned} (\mathbf{Y}_1'\mathbf{Y}_1 - \hat{l}\mathbf{V}_1'\mathbf{V}_1)\mathbf{b}_k + (\mathbf{Y}_1'\mathbf{X}_1)\mathbf{c}_k &= \mathbf{Y}_1'\mathbf{y} - \hat{l}\mathbf{V}_1'\mathbf{y} \\ (\mathbf{X}_1'\mathbf{Y}_1)\mathbf{b}_k + (\mathbf{X}_1'\mathbf{X}_1)\mathbf{c}_k &= \mathbf{X}_1'\mathbf{y} \end{aligned} \tag{13-35}$$

From (13-8) and (13-10)

$$\mathbf{V}_1 = \mathbf{M}\mathbf{Y}_1$$

so

$$\mathbf{V}_1'\mathbf{V}_1 = \mathbf{Y}_1'\mathbf{M}\mathbf{Y}_1 \quad \text{and} \quad \mathbf{V}_1'\mathbf{y} = \mathbf{Y}_1'\mathbf{M}\mathbf{y}$$

Solving the second equation in (13-35) for $\mathbf{c}_k$ gives

$$\mathbf{c}_k = (\mathbf{X}_1'\mathbf{X}_1)^{-1}\mathbf{X}_1'\mathbf{y} - (\mathbf{X}_1'\mathbf{X}_1)^{-1}\mathbf{X}_1'\mathbf{Y}_1\mathbf{b}_k \tag{13-36}$$

Substituting in the first equation of (13-35) and simplifying gives

$$(\mathbf{Y}_1'\mathbf{M}_1\mathbf{Y}_1 - \hat{l}\mathbf{Y}_1'\mathbf{M}\mathbf{Y}_1)\mathbf{b}_k = (\mathbf{Y}_1'\mathbf{M}_1\mathbf{y} - \hat{l}\mathbf{Y}_1'\mathbf{M}\mathbf{y}) \tag{13-37}$$

Comparing (13-34) and (13-37) the k-class estimator $\mathbf{b}_k$ with k equal to $\hat{l}$ is seen to be identical with the LISE estimator $\hat{\boldsymbol{\beta}}$. These equations relate only to the coefficients of the endogenous variables. Equation (13-32) gives the LISE coefficients of the predetermined variables as

$$\begin{aligned} \hat{\boldsymbol{\gamma}} &= (\mathbf{X}_1'\mathbf{X}_1)^{-1}\mathbf{X}_1'\mathbf{Y}_\Delta\hat{\boldsymbol{\beta}}_\Delta \\ &= (\mathbf{X}_1'\mathbf{X}_1)^{-1}\mathbf{X}_1'\mathbf{y} - (\mathbf{X}_1'\mathbf{X}_1)^{-1}\mathbf{X}_1'\mathbf{Y}_1\hat{\boldsymbol{\beta}} \end{aligned} \tag{13-38}$$

[1] The set of $(g + 1)$ equations in (13-31) is constrained to have a solution vector unique up to a factor of proportionality. Thus the solution vector satisfies any subset of g equations.

Comparing (13-38) with (13-36) it is seen that $\hat{\gamma}$ is identical with $\mathbf{c}_k$ when $\hat{\boldsymbol{\beta}}$ on the right-hand side of (13-38) is replaced by its equivalent, $\mathbf{b}_k$. Thus the LISE estimator is a k-class estimator with $k = \hat{l}$.

The family of k-class estimators thus includes the three main estimators that we have considered so far, namely OLS, 2SLS, and LISE. Goldberger has shown that k-class estimators can be interpreted as instrumental variable estimators.[1] The equation to be estimated is, as usual,

$$\mathbf{y} = \mathbf{Y}_1\boldsymbol{\beta} + \mathbf{X}_1\boldsymbol{\gamma} + \mathbf{u}$$

with data matrix $[\mathbf{Y}_1 \quad \mathbf{X}_1]$. Suppose we use as instruments the matrix $[\mathbf{Y}_1 - k\mathbf{V}_1 \quad \mathbf{X}_1]$, then the instrumental variable estimator defined in (9-35) is

$$\begin{bmatrix} (\mathbf{Y}_1 - k\mathbf{V}_1)'\mathbf{Y}_1 & (\mathbf{Y}_1 - k\mathbf{V}_1)'\mathbf{X}_1 \\ \mathbf{X}_1'\mathbf{Y}_1 & \mathbf{X}_1'\mathbf{X}_1 \end{bmatrix} \begin{bmatrix} \mathbf{b} \\ \mathbf{c} \end{bmatrix} = \begin{bmatrix} (\mathbf{Y}_1 - k\mathbf{V}_1)'\mathbf{y} \\ \mathbf{X}_1'\mathbf{y} \end{bmatrix} \tag{13-39}$$

It remains to show that this is equivalent to (13-33). It can be seen that only the top two terms on the left-hand side differ. Starting with those in (13-33)

$$\mathbf{Y}_1'\mathbf{Y}_1 - k\mathbf{V}_1'\mathbf{V}_1 = \mathbf{Y}_1'\mathbf{Y}_1 - k\mathbf{Y}_1'\mathbf{M}\mathbf{Y}_1$$

since

$$\mathbf{V}_1 = \mathbf{M}\mathbf{Y}_1 \quad \text{where} \quad \mathbf{M} = \mathbf{I} - \mathbf{X}(\mathbf{X}'\mathbf{X})^{-1}\mathbf{X}'$$

Thus

$$\mathbf{Y}_1'\mathbf{Y}_1 - k\mathbf{V}_1'\mathbf{V}_1 = (\mathbf{Y}_1 - k\mathbf{V}_1)'\mathbf{Y}_1$$

and

$$\begin{aligned} \mathbf{Y}_1'\mathbf{X}_1 &= \mathbf{Y}_1'\mathbf{X}_1 - k\mathbf{Y}_1'\mathbf{M}'\mathbf{X}_1 \quad \text{for } \mathbf{M}'\mathbf{X}_1 = \mathbf{0} \\ &= (\mathbf{Y}_1 - k\mathbf{V}_1)'\mathbf{X}_1 \end{aligned}$$

Equations (13-33) and (13-39) are thus identical and k-class estimators are indeed instrumental variable estimators with $[\mathbf{Y}_1 - k\mathbf{V}_1 \quad \mathbf{X}_1]$ used as instruments.

Instrumental variable estimators are consistent provided[2]

$$\text{plim}\,\frac{1}{n}(\mathbf{Z}'\mathbf{u}) = \mathbf{0}$$

where $\mathbf{Z}$ denotes the instruments. Thus k-class estimators will be consistent provided

$$\text{plim}\,\frac{1}{n}(\mathbf{Y}_1 - k\mathbf{V}_1)'\mathbf{u} = \mathbf{0} \quad \text{and} \quad \text{plim}\left(\frac{1}{n}\mathbf{X}_1'\mathbf{u}\right) = \mathbf{0}$$

[1] A. Goldberger, "An Instrumental Variable Interpretation of k-class Estimation," *The Indian Economic Journal*, vol. 13, pp. 424–431, 1965.

[2] Provided plim $[(1/n)\mathbf{Z}'\mathbf{Z}]$ exists.

There is no difficulty about the second of these conditions. As regards the first

$$\mathbf{Y}_1 - k\mathbf{V}_1 = \mathbf{Y}_1 - k[\mathbf{I} - \mathbf{X}(\mathbf{X}'\mathbf{X})^{-1}\mathbf{X}']\mathbf{Y}_1$$
$$= [(1-k)\mathbf{I} + k\mathbf{X}(\mathbf{X}'\mathbf{X})^{-1}\mathbf{X}']\mathbf{Y}_1$$

So

$$\operatorname{plim}\frac{1}{n}(\mathbf{Y}_1 - k\mathbf{V}_1)'\mathbf{u} = \operatorname{plim}(1-k)\cdot\operatorname{plim}\left(\frac{1}{n}\mathbf{Y}_1'\mathbf{u}\right) +$$
$$\operatorname{plim} k \cdot \operatorname{plim} \mathbf{Y}_1'\mathbf{X}(\mathbf{X}'\mathbf{X})^{-1} \cdot \operatorname{plim}\left(\frac{1}{n}\mathbf{X}'\mathbf{u}\right)$$

The second term on the right-hand side is zero since

$$\operatorname{plim}\left(\frac{1}{n}\mathbf{X}'\mathbf{u}\right) = \mathbf{0}$$

and plim $\mathbf{Y}_1'\mathbf{X}(\mathbf{X}'\mathbf{X})^{-1}$ is equal to a constant matrix, namely a sub-matrix of $\mathbf{\Pi}$. In the first term

$$\operatorname{plim}\left(\frac{1}{n}\mathbf{Y}_1'\mathbf{u}\right) \neq \mathbf{0}$$

since disturbances and endogenous variables are in general correlated in simultaneous models. Thus k-class estimators will only be consistent if

$$\operatorname{plim}(1-k) = 0$$

This condition is satisfied for both 2SLS and LISE estimators but not for OLS.

The basic result on the asymptotic variance matrix of the instrumental variable estimator derived in Section 3 of Chap. 9 may be applied to obtain the asymptotic matrix of a k-class estimator. For example, applying formula (9-38) with $[\mathbf{Y}_1 - k\mathbf{V}_1 \quad \mathbf{X}_1]$ serving as instruments for $[\mathbf{Y}_1 \quad \mathbf{X}_1]$ and replacing k by unity will give the estimated asymptotic variance matrix for 2SLS (and LISE) already derived in (13-19). The demonstration of the equivalence is left to the reader as an exercise. Goldberger has also demonstrated an attractive feature of LISE estimators in the same article, namely that if one wishes the estimates of the structural coefficients to be invariant to the choice of endogenous variable for the left-hand side of the equation (in the sense that choosing different endogenous variables on the left-hand side gives estimated coefficients proportional to those obtained from any other choice) then k must be set equal to $\hat{l}$.

So far we have dealt only with asymptotic properties of certain k-class estimators. Nagar has obtained expressions for the bias of a k-class estimator (to the order of n^{-1}) and for its moment matrix about the true parameter values (to the order of n^{-2}).[1] If we define

$$k = 1 + \frac{h}{n}$$

where h is a real number independent of n, it turns out that the bias depends, *inter alia*, on h and L, where L is the difference between the number of predetermined variables in the complete model and the number of parameters to be estimated in the structural equation under consideration. Considering only zero-type restrictions L is thus a measure of the degree of overidentification of the equation, for L is zero for an exactly identified equation and will be a positive number for an overidentified equation. To the order of n^{-1} the bias vanishes for

$$k = 1 + \frac{L - 1}{n}$$

More importantly Nagar shows how to determine the value of h (and hence of k) which will minimize the determinant of the moment matrix.[2] In some illustrative calculations with three equations of Klein's simple macromodel of the U.S. economy Nagar finds the optimal h in each case to be negative so that the optimal k is less than one and in nearly all cases the optimal k point estimates lie between the OLS and 2SLS estimates. For the LISE estimator $k(= \hat{l})$ is always greater than one and most of the LISE point estimates in this example lie outside the range defined by the OLS and 2SLS estimates. We note, in passing, that minimizing the generalized second moment is only one of many possible definitions of an optimal estimator. Given the definition, however, Nagar expects the optimal k to be generally below unity.

Further evidence on the relationship between different k-class estimators has recently been obtained by Maeshiro and Oi.[3] Maeshiro considers the special case where only one endogenous variable appears on the right-hand side of the relation. His two main results are that, for that case, 2SLS point estimates will lie between those obtained by OLS and LISE, and that LISE estimates are likely to be the most unstable of the three, in the sense that small changes in the sample data may produce more widely differing estimates by the LISE method than by the other methods. Oi works with the

[1] A. L. Nagar, "The Bias and Moment Matrix of the General k-class Estimators of the Parameters in Simultaneous Equations," *Econometrica*, 27, 575–594, 1959.

[2] In multivariate situations the generalized variance is defined as the determinant of the variance–covariance matrix. Nagar's approach is thus to minimize the generalized second moment.

[3] A. Maeshiro, "A Simple Mathematical Relationship among k-class Estimators," *J. Am. Statist. Assoc.*, vol. 61, pp. 368–374, 1966. W. Y. Oi, "On the Relationship among Different Members of the k-class," *Intern. Econ. Rev.*, vol. 10, pp. 36–46, 1969.

general structural equation in which $\mathbf{Y}_1$ is not restricted to a single vector. He shows that Maeshiro's first result is still true for the coefficients of the endogenous variables, but no simple inference is possible for the coefficients of the predetermined variables, except in the simple case considered by Maeshiro. Oi's work also emphasizes the fact that, in models where the reduced form equations account for a very high proportion of the variance of the endogenous variables, the estimates of the structural coefficients given by OLS, 2SLS, and LISE are likely to lie within a fairly narrow range. Where the proportion of the variance explained is less high the range of the estimates is likely to widen, OLS bias is likely to increase but so too will the sampling variances of 2SLS and LISE.

Returning again to asymptotic properties, Fisher has compared the probability limits of 2SLS and LISE under specification error (exclusion of variables).[1] Letting $\mathbf{d}$ denote a k-class estimator of $\boldsymbol{\delta}$ and $\mathbf{C}$ any positive definite or positive semidefinite matrix, he employed the quadratic loss function

$$(\mathbf{d} - \boldsymbol{\delta})'\mathbf{C}(\mathbf{d} - \boldsymbol{\delta})$$

The main result is the rather negative one that there exists no case in which one estimator is uniformly more robust than the other.

13-5 2SLS AND PRINCIPAL COMPONENTS

In estimating the relation $\mathbf{y} = \mathbf{Y}_1\boldsymbol{\beta} + \mathbf{X}_1\boldsymbol{\gamma} + \mathbf{u}$ by 2SLS the first stage consists of regressing $\mathbf{Y}_1$ on $\mathbf{X} = [\mathbf{X}_1 \quad \mathbf{X}_2]$. The $\mathbf{X}_1$ matrix is of order $(n \times k)$ and the $\mathbf{X}_2$ matrix of order $n \times (K - k)$, where K denotes the total number of predetermined variables in the complete model. Thus in each of these regressions we are estimating K reduced form parameters. In very small models this may cause no difficulty, but in medium and large models the number of predetermined variables (K) may easily exceed the number of sample observations (n), and so the first stage of 2SLS breaks down, or even if $K < n$ we may have an unsatisfactorily small number of degrees of freedom for the regressions.

Kloek and Mennes have suggested replacing $\mathbf{X}_2$ by a small number of principal components in order to avoid these difficulties.[2] The new problem is the choice of principal components. It is clear that we must include at least g principal components for identification requires that the $\mathbf{X}_2$ matrix (and hence any matrix that replaces it) should have at least g columns.

[1] F. M. Fisher, "The Relative Sensitivity to Specification Error of Different k-Class Estimators," *J. Am. Statist. Assoc.*, vol. 61, pp. 345–356, 1966.

[2] T. Kloek and L. B. M. Mennes, "Simultaneous Equation Estimation Based on Principal Components of Predetermined Variables," *Econometrica*, vol. 28, pp. 45-61, 1960.

Suppose the principal components are denoted by a matrix $\mathbf{F}$. Let

$$\mathbf{Z} = [\mathbf{X}_1 \quad \mathbf{F}] \tag{13-40}$$

The $\mathbf{Z}$ matrix thus takes the place of the $\mathbf{X}$ matrix in the previous development and from (13-12) the 2SLS estimator based on the principal components is given by

$$\begin{bmatrix} \mathbf{Y}_1'\mathbf{Z}(\mathbf{Z}'\mathbf{Z})^{-1}\mathbf{Z}'\mathbf{Y}_1 & \mathbf{Y}_1'\mathbf{X}_1 \\ \mathbf{X}_1'\mathbf{Y}_1 & \mathbf{X}_1'\mathbf{X}_1 \end{bmatrix} \begin{bmatrix} \mathbf{b} \\ \mathbf{c} \end{bmatrix} = \begin{bmatrix} \mathbf{Y}_1'\mathbf{Z}(\mathbf{Z}'\mathbf{Z})^{-1}\mathbf{Z}'\mathbf{y} \\ \mathbf{X}_1'\mathbf{y} \end{bmatrix} \tag{13-41}$$

An obvious choice would be to base the principal components on the $\mathbf{X}_2$ matrix. Let us assume that the variables in $\mathbf{X}_2$ have been normalized, that is, adjusted to have zero means and unit variances. If the variables were not measured in the same units normalization is in any case required before computing principal components. Thus $\mathbf{X}_2'\mathbf{X}_2$ is now a zero-order correlation matrix. From the results of Chap. 11 we know that the equation

$$(\mathbf{X}_2'\mathbf{X}_2 - \lambda\mathbf{I})\boldsymbol{\alpha} = \mathbf{0} \tag{13-42}$$

defines the latent roots, λ, and latent vectors, $\boldsymbol{\alpha}$, of $\mathbf{X}_2'\mathbf{X}_2$. The jth principal component is

$$\mathbf{f}_j = \mathbf{X}_2\boldsymbol{\alpha}_j \qquad j = 1, 2, \ldots, K - k$$

It has been suggested that a possible drawback to this method is that one or more of the components may be highly correlated with some of the variables in $\mathbf{X}_1$, though this may not be too serious since the main objective of the first stage in 2SLS is a good estimation of $\hat{\mathbf{Y}}_1$ and this can often be achieved even though some of the individual reduced form coefficients are not very precisely estimated. However, as $\mathbf{Z}'\mathbf{Z}$ approaches singularity computation of its inverse becomes extremely difficult and liable to error. Leaving this possible difficulty on one side one takes at least the first g principal components with the greatest variance corresponding to the largest roots of (13-42).

If it is desired to avoid the correlation problem Kloek and Mennes suggest selecting the components with the greatest θ_j where

$$\theta_j = \lambda_j(1 - R_j^2) \qquad j = 1, 2, \ldots, K - k \tag{13-43}$$

and R_j is the coefficient of multiple correlation when $\mathbf{f}_j$ is regressed on $\mathbf{X}_1$. This amounts to picking the principal components which are least correlated with $\mathbf{X}_1$. For

$$R_j^2 = \frac{\mathbf{f}_j'\mathbf{X}_1(\mathbf{X}_1'\mathbf{X}_1)^{-1}\mathbf{X}_1'\mathbf{f}_j}{\mathbf{f}_j'\mathbf{f}_j}$$

and so

$$\lambda_j(1 - R_j^2) = \mathbf{f}_j'[\mathbf{I} - \mathbf{X}_1(\mathbf{X}_1'\mathbf{X}_1)^{-1}\mathbf{X}_1']\mathbf{f}_j \quad \text{since } \mathbf{f}_j'\mathbf{f}_j = \lambda_j$$

The right-hand side is seen to be the residual sum of squares when $\mathbf{f}_j$ is regressed on $\mathbf{X}_1$.

A disadvantage of both of the above methods if one is estimating more than one equation of a model is that a fresh set of principal components has to be computed for each equation since $\mathbf{X}_2$ is almost certain to vary from equation to equation. A further possibility, therefore, is to compute the principal components of $\mathbf{X}'\mathbf{X}$ and then to select for each equation those which are least correlated with the $\mathbf{X}_1$ of that equation. Amemiya, however, has shown that using the asymptotic generalized mean square error as a criterion several major decision procedures indicate the use of principal components based on $\mathbf{X}_2$.[1] A very interesting study by Klein contains yet another suggested way of using principal components in 2SLS estimation.[2] In estimating a revised version of the Klein–Goldberger model of the U.S. economy he chose the principal components corresponding (a) to the four largest and (b) to the eight largest latent roots of $\mathbf{X}'\mathbf{X}$, where $\mathbf{X}$ was the matrix of all predetermined variables in the model and then used just these principal components in the first stage regressions. A comparison of the 2SLS estimates based on four and eight principal components respectively with OLS and with full-information maximum-likelihood (FIML) suggest that the 2SLS estimates based on just four principal components were the best of the four.

13-6 THREE-STAGE LEAST-SQUARES (3SLS) AND FULL-INFORMATION MAXIMUM-LIKELIHOOD (FIML)

Zellner and Theil have proposed three-stage least-squares as an estimation method which takes account of all the equations in a model and which in certain circumstances may have greater asymptotic efficiency than 2SLS.[3] Consider a general linear model containing G jointly dependent endogenous variables and K predetermined variables. The ith equation may be written

$$\mathbf{y}_i = \mathbf{Y}_i\boldsymbol{\beta}_i + \mathbf{X}_i\boldsymbol{\gamma}_i + \mathbf{u}_i \qquad i = 1, \ldots, G \tag{13-44}$$

where $\mathbf{y}_i$ is an $n \times 1$ vector of sample observations on the dependent variable in the ith equation, $\mathbf{Y}_i$ is an $(n \times g_i)$ matrix of observations on the other

[1] T. Amemiya, "On the Use of Principal Components of Independent Variables in 2SLS Estimation," *Intern. Econ. Rev.*, vol. 7, pp. 283-303, 1966.

[2] L. R. Klein, "Estimation of Interdependent Systems in Macro-econometrics," *Econometrica*, vol. 37, pp. 171–192, 1969.

[3] A. Zellner and H. Theil, "Three-stage, Least-squares: Simultaneous Estimation of Simultaneous Equations," *Econometrica*, vol. 30, pp. 54–78, 1962.

endogenous variables in the equation, $\mathbf{X}_i$ an $(n \times k_i)$ matrix of observations on the predetermined variables in the equation, $\boldsymbol{\beta}_i$ and $\boldsymbol{\gamma}_i$ vectors of parameters and $\mathbf{u}_i$ a vector of disturbances. Rewrite (13-44) as

$$\mathbf{y}_i = \mathbf{Z}_i\boldsymbol{\delta}_i + \mathbf{u}_i \qquad i = 1, \ldots, G \tag{13-45}$$

where

$$\mathbf{Z}_i = [\mathbf{Y}_i \quad \mathbf{X}_i] \quad \text{and} \quad \boldsymbol{\delta}_i = \begin{bmatrix} \boldsymbol{\beta}_i \\ \boldsymbol{\gamma}_i \end{bmatrix} \tag{13-46}$$

If (13-45) is premultiplied by $\mathbf{X}'$, where $\mathbf{X}$ is the $(n \times K)$ matrix of all predetermined variables in the model, then

$$\mathbf{X}'\mathbf{y}_i = \mathbf{X}'\mathbf{Z}_i\boldsymbol{\delta}_i + \mathbf{X}'\mathbf{u}_i \qquad i = 1, \ldots, G \tag{13-47}$$

If we consider (13-47) as a relation between the dependent variable $\mathbf{X}'\mathbf{y}_i$ and explanatory variables $\mathbf{X}'\mathbf{Z}_i$ with disturbance vector $\mathbf{X}'\mathbf{u}_i$ the variance–covariance matrix of the disturbance is

$$E(\mathbf{X}'\mathbf{u}_i\mathbf{u}_i'\mathbf{X}) = \sigma_{ii}\mathbf{X}'\mathbf{X} \tag{13-48}$$

where σ_{ii} is the constant variance of the disturbance in the ith equation. Because of (13-48) the vector $\boldsymbol{\delta}_i$ in (13-47) should be estimated by generalized least-squares, giving the estimator,

$$\mathbf{d}_i = [\mathbf{Z}_i'\mathbf{X}(\mathbf{X}'\mathbf{X})^{-1}\mathbf{X}'\mathbf{Z}_i]^{-1}\mathbf{Z}_i'\mathbf{X}(\mathbf{X}'\mathbf{X})^{-1}\mathbf{X}'\mathbf{y}_i \tag{13-49}$$

Equation (13-49) is simply another way of writing the 2SLS estimator of (13-44) as may easily be verified by substituting for $\mathbf{Z}_i$ from (13-46) and multiplying out.

Let us now write out the complete set of equations in (13-47) as

$$\begin{bmatrix} \mathbf{X}'\mathbf{y}_1 \\ \mathbf{X}'\mathbf{y}_2 \\ \vdots \\ \mathbf{X}'\mathbf{y}_G \end{bmatrix} = \begin{bmatrix} \mathbf{X}'\mathbf{Z}_1 & \mathbf{0} & \cdots & \mathbf{0} \\ \mathbf{0} & \mathbf{X}'\mathbf{Z}_2 & \cdots & \mathbf{0} \\ \vdots & \vdots & & \vdots \\ \mathbf{0} & \mathbf{0} & \cdots & \mathbf{X}'\mathbf{Z}_G \end{bmatrix} \begin{bmatrix} \boldsymbol{\delta}_1 \\ \boldsymbol{\delta}_2 \\ \vdots \\ \boldsymbol{\delta}_G \end{bmatrix} + \begin{bmatrix} \mathbf{X}'\mathbf{u}_1 \\ \mathbf{X}'\mathbf{u}_2 \\ \vdots \\ \mathbf{X}'\mathbf{u}_G \end{bmatrix} \tag{13-50}$$

The variance–covariance matrix of the disturbance vector in (13-50) is then

$$\mathbf{V} = \begin{bmatrix} \sigma_{11}\mathbf{X}'\mathbf{X} & \sigma_{12}\mathbf{X}'\mathbf{X} & \cdots & \sigma_{1G}\mathbf{X}'\mathbf{X} \\ \sigma_{21}\mathbf{X}'\mathbf{X} & \sigma_{22}\mathbf{X}'\mathbf{X} & \cdots & \sigma_{2G}\mathbf{X}'\mathbf{X} \\ \vdots & \vdots & & \vdots \\ \sigma_{G1}\mathbf{X}'\mathbf{X} & \sigma_{G2}\mathbf{X}'\mathbf{X} & \cdots & \sigma_{GG}\mathbf{X}'\mathbf{X} \end{bmatrix} \tag{13-51}$$

where σ_{ij} denotes the contemporaneous covariance of the structural disturbances of the ith and jth equation. Collecting the σ_{ij} in a matrix $\mathbf{\Sigma}$

$$\mathbf{V} = \mathbf{\Sigma} \otimes (\mathbf{X}'\mathbf{X})$$

and

$$\mathbf{V}^{-1} = \mathbf{\Sigma}^{-1} \otimes (\mathbf{X}'\mathbf{X})^{-1}$$

Generalized least-squares is an appropriate estimator for (13-50). However, it involves $\mathbf{V}$ and the $\mathbf{\Sigma}$ matrix appearing in $\mathbf{V}$ is unknown. The Zellner–Theil suggestion is that the σ_{ij} should be estimated from the disturbances calculated from 2SLS estimates, that is, the 2SLS estimator $\mathbf{d}_i$ should be computed for each structural equation from (13-49) and then substituted in (13-45) to yield a calculated vector $\hat{\mathbf{u}}_i (i = 1, \ldots, G)$ from which estimates s_{ij} of the σ_{ij} are computed. The 3SLS estimator $\hat{\boldsymbol{\delta}}$ is then given by

$$\hat{\boldsymbol{\delta}} = \left\{ \begin{bmatrix} \mathbf{Z}_1'\mathbf{X} & \mathbf{0} & \cdots & \mathbf{0} \\ \mathbf{0} & \mathbf{Z}_2'\mathbf{X} & \cdots & \mathbf{0} \\ \vdots & \vdots & & \vdots \\ \mathbf{0} & \mathbf{0} & \cdots & \mathbf{Z}_G'\mathbf{X} \end{bmatrix} \begin{bmatrix} s^{11}(\mathbf{X}'\mathbf{X})^{-1} & s^{12}(\mathbf{X}'\mathbf{X})^{-1} & \cdots & s^{1G}(\mathbf{X}'\mathbf{X})^{-1} \\ \vdots & \vdots & & \vdots \\ s^{G1}(\mathbf{X}'\mathbf{X})^{-1} & s^{G2}(\mathbf{X}'\mathbf{X})^{-1} & \cdots & s^{GG}(\mathbf{X}'\mathbf{X})^{-1} \end{bmatrix} \right.$$

$$\left. \times \begin{bmatrix} \mathbf{X}'\mathbf{Z}_1 & \mathbf{0} & \cdots & \mathbf{0} \\ \mathbf{0} & \mathbf{X}'\mathbf{Z}_2 & \cdots & \mathbf{0} \\ \vdots & \vdots & & \vdots \\ \mathbf{0} & \mathbf{0} & \cdots & \mathbf{X}'\mathbf{Z}_G \end{bmatrix} \right\}^{-1}$$

$$\times \begin{bmatrix} \mathbf{Z}_1'\mathbf{X} & \mathbf{0} & \cdots & \mathbf{0} \\ \mathbf{0} & \mathbf{Z}_2'\mathbf{X} & \cdots & \mathbf{0} \\ \vdots & \vdots & & \vdots \\ \mathbf{0} & \mathbf{0} & \cdots & \mathbf{Z}_G'\mathbf{X} \end{bmatrix} \begin{bmatrix} s^{11}(\mathbf{X}'\mathbf{X})^{-1} & \cdots & s^{1G}(\mathbf{X}'\mathbf{X})^{-1} \\ \vdots & & \vdots \\ s^{G1}(\mathbf{X}'\mathbf{X})^{-1} & \cdots & s^{GG}(\mathbf{X}'\mathbf{X})^{-1} \end{bmatrix} \begin{bmatrix} \mathbf{X}'\mathbf{y}_1 \\ \vdots \\ \mathbf{X}'\mathbf{y}_G \end{bmatrix}$$

where the s^{ij} indicate the elements of $[s_{ij}]^{-1}$. Simplifying gives

$$\hat{\boldsymbol{\delta}} = \begin{bmatrix} s^{11}\mathbf{Z}_1'\mathbf{X}(\mathbf{X}'\mathbf{X})^{-1}\mathbf{X}'\mathbf{Z}_1 & \cdots & s^{1G}\mathbf{Z}_1'\mathbf{X}(\mathbf{X}'\mathbf{X})^{-1}\mathbf{X}'\mathbf{Z}_G \\ \vdots & & \vdots \\ s^{G1}\mathbf{Z}_G'\mathbf{X}(\mathbf{X}'\mathbf{X})^{-1}\mathbf{X}'\mathbf{Z}_1 & \cdots & s^{GG}\mathbf{Z}_G'\mathbf{X}(\mathbf{X}'\mathbf{X})^{-1}\mathbf{X}'\mathbf{Z}_G \end{bmatrix}^{-1}$$

$$\times \begin{bmatrix} \sum_{j=1}^{G} s^{1j}\mathbf{Z}_1'\mathbf{X}(\mathbf{X}'\mathbf{X})^{-1}\mathbf{X}'\mathbf{y}_j \\ \vdots \\ \sum_{j=1}^{G} s^{Gj}\mathbf{Z}_G'\mathbf{X}(\mathbf{X}'\mathbf{X})^{-1}\mathbf{X}'\mathbf{y}_j \end{bmatrix} \qquad (13\text{-}52)$$

with an estimate of the asymptotic variance matrix given by the inverse matrix on the right-hand side of (13-52).

The 3SLS procedure is clearly an extension to simultaneous-equation systems of the Zellner treatment of groups of seemingly unrelated regression equations described in Chap. 7. There is only a gain in asymptotic efficiency over 2SLS if the $\boldsymbol{\Sigma}$ matrix is not diagonal, that is if the disturbances in various structural equations are contemporaneously correlated. To apply the approach in practice the following points should be noted.

(a) Any definitional equations (identities) should be left out of the system before calculations begin.

(b) Likewise any unidentified equations should be omitted.

(c) This leaves just identified and/or overidentified equations. It is computationally efficient to apply 3SLS to each of these groups *separately*.

(d) For the group of overidentified equations compute the 3SLS estimator defined in (13-52) above, taking G as the number of overidentified equations. If there is only one overidentified equation 3SLS degenerates to 2SLS.

(e) For the group of just-identified equations, the computational procedure is somewhat more complicated and the interested reader is referred to the Zellner–Theil article for details.

(f) If the covariance matrix $\boldsymbol{\Sigma}$ of the structural disturbances is block diagonal the 3SLS technique outlined in (a) to (e) may be applied separately to the group of equations corresponding to each block.

Full information maximum-likelihood (FIML) is a complete system method of estimation. It is computationally the most expensive of all the estimation methods that we have considered, as it involves the solution of nonlinear equations, and in addition it is likely to run into trouble over degrees of freedom in anything other than fairly small models. Consider the general linear model in G current endogenous variables

$$\mathbf{B}\mathbf{y}_t + \boldsymbol{\Gamma}\mathbf{x}_t = \mathbf{u}_t \qquad t = 1, \ldots, n \tag{13-53}$$

with

$$E(\mathbf{u}_t) = \mathbf{0} \qquad t = 1, \ldots, n$$

and

$$E(\mathbf{u}_t\mathbf{u}_t') = \boldsymbol{\Sigma} \qquad t = 1, \ldots, n$$

where $\boldsymbol{\Sigma}$ is a positive definite matrix. If it is assumed that the disturbances are normally distributed we can write

$$\mathbf{u}_t \text{ is } N(\mathbf{0}, \boldsymbol{\Sigma})$$

and

$$f(\mathbf{u}_t) = \frac{1}{(2\pi)^{G/2}(\det \mathbf{\Sigma})^{1/2}} \exp\left(-\tfrac{1}{2}\mathbf{u}_t'\mathbf{\Sigma}^{-1}\mathbf{u}_t\right) \tag{13-54}$$

Assuming the $\mathbf{u}$ vectors to be serially uncorrelated the likelihood for the n vectors $\mathbf{u}_1, \mathbf{u}_2, \ldots, \mathbf{u}_n$ is then

$$\begin{aligned} p(\mathbf{u}_1, \mathbf{u}_2, \ldots, \mathbf{u}_n) &= \prod_{t=1}^{n} f(\mathbf{u}_t) \\ &= (2\pi)^{-nG/2}(\det \mathbf{\Sigma})^{-n/2} \exp\left(-\frac{1}{2}\sum_{t=1}^{n} \mathbf{u}_t'\mathbf{\Sigma}^{-1}\mathbf{u}_t\right) \end{aligned} \tag{13-55}$$

The likelihood for $(\mathbf{y}_1, \ldots, \mathbf{y}_n)$ is then

$$\begin{aligned} p(\mathbf{y}_1, \mathbf{y}_2, \ldots, \mathbf{y}_n) &= (2\pi)^{-nG/2}|\det \mathbf{B}|^n(\det \mathbf{\Sigma})^{-n/2} \\ &\quad \times \exp\left\{-\frac{1}{2}\sum_{t=1}^{n} (\mathbf{B}\mathbf{y}_t + \mathbf{\Gamma}\mathbf{x}_t)'\mathbf{\Sigma}^{-1}(\mathbf{B}\mathbf{y}_t + \mathbf{\Gamma}\mathbf{x}_t)\right\} \end{aligned} \tag{13-56}$$

If we write

$$\mathbf{B}\mathbf{y}_t + \mathbf{\Gamma}\mathbf{x}_t = [\mathbf{B} \quad \mathbf{\Gamma}]\begin{bmatrix} \mathbf{y}_t \\ \mathbf{x}_t \end{bmatrix} = \mathbf{A}\mathbf{z}_t$$

the exponent in the likelihood (13-56) can be written

$$\begin{aligned} -\frac{1}{2}\sum_{t=1}^{n} \mathbf{z}_t'\mathbf{A}'\mathbf{\Sigma}^{-1}\mathbf{A}\mathbf{z}_t &= -\tfrac{1}{2}\operatorname{tr}(\mathbf{Z}\mathbf{A}'\mathbf{\Sigma}^{-1}\mathbf{A}\mathbf{Z}') \\ &= -\tfrac{1}{2}\operatorname{tr}(\mathbf{\Sigma}^{-1}\mathbf{A}\mathbf{Z}'\mathbf{Z}\mathbf{A}') \end{aligned}$$

where

$$\mathbf{Z} = [\mathbf{Y} \quad \mathbf{X}] = \begin{bmatrix} \mathbf{y}_1' & \mathbf{x}_1' \\ \vdots & \vdots \\ \mathbf{y}_n' & \mathbf{x}_n' \end{bmatrix}$$

is the $n \times (G + K)$ matrix of observations on all the endogenous and predetermined variables. Defining

$$\mathbf{M} = \frac{1}{n}\mathbf{Z}'\mathbf{Z} \tag{13-57}$$

$$\operatorname{tr}(\mathbf{\Sigma}^{-1}\mathbf{A}\mathbf{Z}'\mathbf{Z}\mathbf{A}') = n \operatorname{tr}(\mathbf{\Sigma}^{-1}\mathbf{A}\mathbf{M}\mathbf{A}')$$

and so the logarithm of the likelihood in (13-56) may be written

$$L(\mathbf{A}, \mathbf{\Sigma}) = \text{constant} + n \log|\det \mathbf{B}| - \frac{n}{2}\log \det \mathbf{\Sigma} - \frac{n}{2}\operatorname{tr}(\mathbf{\Sigma}^{-1}\mathbf{A}\mathbf{M}\mathbf{A}') \tag{13-58}$$

Maximization of $L(\mathbf{A}, \boldsymbol{\Sigma})$ with respect to the elements of $\mathbf{A}$ and $\boldsymbol{\Sigma}$ yields the FIML estimators. We will not present the details here as the resultant equations are computationally expensive and the least used of all the simultaneous estimation methods.[1]

13-7 PREDICTION AND SIMULTANEOUS CONFIDENCE INTERVALS

Econometric models are usually constructed for one or both of two major reasons. One is to obtain knowledge about structural and/or reduced form coefficients: the other is to make conditional predictions for the endogenous variables, given certain assumptions about the exogenous variables. If interest centers on structural coefficients we have seen that consistent estimators are available and furthermore that the sample data can be employed to estimate the asymptotic variances of the estimates. If interest centers on the reduced form coefficients unbiased and consistent estimators may be obtained by applying OLS to each equation in turn, and estimates made of the sampling variances. But this method may be improved upon. For instance if one suspects the disturbances in different reduced form equations to be contemporaneously correlated the Zellner estimator for seemingly unrelated regressions of Chap. 7 may be employed. Neither simple least-squares nor the Zellner method, however, impose any restrictions on the parameters of the reduced form equations. Yet such restrictions do exist and are embodied in the set of equations connecting structural and reduced form parameters, namely $\boldsymbol{\Pi} = -\mathbf{B}^{-1}\boldsymbol{\Gamma}$. Klein has argued that, if the specification of the model in terms of the $\mathbf{B}$ and $\boldsymbol{\Gamma}$ matrices is correct, more efficient estimates of $\boldsymbol{\Pi}$ will be obtained by estimating $\hat{\mathbf{B}}$ and $\hat{\boldsymbol{\Gamma}}$ by some consistent method and then estimating $\boldsymbol{\Pi}$ by $\hat{\boldsymbol{\Pi}} = -\hat{\mathbf{B}}^{-1}\hat{\boldsymbol{\Gamma}}$.[2] $\hat{\boldsymbol{\Pi}}$ obtained in this way will certainly be a consistent estimator. However, it is desirable to be able to form estimates of the sampling variances of the elements of $\hat{\boldsymbol{\Pi}}$. The problem may be stated as follows. Given consistent estimators $\hat{\mathbf{B}}$ and $\hat{\boldsymbol{\Gamma}}$ with known asymptotic variance–covariance matrices, what is the asymptotic variance–covariance matrix for the elements of $\hat{\boldsymbol{\Pi}}$?

To answer this let us first recapitulate some elementary results. Suppose $\hat{\alpha}$ denotes an estimator of a parameter α with asymptotic expectation

$$\mathscr{E}(\hat{\alpha}) = \alpha \tag{13-59}$$

and asymptotic variance

$$\text{asy var}(\hat{\alpha}) = v/n \tag{13-60}$$

[1] For derivations the reader should consult P. R. Fisk, *Stochastically Dependent Equations*, Griffin, London, 1967, and W. C. Hood and T. C. Koopmans (editors), *Studies in Econometric Method*, Wiley, New York, 1953.

[2] L. R. Klein, "The Efficiency of Estimation in Econometric Models," Cowles Foundation Paper No. 157, Yale University, 1960.

where v is a finite constant. As a consequence of (13-59) and (13-60)

$$\text{plim } \hat{\alpha} = \alpha \tag{13-61}$$

Let us suppose also that plim $n(\hat{\alpha} - \alpha)^2$ exists and is equal to v, so that we have the alternative way of writing the asymptotic variance as

$$\text{asy var}(\hat{\alpha}) = n^{-1} \text{ plim } n(\hat{\alpha} - \alpha)^2 = v/n \tag{13-62}$$

Now let $\hat{\pi}$ be a single-valued function of $\hat{\alpha}$, $f(\hat{\alpha})$. As a consequence of (13-61)

$$\text{plim } \hat{\pi} = \text{plim } f(\hat{\alpha}) = f(\alpha) = \pi, \text{ say.} \tag{13-63}$$

Expanding $\hat{\pi}$ in a Taylor series around α and neglecting terms in the second and higher powers of $(\hat{\alpha} - \alpha)$

$$\hat{\pi} = f(\alpha) + \frac{df}{d\hat{\alpha}} \cdot (\hat{\alpha} - \alpha)$$

where the derivative is evaluated at α. Thus

$$\hat{\pi} - \pi = \frac{df}{d\hat{\alpha}} \cdot (\hat{\alpha} - \alpha)$$

Multiplying by $\sqrt{n}$ and squaring

$$[\sqrt{n}(\hat{\pi} - \pi)]^2 = \left(\frac{df}{d\hat{\alpha}}\right)^2 \cdot n(\hat{\alpha} - \alpha)^2$$

Hence

$$n^{-1} \text{ plim } [\sqrt{n}(\hat{\pi} - \pi)]^2 = n^{-1}\left(\frac{df}{d\hat{\alpha}}\right)^2 \text{ plim } n(\hat{\alpha} - \alpha)^2$$

$$= \left(\frac{df}{d\hat{\alpha}}\right)^2 \cdot \frac{v}{n} \tag{13-64}$$

that is, the asymptotic variance of $\hat{\pi}$ is $(df/d\hat{\alpha})^2$ times the asymptotic variance of $\hat{\alpha}$.

Now suppose $\hat{\boldsymbol{\alpha}}$ denotes a vector of consistent estimators of the elements of the vector $\boldsymbol{\alpha}$. That is

$$\text{plim } (\hat{\boldsymbol{\alpha}}) = \boldsymbol{\alpha} \tag{13–65}$$

$$n^{-1} \text{ plim } [\sqrt{n}(\hat{\boldsymbol{\alpha}} - \boldsymbol{\alpha})][\sqrt{n}(\hat{\boldsymbol{\alpha}} - \boldsymbol{\alpha})]' = n^{-1}\mathbf{V} \tag{13-66}$$

where $\mathbf{V}$ is a matrix of finite constants. If $\hat{\pi} = f(\hat{\boldsymbol{\alpha}})$, then plim $\hat{\pi} = f(\boldsymbol{\alpha}) = \pi$ (say), as a consequence of (13-65). Again expanding $f(\hat{\boldsymbol{\alpha}})$ in a Taylor series around $\boldsymbol{\alpha}$ and ignoring terms of second and higher degrees

$$\hat{\pi} = f(\hat{\boldsymbol{\alpha}}) = f(\boldsymbol{\alpha}) + \left(\frac{\partial f}{\partial \hat{\boldsymbol{\alpha}}}\right)'(\hat{\boldsymbol{\alpha}} - \boldsymbol{\alpha}) \tag{13-67}$$

where $(\partial f/\partial \boldsymbol{\alpha})'$ denotes the row vector of partial derivatives of f with respect to the elements of $\hat{\boldsymbol{\alpha}}$. It then follows simply from (13-67) that the asymptotic variance of $\hat{\pi}$ is given by

$$\text{asy var}(\hat{\pi}) = n^{-1}\left(\frac{\partial f}{\partial \hat{\boldsymbol{\alpha}}}\right)'\mathbf{V}\left(\frac{\partial f}{\partial \hat{\boldsymbol{\alpha}}}\right) \tag{13-68}$$

Finally, if $\hat{\boldsymbol{\pi}}$ denotes a vector of estimates, each of which is some function of $\hat{\boldsymbol{\alpha}}$, that is $\hat{\pi}_i = f_i(\hat{\boldsymbol{\alpha}})$ for $i = 1, 2, \ldots$, an expression of the form (13-68) will give the asymptotic variance of each $\hat{\pi}_i$, and it is easily seen that the asymptotic covariance for $\hat{\pi}_i, \hat{\pi}_j$ is

$$\text{asy cov}(\hat{\pi}_i, \hat{\pi}_j) = n^{-1}\left(\frac{\partial f_i}{\partial \hat{\boldsymbol{\alpha}}}\right)'\mathbf{V}\left(\frac{\partial f_j}{\partial \hat{\boldsymbol{\alpha}}}\right)$$

Collecting these variances and covariances the asymptotic variance matrix for $\hat{\boldsymbol{\pi}}$ is

$$\text{asy var}(\hat{\boldsymbol{\pi}}) = n^{-1} \cdot \mathbf{D}'\mathbf{V}\mathbf{D} \tag{13-69}$$

where

$$\mathbf{D} = \frac{\partial \hat{\boldsymbol{\pi}}}{\partial \hat{\boldsymbol{\alpha}}} = \left(\frac{\partial \hat{\pi}_1}{\partial \hat{\boldsymbol{\alpha}}} \quad \frac{\partial \hat{\pi}_2}{\partial \hat{\boldsymbol{\alpha}}} \quad \cdots\right)_{\hat{\boldsymbol{\alpha}}=\boldsymbol{\alpha}} \tag{13-70}$$

is the matrix of partial derivatives of each element of $\hat{\boldsymbol{\pi}}$ with respect to each element of $\hat{\boldsymbol{\alpha}}$, evaluated at $\hat{\boldsymbol{\alpha}} = \boldsymbol{\alpha}$.

Formula (13-69) is the basic result from which the asymptotic variances and covariances of the reduced form coefficients may be derived.[1]

Let $\boldsymbol{\alpha}$ be the column vector whose transpose is the row vector

$$\boldsymbol{\alpha}' = [\beta_{11} \cdots \beta_{1G}\gamma_{11} \cdots \gamma_{1K}\beta_{21} \cdots\cdots \beta_{G1} \cdots \beta_{GG}\gamma_{G1} \cdots \gamma_{GK}]$$

with the coefficients of the first structural equation followed by those of the second, and *seriatim* for the G structural equations. Let $\boldsymbol{\pi}$ denote the column vector containing all the reduced form coefficients,

$$\boldsymbol{\pi}' = [\pi_{11} \cdots \pi_{1K}\pi_{21} \cdots \pi_{2K} \cdots \pi_{G1} \cdots \pi_{GK}]$$

$\boldsymbol{\alpha}$ is thus a vector of $G(G + k)$ elements and $\boldsymbol{\pi}$ a vector of GK elements. The matrix $\mathbf{D}$ of (13-70) is then of order $G(G + K)$ by GK. The matrix should be evaluated at $\hat{\boldsymbol{\alpha}} = \boldsymbol{\alpha}$ which is equivalent to setting

$$\mathbf{D} = \frac{\partial \boldsymbol{\pi}}{\partial \boldsymbol{\alpha}}$$

[1] See A. S. Goldberger, A. L. Nagar, and H. S. Odeh, "The Covariance Matrices of Reduced-Form Coefficients and of Forecasts for a Structural Econometric Model," *Econometrica*, vol. 29, pp. 556–573, 1961.

Goldberger, Nagar, and Odeh have shown that[1]

$$\frac{\partial \pi}{\partial \boldsymbol{\alpha}} = (\mathbf{B}^{-1})' \otimes \begin{bmatrix} \boldsymbol{\Pi} \\ \mathbf{I}_K \end{bmatrix} \tag{13-71}$$

$$= \begin{bmatrix} \beta^{11}\begin{bmatrix} \boldsymbol{\Pi} \\ \mathbf{I} \end{bmatrix} & \beta^{21}\begin{bmatrix} \boldsymbol{\Pi} \\ \mathbf{I} \end{bmatrix} & \cdots & \beta^{G1}\begin{bmatrix} \boldsymbol{\Pi} \\ \mathbf{I} \end{bmatrix} \\ \vdots & \vdots & & \vdots \\ \beta^{1G}\begin{bmatrix} \boldsymbol{\Pi} \\ \mathbf{I} \end{bmatrix} & \beta^{2G}\begin{bmatrix} \boldsymbol{\Pi} \\ \mathbf{I} \end{bmatrix} & \cdots & \beta^{GG}\begin{bmatrix} \boldsymbol{\Pi} \\ \mathbf{I} \end{bmatrix} \end{bmatrix} \tag{13-72}$$

The true coefficients appearing in (13-71) and (13-72) are, of course, unknown but consistent estimates are provided by $\hat{\mathbf{B}}$ and $\hat{\boldsymbol{\Gamma}}$. The remaining term in (13-69) is $n^{-1}\mathbf{V}$, the asymptotic variance–covariance matrix of the structural estimators. If 3SLS has been used to compute $\hat{\mathbf{B}}$ and $\hat{\boldsymbol{\Gamma}}$ a consistent estimator of this dispersion matrix is provided by the inverse matrix on the right-hand side of (13-52). If 2SLS has been used we only have the error variance matrices for each equation separately, which constitute the matrices on the principal diagonal of $n^{-1}\mathbf{V}$; the off-diagonal matrices giving the estimated sampling covariances of the coefficients in any pair of equations

$$\mathbf{y}_i = \mathbf{Y}_i\boldsymbol{\beta}_i + \mathbf{X}_i\boldsymbol{\gamma}_i + \mathbf{u}_i$$

$$\mathbf{y}_j = \mathbf{Y}_j\boldsymbol{\beta}_j + \mathbf{X}_j\boldsymbol{\gamma}_j + \mathbf{u}_j$$

may be computed from[2]

$$s_{ij}\begin{bmatrix} \mathbf{Y}_i'\mathbf{Y}_i - \mathbf{V}_i'\mathbf{V}_i & \mathbf{Y}_i'\mathbf{X}_i \\ \mathbf{X}_i'\mathbf{Y}_i & \mathbf{X}_i'\mathbf{X}_i \end{bmatrix}^{-1} \begin{bmatrix} \mathbf{Y}_i'\mathbf{Y}_j - \mathbf{V}_i'\mathbf{V}_j & \mathbf{Y}_i'\mathbf{X}_j \\ \mathbf{X}_i'\mathbf{Y}_j & \mathbf{X}_i'\mathbf{X}_j \end{bmatrix}$$

$$\times \begin{bmatrix} \mathbf{Y}_j'\mathbf{Y}_j - \mathbf{V}_j'\mathbf{V}_j & \mathbf{Y}_j'\mathbf{X}_j \\ \mathbf{X}_j'\mathbf{Y}_j & \mathbf{X}_j'\mathbf{X}_j \end{bmatrix}^{-1} \tag{13-73}$$

where s_{ij} is the estimated covariance between $\mathbf{u}_i$ and $\mathbf{u}_j$. Thus error variances for the reduced form coefficients are found from (13-69) where the **D** matrix is defined in (13-71) and (13-72). A numerical example is given in the Goldberger, Nagar, Odeh article.

The second problem mentioned at the beginning of this section is that of predicting the endogenous variables for given values of the exogenous variables. Point forecasts are simply produced by substitution in the estimated reduced form equations. Thus if $\mathbf{x}_f$ denotes a vector of forecast values

[1] Goldberger, Nagar, and Odeh, *op. cit.*, pp. 558–561.

[2] H. Theil, *Economic Forecasts and Policy*, 2nd ed., North-Holland Publishing Co., Amsterdam, 1961, p. 342.

for the predetermined variables the point forecasts for the endogenous variables are given by the $\hat{\mathbf{y}}_f$ vector,

$$\hat{\mathbf{y}}_f = \hat{\mathbf{\Pi}}\mathbf{x}_f$$

The determination of a confidence region for these forecasts depends upon the method by which $\hat{\mathbf{\Pi}}$ has been obtained. As indicated earlier, $\hat{\mathbf{\Pi}}$ is in general obtained either by OLS applied to the reduced form equations or by $\hat{\mathbf{\Pi}} = -\hat{\mathbf{B}}^{-1}\hat{\mathbf{\Gamma}}$ where the structural coefficients have been estimated by some consistent method. Given true specifications the latter is preferable, but if one is none too certain about the exact specification of the structural equations it may be sensible to estimate the reduced form equations by OLS.[1]

In the latter case

$$\hat{\mathbf{\Pi}} = \mathbf{Y}'\mathbf{X}(\mathbf{X}'\mathbf{X})^{-1} \tag{13-74}$$

where $\mathbf{Y}$ is the $(n \times G)$ matrix of observations on all the endogenous variables and $\mathbf{X}$ is the $(n \times K)$ matrix of observations on all the predetermined variables in the model. The true values of the endogenous variables in the forecast period are

$$\mathbf{y}_f = \mathbf{\Pi}\mathbf{x}_f + \mathbf{v}_f$$

where $\mathbf{v}_f$ denotes the vector of reduced form disturbances in the forecast period. The error of forecast is thus

$$\hat{\mathbf{y}}_f - \mathbf{y}_f = (\hat{\mathbf{\Pi}} - \mathbf{\Pi})\mathbf{x}_f - \mathbf{v}_f \tag{13-75}$$

Since $E(\hat{\mathbf{\Pi}}) = \mathbf{\Pi}$ and $E(\mathbf{v}_f) = \mathbf{0}$ the forecasts are unbiased. The variance–covariance matrix of the forecast error is

$$\mathbf{\Sigma}_{ff} = E[(\hat{\mathbf{y}}_f - \mathbf{y}_f)(\hat{\mathbf{y}}_f - \mathbf{y}_f)'] \tag{13-76}$$

Substituting from (13-75) on the right-hand side of (13-76) the cross-product terms are seen to vanish as $\hat{\mathbf{\Pi}}$ and $\mathbf{v}_f$ are independent on the usual assumption of serial independence in the structural (and hence in the reduced-form) disturbances. Thus

$$\Sigma_{ff} = E[(\hat{\mathbf{\Pi}} - \mathbf{\Pi})\mathbf{x}_f\mathbf{x}_f'(\hat{\mathbf{\Pi}} - \mathbf{\Pi})] + E[\mathbf{v}_f\mathbf{v}_f'] \tag{13-77}$$

Assuming constant variances and nonzero contemporaneous covariances but zero lagged covariances for the reduced form disturbances we can set

$$E(\mathbf{v}_f\mathbf{v}_f') = \mathbf{\Sigma}_{vv} \tag{13-78}$$

[1] See J. W. Hooper and A. Zellner, "The Error of Forecast for Multivariate Regression Models," *Econometrica*, vol. 29, pp. 544-555, 1961, on which the following results are based.

and so it only remains to evaluate the first term on the right-hand side of (13-77). The set of true reduced form equations can be written

$$\mathbf{Y} = \mathbf{X\Pi}' + \mathbf{V} \tag{13-79}$$

where

$$\mathbf{V} = [\mathbf{v}_1 \cdots \mathbf{v}_i \cdots \mathbf{v}_G] \tag{13-80}$$

so that $\mathbf{V}$ is the $(n \times G)$ matrix of reduced form disturbances, $\mathbf{v}_i$ indicating the column vector of disturbances in the reduced form equation for Y_i. Substituting (13-79) in (13-74) gives

$$\hat{\mathbf{\Pi}} - \mathbf{\Pi} = \mathbf{V}'\mathbf{X}(\mathbf{X}'\mathbf{X})^{-1}$$

and using this with (13-80) gives

$$E[(\hat{\mathbf{\Pi}} - \mathbf{\Pi})\mathbf{x}_f\mathbf{x}_f'(\hat{\mathbf{\Pi}} - \mathbf{\Pi})']$$

$$= E\begin{bmatrix} \mathbf{v}_1'\mathbf{M}'\mathbf{M}\mathbf{v}_1 & \mathbf{v}_1'\mathbf{M}'\mathbf{M}\mathbf{v}_2 & \cdots & \mathbf{v}_1'\mathbf{M}'\mathbf{M}\mathbf{v}_G \\ \vdots & \vdots & & \vdots \\ \mathbf{v}_G'\mathbf{M}'\mathbf{M}\mathbf{v}_1 & \mathbf{v}_G'\mathbf{M}'\mathbf{M}\mathbf{v}_2 & \cdots & \mathbf{v}_G'\mathbf{M}'\mathbf{M}\mathbf{v}_G \end{bmatrix} \tag{13-81}$$

where

$$\mathbf{M} = \mathbf{x}_f'(\mathbf{X}'\mathbf{X})^{-1}\mathbf{X}' \tag{13-82}$$

To evaluate the matrix in (13-81), consider first of all terms on the principal diagonal.

$$\begin{aligned} E(\mathbf{v}_i'\mathbf{M}'\mathbf{M}\mathbf{v}_i) &= E(\text{tr}\,(\mathbf{v}'_i\mathbf{M}'\mathbf{M}\mathbf{v}_i)] \\ &= E[\text{tr}\,(\mathbf{M}\mathbf{v}_i\mathbf{v}_i'\mathbf{M}')] \\ &= \text{tr}\,[\mathbf{M}E(\mathbf{v}_i\mathbf{v}_i')\mathbf{M}'] \\ &= \sigma_{ii}\,\text{tr}\,(\mathbf{MM}') \end{aligned}$$

since $E(\mathbf{v}_i\mathbf{v}_i') = \sigma_{ii}\mathbf{I}_n$ on the usual assumptions about reduced form disturbances, σ_{ii} indicating the variance of the disturbance in the *ith* reduced-form equation. From (13-82)

$$\mathbf{MM}' = \mathbf{x}_f'(\mathbf{X}'\mathbf{X})^{-1}\mathbf{x}_f$$

Thus

$$E(\mathbf{v}_i'\mathbf{M}'\mathbf{M}\mathbf{v}_i) = \sigma_{ii}\mathbf{x}_f'(\mathbf{X}'\mathbf{X})^{-1}\mathbf{x}_f$$

In a similar fashion

$$E(\mathbf{v}_i'\mathbf{M}'\mathbf{M}\mathbf{v}_j) = \sigma_{ij}\mathbf{x}_f'(\mathbf{X}'\mathbf{X})^{-1}\mathbf{x}_f$$

The terms σ_{ii}, σ_{ij} are the elements of $\mathbf{\Sigma}_{vv}$. Thus

$$E[(\hat{\mathbf{\Pi}} - \mathbf{\Pi})\mathbf{x}_f\mathbf{x}_f'(\hat{\mathbf{\Pi}} - \mathbf{\Pi})] = \mathbf{x}_f'(\mathbf{X}'\mathbf{X})^{-1}\mathbf{x}_f\mathbf{\Sigma}_{vv}$$

and so on substitution in (13-77)

$$\mathbf{\Sigma}_{ff} = (1 + \mathbf{x}_f'(\mathbf{X}'\mathbf{X})^{-1}\mathbf{x}_f)\mathbf{\Sigma}_{vv} \tag{13-83}$$

$\mathbf{\Sigma}_{vv}$ is unknown but an unbiased estimator is provided by

$$\begin{aligned} \mathbf{S}_{vv} &= \frac{1}{n-K}(\mathbf{Y} - \mathbf{X}\hat{\mathbf{\Pi}}')'(\mathbf{Y} - \mathbf{X}\hat{\mathbf{\Pi}}') \\ &= \frac{1}{n-K}(\mathbf{Y}'\mathbf{Y} - \hat{\mathbf{\Pi}}\mathbf{X}'\mathbf{Y}) \end{aligned} \tag{13-84}$$

and the estimated variance–covariance matrix of the error of forecast is

$$\mathbf{S}_{ff} = (1 + \mathbf{x}_f'(\mathbf{X}'\mathbf{X})^{-1}\mathbf{x}_f)\mathbf{S}_{vv} \tag{13-85}$$

Hooper and Zellner have shown that Hotelling's T^2 statistic is here

$$T^2 = (\hat{\mathbf{y}}_f - \mathbf{y}_f)'\mathbf{S}_{ff}^{-1}(\hat{\mathbf{y}}_f - \mathbf{y}_f)$$

and that

$$\frac{(n - K - G + 1)T^2}{(n - K)G}$$

has the F distribution with G and $(n - K - G + 1)$ degrees of freedom. If $F_{0.05}$ denotes the value of F giving the upper 5 per cent tail of the appropriate F distribution

$$(\hat{\mathbf{y}}_f - \mathbf{y}_f)'\mathbf{S}_{ff}^{-1}(\hat{\mathbf{y}}_f - \mathbf{y}_f) \leq \frac{(n - K)G}{n - K - G + 1}F_{0.05} \tag{13-86}$$

then defines a concentration ellipsoid for the elements of $\mathbf{y}_f$ with an associated confidence coefficient of 95 per cent. In the case of a single-equation model, $G = 1$, and (13-86) reduces to the result previously obtained in Chap. 5. For a two-equation model $\mathbf{y}_f$ is a two-element vector and (13-86) defines an ellipse, centered at $\hat{\mathbf{y}}_f$, in the y_1, y_2 plane.

For models containing three or more endogenous variables Hymans has suggested that the concentration ellipsoid may be used to determine joint confidence intervals for the elements of $\mathbf{y}_f$ by finding the projections of the ellipsoid on the coordinate axes.[1] Figure 13-1 illustrates the idea for a two-equation model. The projections of the ellipse are MN on the y_1 axis and KL on the y_2 axis. A difficulty with stating MN and KL as simultaneous

[1] S. H. Hymans, "Simultaneous Confidence Intervals in Econometric Forecasting," *Econometrica*, vol. 36, pp. 18-30, 1968.

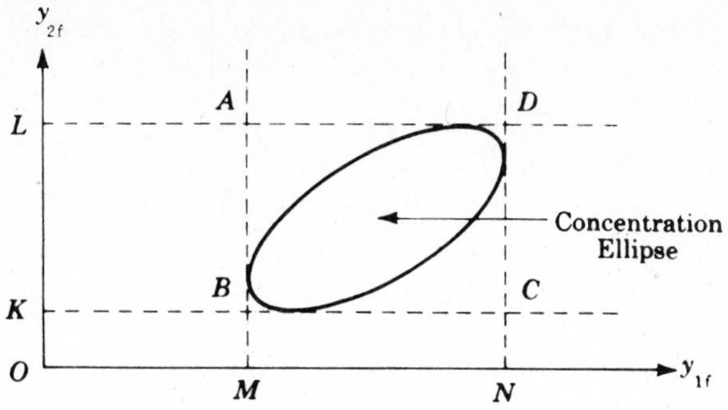

Fig. 13-1.

confidence intervals is that the confidence coefficient to be associated with the implied rectangle ABCD is obviously greater than that of the concentration ellipse, but there is no means of estimating what it is. To illustrate the Hymans technique for the general case rewrite (13-86) in the form

$$(\hat{\mathbf{y}}_f - \mathbf{y}_f)'\mathbf{S}_{vv}^{-1}(\hat{\mathbf{y}}_f - \mathbf{y}_f) \leq \frac{[1 + \mathbf{x}'_f(\mathbf{X}'\mathbf{X})^{-1}\mathbf{x}_f](n - K)G}{n - K - G + 1} F_\alpha \qquad (13\text{-}87)$$

or

$$(\hat{\mathbf{y}}_f - \mathbf{y}_f)'\mathbf{S}_{vv}^{-1}(\hat{\mathbf{y}}_f - \mathbf{y}_f) \leq c \qquad (13\text{-}88)$$

letting c indicate the right-hand side of (13-87). Hyman's basic result shows that the projections of (13-88) on the G coordinate axes are given by

$$\hat{\mathbf{y}}_{if} - \mathbf{y}_{if} = \pm\sqrt{c \cdot s_{ii}} \qquad i = 1, \ldots, G$$

where s_{ii} is the ith element on the principal diagonal of $\mathbf{S}_{vv}$. Thus the G simultaneous confidence intervals are given by

$$\hat{\mathbf{y}}_{if} \pm \sqrt{c \cdot s_{ii}} \qquad i = 1, \ldots, G \qquad (13\text{-}89)$$

The intervals given by (13-89) will be wider than the interval for any y_{if} taken singly. The latter would be of the form

$$\hat{\mathbf{y}}_{if} \pm t_{\alpha/2}\sqrt{s_{ii}}$$

where $t_{\alpha/2}^2 = F_\alpha$. From a comparison of (13-87) and (13-88)

$$c > G \cdot F_\alpha$$

for $(\mathbf{X}'\mathbf{X})$ is positive definite and so $[1 + \mathbf{x}'_f(\mathbf{X}'\mathbf{X})^{-1}\mathbf{x}_f]$ exceeds one. Thus $\sqrt{c} > t_{\alpha/2}\sqrt{G}$ and the difference in the width of the two confidence intervals will be of the order of $\sqrt{G}$.

When the $\hat{\mathbf{\Pi}}$ matrix has been calculated from $\hat{\mathbf{B}}$ and $\hat{\Gamma}$ the variance–covariance matrix for the error of forecast is much more complicated than (13-83). Explicit derivations are given in the Goldberger, Nagar, and Odeh article and the Hymans article also contains an application of the joint confidence interval technique to the more complicated case.

13-8 MONTE CARLO STUDIES

Nearly all the properties of estimators studied in this chapter have been asymptotic properties. In practice one has to work with finite samples and it is therefore important to study the small-sample properties of various estimators. This is often impossible by analytical methods and so numerous Monte Carlo studies have been made in an attempt to shed light on these questions. The essence of a Monte Carlo study is that various sets of parameter values are specified for postulated distributions underlying a model, repeated numerical drawings from the resultant distributions generate a large number of "samples" of finite size, various estimating techniques are applied to these samples, and the sampling distributions of the estimates are studied in relation to the true parameter values and to theoretical expectations about asymptotic distributions. The results are of course conditional on the numerical values used to generate the samples but a range of such studies can build up valuable information.

There are four major questions that one would like such studies to answer. First of all there is the question of whether the asymptotic differences between OLS on the one hand and simultaneous estimators on the other show up clearly in finite samples, and there are various aspects of this comparison. One criterion for comparison is the bias of an estimator, another is its variance about its expected value, and sometimes the two are in conflict if one estimator has a larger bias but a smaller variance than another. The two criteria can be merged in a third which is Mean Square Error, defined as the variance of an estimator about the true value. If $\hat{\beta}$ denotes an estimate of β, then

$$\text{Bias} = E(\hat{\beta}) - \beta$$

$$\text{Variance} = E\{(\hat{\beta} - E\hat{\beta})^2\}$$

$$\text{Mean Square Error (MSE)} = E\{(\hat{\beta} - \beta)^2\}$$

It is easily seen that

$$\begin{aligned} \text{MSE} &= E\{[(\hat{\beta} - E\hat{\beta}) + (E\hat{\beta} - \beta)]^2\} \\ &= \text{Variance} + \text{Square of Bias} \end{aligned}$$

Sometimes the square root of this quantity is computed giving the root mean square error (RMSE). Another aspect of this type of comparison is the proportion of incorrect inferences that might be made using a particular technique.

A second major question concerns the finite sample properties of estimators whose asymptotic properties may be identical, like 2SLS and LISE or 3SLS and FIML, and thirdly one would like to know how the various estimators behave when specification errors are present whether singly or multiply. For instance, what happens if disturbances are autocorrelated, if errors in variables are present, if there is serious collinearity, if variables are wrongly excluded or if various combinations of these things occur? The previous three questions all relate to structural coefficients. In addition one may be interested in similar questions about the reduced form coefficients and in how the system as a whole performs in generating forecasts of the endogenous variable from the reduced form.

The main articles on which the following discussion is based are given below.[1] The reader must be warned that there is no widely accepted method or technique for drawing conclusions from such a varied collection of empirical studies. Different people will stress different aspects. In the last resort the reader must refer to the original sources and decide for himself. In the meantime he should bear in mind the very tentative nature of any conclusions drawn below. We shall try to organize the discussion around the four main points outlined above, but it is not always possible to treat them *seriatim* for they are interwoven in many studies.

[1] G. W. Ladd, "Effects of Shocks and Errors in Estimation: An Empirical Comparison," *J. Farm Economics*, vol. 38, pp. 485–495, 1956.

H. Wagner, "A Monte Carlo Study of Estimates of Simultaneous Linear Structural Equations," *Econometrica*, vol. 26, pp. 117–133, 1958.

R. L. Basmann, *An Experimental Investigation of Some Small Sample Properties of GCL Estimators of Structural Equations, Some Preliminary Results*, General Electric Company, Handford Laboratories, Richland, Washington, 1958, mimeographed.

R. J. Foote, *Analytical Tools for Studying Demand and Price Structures*, U.S. Dept. of Agriculture, Agriculture Handbook 146, 1958.

W. A. Neiswanger and J. A. Yancey, "Parameter Estimates and Autonomous Growth," *J. Am. Statist. Assoc.* vol. 54, pp. 389–402, 1959.

L. R. Klein, "The Efficiency of Estimation in Econometric Models," in *Essays in Economics and Econometrics*, The University of North Carolina Press, Chapel Hill, N.C., 1960.

A. L. Nagar, "A Monte Carlo Study of Alternative Simultaneous Equation Estimators," *Econometrica*, vol. 28, pp. 573-590, 1960.

R. E. Quandt, "Some Small Sample Properties of Certain Structural Equation Estimators," Econometric Research Program, Princeton, Research Memorandum No. 48, December, 1962.

R. Summers, "A Capital Intensive Approach to the Small Sample Properties of Various Simultaneous Equation Estimators," *Econometrica*, vol. 33, pp. 1–41, 1965.

R. E. Quandt, "On Certain Small Sample Properties of *k*-Class Estimators," *Intern. Econ. Rev.*, vol. 6, pp. 92-104, 1965.

J. G. Cragg, "On the Sensitivity of Simultaneous Equation Estimators to the Stochastic Assumptions of the Models," *J. Am. Statist. Assoc.*, vol. 61, pp. 136–151, 1966.

J. G. Cragg, "On the Relative Small Sample Properties of Several Structural Equation Estimators," *Econometrica*, vol. 35, pp. 89–110, 1967.

On the question of bias there is fairly general agreement among the empirical studies. Three main points stand out. The OLS estimates generally display the greatest finite sample bias of all the estimators considered, the consistent estimators show some finite sample bias but the means of the sampling distributions are not usually significantly different from the true values, and the variation in the bias of the consistent estimators is neither large nor systematically in favor of one consistent estimator vis-a-vis another. There is one point, however, on which the evidence about OLS bias is not in complete agreement. Quandt's 1962 study shows that the OLS bias is almost invariably less than the 2SLS bias when there is substantial multicollinearity among the exogenous variables. This is shown in Table 13-1.

Table 13-1[1] Bias of OLS and 2SLS

Type	*Number of cases* *OLS beats*	*Loses to 2SLS*
Model 1, Data Set 1	23	1
Model 1, Data Set 2	2	22
Model 2, Data Set 1	15	9
Model 2, Data Set 2	1	23

[1] Quandt, 1962, Table 2, p. 19.

The correlations of the exogenous variables in this study were greater for Data Set 1 than for Data Set 2, and we see a distinct reversal of the relative positions of the two estimators on bias as we move from one data set to the other. A similar result, however, does not appear in Summers' study. He also uses two different specifications of exogenous variables: his A experiments are based on exogenous variables with zero correlations in the limit, but with fairly small correlations in the sample, while his B experiments have strong correlations in the exogenous variables. Table 13-2 shows some relevant statistics compiled from his detailed tables. In experiments 1 to 4 no specification errors were made, while in experiments 5 and 6 one variable was incorrectly excluded from one of the two equations in the model. Averaging the estimates yielded by a given estimator over the replications within an experiment the estimated bias is simply the difference between the mean of the estimates and the true value of the parameter. Table 13-2 records the number of times each estimator gives the smallest bias of the set of four. Comparing the A and B results there is clearly no difference in the OLS results as one goes from random to collinear exogenous variables. A pairwise comparison of the biases for OLS and 2SLS likewise shows no noticeable difference between the A and B experiments.

Table 13-2[1] Frequencies of best results on bias for structural parameters

Experiments	*OLS*	*2SLS*	*LISE*	*FIML*	*Total*
1A – 4A	1	4	13.5	13.5	32
1B – 4B	2	17	7	6	32
5A and 6A	4	5	5	2	16
5B and 6B	3	7	2	4	16

[1] Compiled from Summers, pp. 34–39, 1965.

More extensive evidence on this point is available from Cragg (1967) who considered six different degrees of collinearity in the exogenous variables, the degree increasing through the indices 1 to 6 in Table 13-3. UBK refers to the unbiased k-class estimator proposed by Nagar. OLS is badly biased even for the Multicollinearity Set 0 and, as the last column shows, the average OLS bias is larger when multicollinearity is present. The rest of the table shows that multicollinearity does have an adverse effect on the consistent estimators also but that the deterioration does not go uniformly with the degree of collinearity, since the results appear to be almost as bad for Set 1 as for Set 6 and less serious in the intermediate sets. Detailed inspection of the Quandt results shows that in many cases the OLS bias was often not a lot greater than the 2SLS bias for the random data set but that multicollinearity produced a greater increase in the bias of 2SLS estimates than in that of the OLS estimates, thus leading to a reversal of the relative positions. The Cragg results suggest that multicollinearity can produce a substantial increase in the bias of the consistent estimators. The Summers' results also show an increase in the bias for both OLS and the consistent estimators

Table 13-3[1] Number of coefficients (out of 15) for which medians were significantly different from population values

Experiment		*OLS*	*2SLS*	*UBK*	*LISE*	*3SLS*	*FIML*	*Typical OLS BIAS*[2]
Multicollinearity	0	14	4	4	0	3	0	−0.13
	1	14	10	9	0	9	0	−0.57
	2	14	5	4	4	6	1	−0.33
	3	15	4	4	2	5	0	−0.34
	4	13	3	2	1	3	0	−0.34
	5	14	4	4	2	4	1	−0.57
	6	15	11	10	5	10	4	−0.85

[1] Cragg, Table VI, p. 99, 1967.
[2] The average of the differences of the OLS medians from the population values divided by the population values of the coefficients.

but do not give any indication of the increase being less for OLS. The one thing that is clear is that multicollinearity has an adverse effect on the bias of all estimators and in some circumstances it can narrow the difference between OLS and the consistent estimators.

The next main result which receives general support is that OLS frequently has the smallest variance (measured around the mean). Table 13-4 gives some relevant summary statistics from the Summers' results. There are eight parameters estimated by four different methods in each of the Summers experiments. Table 13-4 has been produced by simply counting the number of times each estimator has the smallest variance of the set of four. One of the difficulties with any type of ranking is that the estimator ranked first may differ only slightly from that ranked second. In the present case this does not arise for the OLS variances are usually substantially smaller than the variances of the consistent estimators. We see that in the B experiments, where the exogenous variables were strongly correlated, the OLS estimators had the smallest variance in 45 cases out of 48. It is also seen that the relative performance of OLS to the other estimators is better in the mis-specified experiments than in the correctly specified experiments.

Table 13-4[1] **Frequencies of best results on standard deviations for structural parameters**

Experiments	*OLS*	*2SLS*	*LISE*	*FIML*	*Total*
1A – 4A	20	0.5	0	11.5	32
1B – 4B	29	0.5	0	2.5	32
5A and 6A	14	0	0	2	16
5B and 6B	16	0	0	0	16

[1] Compiled from Summers' detailed tables.

When bias and standard deviation are combined to give the root mean square error (RMSE) a somewhat mixed picture emerges. On this criterion the Wagner study found OLS and LISE approximately equal for three parameters and OLS superior to LISE for the fourth. The Nagar study found OLS and 2SLS approximately equal for two parameters, OLS better for another two and 2SLS better for the remaining two. Basmann found OLS to have a lower RMSE than 2SLS in four cases out of five—often considerably so—and both superior to LISE. More comprehensive evidence from Summers' study is given in Table 13-5. For any parameter each estimator has been ranked 1, 2, 3, or 4 in increasing size of RMSE and the rank values totaled for each estimator across groups of experiments. Thus *low* rank values indicate *good* estimators. In the properly specified experiments with independent exogenous variables FIML comes out best with 2SLS second, LISE third, and OLS a poor fourth. When the exogenous variables are correlated 2SLS is now as good as FIML with OLS third, and LISE fourth. In the mis-specification experiments FIML does badly and 2SLS best.

Table 13-5[1] **Rankings by RMSE for structural parameters**

Experiments	*OLS*	*2SLS*	*LISE*	*FIML*	
1A – 4A	107.5	74.5	84	54	320
1B – 4B	85	63	108.5	63.5	320
5A and 6A	38	32	36	54	160
5B and 6B	30	25.5	54	50.5	160

[1] Compiled from Summer's detailed tables.

Further specific comparisons of OLS and 2SLS are provided by Quandt's studies, where two special features of the distribution of estimates were analyzed, namely the proportion within ± 20 per cent of the true value and the proportion in the tails. He found the 2SLS distribution to have a higher density in the 20 per cent range around the true value. On the other hand it had thicker tails than the OLS distribution and gave a greater proportion of estimates with the wrong sign and frequently exhibited a greater maximum absolute deviation from the true value.

More important, however, than any of these characteristics of the sampling distributions of estimators is the likelihood of making correct inferences from a particular estimator. If $\hat{\alpha}$ denotes an estimate of the parameter α and $s_{\hat{\alpha}}$ the estimated standard error of $\hat{\alpha}$ one conventionally employs the ratio $(\hat{\alpha} - \alpha)/s_{\hat{\alpha}}$ for inference purposes, where α denotes a hypothesized value of α. For estimators other than OLS $s_{\hat{\alpha}}$ is an estimate of an asymptotic standard deviation while for OLS it is an estimate of the standard deviation about a biased mean. To examine the approximate validity of the standard test procedures Summers has applied the Kolmogoroff–Smirnov test to see if the sample distributions of $(\hat{\alpha} - \alpha)/s_{\hat{\alpha}}$ diverge significantly from a standard normal distribution at the 5 per cent level. The results are shown in Table 13-6. This table shows up in dramatic fashion the real danger of using OLS estimators in a simultaneous-equation context. The sampling distribution is centered around a biased expectation rather than the true parameter value and hence there is a serious risk of making incorrect inferences. Inference procedures based on the consistent estimators, on the other hand, are likely to work reasonably well. A similar conclusion was reached by Cragg on the basis of fairly extensive experiments. "The standard errors of the consistent

Table 13-6[1] **Frequency of acceptance of the hypothesis that $f[(\hat{\alpha} - \alpha)/s_{\hat{\alpha}}]$ is $N(0, 1)$**

	OLS		*2SLS*		*LISE*	
	Eq. 1	*Eq.* 2	*Eq.* 1	*Eq.* 2	*Eq.* 1	*Eq.* 2
A Experiments	37.5	45.8	100.0	83.3	100.0	79.2
B Experiments	0	29.2	75.0	79.2	83.3	79.2

[1] Summers, Table III, p. 15, 1965.

estimators were reliable for making inferences about the true values of the structural coefficients, those of OLS were less useful."[1]

On the comparison between various consistent estimators there are few very strong indicators. Table 13-2 shows that on the criterion of bias 2SLS would be preferred to LISE and FIML in the B experiments where the exogenous variables were correlated but not in the A experiments. The rankings by RMSE in Table 13-5 would again favor 2SLS for correlated exogenous variables and for the mis-specification experiments. Cragg, who examined Nagar's unbiased *k*-class estimators (UBK) and 3SLS in addition to the four estimators examined by Summers, concluded:

> Differences in the performances of the estimators were not great. The frequency with which one estimator came closer than another to the true values varied significantly over the coefficients for all pairs of methods.
> Given the weakness of the rankings, the results suggested an over-all ranking of the methods into three groups with FIML and 3SLS in the first, 2SLS, UBK and LISE in the second and OLS in the last group. This was not, however, found for all coefficients.[2]

Next we must look at how the estimators perform under various kinds of specification error. Multicollinearity is not, strictly speaking, a specification error, but it is a related problem and we will include it. Tables 13-2, 13-4, and 13-5 suggest that a threefold ranking of estimators in the case of uncorrelated exogenous variables is (a) FIML (b) 2SLS, LISE, and (c) OLS and that when multicollinearity is present the first two groups merge into a single group with 2SLS probably the most robust member. A somewhat stronger change appears in the specification error considered by Summers, namely the incorrect exclusion of a variable in the second equation. FIML is more seriously affected than the single-equation estimators, as is seen from the last two rows of Table 13-5. Summers' detailed results show that 21 out of 32 FIML estimators have distributions whose means are significantly different from the true values and these biased estimators are spread practically equally between the two equations of the model.

[1] J. G. Cragg, *op. cit.*, p. 141, 1966.
[2] J. G. Cragg, *op. cit.*, pp. 140–141, 1966.

The effect of errors of observation has been studied by Ladd, Cragg, and Simister.[1] Ladd compared OLS and LISE for some parameters and found that without observation errors OLS had the larger bias for five of the six parameters; with observation errors in the exogenous variables each method had the larger bias for three parameters and OLS had the smaller RMSE in four cases out of six. In a much more extensive study Cragg (1966) found that measurement errors increased the dispersions of the estimators and that the increases were largest for FIML and 3SLS and least for OLS. There was no real evidence of an increase in bias except for LISE and FIML in the experiment with the largest errors. The relative performance of the estimators came closer together, with FIML and 3SLS closer to LISE and 2SLS and the relative performance of OLS improved. Finally there was no serious effect on the "*t*" ratios, except for OLS where the "*t*" ratios are suspect even without measurement error.[2]

Simister considered measurement errors whose variances were 10 per cent and more of the variances of the corresponding variable measured without error, which are larger than the variances implicit in Cragg's study. His results confirm Cragg's main findings with the exception that the bias of all estimators increases significantly.[3]

Autocorrelated error terms apparently do not have much effect on the various estimators. Cragg found no significant changes in central tendencies nor in the ranking of estimators. The "*t*" ratios were still well-behaved and even improved for the OLS estimators as is shown in Table 13-7. This perhaps fortuitous result for OLS is not confirmed in Simister's

Table 13-7[1] Percentage of all "t" ratios outside a 95 per cent confidence interval

Disturbance	*OLS*	*2SLS*	*UBK*	*LISE*	*3SLS*	*FIML*
Regular	14.1	4.7	4.7	4.0	3.7	2.8
Autocorrelated 1	6.3	3.2	3.3	3.2	3.2	2.3
2	8.5	4.5	4.3	4.1	4.4	2.9
3	4.9	3.7	3.9	3.7	3.1	3.1

[1] Cragg, Table 10, p. 149, 1966.

study nor did he find the "*t*" ratios for other estimators to be unaffected by autocorrelated disturbances. He used a two-equation model and postulated a first order Markov scheme for the disturbances with $\rho_1 = 0.9$ and $\rho_2 = 0.225$. The first disturbance is more strongly autocorrelated than any

[1] L. T. Simister, *Monte Carlo Studies of Simultaneous Equation Systems*, Ph.D Thesis, University of Manchester, 1969.

[2] See J. G. Cragg, *op. cit.*, pp. 141–144, 1966.

[3] See L. T. Simister, *op. cit.*, Chap. 3.

of Cragg's and that may account for the difference. Simister's results will be given in Tables 13-8 and 13-9 below.

It will be seen that most studies have considered one mis-specification at a time. Simister, however, has also studied the effects of having observation errors and autocorrelated disturbances simultaneously present in a model. For the numerical values that he chose, errors of observation appeared as the dominant effect, as is shown in Table 13-8.

Table 13-8[1] **Percentage of "t" ratios with absolute values in excess of two**

Mis-specification	*OLS*	*2SLS*	*LISE*
Nil	21.8 (5.9)	7.5 (6.6)	7.2 (6.9)
Autocorrelated disturbances	22.8 (7.8)	22.5 (7.8)	23.8 (7.8)
Measurement errors	58.4 (17.8)	21.3 (6.9)	19.4 (5.9)
Both	57.8 (19.7)	21.6 (6.9)	19.1 (6.3)

[1] Simister, *op. cit.*, p. 240 and 249.

The main figures in the table come from a model with strongly correlated exogenous variables; those in parentheses are for the same model with substantially uncorrelated exogenous variables. Since Cragg's model had very low correlations in the exogenous variables it is the figures in parentheses in the first two rows which are more directly comparable with his. An interesting study that also stresses the importance of measurement errors is the estimation of a Canadian Econometric Model from various national accounts data.[1] Denton and Kuiper estimate the model by OLS and 2SLS using (a) a set of data consisting of the first published figure for each year, (b) a set of data consisting of the latest published figure for each year and (c) a set of data consisting of a mixture of preliminary, partially revised, and final figures. Their main conclusion is that:

> Variations in parameter estimates are generally much greater between different sets of data than between different methods of estimation, at least for the model and methods used in this paper.[2]

and they speculate on the possibility that "in practical econometric work errors in data may sometimes be much more important than the choice of estimating procedure." One can see what they mean and the point is an important one, but it is also very important to realize that at any given level

[1] F. T. Denton and J. Kuiper, "The Effect of Measurement Errors on Parameter Estimates and Forecasts, A Case Study Based on the Canadian Preliminary National Accounts," *Rev. Economics and Statistics*, vol. 47, pp. 198–206, 1965.

[2] Denton and Kuiper, *op. cit.*, p. 201.

of measurement error some estimators are better than others. Lines one, three, and four of Table 13-8, for example, show three circumstances in which OLS is clearly inferior to LISE and 2SLS.

Finally we may note an interesting effect of variations in the **B** and **Σ** matrices on the estimates of the structural coefficients. The **Σ** matrix is the variance–covariance matrix of the structural disturbances. In the derivation of the simultaneous equation estimators no restrictions were placed on the off-diagonal elements of **Σ**, in other words the disturbances in various structural equations may be contemporaneously correlated. Cragg has compared the effect of a structure 1 in which **Σ** has large off-diagonal elements and a structure 2 in which the off-diagonal elements of **Σ** are very small. His main conclusion is:

> The experiment using structure 2 did not produce the same ranking of the estimators. Differences in the rankings of the full model methods from the consistent *k*-Class estimators were neglible. The inferiority of OLS was not as pronounced.[1]

This is, of course, a very plausible result. Quandt also found that as the sparseness (number of zero coefficients) of the **B** matrix increased the mean bias of *k*-class estimators (including OLS and 2SLS) decreased.

The state of current knowledge on the various structural coefficient estimators is well summarized in the conclusions of Cragg after a study which contained substantial variations in the postulated parameter values. The methods studied were OLS, 2SLS, UBK, LISE, 3SLS, and FIML.[2]

> 1. The differences in the performances of the methods are not at all pronounced.
> 2. The frequency with which one estimator came closer to the true values of the structural coefficients than another varied significantly over the different coefficients of an experiment. The variation was sufficient to make the rankings of the estimators for different coefficients different.
> 3. The frequencies with which one method came closer to the true values of the structural coefficients than another depended on the exact set of exogenous data used, the true values of the structural coefficients, the correlations between the structural disturbances and the sizes of the structural disturbances. This variability could change the rankings of the estimators for some coefficients.
> 4. Given the small differences among the estimators and the variability in their relative performances, OLS was usually the poorest member and 3SLS and FIML were better than 2SLS, UBK and LISE.
> 5. In most cases differences in the central tendencies of the distributions of the consistent estimators from the true values of the coefficients were not very serious, but large disturbances and multicollinearity could change this conclusion. On this criterion, FIML and LISE seemed slightly superior to other methods. The differences of its medians from the true values was a serious problem for OLS. This feature, rather than wide dispersions, was the reason for the poor rankings of OLS. It weighed more heavily against OLS when larger samples were used.

[1] Cragg, *op. cit.*, p. 141, 1966.
[2] J. G. Cragg, *Econometrica*, vol. 35, pp. 108–109, 1967.

6. Usually use of the standard errors of the consistent methods would lead to reliable inferences, but this was not always the case. The standard errors of OLS were not useful for making inferences about the true values of coefficients.

The experiments conducted give no clear guide lines for the choice of an estimator for econometric models. They indicate that the ambiguities to be found in earlier sampling experiments genuinely reflect properties of the simultaneous-equation estimators. The results suggest that, because the consistent estimators do not differ greatly and their relative performances are sensitive to the data and structure studied, 2SLS may well be the best estimator to choose since it is the cheapest and easiest method to compute. The choice of OLS also may be sensible even for very simple models conforming to the assumptions under which the simultaneous-equation estimators were derived and the experiments conducted.

Economists have a genuine interest in structural parameters since many of them correspond to fundamental parameters in economic theory. To some extent this is also true of reduced form parameters for some of these are important impact multipliers. However, the major use of reduced-form systems is the production of forecasts of endogenous variables conditional on specified exogenous variables. Such forecasts depend upon all the reduced form coefficients and their accuracy reflects the performance of the whole model. Summers has given this aspect major prominence in his study. Given any set of estimates of the structural parameters $\hat{\mathbf{B}}$ and $\hat{\mathbf{\Gamma}}$ the corresponding reduced-form coefficients can be derived from

$$\hat{\mathbf{\Pi}} = -\hat{\mathbf{B}}^{-1}\hat{\mathbf{\Gamma}}$$

In addition the reduced-form coefficients may be estimated by the direct application of OLS to each reduced-form equation separately. This method takes no account of any restrictions on the reduced-form coefficients implied by restrictions on the $\mathbf{B}$ and $\mathbf{\Gamma}$ matrices, and is known as least-squares with no restrictions (LSNR). Notice that LSNR and OLS are two *different* methods of estimating reduced-form coefficients. The former has just been defined. The latter consists of estimating $\mathbf{B}$ and $\mathbf{\Gamma}$ by OLS and then substituting in $\hat{\mathbf{\Pi}} = -\hat{\mathbf{B}}^{-1}\hat{\mathbf{\Gamma}}$.

Summers applies nonparametric tests to judge the significance of the difference between the mean absolute error of forecast given by any pair of methods. The disadvantage of the procedure is that the comparisons have to be made a pair at a time and it is difficult to derive a general ranking of the methods. His main conclusions are as follows.

In almost every individual contest OLS was revealed inferior to its opponent. The aggregate statistics for the various groups in every case reveal FIML, LISE, 2SLS and LSNR to be superior to OLS. The significant differences for the other pairwise comparisons are not as striking, however.[1]

···any ranking of these four methods (FIML, LISE, 2SLS and LSNR) must be extremely tentative. The least ambiguous case will be examined first. In the mis-

[1] Summers, *op. cit.*, p. 18.

specification experiments, 2SLS is distinctly inferior to the other three methods when the predetermined variables are not highly intercorrelated, it performs much better, relatively, when they are. This may only be a consequence of an inability to perceive the inferiority of 2SLS because of lack of power. On balance, it seems appropriate to rank 2SLS low. Surprisingly, FIML appears somewhat better than the others. It was expected that FIML would be thrown off the scent more than the others by the mis-specification. Surely for large enough values of γ_{21} this would happen. Also surprisingly, LSNR did not distinguish itself in these experiments. It appears that when dealing with a small sample, exploiting the *a priori* information about the model through the use of FIML or LISE will more than compensate for slight errors in specifying the model. LSNR is not misled by the incorrect constraint on the π's, but at the same time it does not make use of the correct one; on balance, in competing with LISE and FIML, LSNR is the loser for the compromise when the degree of inaccuracy of the constraint is not too great.

The differences between the methods in the first four experiments were quite small. One would be rash here to conclude more than that LSNR is relatively weak. FIML's performance is again surprising. On the basis of its optimum large sample properties, one would have expected it to stand out much more in comparison with the other methods. In the region of the parameter space covered by the first four experiments, it appears that, as far as conditional predictions are concerned, economy in computation can safely supplant statistical efficiency as a basis for choosing FIML, LISE, 2SLS and LSNR.[1]

Klein took the structural equations of Ladd's error in variables model, that had been estimated by OLS and LISE, and derived the corresponding reduced form coefficients as well as estimating reduced form coefficients by LSNR. On the RMSE criterion LISE was the best estimator of the reduced form coefficients, which reverses the OLS, LISE ranking for the structural parameters. Foote compared the forecasting accuracy of LISE and LSNR and found fairly small absolute differences in the mean-square errors. On the usual ranking basis LISE was the better method in a majority of the cases.

Table 13-9* RMSE for predictions by various methods

Method	y_1				y_2			
	N	*S*	*E*	*SE*	*N*	*S*	*E*	*SE*
OLS	17.23	6.54	11.45	13.15	66.54	8.84	45.38	43.86
2SLS	4.80	7.04	8.80	10.81	5.40	10.03	16.81	16.07
LISE	4.84	61.04	8.44	10.69	5.22	173.67	15.66	16.09
LSNR	5.43	14.31	18.54	11.32	6.30	13.17	29.85	16.55

* Simister, *op. cit.*, pp. 122, 123, 181, 226.
N—no specification error.
S—serially correlated disturbances.
E—errors of measurement.
SE—both *S* and *E*.
y_1 and y_2—endogenous variables to be predicted.

[1] *Idem.*, p. 21.

Simister has analyzed predictions when certain specification errors are made. His main results are shown in Table 13-9. When there is no specification error we see from the N column that 2SLS and LISE are joint best, fairly closely followed by LSNR with OLS a very bad third. When a strong serial correlation is inserted in the first equation and a weaker one in the second, OLS is best for predicting both variables, followed by 2SLS and LSNR but the variance of the LISE method increases alarmingly due to a small number of extreme estimates. When measurement errors are present and also when both complications are present simultaneously 2SLS and LISE are joint best. Taking the table as a whole one would be inclined to regard 2SLS as the most robust and useful method. Table 13-9 is based on the experiments with correlated exogenous variables. When a similar table is compiled for the experiments with approximately uncorrelated exogenous variables the differences between the figures are almost everywhere quite small, LISE no longer produces extreme estimates and 2SLS and LISE would narrowly appear as joint best.

PROBLEMS

13-1 Prove the equivalence of (13-9) and (13-13).

13-2 Prove that for an exactly identified equation 2SLS estimates are equal to indirect least-squares estimates.

13-3. If $\mathbf{Z} = [\mathbf{Y}_1 - \mathbf{V}_1 \quad \mathbf{X}_1]$ and $\mathbf{W} = [\mathbf{Y}_1 \quad \mathbf{X}_1]$ where $\mathbf{V}_1 = [\mathbf{I} - \mathbf{X}(\mathbf{X}'\mathbf{X})^{-1}\mathbf{X}']\mathbf{Y}_1$ show that

$$(\mathbf{Z}'\mathbf{W})^{-1}(\mathbf{Z}'\mathbf{Z})(\mathbf{W}'\mathbf{Z})^{-1} = \begin{bmatrix} \mathbf{Y}_1'\mathbf{X}(\mathbf{X}'\mathbf{X})^{-1}\mathbf{X}'\mathbf{Y}_1 & \mathbf{Y}_1'\mathbf{X}_1 \\ \mathbf{X}_1'\mathbf{Y}_1 & \mathbf{X}_1'\mathbf{X}_1 \end{bmatrix}^{-1}$$

(Compare formulae (9-38) and (13-19) in the light of the discussion of k-class estimators in this chapter).

13-4. Prove that when an equation is exactly identified the estimates yielded by 2SLS and LISE, are identical.

13-5. Discuss the identifiability and estimation of the parameters of the model

$$y_{1t} - y_{1(t-1)} = \alpha_{10} + \alpha_{11}(y_{1t} + y_{1(t-1)}) + \alpha_{12}(y_{2t} + y_{2(t-1)}) + u_{1t}$$

$$y_{2t} - y_{2(t-1)} = \alpha_{20} + \alpha_{22}(y_{2t} + y_{2(t-1)}) + \alpha_{23}(y_{3t} + y_{3(t-1)}) + u_{2t}$$

$$y_{3t} - y_{3(t-1)} = \alpha_{30} + \alpha_{31}(y_{1t} + y_{1(t-1)}) + \alpha_{32}(y_{2t} + y_{2(t-1)})$$

$$+ \alpha_{33}(y_{3t} + y_{3(t-1)}) + u_{3t}$$

where

$$E(u_{it}) = 0$$

$$E(u_{it}^2) = \sigma_i^2$$

$$E(u_{it}u_{jt}) = \sigma_{ij} \qquad i \neq j$$

$$E(u_{it}u_{j(t-r)}) = 0 \qquad r \neq 0$$

(L.S.E. 1963)

13-6. Consider the following model

$$y_{1t} = \beta_{12}y_{2t} + \gamma_{11}x_{1t} + \gamma_{12}x_{2t} + \gamma_{13}x_{3t} + \gamma_{14}x_{4t} + u_{1t}$$

$$y_{2t} = \beta_{21}y_{1t} + \gamma_{21}x_{1t} + \gamma_{22}x_{2t} + \gamma_{23}x_{3t} + \gamma_{24}x_{4t} + u_{2t}$$

where the x_{it} are fixed numbers and the u_{it} are serially uncorrelated random disturbances with zero means. Using zero-type restrictions specify three alternative structures for which the simplest consistent estimating procedures are ordinary least-squares, indirect least-squares, and two-stage least-squares respectively. Show that indirect least-squares and two-stage least-squares are equivalent when applied to an equation which is exactly identified.

(L.S.E. 1966)

13-7. In the model

$$y_{1t} = \gamma_{12}x_{2t} + u_{1t}$$

$$y_{2t} = \beta_{21}y_{1t} + \gamma_{21}x_{1t} + u_{2t}$$

$$y_{3t} = \beta_{31}y_{1t} + \gamma_{32}x_{2t} + u_{3t}$$

the x_{it} are predetermined variables and the u_{it} are serially uncorrelated random disturbances with zero means. Given that $E(u_{1t}u_{3t}) = 0$, consider the identifiability of each equation and indicate suitable methods of estimation. (L.S.E. 1966)

13-8. "With large computers and appropriate programs at our disposal, there is no longer any justification for using, for instance, two-stage least-squares rather than full information maximum likelihood, or three-stage least-squares in estimating equation systems." Discuss.

(Oxford Diploma, 1965)

13-9. The $\mathbf{X'X}$ matrix for all the exogenous variables in a model is

$$\mathbf{X'X} = \begin{bmatrix} 7 & 0 & 3 & 1 \\ 0 & 2 & -2 & 0 \\ 3 & -2 & 5 & 1 \\ 1 & 0 & 1 & 1 \end{bmatrix}$$

Only the first of these exogenous variables has a nonzero coefficient in a structural equation to be estimated by two-stage least-squares. This equation includes two endogenous variables and the least-squares estimates of the reduced form coefficients for these two variables are

$$\begin{bmatrix} 0 & 1 & 3 & 2 \\ 1 & -1 & 1 & -1 \end{bmatrix}$$

Taking the first endogenous variable as the dependent variable, state and solve the equation for the two-stage least-squares estimates.

13-10. Derive the three-stage least-squares estimator for the model

$$\mathbf{B}\mathbf{y}_t + \mathbf{\Gamma}\mathbf{x}_t = u_t$$

where

$$\mathbf{B} = \begin{bmatrix} 1 & \beta_{12} \\ \beta_{21} & 1 \end{bmatrix} \quad \text{and} \quad \mathbf{\Gamma} = \begin{bmatrix} 0 & \gamma_{12} & 0 & \gamma_{14} \\ \gamma_{21} & 0 & \gamma_{23} & 0 \end{bmatrix}$$

while the covariance matrix of the disturbances is

$$\mathbf{\Sigma} = \begin{bmatrix} \sigma_{11} & \sigma_{12} \\ \sigma_{21} & \sigma_{22} \end{bmatrix}$$

Indicate how $\mathbf{\Sigma}$ is estimated. Assume that $\sigma_{12} = \sigma_{21} = 0$ and compare the 3SLS estimator in this special case with the 2SLS estimator. (L.S.E. 1969)

13-11. For the model

$$y_{1t} = \beta_{12}y_{2t} + \gamma_{11}x_{1t} + u_{1t}$$

$$y_{2t} = \beta_{21}y_{1t} + \gamma_{22}x_{2t} + \gamma_{23}x_{3t} + u_{2t}$$

you are given the following information:

(a) The least-squares estimates of the reduced form coefficients are

$$\begin{bmatrix} 5 & 10 & 2 \\ 10 & 10 & 5 \end{bmatrix}$$

(b) The estimates of variance of the errors of the coefficients in the first reduced form equation are 1, 0.5, 0.1.

(c) The corresponding covariances are estimated to be all zero.

(d) The estimated variance of the error on the first reduced form equation is 2.0.

Use this information to reconstruct the 2SLS equations for the estimates of the coefficients of the first structural equation, and compute these estimates. (L.S.E. 1969)

13-12.

$$y_{1t} = \beta_{12}y_{2t} + \beta_{13}y_{3t} + \gamma_{11}x_{1t} + u_{1t}$$

is one equation in a three-equation model which contains three other exogenous variables x_{2t}, x_{3t}, and x_{4t}. Observations give the following matrices

$$\mathbf{Y'Y} = \begin{bmatrix} 20 & 15 & -5 \\ 15 & 60 & -45 \\ -5 & -45 & 70 \end{bmatrix} \qquad \mathbf{Y'X} = \begin{bmatrix} 2 & 2 & 4 & 5 \\ 0 & 4 & 12 & -5 \\ 0 & -2 & -12 & 10 \end{bmatrix}$$

$$\mathbf{X'X} = \begin{bmatrix} 1 & 0 & 0 & 0 \\ 0 & 2 & 0 & 0 \\ 0 & 0 & 4 & 0 \\ 0 & 0 & 0 & 5 \end{bmatrix}$$

Obtain 2SLS estimates of the parameters of the equation and estimate their standard errors. (L.S.E. 1968)

13-13.

$$y_{1t} = \beta_{12}y_{2t} + \gamma_{11}x_{1t} + u_{1t}$$

$$y_{2t} = \beta_{21}y_{1t} + \gamma_{22}x_{2t} + \gamma_{23}x_{3t} + u_{2t}$$

Find direct least-squares and 2SLS estimates of β_{12} and γ_{11} if the matrix of sums of products of observed values is as follows:

$$\begin{array}{c|ccccc} & y_1 & y_2 & x_1 & x_2 & x_3 \\ \hline y_1 & 100 & 200 & 30 & 20 & 40 \\ y_2 & 200 & 900 & 0 & 50 & 160 \\ x_1 & 30 & 0 & 100 & 0 & 0 \\ x_2 & 20 & 50 & 0 & 50 & 0 \\ x_3 & 40 & 60 & 0 & 0 & 40 \end{array}$$

Given that the estimate of the variance of u_1 is 1.1 when the direct least-squares procedure is used, and is 1.4 when the 2SLS procedure is used, obtain estimates of the sampling variances of the two estimates of β_{12} and γ_{11}. Taking the difference between the two estimates as an estimate of the bias of direct least-squares, discuss the relative merits of the two estimates. How would the comparison be affected if you knew that $\beta_{21} = 0$ and that u_{1t} and u_{2t} were independent?

(L.S.E. 1967)

13-14. Show that if every equation in a linear stochastic model is just-identified then the 3SLS estimates are the indirect least-squares estimates of the coefficients. If only one equation of the model is just-identified how do the 3SLS estimates of its coefficients differ from the indirect least-squares estimates? (L.S.E. 1968)

Table A-1 Normal distribution. Ordinates Y at $\pm z$, and areas A between $-z$ and $+z$, of the normal distribution[1]

z	X	Y	A	$1 - A$	z	X	Y	A	$1 - A$
0	μ	0.399	0.0000	1.0000	±1.50	$\mu \pm 1.50\sigma$	0.1295	0.8664	0.1336
±0.05	$\mu \pm 0.05\sigma$	0.398	0.0399	0.9601	±1.55	$\mu \pm 1.55\sigma$	0.1200	0.8789	0.1211
±0.10	$\mu \pm 0.10\sigma$	0.397	0.0797	0.9203	±1.60	$\mu \pm 1.60\sigma$	0.1109	0.8904	0.1096
±0.15	$\mu \pm 0.15\sigma$	0.394	0.1192	0.8808	±1.65	$\mu \pm 1.65\sigma$	0.1023	0.9011	0.0989
±0.20	$\mu \pm 0.20\sigma$	0.391	0.1585	0.8415	±1.70	$\mu \pm 1.70\sigma$	0.0940	0.9109	0.0891
±0.25	$\mu \pm 0.25\sigma$	0.387	0.1974	0.8026	±1.75	$\mu \pm 1.75\sigma$	0.0863	0.9199	0.0801
±0.30	$\mu \pm 0.30\sigma$	0.381	0.2358	0.7642	±1.80	$\mu \pm 1.80\sigma$	0.0790	0.9281	0.0719
±0.35	$\mu \pm 0.35\sigma$	0.375	0.2737	0.7263	±1.85	$\mu \pm 1.85\sigma$	0.0721	0.9357	0.0643
±0.40	$\mu \pm 0.40\sigma$	0.368	0.3108	0.6892	±1.90	$\mu \pm 1.90\sigma$	0.0656	0.9426	0.0574
±0.45	$\mu \pm 0.45\sigma$	0.361	0.3473	0.6527	±1.95	$\mu \pm 1.95\sigma$	0.0596	0.9488	0.0512
±0.50	$\mu \pm 0.50\sigma$	0.352	0.3829	0.6171	±2.00	$\mu \pm 2.00\sigma$	0.0540	0.9545	0.0455
±0.55	$\mu \pm 0.55\sigma$	0.343	0.4177	0.5823	±2.05	$\mu \pm 2.05\sigma$	0.0488	0.9596	0.0404
±0.60	$\mu \pm 0.60\sigma$	0.333	0.4515	0.5485	±2.10	$\mu \pm 2.10\sigma$	0.0440	0.9643	0.0357
±0.65	$\mu \pm 0.65\sigma$	0.323	0.4843	0.5157	±2.15	$\mu \pm 2.15\sigma$	0.0396	0.9684	0.0316
±0.70	$\mu \pm 0.70\sigma$	0.312	0.5161	0.4839	±2.20	$\mu \pm 2.20\sigma$	0.0355	0.9722	0.0278
±0.75	$\mu \pm 0.75\sigma$	0.301	0.5467	0.4533	±2.25	$\mu \pm 2.25\sigma$	0.0317	0.9756	0.0244
±0.80	$\mu \pm 0.80\sigma$	0.290	0.5763	0.4237	±2.30	$\mu \pm 2.30\sigma$	0.0283	0.9786	0.0214
±0.85	$\mu \pm 0.85\sigma$	0.278	0.6047	0.3953	±2.35	$\mu \pm 2.35\sigma$	0.0252	0.9812	0.0188
±0.90	$\mu \pm 0.90\sigma$	0.266	0.6319	0.3681	±2.40	$\mu \pm 2.40\sigma$	0.0224	0.9836	0.0164
±0.95	$\mu \pm 0.95\sigma$	0.254	0.6579	0.3421	±2.45	$\mu \pm 2.45\sigma$	0.0198	0.9857	0.0143

±1.00	$\mu \pm 1.00\sigma$	0.242	0.6827	0.3173	±2.50	$\mu \pm 2.50\sigma$	0.0175	0.9876	0.0124
±1.05	$\mu \pm 1.05\sigma$	0.230	0.7063	0.2937	±2.55	$\mu \pm 2.55\sigma$	0.0154	0.9892	0.0108
±1.10	$\mu \pm 1.10\sigma$	0.218	0.7287	0.2713	±2.60	$\mu \pm 2.60\sigma$	0.0136	0.9907	0.0093
±1.15	$\mu \pm 1.15\sigma$	0.206	0.7499	0.2501	±2.65	$\mu \pm 2.65\sigma$	0.0119	0.9920	0.0080
±1.20	$\mu \pm 1.20\sigma$	0.194	0.7699	0.2301	±2.70	$\mu \pm 2.70\sigma$	0.0104	0.9931	0.0069
±1.25	$\mu \pm 1.25\sigma$	0.183	0.7887	0.2113	±2.75	$\mu \pm 2.75\sigma$	0.0091	0.9940	0.0060
±1.30	$\mu \pm 1.30\sigma$	0.171	0.8064	0.1936	±2.80	$\mu \pm 2.80\sigma$	0.0079	0.9949	0.0051
±1.35	$\mu \pm 1.35\sigma$	0.160	0.8230	0.1770	±2.85	$\mu \pm 2.85\sigma$	0.0069	0.9956	0.0044
±1.40	$\mu \pm 1.40\sigma$	0.150	0.8385	0.1615	±2.90	$\mu \pm 2.90\sigma$	0.0060	0.9963	0.0037
±1.45	$\mu \pm 1.45\sigma$	0.139	0.8529	0.1471	±2.95	$\mu \pm 2.95\sigma$	0.0051	0.9968	0.0032
±1.50	$\mu \pm 1.50\sigma$	0.130	0.8664	0.1336	±3.00	$\mu \pm 3.00\sigma$	0.0044	0.9973	0.0027
					±4.00	$\mu \pm 4.00\sigma$	0.0001	0.99994	0.00006
					±5.00	$\mu \pm 5.00\sigma$	0.000001	0.9999994	0.0000006
±0.000	μ	0.3989	0.0000	1.0000	±1.036	$\mu \pm 1.036\sigma$	0.2331	0.7000	0.3000
±0.126	$\mu \pm 0.126\sigma$	0.3958	0.1000	0.9000	±1.282	$\mu \pm 1.282\sigma$	0.1755	0.8000	0.2000
±0.253	$\mu \pm 0.253\sigma$	0.3863	0.2000	0.8000	±1.645	$\mu \pm 1.645\sigma$	0.1031	0.9000	0.1000
±0.385	$\mu \pm 0.385\sigma$	0.3704	0.3000	0.7000	±1.960	$\mu \pm 1.960\sigma$	0.0584	0.9500	0.0500
±0.524	$\mu \pm 0.524\sigma$	0.3477	0.4000	0.6000	±2.576	$\mu \pm 2.576\sigma$	0.0145	0.9900	0.0100
±0.674	$\mu \pm 0.674\sigma$	0.3178	0.5000	0.5000	±3.291	$\mu \pm 3.291\sigma$	0.0018	0.9990	0.0010
±0.842	$\mu \pm 0.842\sigma$	0.2800	0.6000	0.4000	±3.891	$\mu \pm 3.891\sigma$	0.0002	0.9999	0.0001

[1] Reprinted with permission from W. J. Dixon and F. J. Massey, Jr., *Introduction to Statistical Analysis*, Third edition, McGraw-Hill, 1969.

Table A-2 Percentiles of the *t* distribution[1]

df	$t_{0.60}$	$t_{0.70}$	$t_{0.80}$	$t_{0.90}$	$t_{0.95}$	$t_{0.975}$	$t_{0.99}$	$t_{0.995}$
1	0.325	0.727	1.376	3.078	6.314	12.706	31.821	63.657
2	0.289	0.617	1.061	1.886	2.920	4.303	6.965	9.925
3	0.277	0.584	0.978	1.638	2.353	3.182	4.541	5.841
4	0.271	0.569	0.941	1.533	2.132	2.776	3.747	4.604
5	0.267	0.559	0.920	1.476	2.015	2.571	3.365	4.032
6	0.265	0.553	0.906	1.440	1.943	2.447	3.143	3.707
7	0.263	0.549	0.896	1.415	1.895	2.365	2.998	3.499
8	0.262	0.546	0.889	1.397	1.860	2.306	2.896	3.355
9	0.261	0.543	0.883	1.383	1.833	2.262	2.821	3.250
10	0.260	0.542	0.879	1.372	1.812	2.228	2.764	3.169
11	0.260	0.540	0.876	1.363	1.796	2.201	2.718	3.106
12	0.259	0.539	0.873	1.356	1.782	2.179	2.681	3.055
13	0.259	0.538	0.870	1.350	1.771	2.160	2.650	3.012
14	0.258	0.537	0.868	1.345	1.761	2.145	2.624	2.977
15	0.258	0.536	0.866	1.341	1.753	2.131	2.602	2.947
16	0.258	0.535	0.865	1.337	1.746	2.120	2.583	2.921
17	0.257	0.534	0.863	1.333	1.740	2.110	2.567	2.898
18	0.257	0.534	0.862	1.330	1.734	2.101	2.552	2.878
19	0.257	0.533	0.861	1.328	1.729	2.093	2.539	2.861
20	0.257	0.533	0.860	1.325	1.725	2.086	2.528	2.845
21	0.257	0.532	0.859	1.323	1.721	2.080	2.518	2.831
22	0.256	0.532	0.858	1.321	1.717	2.074	2.508	2.819
23	0.256	0.532	0.858	1.319	1.714	2.069	2.500	2.807
24	0.256	0.531	0.857	1.318	1.711	2.064	2.492	2.797
25	0.256	0.531	0.856	1.316	1.708	2.060	2.485	2.787
26	0.256	0.531	0.856	1.315	1.706	2.056	2.479	2.779
27	0.256	0.531	0.855	1.314	1.703	2.052	2.473	2.771
28	0.256	0.530	0.855	1.313	1.701	2.048	2.467	2.763
29	0.256	0.530	0.854	1.311	1.699	2.045	2.462	2.756
30	0.256	0.530	0.854	1.310	1.697	2.042	2.457	2.750
40	0.255	0.529	0.851	1.303	1.684	2.021	2.423	2.704
60	0.254	0.527	0.848	1.296	1.671	2.000	2.390	2.660
120	0.254	0.526	0.845	1.289	1.658	1.980	2.358	2.617
∞	0.253	0.524	0.842	1.282	1.645	1.960	2.326	2.576
df	$-t_{0.40}$	$-t_{0.30}$	$-t_{0.20}$	$-t_{0.10}$	$-t_{0.05}$	$-t_{0.025}$	$-t_{0.01}$	$-t_{0.005}$

When the table is read from the foot, the tabled values are to be prefixed with a negative sign. Interpolation should be performed using the reciprocals of the degrees of freedom.

[1] The data of this table extracted from Table III of Fisher and Yates, *Statistical Tables for Biological, Agricultural and Medical Research,* with the permission of the authors and publishers, Oliver & Boyd, Ltd., Edinburgh. Also reprinted in Dixon and Massey, *op. cit.*

Table A-3 Percentiles of the χ^2 distribution[1]

df	Per cent									
	0.5	1	2.5	5	10	90	95	97.5	99	99.5
1	0.000039	0.00016	0.00098	0.0039	0.0158	2.71	3.84	5.02	6.63	7.88
2	0.0100	0.0201	0.0506	0.1026	0.2107	4.61	5.99	7.38	9.21	10.60
3	0.0717	0.115	0.216	0.352	0.584	6.25	7.81	9.35	11.34	12.84
4	0.207	0.297	0.484	0.711	1.064	7.78	9.49	11.14	13.28	14.86
5	0.412	0.554	0.831	1.15	1.61	9.24	11.07	12.83	15.09	16.75
6	0.676	0.872	1.24	1.64	2.20	10.64	12.59	14.45	16.81	18.55
7	0.989	1.24	1.69	2.17	2.83	12.02	14.07	16.01	18.48	20.28
8	1.34	1.65	2.18	2.73	3.49	13.36	15.51	17.53	20.09	21.96
9	1.73	2.09	2.70	3.33	4.17	14.68	16.92	19.02	21.67	23.59
10	2.16	2.56	3.25	3.94	4.87	15.99	18.31	20.48	23.21	25.19
11	2.60	3.05	3.82	4.57	5.58	17.28	19.68	21.92	24.73	26.76
12	3.07	3.57	4.40	5.23	6.30	18.55	21.03	23.34	26.22	28.30
13	3.57	4.11	5.01	5.89	7.04	19.81	22.36	24.74	27.69	29.82
14	4.07	4.66	5.63	6.57	7.79	21.06	23.68	26.12	29.14	31.32
15	4.60	5.23	6.26	7.26	8.55	22.31	25.00	27.49	30.58	32.80
16	5.14	5.81	6.91	7.96	9.31	23.54	26.30	28.85	32.00	34.27
18	6.26	7.01	8.23	9.39	10.86	25.99	28.87	31.53	34.81	37.16
20	7.43	8.26	9.59	10.85	12.44	28.41	31.41	34.17	37.57	40.00
24	9.89	10.86	12.40	13.85	15.66	33.20	36.42	39.36	42.98	45.56
30	13.79	14.95	16.79	18.49	20.60	40.26	43.77	46.98	50.89	53.67
40	20.71	22.16	24.43	26.51	29.05	51.81	55.76	59.34	63.69	66.77
60	35.53	37.48	40.48	43.19	46.46	74.40	79.08	83.30	88.38	91.95
120	83.85	86.92	91.58	95.70	100.62	140.23	146.57	152.21	158.95	163.64

For large values of degrees of freedom the approximate formula

$$\chi_\alpha^2 = n\left(1 - \frac{2}{9n} + z_\alpha\sqrt{\frac{2}{9n}}\right)^3$$

where z_α is the normal deviate and n is the number of degrees of freedom, may be used. For example $\chi^2_{0.99} = 60[1 - 0.00370 + 2.326(0.06086)]^3 = 60(1.1379)^3 = 88.4$ for the 99th percentile for 60 degrees of freedom.

[1] Reprinted with permission from Dixon and Massey, *op. cit.*

Table A-4a ***F* Distribution, upper 5% points ($F_{0.95}$).**[1]

Degrees of freedom for numerator

Degrees of freedom for denominator	1	2	3	4	5	6	7	8	9	10	12	15	20	24	30	40	60	120	∞
1	161	200	216	225	230	234	237	239	241	242	244	246	248	249	250	251	252	253	254
2	18.5	19.0	19.2	19.2	19.3	19.3	19.4	19.4	19.4	19.4	19.4	19.4	19.4	19.5	19.5	19.5	19.5	19.5	19.5
3	10.1	9.55	9.28	9.12	9.01	8.94	8.89	8.85	8.81	8.79	8.74	8.70	8.66	8.64	8.62	8.59	8.57	8.55	8.53
4	7.71	6.94	6.59	6.39	6.26	6.16	6.09	6.04	6.00	5.96	5.91	5.86	5.80	5.77	5.75	5.72	5.69	5.66	5.63
5	6.61	5.79	5.41	5.19	5.05	4.95	4.88	4.82	4.77	4.74	4.68	4.62	4.56	4.53	4.50	4.46	4.43	4.40	4.37
6	5.99	5.14	4.76	4.53	4.39	4.28	4.21	4.15	4.10	4.06	4.00	3.94	3.87	3.84	3.81	3.77	3.74	3.70	3.67
7	5.59	4.74	4.35	4.12	3.97	3.87	3.79	3.73	3.68	3.64	3.57	3.51	3.44	3.41	3.38	3.34	3.30	3.27	3.23
8	5.32	4.46	4.07	3.84	3.69	3.58	3.50	3.44	3.39	3.35	3.28	3.22	3.15	3.12	3.08	3.04	3.01	2.97	2.93
9	5.12	4.26	3.86	3.63	3.48	3.37	3.29	3.23	3.18	3.14	3.07	3.01	2.94	2.90	2.86	2.83	2.79	2.75	2.71
10	4.96	4.10	3.71	3.48	3.33	3.22	3.14	3.07	3.02	2.98	2.91	2.85	2.77	2.74	2.70	2.66	2.62	2.58	2.54
11	4.84	3.98	3.59	3.36	3.20	3.09	3.01	2.95	2.90	2.85	2.79	2.72	2.65	2.61	2.57	2.53	2.49	2.45	2.40
12	4.75	3.89	3.49	3.26	3.11	3.00	2.91	2.85	2.80	2.75	2.69	2.62	2.54	2.51	2.47	2.43	2.38	2.34	2.30
13	4.67	3.81	3.41	3.18	3.03	2.92	2.83	2.77	2.71	2.67	2.60	2.53	2.46	2.42	2.38	2.34	2.30	2.25	2.21
14	4.60	3.74	3.34	3.11	2.96	2.85	2.76	2.70	2.65	2.60	2.53	2.46	2.39	2.35	2.31	2.27	2.22	2.18	2.13
15	4.54	3.68	3.29	3.06	2.90	2.79	2.71	2.64	2.59	2.54	2.48	2.40	2.33	2.29	2.25	2.20	2.16	2.11	2.07
16	4.49	3.63	3.24	3.01	2.85	2.74	2.66	2.59	2.54	2.49	2.42	2.35	2.28	2.24	2.19	2.15	2.11	2.06	2.01
17	4.45	3.59	3.20	2.96	2.81	2.70	2.61	2.55	2.49	2.45	2.38	2.31	2.23	2.19	2.15	2.10	2.06	2.01	1.96
18	4.41	3.55	3.16	2.93	2.77	2.66	2.58	2.51	2.46	2.41	2.34	2.27	2.19	2.15	2.11	2.06	2.02	1.97	1.92
19	4.38	3.52	3.13	2.90	2.74	2.63	2.54	2.48	2.42	2.38	2.31	2.23	2.16	2.11	2.07	2.03	1.98	1.93	1.88
20	4.35	3.49	3.10	2.87	2.71	2.60	2.51	2.45	2.39	2.35	2.28	2.20	2.12	2.08	2.04	1.99	1.95	1.90	1.84
21	4.32	3.47	3.07	2.84	2.68	2.57	2.49	2.42	2.37	2.32	2.25	2.18	2.10	2.05	2.01	1.96	1.92	1.87	1.81
22	4.30	3.44	3.05	2.82	2.66	2.55	2.46	2.40	2.34	2.30	2.23	2.15	2.07	2.03	1.98	1.94	1.89	1.84	1.78
23	4.28	3.42	3.03	2.80	2.64	2.53	2.44	2.37	2.32	2.27	2.20	2.13	2.05	2.01	1.96	1.91	1.86	1.81	1.76
24	4.26	3.40	3.01	2.78	2.62	2.51	2.42	2.36	2.30	2.25	2.18	2.11	2.03	1.98	1.94	1.89	1.84	1.79	1.73
25	4.24	3.39	2.99	2.76	2.60	2.49	2.40	2.34	2.28	2.24	2.16	2.09	2.01	1.96	1.92	1.87	1.82	1.77	1.71
30	4.17	3.32	2.92	2.69	2.53	2.42	2.33	2.27	2.21	2.16	2.09	2.01	1.93	1.89	1.84	1.79	1.74	1.68	1.62
40	4.08	3.23	2.84	2.61	2.45	2.34	2.25	2.18	2.12	2.08	2.00	1.92	1.84	1.79	1.74	1.69	1.64	1.58	1.51
60	4.00	3.15	2.76	2.53	2.37	2.25	2.17	2.10	2.04	1.99	1.92	1.84	1.75	1.70	1.65	1.59	1.53	1.47	1.39
120	3.92	3.07	2.68	2.45	2.29	2.18	2.09	2.02	1.96	1.91	1.83	1.75	1.66	1.61	1.55	1.50	1.43	1.35	1.25
∞	3.84	3.00	2.60	2.37	2.21	2.10	2.01	1.94	1.88	1.83	1.75	1.67	1.57	1.52	1.46	1.39	1.32	1.22	1.00

Interpolation should be performed using reciprocals of the degrees of freedom.

[1] This table is reproduced with the permission of the Biometrika Trustees from M. Merrington, C. M. Thompson, "Tables of percentage points of the inverted beta (*F*) distribution," *Biometrika*, vol. 33, p. 73, 1943. Also reprinted in Dixon and Massey, *op. cit.*

Table A-4b ***F* Distribution, upper 1% points ($F_{0.99}$)[1].**

Degrees of freedom for numerator (rows: Degrees of freedom for denominator)

	1	2	3	4	5	6	7	8	9	10	12	15	20	24	30	40	60	120	∞
1	4,052	5,000	5,403	5,625	5,764	5,859	5,928	5,982	6,023	6,056	6,106	6,157	6,209	6,235	6,261	6,287	6,313	6,339	6,366
2	98.5	99.0	99.2	99.2	99.3	99.3	99.4	99.4	99.4	99.4	99.4	99.4	99.4	99.5	99.5	99.5	99.5	99.5	99.5
3	34.1	30.8	29.5	28.7	28.2	27.9	27.7	27.5	27.3	27.2	27.1	26.9	26.7	26.6	26.5	26.4	26.3	26.2	26.1
4	21.2	18.0	16.7	16.0	15.5	15.2	15.0	14.8	14.7	14.5	14.4	14.2	14.0	13.9	13.8	13.7	13.7	13.6	13.5
5	16.3	13.3	12.1	11.4	11.0	10.7	10.5	10.3	10.2	10.1	9.89	9.72	9.55	9.47	9.38	9.29	9.20	9.11	9.02
6	13.7	10.9	9.78	9.15	8.75	8.47	8.26	8.10	7.98	7.87	7.72	7.56	7.40	7.31	7.23	7.14	7.06	6.97	6.88
7	12.2	9.55	8.45	7.85	7.46	7.19	6.99	6.84	6.72	6.62	6.47	6.31	6.16	6.07	5.99	5.91	5.82	5.74	5.65
8	11.3	8.65	7.59	7.01	6.63	6.37	6.18	6.03	5.91	5.81	5.67	5.52	5.36	5.28	5.20	5.12	5.03	4.95	4.86
9	10.6	8.02	6.99	6.42	6.06	5.80	5.61	5.47	5.35	5.26	5.11	4.96	4.81	4.73	4.65	4.57	4.48	4.40	4.31
10	10.0	7.56	6.55	5.99	5.64	5.39	5.20	5.06	4.94	4.85	4.71	4.56	4.41	4.33	4.25	4.17	4.08	4.00	3.91
11	9.65	7.21	6.22	5.67	5.32	5.07	4.89	4.74	4.63	4.54	4.40	4.25	4.10	4.02	3.94	3.86	3.78	3.69	3.60
12	9.33	6.93	5.95	5.41	5.06	4.82	4.64	4.50	4.39	4.30	4.16	4.01	3.86	3.78	3.70	3.62	3.54	3.45	3.36
13	9.07	6.70	5.74	5.21	4.86	4.62	4.44	4.30	4.19	4.10	3.96	3.82	3.66	3.59	3.51	3.43	3.34	3.25	3.17
14	8.86	6.51	5.56	5.04	4.70	4.46	4.28	4.14	4.03	3.94	3.80	3.66	3.51	3.43	3.35	3.27	3.18	3.09	3.00
15	8.68	6.36	5.42	4.89	4.56	4.32	4.14	4.00	3.89	3.80	3.67	3.52	3.37	3.29	3.21	3.13	3.05	2.96	2.87
16	8.53	6.23	5.29	4.77	4.44	4.20	4.03	3.89	3.78	3.69	3.55	3.41	3.26	3.18	3.10	3.02	2.93	2.84	2.75
17	8.40	6.11	5.19	4.67	4.34	4.10	3.93	3.79	3.68	3.59	3.46	3.31	3.16	3.08	3.00	2.92	2.83	2.75	2.65
18	8.29	6.01	5.09	4.58	4.25	4.01	3.84	3.71	3.60	3.51	3.37	3.23	3.08	3.00	2.92	2.84	2.75	2.66	2.57
19	8.19	5.93	5.01	4.50	4.17	3.94	3.77	3.63	3.52	3.43	3.30	3.15	3.00	2.92	2.84	2.76	2.67	2.58	2.49
20	8.10	5.85	4.94	4.43	4.10	3.87	3.70	3.56	3.46	3.37	3.23	3.09	2.94	2.86	2.78	2.69	2.61	2.52	2.42
21	8.02	5.78	4.87	4.37	4.04	3.81	3.64	3.51	3.40	3.31	3.17	3.03	2.88	2.80	2.72	2.64	2.55	2.46	2.36
22	7.95	5.72	4.82	4.31	3.99	3.76	3.59	3.45	3.35	3.26	3.12	2.98	2.83	2.75	2.67	2.58	2.50	2.40	2.31
23	7.88	5.66	4.76	4.26	3.94	3.71	3.54	3.41	3.30	3.21	3.07	2.93	2.78	2.70	2.62	2.54	2.45	2.35	2.26
24	7.82	5.61	4.72	4.22	3.90	3.67	3.50	3.36	3.26	3.17	3.03	2.89	2.74	2.66	2.58	2.49	2.40	2.31	2.21
25	7.77	5.57	4.68	4.18	3.86	3.63	3.46	3.32	3.22	3.13	2.99	2.85	2.70	2.62	2.53	2.45	2.36	2.27	2.17
30	7.56	5.39	4.51	4.02	3.70	3.47	3.30	3.17	3.07	2.98	2.84	2.70	2.55	2.47	2.39	2.30	2.21	2.11	2.01
40	7.31	5.18	4.31	3.83	3.51	3.29	3.12	2.99	2.89	2.80	2.66	2.52	2.37	2.29	2.20	2.11	2.02	1.92	1.80
60	7.08	4.98	4.13	3.65	3.34	3.12	2.95	2.82	2.72	2.63	2.50	2.35	2.20	2.12	2.03	1.94	1.84	1.73	1.60
120	6.85	4.79	3.95	3.48	3.17	2.96	2.79	2.66	2.56	2.47	2.34	2.19	2.03	1.95	1.86	1.76	1.66	1.53	1.38
∞	6.63	4.61	3.78	3.32	3.02	2.80	2.64	2.51	2.41	2.32	2.18	2.04	1.88	1.79	1.70	1.59	1.47	1.32	1.00

Interpolation should be performed using reciprocals of the degrees of freedom.

[1] This table is reproduced with the permission of the Biometrika Trustees from M. Merrington, C. M. Thompson, "Tables of percentage points of the inverted beta (*F*) distribution," *Biometrika*, vol. 33, p. 73, 1943. Also reprinted in Dixon and Massey, *op. cit.*

Table A-5a[1] Durbin-Watson statistic (d). Significance points of d_L and d_U: 5%

n	$k' = 1$		$k' = 2$		$k' = 3$		$k' = 4$		$k' = 5$	
	d_L	d_U	d_L	d_U	d_L	d_U	d_L	d_U	d_L	d_U
15	1.08	1.36	0.95	1.54	0.82	1.75	0.69	1.97	0.56	2.21
16	1.10	1.37	0.98	1.54	0.86	1.73	0.74	1.93	0.62	2.15
17	1.13	1.38	1.02	1.54	0.90	1.71	0.78	1.90	0.67	2.10
18	1.16	1.39	1.05	1.53	0.93	1.69	0.82	1.87	0.71	2.06
19	1.18	1.40	1.08	1.53	0.97	1.68	0.86	1.85	0.75	2.02
20	1.20	1.41	1.10	1.54	1.00	1.68	0.90	1.83	0.79	1.99
21	1.22	1.42	1.13	1.54	1.03	1.67	0.93	1.81	0.83	1.96
22	1.24	1.43	1.15	1.54	1.05	1.66	0.96	1.80	0.86	1.94
23	1.26	1.44	1.17	1.54	1.08	1.66	0.99	1.79	0.90	1.92
24	1.27	1.45	1.19	1.55	1.10	1.66	1.01	1.78	0.93	1.90
25	1.29	1.45	1.21	1.55	1.12	1.66	1.04	1.77	0.95	1.89
26	1.30	1.46	1.22	1.55	1.14	1.65	1.06	1.76	0.98	1.88
27	1.32	1.47	1.24	1.56	1.16	1.65	1.08	1.76	1.01	1.86
28	1.33	1.48	1.26	1.56	1.18	1.65	1.10	1.75	1.03	1.85
29	1.34	1.48	1.27	1.56	1.20	1.65	1.12	1.74	1.05	1.84
30	1.35	1.49	1.28	1.57	1.21	1.65	1.14	1.74	1.07	1.83
31	1.36	1.50	1.30	1.57	1.23	1.65	1.16	1.74	1.09	1.83
32	1.37	1.50	1.31	1.57	1.24	1.65	1.18	1.73	1.11	1.82
33	1.38	1.51	1.32	1.58	1.26	1.65	1.19	1.73	1.13	1.81
34	1.39	1.51	1.33	1.58	1.27	1.65	1.21	1.73	1.15	1.81
35	1.40	1.52	1.34	1.58	1.28	1.65	1.22	1.73	1.16	1.80
36	1.41	1.52	1.35	1.59	1.29	1.65	1.24	1.73	1.18	1.80
37	1.42	1.53	1.36	1.59	1.31	1.66	1.25	1.72	1.19	1.80
38	1.43	1.54	1.37	1.59	1.32	1.66	1.26	1.72	1.21	1.79
39	1.43	1.54	1.38	1.60	1.33	1.66	1.27	1.72	1.22	1.79
40	1.44	1.54	1.39	1.60	1.34	1.66	1.29	1.72	1.23	1.79
45	1.48	1.57	1.43	1.62	1.38	1.67	1.34	1.72	1.29	1.78
50	1.50	1.59	1.46	1.63	1.42	1.67	1.38	1.72	1.34	1.77
55	1.53	1.60	1.49	1.64	1.45	1.68	1.41	1.72	1.38	1.77
60	1.55	1.62	1.51	1.65	1.48	1.69	1.44	1.73	1.41	1.77
65	1.57	1.63	1.54	1.66	1.50	1.70	1.47	1.73	1.44	1.77
70	1.58	1.64	1.55	1.67	1.52	1.70	1.49	1.74	1.46	1.77
75	1.60	1.65	1.57	1.68	1.54	1.71	1.51	1.74	1.49	1.77
80	1.61	1.66	1.59	1.69	1.56	1.72	1.53	1.74	1.51	1.77
85	1.62	1.67	1.60	1.70	1.57	1.72	1.55	1.75	1.52	1.77
90	1.63	1.68	1.61	1.70	1.59	1.73	1.57	1.75	1.54	1.78
95	1.64	1.69	1.62	1.71	1.60	1.73	1.58	1.75	1.56	1.78
100	1.65	1.69	1.63	1.72	1.61	1.74	1.59	1.76	1.57	1.78

n = number of observations.
k' = number of explanatory variables.

[1] This Table is reproduced from *Biometrika*, vol. 41, p. 173, 1951, with the permission of the Trustees.

Table A-5b[1] Durbin-Watson statistic (d). Significance points of d_L and d_U: 1%

	$k' = 1$		$k' = 2$		$k' = 3$		$k' = 4$		$k' = 5$	
n	d_L	d_U	d_L	d_U	d_L	d_U	d_L	d_U	d_L	d_U
15	0.81	1.07	0.70	1.25	0.59	1.46	0.49	1.70	0.39	1.96
16	0.84	1.09	0.74	1.25	0.63	1.44	0.53	1.66	0.44	1.90
17	0.87	1.10	0.77	1.25	0.67	1.43	0.57	1.63	0.48	1.85
18	0.90	1.12	0.80	1.26	0.71	1.42	0.61	1.60	0.52	1.80
19	0.93	1.13	0.83	1.26	0.74	1.41	0.65	1.58	0.56	1.77
20	0.95	1.15	0.86	1.27	0.77	1.41	0.68	1.57	0.60	1.74
21	0.97	1.16	0.89	1.27	0.80	1.41	0.72	1.55	0.63	1.71
22	1.00	1.17	0.91	1.28	0.83	1.40	0.75	1.54	0.66	1.69
23	1.02	1.19	0.94	1.29	0.86	1.40	0.77	1.53	0.70	1.67
24	1.04	1.20	0.96	1.30	0.88	1.41	0.80	1.53	0.72	1.66
25	1.05	1.21	0.98	1.30	0.90	1.41	0.83	1.52	0.75	1.65
26	1.07	1.22	1.00	1.31	0.93	1.41	0.85	1.52	0.78	1.64
27	1.09	1.23	1.02	1.32	0.95	1.41	0.88	1.51	0.81	1.63
28	1.10	1.24	1.04	1.32	0.97	1.41	0.90	1.51	0.83	1.62
29	1.12	1.25	1.05	1.33	0.99	1.42	0.92	1.51	0.85	1.61
30	1.13	1.26	1.07	1.34	1.01	1.42	0.94	1.51	0.88	1.61
31	1.15	1.27	1.08	1.34	1.02	1.42	0.96	1.51	0.90	1.60
32	1.16	1.28	1.10	1.35	1.04	1.43	0.98	1.51	0.92	1.60
33	1.17	1.29	1.11	1.36	1.05	1.43	1.00	1.51	0.94	1.59
34	1.18	1.30	1.13	1.36	1.07	1.43	1.01	1.51	0.95	1.59
35	1.19	1.31	1.14	1.37	1.08	1.44	1.03	1.51	0.97	1.59
36	1.21	1.32	1.15	1.38	1.10	1.44	1.04	1.51	0.99	1.59
37	1.22	1.32	1.16	1.38	1.11	1.45	1.06	1.51	1.00	1.59
38	1.23	1.33	1.18	1.39	1.12	1.45	1.07	1.52	1.02	1.58
39	1.24	1.34	1.19	1.39	1.14	1.45	1.09	1.52	1.03	1.58
40	1.25	1.34	1.20	1.40	1.15	1.46	1.10	1.52	1.05	1.58
45	1.29	1.38	1.24	1.42	1.20	1.48	1.16	1.53	1.11	1.58
50	1.32	1.40	1.28	1.45	1.24	1.49	1.20	1.54	1.16	1.59
55	1.36	1.43	1.32	1.47	1.28	1.51	1.25	1.55	1.21	1.59
60	1.38	1.45	1.35	1.48	1.32	1.52	1.28	1.56	1.25	1.60
65	1.41	1.47	1.38	1.50	1.35	1.53	1.31	1.57	1.28	1.61
70	1.43	1.49	1.40	1.52	1.37	1.55	1.34	1.58	1.31	1.61
75	1.45	1.50	1.42	1.53	1.39	1.56	1.37	1.59	1.34	1.62
80	1.47	1.52	1.44	1.54	1.42	1.57	1.39	1.60	1.36	1.62
85	1.48	1.53	1.46	1.55	1.43	1.58	1.41	1.60	1.39	1.63
90	1.50	1.54	1.47	1.56	1.45	1.59	1.43	1.61	1.41	1.64
95	1.51	1.55	1.49	1.57	1.47	1.60	1.45	1.62	1.42	1.64
100	1.52	1.56	1.50	1.58	1.48	1.60	1.46	1.63	1.44	1.65

n = number of observations.
k' = number of explanatory variables.

[1] This Table is reproduced from *Biometrika*, vol. 41, p. 175, 1951, with the permission of the Trustees.

Table A-6[1] Critical values of the von Neumann ratio

$$P\left(\frac{\delta^2}{s^2} < k\right) = \int_0^k \omega\left(\frac{\delta^2}{s^2}\right) d\left(\frac{\delta^2}{s^2}\right)$$

k \ n	4	5	6	7	8	9	10	11	12
0.25				0.00001	0.00001	0.00001	0.00001		
0.30				0.00007	0.00007	0.00005	0.00004	0.00002	0.00001
0.35			0.00006	0.00027	0.00021	0.00014	0.00009	0.00005	0.00003
0.40			0.00047	0.00065	0.00047	0.00031	0.00019	0.00012	0.00007
0.45			0.00126	0.00126	0.00088	0.00059	0.00038	0.00025	0.00016
0.50		0.00038	0.00246	0.00214	0.00150	0.00103	0.00069	0.00046	0.00031
0.55		0.00223	0.00409	0.00333	0.00237	0.00168	0.00116	0.00080	0.00055
0.60		0.00493	0.00615	0.00486	0.00355	0.00259	0.00185	0.00132	0.00094
0.65		0.00830	0.00865	0.00678	0.00511	0.00382	0.00282	0.00208	0.00152
0.70		0.01225	0.01161	0.00913	0.00710	0.00544	0.00414	0.00313	0.00235
0.75		0.01673	0.01505	0.01197	0.00958	0.00753	0.00587	0.00455	0.00351
0.80	0.00356	0.02171	0.01900	0.01534	0.01263	0.01015	0.00809	0.00642	0.00508
0.85	0.01302	0.02717	0.02348	0.01932	0.01631	0.01338	0.01089	0.00883	0.00714
0.90	0.02257	0.03310	0.02851	0.02403	0.02068	0.01729	0.01436	0.01188	0.00980
0.95	0.03223	0.03949	0.03412	0.02957	0.02579	0.02196	0.01858	0.01565	0.01316
1.00	0.04199	0.04634	0.04035	0.03598	0.03171	0.02745	0.02363	0.02025	0.01733
1.05	0.05186	0.05364	0.04728	0.04325	0.03849	0.03384	0.02959	0.02578	0.02241
1.10	0.06184	0.06140	0.05500	0.05137	0.04618	0.04120	0.03655	0.03232	0.02852
1.15	0.07194	0.06963	0.06361	0.06036	0.05482	0.04957	0.04458	0.03997	0.03577
1.20			0.07323	0.07020	0.06445	0.05901	0.05375	0.04882	0.04425
1.25						0.06956	0.06412	0.05894	0.05407
1.30								0.07040	0.06531

[1] This Table is reproduced from *The Annals of Mathematical Statistics*, vol. 13, p. 213, 1942, with the permission of the editors.

Table A-6[1] Critical values of the von Neumann ratio—continued

k \ n	15	20	25	30	40	50	60
0.35	0.00001						
0.40	0.00002						
0.45	0.00004						
0.50	0.00009	0.00001					
0.55	0.00018	0.00002					
0.60	0.00033	0.00005	0.00001				
0.65	0.00059	0.00012	0.00002				
0.70	0.00100	0.00024	0.00005	0.00001			
0.75	0.00161	0.00044	0.00011	0.00003			
0.80	0.00250	0.00076	0.00023	0.00007	0.00001		
0.85	0.00375	0.00127	0.00044	0.00015	0.00002		
0.90	0.00547	0.00206	0.00079	0.00030	0.00004	0.00001	
0.95	0.00778	0.00323	0.00135	0.00057	0.00010	0.00002	
1.00	0.01079	0.00489	0.00222	0.00102	0.00022	0.00005	0.00001
1.05	0.01465	0.00720	0.00355	0.00176	0.00044	0.00012	0.00003
1.10	0.01950	0.01033	0.00550	0.00294	0.00085	0.00026	0.00008
1.15	0.02550	0.01448	0.00826	0.00474	0.00158	0.00054	0.00019
1.20	0.03280	0.01986	0.01208	0.00738	0.00280	0.00108	0.00043
1.25	0.04155	0.02670	0.01723	0.01117	0.00476	0.00206	0.00092
1.30	0.05189	0.03524	0.02402	0.01644	0.00780	0.00376	0.00185
1.35	0.06396	0.04571	0.03276	0.02357	0.01235	0.00656	0.00355
1.40	0.07787	0.05834	0.04379	0.03298	0.01892	0.01098	0.00649
1.45		0.07333	0.05743	0.04511	0.02810	0.01769	0.01133
1.50			0.07398	0.06038	0.04055	0.02750	0.01893
1.55				0.07920	0.05696	0.04131	0.03034
1.60					0.07797	0.06006	0.04675
1.65						0.08465	0.06942
1.70							0.09949

Values of k for which $P\left(\frac{\delta^2}{s^2} < k\right) = 0$

n	k	n	k
4	0.7811	15	0.0468
5	0.4775	20	0.0259
6	0.3215	25	0.0164
7	0.2311	30	0.0113
8	0.1740	40	0.0063
9	0.1357	50	0.0040
10	0.1088	60	0.0028
11	0.0891		
12	0.0743		

Index